Handbook of Methods of Applied Statistics

Volume I

Handbook of Methods of Applied Statistics

Volume I

Techniques of Computation, Descriptive Methods, and Statistical Inference

I. M. CHAKRAVARTI

University of North Carolina

R. G. LAHA

Catholic University

J. ROY

Indian Statistical Institute

John Wiley & Sons, Inc.

New York · London · Sydney

Preface

The addition of one more new title to the long list of books already existing on basic statistical methods perhaps calls for a few words of explanation. The many excellent textbooks on this subject which are available today fall mainly into three broad classes. In some books, starting from basic concepts of probability and inductive inference, the authors develop a battery of statistical tools and techniques by rigorous mathematical reasoning. Either by choice or because of limitations of space, these books do not attempt to describe the manifold applications of the techniques in different fields. On the other hand, there are books dealing with the application of statistical methods in a selected field, and concerned primarily with problems of quantitative inference pertinent to that field. These books describe how standard statistical techniques can be used in solving specific problems, with, however, little or no emphasis on the theoretical basis or general applicability of the methods to other fields. Books in the third category, in trying to treat both the theory and applications of statistical methods, do so by restricting the coverage to selected topics.

If one accepts the view of the late Sir Ronald A. Fisher that statistics is the key technology of the present day, he is immediately struck by the scarcity of handbooks or reference books in statistics wherein practicing statisticians working in diverse fields can find collected all the important tools and techniques of statistics, with precise explanations of their theoretical bases and illustrative examples of their usage. The purpose of this book is to fill this gap in current statistical literature. The two volumes bring together under one title, in a logically arranged, documented, and readily usable form, most of the essential techniques of quantitative inference. The theoretical basis of each technique is described in some detail, but formal proofs are omitted.

This book is intended for (1) students in graduate and senior under-graduate courses who are interested in the applications of statistical methods in various fields, (2) practicing statisticians dealing with the condensation of statistical data and their subsequent analysis and interpretation with the help of statistical methods, and (3) research workers carrying out experiments in their own fields of specialization and applying modern statistical techniques to their experimental data in order to draw valid objective conclusions therefrom.

Volume I is divided into three parts. Part I deals with the standard techniques of desk computation. Part II describes the methods of condensation of data (univariate as well as multivariate) and includes a discussion of standard discrete and continuous distributions and regression and correlation techniques. In Part III are presented the methods of statistical inference, estimation of parameters and tests of statistical hypotheses, analysis of variance, multivariate analysis, and sequential procedures. Volume II describes methods of collection of information through sample surveys and controlled experiments.

In each part, every basic statistical method is described in detail with a precise explanation of its theoretical foundation. Then the computational procedure is discussed and illustrated by numerical examples completely worked out. These are followed by a large collection of selected and graded exercises to be done by the students. The examples and exercises are based on statistical data taken from different branches of science and technology, such as the physical sciences and engineering, biometry and agronomy, demography, anthropology, psychometry, and econometrics.

The writing of the manuscript started in 1956 when all three of us were teaching at the Research and Training School of the Indian Statistical Institute in Calcutta. In the course of writing, we have used freely materials from lecture notes and examination questions prepared by some of our colleagues at the Indian Statistical Institute. During the past years, various parts and sections of the manuscript have been tried out in different courses of the Indian Statistical Institute and also in the graduate and undergraduate courses in some universities and technological institutes in the United States.

We express our sincere thanks to our colleagues at the Research and Training School of the Indian Statistical Institute, and particularly to Professor C. R. Rao, the Director, for valuable advice and suggestions. We are grateful to Mr. R. K. Naha and Mr. M. Chatterjee of the Indian Statistical Institute for working out the illustrative examples and also to many students of the Research and Training School for checking the computations. Our thanks are also due to Mr. G. Das and Mr. K. Bhattacharya of the Indian Statistical Institute for typing many earlier versions and to Mrs. P. Spathelf of the Catholic University of America for typing the final version of the manuscript.

The material for illustrative examples and exercises was collected from textbooks, journals, laboratory records, and examination papers. We have referred to the original source whenever we could locate it. Since much of the material was derived from secondary sources, it is quite possible that in some instances we have failed to give proper credit. We offer our regrets and apologies to the authors of such material.

We should appreciate it greatly if readers will bring to our attention any errors which they detect.

I. M. Chakravarti

R. G. Laha

J. Roy

January, 1967

Contents

series expansion 153 Normalization 154 4.3 Pearsonian system of distributions 155 *Type I 155 Type II 156 Type III 157 Type IV 157 Type V 158 Type VI 158 Type VII 159* 4.4 Distributions occurring in sampling theory 161 *t distribution 161 Chi-square distribution 161 Variance ratio or F distribution 161 Beta distribution 162* 4.5 Mixture of distributions 162 *Non-central chi-square distribution 162 Non-central beta distribution of Types I and II 163* 4.6 Exercises (36) 163

5   Bivariate Data: Regression and Correlation   169

5.1 Bivariate distribution 169 *Marginal and conditional distribution 169 Regression and correlation 170* 5.2 Least-squares approximation to regression functions 171 *Linear approximation 171 Polynomial approximation 173 Orthogonal polynomials 173* 5.3 Computation of regression and correlation from a bivariate frequency table 174 5.4 Bivariate normal distribution 178 5.5 Other measures of correlation 180 *Rank correlation 180 Point-biserial correlation 180 Tetrachoric correlation 181 Grade correlation 181* 5.6 Exercises (26) 182

6   Multivariate Data: Multiple Regression and Correlation   196

6.1 Multivariate distribution 196 *Linear regression 196* 6.2 Multiple and partial correlation ceofficients 197 6.3 Computation of multiple and partial correlation and regression 198 6.4 Multivariate normal distribution 203 6.5 Exercises (7) 204

7   Analysis of Time Series   212

7.1 Time Series 212 7.2 Trend 212 *Free-hand smoothing 212 Moving averages 212 Polynomial trend 213 Other mathematical functions 221* 7.3 Seasonal index 223 *Ratios to trend 223 Link relatives 225* 7.4 Cyclical fluctuations 228 *Periodogram analysis 228* 7.5 Correlogram 232 *Serial correlation 232 Lag correlation 232* 7.6 Exercises (18) 223

PART III
STATISTICAL INFERENCE   243

1   Probability

1.1 Definition 245 *Random experiment 245 Sample space 246 Event 246* 1.2 Probability calculus 247 *Combination of events 247 Conditional probability, stochastic independence 248* 1.3 Random variables and probability distributions 249 *Univariate distributions 249 Bivariate distributions 250 p-Variate distributions (p > 2) 251 Functions of random variables 252* 1.4 Mathematical expectations 253 *Expectation of sum and product of random variables 253 Moments 254 Chebycheff's inequality 254* 1.5 Limit

PART I

Techniques of Computation

CHAPTER 1

Use of Computing Equipment

1.1 AIDS TO COMPUTATION

It is in the nature of a statistician's job that he has to undertake or supervise heavy numerical computations. To facilitate his work, various aids to computation are now available, the most important being a *desk calculator* and a collection of *mathematical tables*. Among inexpensive equipment, mention may be made of the *abacus** and the *slide rule*. For very large scale work, *punched card machines* and *electronic computers* are used.

Desk Calculators. The many different types of desk calculators now available for computations are designed to perform all routine arithmetic operations. In a "manual type" calculator, operations are performed by rotating a crank. In an automatic calculator, we have to push buttons. The general principles of operating a calculator are more or less the same, with exceptions in minor details of arrangement of different registers, keyboards, and buttons.

Every type of calculator has its own manual which explains how to operate it, what can be done on it, and what short-cut techniques are available. With the help of a manual, we can learn to operate a calculator in a short time, but it takes a little longer to acquire facility in complicated computations.

Mathematical Tables. Values of squares, cubes, and higher powers, factorials, square roots, cube roots, logarithms, exponentials, sines, cosines, tangents, and other trigonometrical functions and numerical values of various other mathematical functions are often required in computational work. These are available in a large number of mathematical tables with which every statistician should be well acquainted.

---

* The abacus uses several rows of beads, each row containing ten beads to correspond to ten digits. Each row corresponds to a definite digit-position in a number.

Some of these tables which are commonly used are described below. Other tables of limited or special use are discussed in appropriate chapters.

BARLOW's *Tables.* These tables, published by E. and F. N. Spon, London (Spon and Chamberlain, New York), 1890, give the squares, cubes, square roots, cube roots, and reciprocals of all integers up to 12,500. In addition, they give factorials and powers up to ten of all integers up to 100. Values of some useful constants are also tabulated.

CHAMBERS' *Seven-Figure Mathematical Tables.* These tables, published by W. and R. Chambers, London, 1858, give logarithms to seven figures of numbers up to 100,000 and also their first differences. Values of trigonometric functions and some useful mathematical constants are also provided.

Tables of the Incomplete Gamma Function. These tables, edited by K. Pearson and published by Cambridge University Press, 1951, give values of

$$I(u, p) = \int_0^{u/\sqrt{p+1}} e^{-v}v^p \, dv \Big/ \int_0^\infty e^{-v}v^p \, dv$$

to seven figures for $p = -1.0 \ (0.05) \ 0.0 \ (0.1) \ 5.0 \ (0.2) \ 50.0$ and $u = 0.0 \ (0.1) \ 5.0$ for negative values of p, and $u = 0.0 \ (0.1) \ 50.0$ for positive values of p. Values of some other functions related to the gamma function are also tabulated.

Tables of the Incomplete Beta Function. These tables, edited by K. Pearson and published by Cambridge University Press, 1934, give values of the beta function

$$\beta(p, q) = \int_0^1 x^{p-1}(1 - x)^{q-1} \, dx$$

and the incomplete beta function ratio

$$I_x(p, q) = \frac{1}{\beta(p, q)} \int_0^x t^{p-1}(1 - t)^{q-1} \, dt$$

to seven places of decimals for $p \geq q = 0.5 \ (0.5) \ 11.0 \ (1.0) \ 50.0$ and $x = 0.01 \ (0.01) \ 1.00$.

Statistical Tables for Biological, Agricultural, and Medical Research. This very useful collection by R. A. Fisher and F. Yates, published by Oliver and Boyd, London (Hafner, New York), 1963, contains tables of area and ordinates of normal distribution; tables of percentiles of the distributions of t, chi square, correlation coefficient, and variance ratio; tables for tests of significance and estimation; tables of probits and other transformations. Latin squares, balanced incomplete block designs, and random numbers and permutations are provided to facilitate the designing of experiments. Limited tables of logarithms, squares, square roots, reciprocals, factorials, natural sines, and tangents are also given.

Biometrika Tables for Statisticians, Vol. I, by E. S. Pearson and H. O. Hartley. This book, published by Cambridge University Press, 1958, presents a selection of tables needed by statisticians and experimenters in the analysis of their data. Tables of binomial, Poisson, and normal probability functions, and percentage points of Pearson's frequency curves and of commonly used statistics like t, chi square, variance ratio, product moment and rank correlation coefficients, range, extreme deviates, etc., are provided. Auxiliary tables of powers, sums of powers, orthogonal polynomials, and values of some useful constants are also given.

1.2 CALCULATIONS WITH APPROXIMATE NUMBERS

Rounding Off. Because of the limited digit capacity of all computing equipment, computations must generally be carried out with numbers rounded off suitably. To round off a number to n digits, replace all digits to the right of the nth digit by zeros. If the discarded number contributes less than half a unit in the nth place, leave the nth digit unaltered; if it is greater than half a unit, increase the nth digit by unity; if it is exactly half a unit, leave the nth digit unaltered when it is an even number and increase it by unity when it is an odd number. For example, the numbers 237,582, 46.85, 3.735 when rounded off to three digits would become 238,000, 46.8, and 3.74, respectively.

Significant Figures. In a rounded-off number, the significant figures are the digits $1, 2, \ldots, 9$. Zero (0) is also a significant figure except when it is used to fix the decimal point or to fill the places of unknown or discarded digits. Thus in 0.002603 the number of significant figures is only four. Given a number like 58,100, we cannot say whether the zeros are significant figures or not; to be specific we should write it in the form 5.81×10^4, 5.810×10^4, or 5.8100×10^4 to indicate respectively that the number of significant figures is three, four, or five.

Error Involved in the Use of Approximate Numbers. If u is the true value of a number and u_0 an approximation to it, then the error involved is

$$E = u - u_0,$$

the relative error is

$$e = \frac{u - u_0}{u},$$

and the percentage error is

$$p = \frac{100(u - u_0)}{u}.$$

If a function $F = F(u_1, u_2, \ldots, u_n)$ is evaluated by using approximations $u_i{}^0 = u_i - E_i$ for u_i, where E_i is the error in $u_i{}^0$ ($i = 1, 2, \ldots, n$), the approximation F_0 to F is given by

$$F_0 = F(u_1{}^0, u_2{}^0, \ldots, u_n{}^0) = F - \sum_{i=1}^{n} E_i f_i{}^0$$

(neglecting products, squares, and higher powers of E_i's), where $f_i{}^0$ is the partial derivative $\delta F / \delta u_i$, evaluated at the point $(u_1{}^0, u_2{}^0, \ldots, u_n{}^0)$. The error E in F_0 is thus given approximately by

(1.2.1) $$E = \sum_{i=1}^{n} E_i f_i{}^0.$$

As a corollary, we obtain the following rules:

For a sum or a difference, the absolute value of the error is not greater than the sum of the absolute values of the errors of the components in the sum or difference.

For a product or a quotient, the absolute value of the relative error is not greater than the sum of the absolute values of the relative errors of the components in this product or quotient.

Illustrative Example 1.1. The length of the smaller arc of a circle, standing on a chord of length $c = 1.5$ meters, is $a = 5$ meters. Find the radius of the circle. If the length measurements are correct to the nearest centimeter, assess the accuracy of the estimate of radius.

Let r be the radius of the circle in meters, and 2θ the angle in radians subtended by the chord at the center. Then

$$a = 2r\theta \quad \text{and} \quad c = 2r \sin \theta,$$

which gives

$$\frac{\sin \theta}{\theta} = \frac{c}{a} = 0.3.$$

Solving this equation by methods described in Chapter 3, we obtain $\theta = 2.35644$ in radians. See illustrative example 3.1 for details. Then, we find $r = a/2\theta = 1.06092$ in meters.

To assess the accuracy of this estimate of radius, let δc and δa denote, respectively, the errors in c and a. Then, neglecting squares, products, and higher-order terms, the errors δr and $\delta\theta$ in r and θ, respectively, are obtained from

$$\delta a = 2\theta \, \delta r + 2r \, \delta\theta,$$

$$\delta c = 2 \sin \theta \, \delta r + 2r \cos \theta \, \delta\theta.$$

Thus solving,

$$\delta r = \frac{\tfrac{1}{2}\delta c - \tfrac{1}{2} \cos \theta \, \delta a}{\sin \theta - \theta \cos \theta},$$

so that

$$|\delta r| \leq \frac{\frac{1}{2}|\delta c| + \frac{1}{2}|\cos\theta| \, |\delta a|}{|\sin\theta - \theta\cos\theta|}.$$

Now, since the length measurements are correct to the nearest centimeter, we have $|\delta c| \leq 0.005$, $|\delta a| \leq 0.005$.

Therefore, putting $|\delta c| = |\delta a| = 0.005$ and $\theta = 2.35644$ radians, we find

$$|\delta r| \leq \frac{0.0025 + 0.0017682}{2.3735987} = 0.00180.$$

The error in r is thus of the order of 0.002; the computed value of r may therefore be in error by as much as two units in the third decimal place.

1.3 MISTAKES IN COMPUTATION: HOW TO AVOID THEM

However fine techniques a statistician may use, if computations are inaccurate, the conclusions he draws from an analysis of numerical data will generally be wrong and very often misleading. It is essential therefore that every student of statistics should acquire some knowledge about the sources of inaccuracies in numerical computations and the ways to avoid them.

Types of Inaccuracies. It is convenient at the start to make a distinction between different types of inaccuracies in computational work. A *blunder* is a gross inaccuracy arising through ignorance. A statistician who knows his theory rarely commits a blunder. But even when we know the procedure in detail and use machines for computations, we sometimes make *mistakes*. There is a third type of inaccuracy, which we shall call an *error*. This is different from the other two types in that it is usually impracticable and sometimes even impossible to avoid. Errors may arise from one or more of the following sources: (a) the mathematical formulation is only an idealized and very seldom an exact description of reality; (b) parameters occurring in mathematical formulae are almost always subject to errors of estimation; (c) many mathematical problems can only be solved by an infinite process, whereas all computations have to be terminated after a finite number of steps; (d) because of the limited digit capacity of computing equipment, computations have to be carried with numbers rounded off conveniently. However, it is not necessary to try to avoid all errors, because usually the final answer need be correct only to a certain number of figures. The theory of calculations with approximate numbers will be found in most treatises on numerical computations, and a brief description was given in this book in Section 1.2. For the present we shall be concerned only with the problem of mistakes in computation.

How and Where Mistakes Arise. The only way to avoid mistakes is, of course, to work carefully, but a general knowledge about the nature of mistakes and how they arise helps us to work carefully. Most mistakes arise at the stage of *copying* from the original material to the worksheet or from one worksheet to another, *transferring* from the worksheet onto the calculating machine or vice versa, and *reading* from mathematical tables. It is a good idea in any computational program to cut down copying and transferring operations as much as possible. A person who computes should always do things neatly in the first instance and never indulge in the habit of doing "rough work" and then making a fair copy. Computational steps should be broken up into the minimum possible number of *unit operations*—operations that can be carried out on the calculating machine without having to write down any intermediate answer. Finally the work should be so arranged that it is not necessary to refer to mathematical tables every now and then. As far as possible, all references to such tables should be made together at the same time: this minimizes the possibility of referring to a wrong page and of making gross mistakes in reading similar numbers from the same table. In many mathematical tables, when the first few digits occur repeatedly, they are separated from the body of the table and put separately in a corner; a change in these leading digits in the middle of a row is indicated by a line or some other suitable symbol. We should be careful to read the leading digits correctly from such tables.

Classification of Mistakes. Mistakes in copying, transferring, and reading fall into three broad classes: digit *substitution*, *juxtaposition*, and *repetition*. One mistake is to substitute hurriedly one digit for another in a number, for instance, 0 for 6, 0 for 9, 1 for 7, 1 for 4, 3 for 8, or 7 for 9. The only remedy is to write the digits distinctly. Another mistake is to alter the arrangement of the digits in a number, to write 32 for 23 or 547 for 457. The third type of mistake occurs when the same number or digit occurs repeatedly. For instance, 12,225 may be copied as 1225, or in the series of numbers 71, 63, 64, 64, 64, . . . , one or more of the 64's may be forgotten. We should be especially careful to avoid these mistakes.

Precautions. Certain general precautions should be taken to avoid mistakes in computations. Whenever possible, we should make provision for checking the accuracy of computation. One way is to make use of mathematical identities and compute the same quantity by different methods. Computations should be properly laid out, in tabular form, with check columns whenever possible. A good tabular arrangement of computations helps in many ways—it reduces the number of unit operations, makes it unnecessary to refer to tables every now and then, makes the actual computation a routine affair, and, most important of all, indicates mistakes by comparison of similar entries in the same row or column. The few minutes devoted to devising an appropriate tabular form for a piece of computation should not therefore be considered wasted; it is time most fruitfully spent. Before starting on the detailed computations a few extra minutes may be taken for computing mentally a rough answer, the first digit and the order of the answer. This serves as a check on the final detailed computation and prevents putting the decimal point in the wrong place. To summarize, we may lay down the following five principles for avoiding mistakes in computation:

> Write the digits distinctly.
> Cut down copying and transferring operations.
> Use tabular arrangement for computations.
> Keep provision for checking.
> Guess the answer beforehand.

A last word of warning may be helpful. If a mistake is made, it is almost impossible to locate and correct the mistake by going through the original computation, even if this is done a number of times. The best way out is to work the whole thing afresh, perhaps using a different computational layout altogether.

1.4 EXERCISES

1.1. Evaluate each of the following, correct to five decimal places:

(a) $\dfrac{1.2345 \times 2.3456}{0.34567}$.

(b) x^{x^x}, where $x = 0.6543$.

(c) $\log_{0.2468} (\tan \sin^{-1} 0.3157)$.

1.2. Find the percentage error in the approximation:

$$\log n! \sim \tfrac{1}{2}\log 2\pi + (n + \tfrac{1}{2})\log n - n \log e$$

for $n = 5, 10, 15, 20$.

1.3. Extract the square root, correct to five decimal places, of 23.45678, using: (a) proportional parts (linear interpolation) in Barlow's *Tables*, (b) logarithms, (c) successive approximation $x_{n+1} = \tfrac{1}{2}(x_n + N/x_n)$, where x_n is the nth approximation to the square root of N, and $x_1 = 4.8$.

1.4. Evaluate correctly to ten places of decimals: 1,234,567,898 ÷ 2,345,678,987.

1.5–1.8. All the numbers are correct to within half a unit of the last place. All answers should also be rounded off so that the absolute error in the last digit retained is less than half a unit.

1.5. Round off each of these numbers to four significant figures: .0063945; 83,615; 363,042; 0.90038.

1.6. Find the sum of the following numbers: 136.421, 28.3, 321, 68.243, 17.428.

1.7. Find the difference of 48.392 and 6852.4.

1.8. Evaluate $\dfrac{1.234 \times 2.345}{3.456}$.

1.9. Find the value, correct to five significant figures, of $\sqrt{10} - \pi$, where 10 is an exact number.

1.10. Evaluate $a - b$, a/b, and $a^{1/2} \cdot b^{1/3}$, where $a = 3.344 \pm 0.002$ and $b = 4.455 \pm 0.003$ are two approximate numbers.

1.11. Which of the following measurements has the smallest relative error: (a) a distance of 1 mile measured to the nearest yard, (b) a 10-ft rod measured to the nearest eighth of an inch, or (c) a half-inch bolt measured to the nearest thousandth of an inch?

1.12. How accurately should the length l and time T of vibration of a simple pendulum be measured so that the value of g (the acceleration due to gravity) can be determined to within 0.05% of its true value from the formula $T = 2\pi\sqrt{l/g}$?

1.13. Find the number of terms required in the expansion

$$e = 1 + \frac{1}{1!} + \frac{1}{2!} + \frac{1}{3!} + \cdots$$

to compute e correct to seven places of decimals.

1.14. Van der Waals' equation of state for a real gas is expressed as

$$V^3 - \left(b + \frac{RT}{p}\right)V^2 + \frac{a}{p}V - \frac{ab}{p} = 0,$$

where a, b, and R are constants. The equation becomes a cubic in V (volume) for constant values of p (pressure) and T (temperature).

Assume that for a certain gas there exist $p = p_c$ and $T = T_c$ such that the cubic equation in V has all roots real and equal. Let V_c denote the value of the root. Find the accuracy required in the determination of the constants a, b, and R so that V_c, p_c, and T_c may be determined to within 0.05% of their respective true values.

1.15. If n balls are distributed at random in f distinct cells, the probability of finding exactly u cells occupied is

$$p(n, u) = \begin{cases} f^{-n}\dbinom{f}{u}\Delta^u 0^n & \text{for } u \leq n, \\ 0 & \text{for } u > n, \end{cases}$$

where

$$\binom{f}{u} = \frac{f!}{u!\,(f-u)!}.$$

For $n = 36$ and $f = 9$, find r, the largest integer for which

$$P = \sum_{u=1}^{r} p(n, u) \leq 0.05,$$

and compute this value of P correct to four places of decimals.

The table below gives the values of $\Delta^u 0^{36}/u!$ for $u = 1, 2, \ldots, 10$.

u	$\Delta^u 0^{36}/u!$					
1						1
2				3	43,597	38,367
3			25	01,573	81,897	61,486
4		1	96,740	25,436	41,989	19,901
5		1,210	69,207	47,415	14,112	98,300
6	1	42,044	22,416	13,289	69,511	97,888
7	51	18,720	82,780	24,639	62,695	36,244
8	752	95,807	59,157	03,606	06,085	85,183
9	5,429	43,405	36,065	70,049	63,584	47,625
10	21,742	81,564	50,300	65,712	75,062	23,115

CHAPTER 2

Interpolation

2.1 GENERAL FORMULAE FOR INTERPOLATION

The problem of evaluating a function $y = f(x)$ for a given value of the argument x, making use only of tabulated values of the function at certain values of the argument, say $x = \ldots, x_{-3}, x_{-2}, x_{-1}, x_0, x_1, x_2, \ldots$, etc., is known as interpolation. The usual method is to approximate the function $f(x)$ by a polynomial $P(x)$ which coincides with the tabulated values of the function $f(x)$ in the neighborhood of the given point x. Rational functions and trigonometric functions are also used at times as approximating functions.

The polynomial $P_n(x)$ of degree n in x, which coincides with the function $f(x)$ for $x = x_0, x_1, \ldots, x_n$, is given by the following formulae.

Newton's General Divided Difference Formula

$$(2.1.1) \quad P_n(x) = f(x_0) + (x - x_0)f(x_0, x_1)$$
$$+ (x - x_0)(x - x_1)f(x_0, x_1, x_2) + \cdots$$
$$+ (x - x_0)(x - x_1) \cdots (x - x_{n-1})f(x_0, x_1, \ldots, x_n),$$

where $f(x_0, x_1), f(x_0, x_1, x_2), \ldots$, etc., are called the divided differences of the function $f(x)$. Divided differences of the first order are defined by

$$f(x_i, x_{i+1}) = \frac{f(x_{i+1}) - f(x_i)}{x_{i+1} - x_i}.$$

Divided differences of the second order are then defined by

$$f(x_i, x_{i+1}, x_{i+2}) = \frac{f(x_{i+1}, x_{i+2}) - f(x_i, x_{i+1})}{x_{i+2} - x_i}.$$

Generally divided differences of the rth order are defined by

$$f(x_i, x_{i+1}, \ldots, x_{i+r}) = \frac{f(x_{i+1}, \ldots, x_{i+r}) - f(x_i, \ldots, x_{i+r-1})}{x_{i+r} - x_i}.$$

An alternative form for this polynomial is as follows.
Lagrange's Formula

(2.1.2) $$P_n(x) = \sum_{i=0}^{n} y_i L_i(x),$$

where

$$L_i(x) = \frac{(x - x_0) \cdots (x - x_{i-1})(x - x_{i+1}) \cdots (x - x_n)}{(x_i - x_0) \cdots (x_i - x_{i-1})(x_i - x_{i+1}) \cdots (x_i - x_n)},$$

and $y_i = f(x_i)$. The values of the coefficients $L_i(x)$ when arguments are equally spaced at unit intervals, that is, when $x_{i+1} - x_i = 1$, are available in special tables of interpolation coefficients; see, for instance, *The Kelley Statistical Tables*, by T. L. Kelley, Harvard University Press, Cambridge, Mass., 1948.

The difference $R(x) = f(x) - P_n(x)$, called the *error* in the interpolation formula, is given by

(2.1.3) $$R(x) = (x - x_0)(x - x_1) \cdots (x - x_n)f(x, x_0, x_1, \ldots, x_n)$$

$$= \frac{1}{(n + 1)!} (x - x_0)(x - x_1) \cdots (x - x_n)f^{(n+1)}(\xi),$$

where $f^{(n+1)}(x)$ denotes the $(n + 1)$th-order derivative of $f(x)$, and ξ is some point in the interval containing the points $x_0, x_1, \ldots, x_n$ and also x.

Illustrative Example 2.1. The first two columns of the table below show the values of x and the corresponding values of $f(x)$; the other columns give the divided differences. Use this table to evaluate $f(0.182)$.

| x | $f(x)$ | Divided differences | | |
		First order	Second order	Third order
$x_0 = 0.00$	$f(x_0) =$ 0.3989423			
		$f(x_0, x_1) =$ −0.0099680		
$x_1 = 0.05$	0.3984439		$f(x_0, x_1, x_2) =$ −0.1978533	
		−0.0396460		$f(x_0, x_1, x_2, x_3) =$ 0.0244350
$x_2 = 0.15$	0.3944793		−0.1905228	
		−0.0872767		
$x_3 = 0.30$	0.3813878			

Here $x = 0.182$, so that from Newton's general divided difference formula 2.1.1 we have

$$f(0.182) = 0.3989423 + (0.182 - 0.00)(-0.0099680)$$
$$+ (0.182 - 0.00)(0.182 - 0.05)(-0.1978533)$$
$$+ (0.182 - 0.00)(0.182 - 0.05)(0.182 - 0.15)(0.0244350)$$
$$= 0.3923937,$$

neglecting the error in interpolation.

For an illustration of Lagrange's interpolation formula see illustrative example 2.4.

2.2　INTERPOLATION WITH EQUIDISTANT ARGUMENTS

Difference Table. The above formulae can be used for any given values of the arguments $x_0, x_1, \ldots, x_n$. However, functions are usually tabulated at equal intervals of the values of the argument, that is, for values $x_i = x_0 + ih$, $i = \ldots, -2, -1, 0, 1, 2, \ldots$, where h is called the *interval of tabulation.* In such a case, interpolation formulae take particularly simple forms through the use of what are called ordinary *differences.* When arguments are equidistant, ordinary differences of various orders are defined by

First-order difference: $\quad \Delta f(x_i) = f(x_{i+1}) - f(x_i),$
Second-order difference: $\quad \Delta^2 f(x_i) = \Delta f(x_{i+1}) - \Delta f(x_i),$

etc., in general, the rth-order difference being defined by

$$\Delta^r f(x_i) = \Delta^{r-1} f(x_{i+1}) - \Delta^{r-1} f(x_i).$$

Ordinary differences are formed successively in a tabular arrangement as shown below. [In whatever follows, we write for the sake of simplicity $y_i = f(x_i)$.]

DIFFERENCE TABLE

x	y	Δ	Δ^2	Δ^3	Δ^4	Δ^5	Δ^6
...	...						
		...					
x_{-2}	y_{-2}		...				
		Δy_{-2}		...			
x_{-1}	y_{-1}		$\Delta^2 y_{-2}$		...		
		Δy_{-1}		$\Delta^3 y_{-2}$		...	
x_0	y_0		$\Delta^2 y_{-1}$		$\Delta^4 y_{-2}$		...
		Δy_0		$\Delta^3 y_{-1}$		...	
x_1	y_1		$\Delta^2 y_0$		...		
		Δy_1		...			
x_2	y_2		...				
		...					
...	...						

The nth-order ordinary or divided difference of a tabulated polynomial of the nth degree is a constant, and the $(n + 1)$th-order difference is zero. Since in a small range of the argument most continuous functions can be approximated by polynomials of low degree, irregularity of higher-order differences usually indicates the occurrence and the location of erroneous values in tabulated functions. An illustrative example will make this clear.

Illustrative Example 2.2.   The following table gives the values of the function $(\sin \theta)/\theta$ for various values of the angle θ measured in radians. Prepare a difference table to locate errors, if any.

$18\theta/\pi$	$(\sin \theta)/\theta$	$18\theta/\pi$	$(\sin \theta)/\theta$
9	0.63662	14	0.26306
10	0.56425	15	0.19099
11	0.48946	16	0.12248
12	0.41350	17	0.05852
13	0.33962	18	0.00000

Writing $y = (\sin \theta)/\theta \times 10^5$, we have the following difference table:

y	Δ	Δ^2	Δ^3	Δ^4	Δ^5	Δ^6
63,662						
	−7237					
56,425		−242				
	−7479		+125			
48,946		−117		+200		
	−7596		+325		−1001	
41,350		+208		−801		+2995
	−7388		−476		+1994	
33,962		−268		+1193		−3997
	−7656		+717		−2003	
26,306		+449		−810		+3005
	−7207		−93		+1002	
19,099		+356		+192		−1204
	−6851		+99		−202	
12,248		+455		−10		
	−6396		+89			
5,852		+544				
	−5852					
0						

On examination of this difference table we find that higher-order differences do not fall off. On the contrary, fourth- and higher-order differences are symmetrically distributed with alternating plus and minus signs about the horizontal line through $y = 33,962$. This indicates that there is possibly an error in this value of y and that, but for this error, fourth- and higher-order differences would be negligible. If the correct value is $y = 33,962 - \epsilon$, and if with this value fourth- and higher-order differences vanish, we should then have, from the column for Δ^4,

$$0 = 200 - \epsilon = -801 + 4\epsilon = 1193 - 6\epsilon = -810 + 4\epsilon = 192 - \epsilon.$$

Similarly, from the column for Δ^5,

$$0 = -1001 + 5\epsilon = 1994 - 10\epsilon = -2003 + 10\epsilon$$
$$= 1002 - 5\epsilon = -202 + \epsilon,$$

and so on. All these equations are approximately satisfied by

$$\epsilon = 200.$$

This is strong enough evidence to induce us to correct the value $y = 33,962$ to $y = 33,762$. On verification, this is found to be the actual value correct to five places of decimals.

We then write $x = 18\theta/\pi$ and prepare the corrected difference table as shown below for use in problems of interpolation. With each difference, 10^{-5} is understood as a common multiplier.

CORRECTED DIFFERENCE TABLE

$x = 18\theta/\pi$	$(\sin \theta)/\theta$	Δ	Δ^2	Δ^3	Δ^4	Δ^5
9	0.63662					
		−7237				
10	0.56425		−242			
		−7479		+125		
11	0.48946		−117		0	
		−7596		125		−1
12	0.41350		+8		−1	
		−7588		124		−6
13	0.33762		132		−7	
		−7456		117		−3
14	0.26306		249		−10	
		−7207		107		+2
15	0.19099		356		−8	
		−6851		99		−2
16	0.12248		455		−10	
		−6396		89		
17	0.05852		544			
		−5852				
18	0.00000					

In whatever follows, x_0 is the tabular entry nearest to the given point x at which we want to interpolate, and the function $f(x)$ is considered to be tabulated at equal intervals h of the argument. Furthermore, we shall write

$$u = \frac{x - x_0}{h}.$$

A number of polynomial interpolation formulae useful in different situations will now be described.

Newton's Formula. If tabular values only on one side of x_0, say $y_0, y_1, \ldots, y_n$, are to be employed, we use

$$(2.2.1) \quad P_n(x) = y_0 + u\,\Delta y_0 + \frac{u(u-1)}{2!}\Delta^2 y_0 + \cdots$$

$$+ \frac{u(u-1)\cdots(u-n+1)}{n!}\Delta^n y_0.$$

Linear Interpolation. For routine interpolation in tables where the interval of tabulation h is such that second differences are small and x lies between, say, x_0 and x_1 we may use

$$(2.2.2) \quad P_1(x) = f(x_0) + \frac{x - x_0}{x_1 - x_0}\Delta f(x_0)$$

$$= (1 - u)f(x_0) + uf(x_1),$$

where $u = (x - x_0)/(x_1 - x_0)$. For the error $R(x)$ in linear interpolation we have

$$|R(x)| < \frac{h^2}{8} M,$$

where M is the maximum value of $|f''(x)|$ in the interval $x_0 < x < x_1$.

Stirling's Formula. If values on both sides of x_0, namely, those of $y_{-n}, \ldots, y_{-1}, y_0, y_1, \ldots, y_n$ are to be employed, we use

$$(2.2.3) \quad P_{2n}(x) = y_0 + u \cdot \frac{\Delta y_{-1} + \Delta y_0}{2} + \frac{u^2}{2!}\Delta^2 y_{-1} + \cdots$$

$$+ \frac{u(u^2 - 1)}{3!}\frac{\Delta^3 y_{-2} + \Delta^3 y_{-1}}{2} + \cdots$$

$$+ \frac{u^2(u^2 - 1)}{4!}\Delta^4 y_{-2} + \cdots$$

$$+ \frac{u^2(u^2 - 1)\cdots[u^2 - (n-1)^2]}{(2n)!}\Delta^{2n} y_{-n}.$$

Bessel's Formula. On the other hand, if the values of $y_{-n}, y_{-n+1}, \ldots,$ $y_{-1}, y_0, y_1, \ldots, y_{n+1}$ are to be employed, we use

$$(2.2.4) \quad P_{2n+1}(x) = \frac{y_0 + y_1}{2} + v\,\Delta y_0 + \frac{v^2 - \frac{1}{4}}{2!} \frac{\Delta^2 y_{-1} + \Delta^2 y_0}{2}$$

$$+ \frac{v(v^2 - \frac{1}{4})}{3!} \Delta^3 y_{-1} + \frac{(v^2 - \frac{1}{4})(v^2 - \frac{9}{4})}{4!}$$

$$\times \frac{\Delta^4 y_{-2} + \Delta^4 y_{-1}}{2} + \cdots$$

$$+ \frac{v(v^2 - \frac{1}{4})(v^2 - \frac{9}{4}) \cdots [v^2 - (2n-1)^2/4]}{(2n+1)!} \Delta^{2n+1} y_{-n},$$

where $v = u - \frac{1}{2}$. Generally, Bessel's formula is used when interpolating near the middle of an interval, for, say, $u = 0.25$ to 0.75 (that is, $v = -0.25$ to 0.25), and Stirling's formula near the beginning or the end of an interval, for $u = -0.25$ to 0.25, say.

When $u = \frac{1}{2}$ or $v = 0$, Bessel's formula takes the simple form

$$(2.2.5) \quad P_{2n+1}(x_0 + \tfrac{1}{2}) = \frac{y_0 - y_1}{2} - \frac{1}{8} \frac{\Delta^2 y_1 + \Delta^2 y_0}{2}$$

$$+ \frac{3}{128} \frac{\Delta^4 y_2 + \Delta^4 y_1}{2} \cdots,$$

which is used for interpolation at the midpoint of an interval.

Everett's Formula. When tabulating a function $y = f(x)$ it is convenient to compute directly the values of the function at somewhat wide intervals of the values of the argument and then to obtain the intermediate values by interpolation. This is called *subtabulation.* For this purpose, a very useful method requiring only even-order differences is given by

$$(2.2.6) \quad P(x) = vy_0 + uy_1 + \binom{v+1}{3} \Delta^2 y_{-1} + \binom{u+1}{3} \Delta^2 y_0$$

$$+ \binom{v+2}{5} \Delta^4 y_{-2} + \binom{u+2}{5} \Delta^4 y_{-1} + \cdots,$$

where $v = 1 - u$ and $\binom{u}{t} = \frac{u(u-1)\cdots(u-t+1)}{t!}$.

Estimate of Error. The error in each of these interpolation formulae can be obtained from formula 2.1.3. This, however, requires a knowledge of higher-order derivatives of the function. When this is lacking, an estimate of the error is given by the first term neglected in the interpolation formula used.

Illustrative Example 2.3. Using the corrected data from illustrative example 2.2, find by interpolation the values of $(\sin \theta)/\theta$ for (a) $\theta = 1.6$, (b) $\theta = 25\pi/36$, and (c) $18\theta/\pi = 13.2$, 13.4, 13.6, and 13.8.

(a) Let us write $x = 18\theta/\pi$ and $y = (\sin \theta)/\theta$. From the corrected difference table it is seen that fifth differences are negligible. To obtain by interpolation the value of y when $\theta = 1.6$, that is, when $x = 18 \times 1.6/\pi = 9.1673251$, we use Newton's formula 2.2.1. Here $x_0 = 9$, $h = 1$, and $u = (x - x_0)/h = 0.1673251$. We then compute

$$y_0 = +0.63662$$
$$u = +0.1673251 \qquad \Delta y_0 = -0.07237$$
$$\frac{u-1}{2} = -0.4163374 \qquad \binom{u}{2} = -0.0696637 \qquad \Delta^2 y_0 = -0.00242$$
$$\frac{u-2}{3} = -0.6108916 \qquad \binom{u}{3} = +0.0425570 \qquad \Delta^3 y_0 = +0.00125$$
$$\frac{u-3}{4} = -0.7081687 \qquad \binom{u}{4} = -0.0301375 \qquad \Delta^4 y_0 = +0.00000$$

where $\binom{u}{r} = u(u - 1) \cdots (u - r + 1)/r!$ Thus, retaining up to fourth differences, we have by Newton's formula 2.2.1

$$y = y_0 + u\,\Delta y_0 + \binom{u}{2}\Delta^2 y_0 + \cdots = 0.62473.$$

To obtain an estimate of the error, we compute the next term. Here $\binom{u}{5} = 0.0231014$ and $\Delta^5 y_0 = -0.00001$, so that the error is $R = \binom{u}{5}\Delta^5 y_0 = -0.0000002$. The error in the interpolation formula does not therefore affect the result.

(b) When $\theta = 25\pi/36$, we have $x = 12.5$. We take $x_0 = 12$, so that $u = \frac{1}{2}$. We use Bessel's formula 2.2.4, where $v = u - \frac{1}{2} = 0$. Retaining up to fourth differences:

$$y = \frac{1}{2}(y_0 + y_1) - \frac{1}{8} \cdot \frac{1}{2}(\Delta^2 y_{-1} + \Delta^2 y_0) + \frac{3}{128} \cdot \frac{1}{2}(\Delta^4 y_{-2} + \Delta^4 y_{-1})$$
$$= \frac{1}{2}(0.41350 + 0.33762) - 0.125 \cdot \frac{1}{2}(0.00008 + 0.00132)$$
$$\quad + 0.0234375 \cdot \frac{1}{2}(-0.00001 - 0.00007)$$
$$= 0.37547,$$

which again is correct to five places of decimals.

(c) For this problem we take $x_0 = 13$ and use Everett's formula 2.2.5 for $u = 0.2, 0.4, 0.6,$ and 0.8. The required differences are

$x_0 = 13$	$y_0 = 0.33762$	$\Delta^2 y_{-1} = 0.00132$	$\Delta^4 y_{-2} = -0.00007$
$x_1 = 14$	$y_1 = 0.26306$	$\Delta^2 y_0 = 0.00249$	$\Delta^4 y_{-1} = -0.00010$

and the coefficients are

u	$\binom{u+1}{3}$	$\binom{u+2}{5}$
0.2	−0.032	0.006336
0.4	−0.056	0.010752
0.6	−0.064	0.011648
0.8	−0.048	0.008064

Therefore, when $x = 13.2$, that is, $u = 0.2$ and $v = 0.8$, we have

$$y = (0.8)(0.33762) + (0.2)(0.26306) + (-0.048)(0.00132)$$
$$+ (-0.032)(0.00249) + (0.008064)(-0.00007)$$
$$+ (0.006336)(-0.00010) = 0.322564.$$

Similar computations give the following results:

$x = 180/\pi$	$y = (\sin \theta)/\theta$
13.2	0.322564
13.4	0.307570
13.6	0.292649
13.8	0.277809

2.3 INVERSE INTERPOLATION

Given a table of values of the function $y = f(x)$, usually at equal intervals of the argument x, the problem of evaluating the point x at which the function takes a preassigned value, say a, is known as inverse interpolation. Formally, then, the problem here is to obtain a solution of the equation $f(x) = a$, using tabulated values of the function $f(x)$, for which methods given in Chapter 3 of Part I may be applied. On the other hand, if the roles of the function and the argument are reversed, the problem becomes one of interpolation in a table in which the argument is not equally spaced. If this inverse function is single valued in the range under consideration, Newton's general divided difference formula or Lagrange's formula can be used.

Two other methods of inverse interpolation are described below. Let x_0 be the tabular entry nearest to the required value of x, and h the interval of tabulation. Writing $u = (x - x_0)/h$, the problem then is to determine the value of u for which $y = a$. Let the function y be replaced by a suitable interpolation polynomial, say $Q_n(u)$ of the nth degree in u. To solve for u from the equation $Q_n(u) = a$, we may use either of the following methods.

Iterative Method. The equation $Q_n(u) = a$ is first expressed in the form $u = \Phi(u)$. Then, a first approximation u_1 is obtained by solving the equation $Q_1(u) = a$, where $Q_1(u)$ is the linear interpolation formula for y. Successive approximations $u_2, u_3, \ldots$ are then obtained from $u_2 = \Phi(u_1)$, $u_3 = \Phi(u_2), \ldots$, etc.

Reversion of Series. Another method is to revert the polynomial interpolation formula

$$y = a_0 + a_1 u + a_2 u^2 + a_3 u^3 + a_4 u^4 + \cdots$$

in the form:

(2.3.1) $$u = Z + c_2 Z^2 + c_3 Z^3 + c_4 Z^4 + \ldots,$$

where

$$Z = (y - a_0)/a_1,$$

$$c_2 = -b_2, \quad c_3 = -b_3 + 2b_2^2, \quad c_4 = -b_4 + 5b_2 b_3 - 5b_2^3,$$

and

$$b_2 = a_2/a_1, \quad b_3 = a_3/a_1, \quad b_4 = a_4/a_1.$$

Substituting $Z = (a - a_0)/a_1$, the required value of u is obtained.

Illustrative Example 2.4. Using the corrected data from illustrative example 2.2, find by inverse interpolation the value of θ for which $(\sin \theta)/\theta = 0.3$.

To find the value of θ for which $y = (\sin \theta)/\theta = 0.3$ we use y as the argument and $x = 180/\pi$ as the function dependent on y, and employ Lagrange's formula 2.1.2 for interpolation with unequal intervals. We thus have

$$x = L_0 x_0 + L_1 x_1 + \cdots + L_5 x_5,$$

where $x_0 = 11$, $x_1 = 12, \ldots, x_5 = 16$, and

$$
\begin{aligned}
L_0 &= \frac{(y - y_1)(y - y_2) \cdots (y - y_5)}{(y_0 - y_1)(y_0 - y_2) \cdots (y_0 - y_5)} \\
&= \frac{(0.3 - 0.41350)(0.3 - 0.33762) \cdots (0.3 - 0.12248)}{(0.48946 - 0.41350)(0.48946 - 0.33762) \cdots (0.48946 - 0.12248)} \\
&= +0.0106717,
\end{aligned}
$$

computed with the help of seven-digit logarithm tables. Similarly,

$$L_1 = -0.0907400,$$
$$L_2 = +0.5672319,$$
$$L_3 = +0.6084461,$$
$$L_4 = -0.1103303,$$
$$L_5 = +0.0147208.$$

A check on the computations is made from the fact that the sum of the L's should be unity. We have here $L_0 + L_1 + \cdots L_5 = 1.0000002$. Thus $x = 13.5013471$; hence $\theta = x\pi/18 = 2.35643$.

Alternatively, we may use Bessel's formula 2.2.4, setting out from $x_0 = 13$. This gives

$$y = \tfrac{1}{2}(0.33762 + 0.26306) + v(-0.07456) + \frac{(v^2 - \frac{1}{4})}{2}$$
$$\times \tfrac{1}{2}(0.00132 + 0.00249) + \frac{v(v^2 - \frac{1}{4})}{6}(0.00117) + \frac{v^2(v^2 - \frac{1}{4})}{24}$$
$$\times \tfrac{1}{2}(-0.00007 - 0.00010) + \frac{v(v^2 - \frac{1}{4})(v^2 - \frac{9}{4})}{120}(-0.00003),$$

where $v = x - 13.5$.

This may be expressed as a polynomial in v as follows:

$$y = 0.3001019 - 0.0746089v + 0.0009534v^2 + 0.0001956v^3$$
$$- 0.0000035v^4 - 0.0000002v^5.$$

The problem now is to find the value of v for which $y = 0.3$. Reverting this series by means of formula 2.3.1, we have

$$v = Z + 0.0127786Z^2 + 0.0029483Z^3 + \cdots,$$

where $Z = (y - 0.3001019)/0.0746089 = 0.0013658$. Substituting this value of Z in the above equation, we get $v = 0.0013658$. Thus $x = v + 13.5 = 13.5013658$, so that $\theta = x\pi/18 = 2.35643$. This result agrees with the one obtained by the preceding method.

2.4 EXERCISES

2.1. Locate and correct the errors in the following values of a function $f(x)$ by examining the difference table:

x	$f(x)$	x	$f(x)$
0.5	0.19146	1.1	0.36433
0.6	0.22575	1.2	0.38493
0.7	0.25804	1.3	0.40320
0.8	0.28814	1.4	0.41924
0.9	0.31594	1.5	0.43319
1.0	0.34124	1.6	0.44520

2.2. The following table gives the values of $\log_{10} x$ for various values of x. Find by linear interpolation the values of log 1.25132, log 1.25884, log 1.2605, and log 1.26895 and the estimate of the error in linear interpolation. Compute the same values by using polynomial interpolation formulae of appropriate form and degree. Compare the interpolated values with the actual values read from a seven-figure logarithmic table.

x	$\log x$	x	$\log x$
1.250	0.0969100	1.260	0.1003705
1.251	0.0972573	1.261	0.1007151
1.252	0.0976043	1.262	0.1010594
1.253	0.0979511	1.263	0.1014034
1.254	0.0982975	1.264	0.1017471
1.255	0.0986437	1.265	0.1020905
1.256	0.0989896	1.266	0.1024337
1.257	0.0993353	1.267	0.1027766
1.258	0.0996806	1.268	0.1031193
1.259	0.1000257	1.269	0.1034616

2.3. Using the following table of values of the incomplete normal probability integral

$$F(x) = \int_x^\infty (2\pi)^{-\frac{1}{2}} \exp\left(-\tfrac{1}{2}t^2\right) dt,$$

find by interpolation the values of

$$I(x) = \int_{-x}^x (2\pi)^{-\frac{1}{2}} \exp\left(-\tfrac{1}{2}t^2\right) dt$$

for $x = 0.01$, 0.675, and 1.96.

x	$F(x)$	x	$F(x)$	x	$F(x)$
0.00	.50000	0.75	.22663	1.50	.066807
0.05	.48006	0.80	.21186	1.55	.060571
0.10	.46017	0.85	.19766	1.60	.054799
0.15	.44038	0.90	.18406	1.65	.049471
0.20	.42074	0.95	.17106	1.70	.044565
0.25	.40129	1.00	.15866	1.80	.035930
0.30	.38209	1.05	.14686	1.90	.028717
0.35	.36317	1.10	.13567	2.00	.022750
0.40	.34458	1.15	.12507	2.10	.017864
0.45	.32636	1.20	.11507	2.20	.013903
0.50	.30854	1.25	.10565	2.30	.010724
0.55	.29116	1.30	.096800	2.40	.0081975
0.60	.27425	1.35	.088508	2.50	.0062097
0.65	.25785	1.40	.080757	2.60	.0046612
0.70	.24196	1.45	.073529	2.70	.0034670

2.4. The values of a function $y = f(x)$ at the points $x = -1, 0, 1$, and 2 are denoted by y_{-1}, y_0, y_1, and y_2, respectively. Show that the third-degree polynomial interpolation formula for $y_u = f(u)$ $(0 < u < 1)$ may be expressed in the form:

$$y_u = c_{-1}(u)y_{-1} + c_0(u)y_0 + c_1(u)y_1 + c_2(u)y_2,$$

where c's are numerical coefficients depending only on u. Prepare a table of values of $c_i(u)$ for $u = 0.1\ (0.1)\ 0.9$, $i = -1, 0, 1, 2$, where the values of u as indicated are $0.1, 0.2, \ldots, 0.9$.

2.5. The values of $\sin x$ at the points given below are well known. Evaluate $\sin 15°$ and $\sin 75°$ by using a fourth-degree polynomial interpolation formula.

x (in degrees)	0	30	45	60	90
$\sin x$	0	$\frac{1}{2}$	$1/\sqrt{2}$	$\sqrt{3}/2$	1

2.6. The populations in four consecutive age groups in a certain country are given below. Estimate the populations at ages 32 and 37.

Age group	Population
25–29	458,572
30–34	441,424
35–39	423,123
40–44	402,918

2.7. Given that $\sum_{x=1}^{10} f(x) = 500{,}426$, $\sum_{x=4}^{10} f(x) = 329{,}240$, $\sum_{x=7}^{10} f(x) = 175{,}212$, and $f(10) = 40{,}365$, find the values of $f(x)$ for $x = 1, 4$, and 5.

2.8. Given that $f(0) = 23.1234$, $f(6) = 23.7252$, $f(12) = 24.6836$, and $f(18) = 26.1330$, complete the series from $f(6)$ to $f(12)$.

2.9. Using the table in exercise 2.2, find $10^{1/10}$ by inverse interpolation.

2.10. Using the table in exercise 2.3, find by inverse interpolation the value of x for which $I(x) = 0.5$.

2.11. Using the table in exercise 2.3, find by inverse interpolation the value of x for which $F(x) = 0.05$.

2.12. The following table gives the values of $F_0 \equiv F_\alpha(m, n)$ for which

$$\frac{m^{\frac{1}{2}m} n^{\frac{1}{2}n}}{B(\frac{1}{2}m, \frac{1}{2}n)} \int_{F_0}^{\infty} F^{\frac{1}{2}m-1}(n + mF)^{-\frac{1}{2}(m+n)} \, dF = \alpha$$

for $\alpha = 0.05$, $m = 6, 8, 12, 24, \infty$, and $n = 30, 40, 60, 120, \infty$. From this table find by interpolation the values of (a) $F_{0.05}(15, 50)$, (b) $F_{0.95}(30, 25)$, by using $1/m$ and $1/n$ as arguments.

VALUES OF $F_{0.05}(m, n)$

n \ m	6	8	12	24	∞
30	2.42	2.27	2.09	1.89	1.62
40	2.34	2.18	2.00	1.79	1.51
60	2.25	2.10	1.92	1.70	1.39
120	2.17	2.02	1.83	1.61	1.25
∞	2.10	1.94	1.75	1.52	1.00

2.13. A table of values of e^{-x} is to be constructed for values of x in the interval $x = 0$ to $x = 1$. Determine the maximum uniform tabular interval such that linear interpolation in the tables would give seven-figure accuracy.

2.14. The following tables give the values of the integral

$$\alpha(h, k, \rho) = \int_h^\infty \int_k^\infty \frac{1}{2\pi\sqrt{1 - \rho^2}} \exp\left[-\frac{1}{2(1 - \rho^2)}(x^2 + y^2 - 2\rho xy)\right] dx\, dy$$

for different values of h, k, and ρ. Find by interpolation the value of $\alpha(h, k, \rho)$ for $h = 0.16$, $k = 0.14$, and $\rho = 0.875$.

VALUES OF $\alpha(h, k, \rho)$

$\rho = 0.80$

k \ h	0.0	0.1	0.2	0.3
0.0	.3976	.3766	.3538	.3294
0.1		.3583	.3380	.3162
0.2			.3204	.3011
0.3				.2843

$\rho = 0.85$

k \ h	0.0	0.1	0.2	0.3
0.0	.4117	.3905	.3670	.3417
0.1		.3723	.3518	.3292
0.2			.3342	.3145
0.3				.2978

$\rho = 0.90$

k \ h	0.0	0.1	0.2	0.3
0.0	.4282	.4067	.3822	.3552
0.1		.3887	.3678	.3441
0.2			.3504	.3302
0.3				.3135

$\rho = 0.95$

k \ h	0.0	0.1	0.2	0.3
0.0	.4495	.4271	.4005	.3705
0.1		.4099	.3880	.3622
0.2			.3712	.3500
0.3				.3338

Numerical Solution of Equations

A number of computational techniques for evaluating the roots of equations with numerical coefficients are described in this chapter. In most of these techniques we start with an approximate value of a root and then obtain successively closer approximations.

3.1 METHODS FOR LOCATING ROOTS

Real roots of the equation $f(x) = 0$ can be located approximately by drawing the graph of the function $y = f(x)$ and finding the abscissae of the points where it crosses the x-axis. Graphical methods can also be adopted for the purpose of locating roots of simultaneous equations.

If $f(x)$ is continuous, and $f(x_1)$ and $f(x_2)$ are of opposite signs, a root of the equation $f(x) = 0$ lies between x_1 and x_2.

Rolle's Theorem. If $f(x)$ has a continuous derivative $f'(x)$, then between two consecutive real roots of $f(x) = 0$ there is at least one root of $f'(x) = 0$.

Fundamental Theorem of Algebra. If $P_n(x)$ is a polynomial of degree n in x, then the equation $P_n(x) = 0$ has n roots, real or imaginary. Imaginary roots occur in conjugate pairs* if the coefficients of $P_n(x)$ are all real.

Descartes' Rule of Signs. For the polynomial equation $P_n(x) \equiv a_0 x^n + a_1 x^{n-1} + a_2 x^{n-2} + \cdots + a_{n-1} x + a_n = 0$, consider the sequence of signs of the coefficients $a_0, a_1, a_2, \ldots, a_n$ in that order. If the signs of two consecutive coefficients are different, that will be counted as one variation. The zero coefficients are disregarded. Count the number of variations in sign in this sequence. Then the number of positive real roots of the equation is either equal to or less than this by an even integer. For example, consider the equation $x^3 - x - 4 = 0$. The sequence of signs of the coefficients is $+$, 0, $-$, $-$. Disregarding zero, there is just one

---

* For example, the equation $x^2 - 2x + 5 = 0$ has as its roots $1 + 2i, 1 - 2i$, where $i = \sqrt{-1}$.

variation in sign. Therefore there must be one and only one positive real root of this equation.

Sturm's Theorem. Let $F_0 \equiv P_n(x)$ be a polynomial of degree n in x, $F_1 \equiv P_n'(x)$. Let $-F_2$ be the remainder in the division of F_0 by F_1, and Q_1 the corresponding quotient, that is, $F_0 = Q_1 F_1 - F_2$, and similarly $F_1 = Q_2 F_2 - F_3, \ldots$, and finally $F_{n-1} = Q_n F_n$, with the convention that any non-zero constant divides any polynomial exactly. Let $a < b$ be two real numbers. Let V_a and V_b be the number of variations in signs of the sequence of functions $F_0, F_1, \ldots, F_n$ evaluated at a and b, respectively. Then $V_a \geq V_b$, and $V_a - V_b$ is exactly equal to the number of real roots of $P_n(x) = 0$ on the interval (a, b). This is true for simple as well as multiple roots, but each multiple root is to be counted only once.

Thus, if we want to find the number of real roots of the equation

$$F_0 = x^3 - x - 4 = 0$$

between 1 and 2, we evaluate the functions

$$F_1 = 3x^2 - 1, \quad F_2 = \tfrac{2}{3}x + 4, \quad F_3 = -107$$

at points 1 and 2. The signs of these functions at 1 and 2 are as follows:

x	F_0	F_1	F_2	F_3
1	−	+	+	−
2	+	+	+	−

so that $V_1 = 2$, $V_2 = 1$, and $V_1 - V_2 = 1$. Therefore there is just one real root of the equation $x^3 - x - 4 = 0$ in the interval $(1, 2)$.

3.2 EQUATIONS IN ONE UNKNOWN

Regula Falsi (Method of False Position). In this method, to evaluate a root of the equation $f(x) = 0$ we first find, by some method or other, two numbers x_1 and x_2, as close together as possible, such that $y_1 = f(x_1)$ and $y_2 = f(x_2)$ are of opposite signs. If $f(x)$ is continuous, then there is a root x_0 of the equation $f(x) = 0$ in the interval (x_1, x_2). A first approximation $x^{(1)}$ to it can be derived by replacing the function $y = f(x)$ in the interval (x_1, x_2) by the straight line which passes through the points (x_1, y_1) and (x_2, y_2) and finding the abscissa of the point where this line cuts the x axis. This gives

$$(3.2.1) \qquad x^{(1)} = x_1 - \frac{x_1 - x_2}{y_1 - y_2} \cdot y_1.$$

To obtain an even better approximation, we compute $y^{(1)} = f(x^{(1)})$. Then, if y_1 and $y^{(1)}$ are of opposite signs, a root lies in the interval $(x_1, x^{(1)})$. Otherwise $y^{(1)}$ and y_2 must be of opposite signs, and a root lies in the interval $(x^{(1)}, x_2)$. After locating the root in this way, we repeat the above procedure to obtain a closer approximation.

Illustrative Example 3.1.   Find the root of the equation $(\sin \theta)/\theta = 0.3$ to five places of decimals by the method of false position.

Let us write x for the magnitude in degrees of the angle whose radian measure is θ and $f(x) = (\sin \theta)/\theta - 0.3$. We want the value of x for which $f(x) = 0$. Let $x_1 = 130$ and $x_2 = 140$. By direct computation using Chambers' *Seven-Figure Mathematical Tables*, we find $f(x_1) = 0.03762$ and $f(x_2) = -0.03694$, so that a root of $f(x) = 0$ lies between x_1 and x_2. An approximate value of this root is given by formula (3.2.1) as

$$x^{(1)} = 130 - \frac{130 - 140}{0.03762 - (-0.03694)} \, 0.03762 = 135.0456009.$$

To obtain a still better approximation, we compute $f(x^{(1)}) = -0.00024$, so that the root lies between x_1 and $x^{(1)}$. The process can then be continued as shown in the table below. For other methods of solving this equation see illustrative examples 2.4 and 3.3.

x	θ	$f(x) = \dfrac{\sin \theta}{\theta} - 0.3$	Improved value of x
$x_1 \ = 130°$	2.2689277	0.0376240	$x^{(1)} = 135.0456009$
$x^{(1)} = 135°2'.74$	2.3569914	-0.0002353	$x^{(2)} = 135.0142419$
$x^{(2)} = 135°0'.85$	2.3564441	-0.0000005	$x^{(3)} = 135.0141753$
$x^{(3)} = 135°0'.85$	2.3564429		

Newton–Raphson Method.   In this method we start with an approximation $x^{(1)}$ to the required root x_0 of the equation $f(x) = 0$. Then, writing h for the additive correction to be applied to $x^{(1)}$ to obtain x_0, we have $x_0 = x^{(1)} + h$; therefore h satisfies the equation $f(x^{(1)} + h) = 0$. An approximate solution of this equation in h is obtained by expanding the left-hand side in a Taylor series and omitting second and higher powers of h. Applying this procedure to $x^{(1)}$, we obtain $x^{(2)}$, the second approximation to the root:

$$(3.2.2) \qquad x^{(2)} = x^{(1)} - \frac{f(x^{(1)})}{f'(x^{(1)})},$$

where $f'(x)$ is the derivative of $f(x)$. This process may be repeated to obtain further approximations $x^{(3)}, x^{(4)}, \ldots$, etc., successively from the formula

$$x^{(i+1)} = x^{(i)} - \frac{f(x^{(i)})}{f'(x^{(i)})}.$$

The process converges rapidly when the numerical value of the derivative $f'(x)$ is large relative to $f(x)$ in the neighborhood of the required root.

Illustrative Example 3.2. Find by the Newton–Raphson method the root of the equation $P(x) \equiv x^3 - x - 4 = 0$ lying between 1 and 2 correct to five places of decimals.

We find that $P(1) = -4$ and $P(2) = 2$, so that, by linear interpolation, the root is approximately $x^{(1)} = 1.7$. Here $P'(x) = 3x^2 - 1$, and using the formula

$$x^{(i+1)} = x^{(i)} - \frac{P(x^{(i)})}{P'(x^{(i)})},$$

we have successively $x^{(2)} = 1.8026076$, $x^{(3)} = 1.7963463$, $x^{(4)} = 1.7963219$, the last being correct to five places of decimals. The details are shown in the following table.

x	$P(x) = x^3 - x - 4$	$P'(x) = 3x^2 - 1$	$P(x)/P'(x)$
$x^{(1)} = 1.7$	-0.787	7.67	-0.1026076
$x^{(2)} = 1.8026076$	0.0547751	8.7481826	0.0062613
$x^{(3)} = 1.7963463$	0.0002117	8.6805800	0.0000244
$x^{(4)} = 1.963219$			

For an alternative method of solving this equation see illustrative example 3.4.

Method of Straightforward Iteration. This method consists in rewriting the equation $f(x) = 0$ in the form $x = F(x)$. Then, starting with an approximation $x^{(1)}$ to the required root x_0, the next approximation $x^{(2)}$ is obtained as

(3.2.3) $$x^{(2)} = F(x^{(1)}).$$

This process is repeated to get successive approximations $x^{(3)}, x^{(4)}, \ldots$, etc., from the formula $x^{(i+1)} = F(x^{(i)})$, until the desired degree of accuracy is attained. The condition for convergence of this method is that the size of the derivative $F'(x)$ be smaller than unity in the neighborhood of the required root. The smaller the value of $|F'(x)|$ the more rapid is the convergence.

Illustrative Example 3.3. Find the root of the equation $(\sin \theta)/\theta = 0.3$ to five places of decimals by straightforward iteration.

We express the equation in the form $\theta = F(\theta)$, where $F(\theta) = \sin \theta + 0.7\theta$. Writing x for the magnitude in degrees of the angle whose radian measure is θ, we start with the first approximation $x^{(1)} = 130$, the corresponding value of θ being $\theta^{(1)} = 2.2689277$, so that the next approximation is $\theta^{(2)} = F(\theta^{(1)}) = 2.3542938$, the corresponding value of x being $x^{(2)} = 134°53'.47$. Continuing in this way, we obtain $\theta^{(3)} = F(\theta^{(2)}) = 2.3564543$ and $\theta^{(4)} = 2.3564417$, which is correct to five places of decimals. The details are shown in the following table.

x	$\sin \theta$	$\theta = \sin \theta + 0.7\theta$
$x^{(1)} = 130°$		
$\theta^{(1)} = 2.2689277$	0.7660444	$2.3542938 = \theta^{(2)}$
$x^{(2)} = 134°54'.47$	0.7084486	$2.3564543 = \theta^{(3)}$
$x^{(3)} = 135°0'.89$	0.7069237	$2.3564417 = \theta^{(4)}$

Illustrative Example 3.4.   Find the real root of the equation

$$x^3 - x - 4 = 0$$

correct to five places of decimals by straightforward iteration.

Here we choose the iteration scheme $x^{(i+1)} = \sqrt[3]{x^{(i)} + 4}$ in order to satisfy the condition $|F'(x)| < 1$. Starting with $x^{(1)} = 2$, we obtain successively $x^{(2)} = 1.817121$, $x^{(3)} = 1.7984679$, $x^{(4)} = 1.7965435$, $x^{(5)} = 1.7963242$, $x^{(6)} = 1.79632209$, so that the root to five places of decimals is 1.79632.

The following method for solving polynomial equations does not require approximate location of roots.

Graeffe's Root-Squaring Method.   If it is required to find the roots of a polynomial equation $P_n(x) \equiv a_0 x^n + a_1 x^{n-1} + \cdots + a_n = 0$, the first step in this method is to construct another polynomial equation $G_n(x) = g_0 x^n + g_1 x^{n-1} + \cdots + g_n = 0$. In this equation the roots are Nth powers of the roots of $P_n(x) = 0$, where N is a conveniently large integer of the form $N = 2^k$. The polynomial $G_n(x)$ is constructed from the polynomial $P_n(x)$ in k successive stages, in each of which Graeffe's root-squaring process is applied to obtain a polynomial equation whose roots are the squares of the roots of the polynomial equation in the previous stage. One way to construct a polynomial equation $Q_n(x) \equiv b_0 x^n + b_1 x^{n-1} + \cdots + b_n = 0$ whose roots are squares of those of $P_n(x) = 0$ is to make use of the identity $Q_n(x) = (-1)^n P_n(\sqrt{x}) P_n(-\sqrt{x})$. Thus the b's are given by

$$
\begin{aligned}
b_0 &= a_0{}^2, \\
b_1 &= -a_1{}^2 + 2a_0 a_2, \\
b_2 &= a_2{}^2 - 2a_1 a_3 + 2a_0 a_4, \\
b_3 &= -a_3{}^2 + 2a_2 a_4 - 2a_1 a_5 + 2a_0 a_6, \\
\cdots \quad &\cdots \quad \cdots \quad \cdots \quad \cdots
\end{aligned}
$$

Thus, if $\alpha_1, \alpha_2, \ldots, \alpha_n$ are the roots of $P_n(x) = 0$, those of $G_n(x) = 0$ are $\alpha_1^N, \alpha_2^N, \ldots, \alpha_n^N$, so that we have the identities:

$$-g_1/g_0 = \alpha_1^N + \alpha_2^N + \cdots + \alpha_n^N,$$
$$g_2/g_0 = \alpha_1^N\alpha_2^N + \alpha_1^N\alpha_2^N + \cdots + \alpha_{n-1}^N\alpha_n^N,$$
$$\cdots \quad \cdots \quad \cdots \quad \cdots \quad \cdots$$
$$(-1)^n g_n/g_0 = \alpha_1^N\alpha_2^N \cdots \alpha_n^N.$$

If the roots are all real and unequal, $|\alpha_1| > |\alpha_2| > \cdots > |\alpha_n|$, say, then for large N the ratios $(\alpha_2/\alpha_1)^N, \ldots, (\alpha_n/\alpha_{n-1})^N$ are all negligible, so that we have asymptotically

$$\alpha_1^N = -g_1/g_0, \quad \alpha_2^N = -g_2/g_1, \ldots, \quad \alpha_n^N = -g_n/g_{n-1},$$

from which all the roots can be evaluated. Modifications of this method are available for computing imaginary roots or multiple roots of polynomial equations. An example will make this clear.

Illustrative Example 3.5. Find the real root of the equation

$$P(x) \equiv x^3 - x - 4 = 0$$

by Graeffe's root-squaring method.

We find by inspection that the equation $P(x) = 0$ has one real root and two imaginary roots, which are, of course, conjugate to one another. Let us denote the real root by λ and the conjugate pair of imaginary roots* by $\lambda_1 = re^{i\theta}$ and $\lambda_2 = re^{-i\theta}$.

Consequently if the equation

$$G(x) = x^3 + g_1x^2 + g_2x + g_3 = 0$$

is constructed so that the roots of $G(x) = 0$ are the $2m$th $(2m = 2^N)$ powers of the roots of $P(x) = 0$, we must have

$$-g_1 = 2r^{2m} \cos 2m\theta + \lambda^{2m},$$
$$g_2 = r^{4m} + 2r^{2m}\lambda^{2m} \cos 2m\theta,$$
$$-g_3 = r^{4m}\lambda^{2m}.$$

Let us distinguish two cases: (a) $|r| > |\lambda|$ and (b) $|r| < |\lambda|$. In case (a), we have asymptotically

$$-g_1 \doteq 2r^{2m} \cos 2m\theta \quad \text{and} \quad g_2 \doteq r^{4m},$$

* This is another way of expressing conjugate roots. See the footnote in Section 3.1, p. 26.

so that, as m increases, the sign of g_1 may change, but that of g_2 will remain positive. In case (b), we have asymptotically

$$-g_1 \doteq \lambda^{2m} \quad \text{and} \quad g_2 \doteq 2r^{2m}\lambda^{2m} \cos 2m\theta,$$

so that with increasing m the coefficient g_1 will remain negative, but the sign of g_2 may change.

We now carry out the root-squaring process as shown in the following table.

ROOT SQUARING

$2m$	c_0	c_1	c_2	c_3
1	1	0	-1	-4
2	1	-2	1	-16
4	1	-2	-63	-256
8	1	-130	2945	$-65,536$
16	1	$-11,010$	$-8,366,335$	$-4,294,967 \times 10^3$
32	1	$-1,379,528 \times 10^2$	$-2,457,961 \times 10^7$	$-1,844,674 \times 10^{13}$
64	1	$-1,908,013 \times 10^{10}$	$-4,485,402 \times 10^{21}$	$-3,402,822 \times 10^{32}$
128	1	$-3,640,603 \times 10^{26}$	$7,133,574 \times 10^{48}$	$-1,157,920 \times 10^{71}$
256	1	$-1,325,400 \times 10^{59}$	...	...

The c's are computed successively from the relations:

$$c_0' = 1, \quad c_1' = -c_1^2 + 2c_2, \quad c_2' = c_2^2 - 2c_1c_3, \quad c_3' = -c_3^2.$$

For instance, c_1 for the line $2m = 16$ is obtained as

$$c_1 = -(-130)^2 + 2(-8,366,335) = -1,379,528 \times 10^2.$$

Looking at these coefficients, we find that c_1 remains negative throughout, but the sign of c_2 changes. Therefore, we have $|r| < |\lambda|$ and, consequently, $-c_1 \doteq \lambda^{2m}$. Thus

$$\lambda^{256} = 1,325,400 \times 10^{59},$$

so that $256 \log \lambda = 65.1223470$ from Chambers' *Seven-Figure Mathematical Tables*. Thus $\log \lambda = 0.2543842$ and hence $\lambda = 1.79632$. This is correct to five places of decimals.

3.3 EQUATIONS IN MORE THAN ONE UNKNOWN

The techniques described in Section 3.2 for the solution of equations in one unknown can be easily extended to obtain solutions of equations involving more than one unknown. We will discuss two such techniques.

Newton–Raphson's Method for Equations in Several Unknowns. Let the equations involving n unknowns $x_1, x_2, \ldots, x_n$ be $f_i(x_1, x_2, \ldots, x_n) = 0$, $i = 1, 2, \ldots, n$, and let $[x_1^{(1)}, x_2^{(1)}, \ldots, x_n^{(1)}]$ be an approximation to the true solution $(x_1^0, x_2^0, \ldots, x_n^0)$. Then the next approximation $[x_1^{(2)}, x_2^{(2)}, \ldots, x_n^{(2)}]$ is obtained as $x_i^{(2)} = x_i^{(1)} + h_i$, $i = 1, 2, \ldots, n$, where h_i's are the solutions of the linear equations

$$(3.8.1) \qquad \sum_j h_j \frac{\partial f_i}{\partial x_j} = -f_i, \qquad i = 1, 2, \ldots n,$$

and the functions f_i's and the partial derivatives $\left(\dfrac{\partial f_i}{\partial x_j}\right)$'s are to be evaluated at $[x_1^{(1)}, x_2^{(1)}, \ldots, x_n^{(1)}]$. The process is continued iteratively until the desired accuracy is reached.

Method of Straightforward Iteration. This method is applicable by first expressing the simultaneous equations in the form

$$x_i = F_i(x_1, x_2, \ldots, x_n), \qquad i = 1, 2, \ldots, n.$$

Starting with a first approximation $[x_1^{(1)}, x_2^{(1)}, \ldots, x_n^{(1)}]$, the second approximation $[x_1^{(2)}, x_2^{(2)}, \ldots, x_n^{(2)}]$ is obtained from the following formulae:

$$(3.3.2) \qquad \begin{aligned} x_1^{(2)} &= F_1(x_1^{(1)}, x_2^{(1)}, \ldots, x_n^{(1)}), \\ x_2^{(2)} &= F_2(x_1^{(2)}, x_2^{(1)}, \ldots, x_n^{(1)}). \\ &\cdots \quad\cdots \\ x_n^{(2)} &= F_n(x_1^{(2)}, x_2^{(2)}, \ldots, x_{n-1}^{(2)}, x_n^{(1)}). \end{aligned}$$

Further approximations to the required degree of accuracy can be obtained by iteration.

3.4 EXERCISES

3.1. Using properties of differences, tabulate the polynomial $P(x) = 315x^3 - 525x^2 + 231x - 17$ for values of x in the range $(0, 1)$ at intervals of 0.05. Use this table to verify that all the roots of the equation $P(x) = 0$ are real, and obtain from the table approximate values of these roots. Starting with these approximations, evaluate to five significant figures all the roots of the equation $P(x) = 0$, using (a) the Newton–Raphson method and (b) the false-position method.

3.2. Find all the roots of the equation in exercise 3.1 by Graeffe's root-squaring method.

3.3. Find the root of the equation $x/(1 - e^{-x}) = 3.034$ correct to four places of decimals by any suitable method.

3.4. Find the root of the equation $x^2 + 4 \sin x = 0$ correct to four places of decimals by any suitable method.

3.5. An approximate solution of the equations

$$x^7 - 5x^2y^4 + 1510 = 0$$
$$y^5 - 3x^4y - 105 = 0$$

is $x = 2$, $y = 3$. Find this solution correct to four places of decimals.

3.6. Find, correct to five places of decimals, a solution of

$$\sin x = y + 1.32,$$
$$\cos y = x - 0.85.$$

3.7. The length of the smaller arc of a circle is 10 ft, and the length of the chord on which it stands is 8 ft. Find the radius of the circle to the nearest tenth of an inch.

3.8. The probability $P(x)$ that in a random sample of size 5, from a normal population with zero mean and unit standard deviation, the maximum will exceed a specified value x is given by

$$P(x) = 1 - [1 - F(x)]^5,$$

where

$$F(x) = \int_x^\infty (2\pi)^{-\frac{1}{2}} \exp\left(-\tfrac{1}{2}t^2\right) dt$$

is the normal probability integral. Using tables of the normal probability integral, find the value of x for which $P(x) = 0.05$.

3.9. Find for what value of x the function

$$Y_0\left\{1 + \alpha\left[1 + \frac{a(1 - x)}{bx}\right](e^{bxt} - 1)\right\}$$

is a maximum, given that $\alpha = 0.05$, $a = 0.3$, $b = 0.1$, and $t = 15$.

3.10. Find all the roots of the equation

$$\sum_{k=0}^{n} (-1)^k \binom{n}{k}\binom{n+k}{k} x^k = 0,$$

separately for $n = 1, 2, 3, 4$, and 5.

CHAPTER 4

Numerical Differentiation and Integration

4.1 NUMERICAL DIFFERENTIATION

Numerical differentiation is the process of evaluating the derivatives of a function by using only its tabulated values. This is achieved by differentiating a suitable polynomial approximation to the given function. Thus for a function $f(x)$, tabulated at equidistant values of the argument, if we are to evaluate the derivative near the beginning of the tables, we may use Newton's forward difference formula $P_n(x)$ for the polynomial approximation to $f(x)$. Retaining the first five terms and neglecting the error in the interpolation formula, we have

$$f(x) = y_0 + u\,\Delta y_0 + \frac{u(u-1)}{2}\Delta^2 y_0 + \frac{u(u-1)(u-2)}{6}\Delta^3 y_0$$
$$+ \frac{u(u-1)(u-2)(u-3)}{24}\Delta^4 y_0$$

where $u = (x - x_0)/h$, h being the interval of tabulation. Then

$$f'(x) = \frac{1}{h}\left(\Delta y_0 + \frac{2u-1}{2}\Delta^2 y_0 + \frac{3u^2 - 6u + 2}{6}\Delta^3 y_0\right.$$
$$\left.+ \frac{4u^3 - 18u^2 + 22u - 6}{24}\Delta^4 y_0\right),$$

(4.1.1) $\quad f''(x) = \frac{1}{h^2}\left[\Delta^2 y_0 + (u-1)\Delta^3 y_0 + \frac{6u^2 - 18u + 11}{12}\Delta^4 y_0\right],$

$$f'''(x) = \frac{1}{h^3}\left(\Delta^3 y_0 + \frac{2u-3}{2}\Delta^4 y_0\right),$$

$$f^{iv}(x) = \frac{1}{h^4}\,\Delta^4 y_0.$$

Similarly, to obtain the derivatives for points near the middle of the table, we may use a central difference formula. Thus, from Stirling's formula, using the first five terms and neglecting the error, we have

$$f(x) = y_0 + uA_1 + \frac{u^2}{2} A_2 + \frac{u(u^2 - 1)}{6} A_3 + \frac{u^2(u^2 - 1)}{24} A_4,$$

where

$$A_1 = \tfrac{1}{2}(\Delta y_{-1} + \Delta y_0), \quad A_1 = \Delta^2 y_{-1}, \quad A_3 = \tfrac{1}{2}(\Delta^3 y_{-2} + \Delta^3 y_{-1}),$$

$$A_4 = \Delta^4 y_{-2}.$$

Then,

$$f'(x) = \frac{1}{h}\left(A_1 + uA_2 + \frac{3u^2 - 1}{6} A_3 + \frac{2u^3 - u}{12} A_4 \right),$$

$$f''(x) = \frac{1}{h^2}\left(A_2 + uA_3 + \frac{6u^2 - 1}{12} A_4 \right),$$

(4.1.2)

$$f'''(x) = \frac{1}{h^3} (A_3 + uA_4),$$

$$f^{\mathrm{iv}}(x) = \frac{1}{h^4} A_4.$$

Alternately, from Bessel's formula, retaining the first five terms and neglecting the error,

$$f(x) = c_0 + vc_1 + \frac{v^2 - \tfrac{1}{4}}{2} c_2 + \frac{v(v^2 - \tfrac{1}{4})}{6} c_3 + \frac{(v^2 - \tfrac{1}{4})(v^2 - \tfrac{9}{4})}{24} c_4,$$

where

$$v = \frac{x - x_0}{h} - \frac{1}{2}, \quad c_0 = \frac{y_0 + y_1}{2}, \quad c_1 = \Delta y_0,$$

$$c_2 = \tfrac{1}{2}(\Delta^2 y_{-1} + \Delta^2 y_0), \quad c_3 = \Delta^3 y_{-1}, \quad c_4 = \tfrac{1}{2}(\Delta^4 y_{-2} + \Delta^4 y_{-1}),$$

we have

$$f'(x) = \frac{1}{h}\left(c_1 + vc_2 + \frac{3v^2 - \tfrac{1}{4}}{6} c_3 + \frac{4v^3 - 5v}{24} c_4 \right),$$

$$f''(x) = \frac{1}{h^2}\left(c_2 + vc_3 + \frac{12v^2 - 5}{24} c_4 \right),$$

(4.1.3)

$$f'''(x) = \frac{1}{h^3} (c_3 + vc_4),$$

$$f^{\mathrm{iv}}(x) = \frac{1}{h^4} c_4.$$

In a similar manner, other interpolation formulae may be differentiated to obtain computational formulae for numerical differentiation in different situations. In particular, when the interval of tabulation is not constant, Lagrange's formula or Newton's general divided difference formula may be used to obtain the derivatives.

Illustrative Example 4.1.   The following table gives the values of an empirical function $f(x)$ for certain values of x. Find (a) $f'(93)$, (b) the value of x at which $f(x)$ is a maximum, and (c) the maximum value of $f(x)$ in this range of x.

x	60	75	90	105	120
$f(x)$	28.2	38.2	43.2	40.9	37.7

We first prepare the difference table:

x	$y = f(x)$	Δ	Δ^2	Δ^3	Δ^4
60	28.2				
		10.0			
75	38.2		−5.0		
		−5.0		−2.3	
90	43.2		−7.3		8.7
		−2.3		6.4	
105	40.9		−0.9		
		−3.2			
120	37.7				

Taking $x_0 = 90$ as the origin, we have from Stirling's interpolation formula 2.2.3

$$f(x) = A_0 + uA_1 + \frac{u^2}{2}A_2 + \frac{u(u^2 - 1)}{6}A_3 + \frac{u^2(u^2 - 1)}{24}A_4,$$

where $u = (x - x_0)/h$, $h = 15$ in this case, and

$$A_0 = y_0 = 43.2,$$
$$A_1 = \tfrac{1}{2}(\Delta y_{-1} + \Delta y_0) \qquad = \tfrac{1}{2}(5.0 - 2.3) = 1.35,$$
$$A_2 = \Delta^2 y_{-1} \qquad = -7.3,$$
$$A_3 = \tfrac{1}{2}(\Delta^3 y_{-2} + \Delta^3 y_{-1}) \qquad = \tfrac{1}{2}(-2.3 + 6.4) = 2.05,$$
$$A_4 = \Delta^4 y_{-2} \qquad = 8.7.$$

Differentiating, we have

$$f'(x) = \frac{1}{h}\left(A_1 + uA_2 + \frac{3u^2 - 1}{6} A_3 + \frac{2u^3 - u}{12} A_4\right).$$

When $x = 93$, we have $u = (93 - 90)/15 = 0.2$, and therefore

$$f'(93) = \frac{1}{15}\left[1.35 + 0.2(-7.3) + \frac{3(0.2)^2 - 1}{6}(2.05) + \frac{2(0.2)^3 - 0.2}{12}(8.7)\right]$$

$$= -0.036271.$$

To locate the maximum, we have to solve the equation $f'(x) = 0$. In terms of u, this gives

$$A_1 + uA_2 + \frac{3u^2 - 1}{6} A_3 + \frac{2u^3 - u}{12} A_4 = 0$$

or

$$(12A_1 - 2A_3) + (12A_2 - A_4)u + 6A_3u^2 + 2A_4u^3 = 0,$$

that is,

$$12.10 - 96.3u + 12.30u^2 + 17.4u^3 = 0.$$

Solving this equation by the Newton–Raphson process, we get

$$u = 0.128126,$$

and the corresponding value of x is

$$x = x_0 + hu = 90 + 15(0.128126)$$

$$= 91.92189.$$

Also the value of $f(x)$ at this point is obtained by the substitution of $u = 0.128126$ in Stirling's formula; this turns out to be

$$f(91.92189) = 43.2641.$$

4.2 NUMERICAL INTEGRATION

Numerical integration is the process of evaluating a definite integral

$$I = \int_a^b f(x)\, dx$$

using a given set of tabulated values of the integrand $f(x)$. This method is generally used when the integrand is empirically determined or when it has a complicated expression difficult to treat analytically. The common procedure is to divide the range of integration (a, b) into a number of contiguous non-overlapping intervals. In each interval the integrand is approximated by a suitable interpolation polynomial and the integral is evaluated by integrating this polynomial. These integrals are then added up to obtain the integral for the entire range (a, b).

Trapezoidal Rule. Suppose that the values of the function $f(x)$ are tabulated at $n + 1$ equidistant points, $a = x_0, x_1, \ldots, x_n = b$, where $x_i = x_0 + ih$, $h = (b - a)/n$, and $f(x_i) = y_i$, $i = 0, 1, \ldots, n$. Then we might decide to take (x_0, x_1) as one interval and replace the integrand in this range by a first-degree polynomial. To find the value of the integral in this interval, we use

$$(4.2.1) \qquad \int_{x_0}^{x_1} f(x)\, dx = \frac{h}{2} (y_0 + y_1) + E.$$

Here E, the error term, is given by $E = -(h^3/12)f''(\lambda)$, where $x_0 < \lambda < x_1$.

Simpson's One-Third Rule. We might decide to take (x_0, x_2) as one interval and to replace the integrand in this range by a second-degree polynomial. Then, to obtain the value of the integral in this interval, we use

$$(4.2.2) \qquad \int_{x_0}^{x_2} f(x)\, dx = \frac{h}{3} (y_0 + 4y_1 + y_2) + E.$$

Here E, the error term, is given by $E = -(h^5/90)f^{iv}(\lambda)$, where $x_0 < \lambda < x_2$.

Weddle's Rule. Instead, we might decide to take (x_0, x_6) as one interval and to replace the integrand in this range by a sixth-degree polynomial. Then, to obtain the value of the integral in this range, we use

$$(4.2.3) \quad \int_{x_0}^{x_6} f(x)\, dx = \frac{3h}{10} (y_0 + 5y_1 + y_2 + 6y_3 + y_4 + 5y_5 + y_6) + E.$$

Here E, the error term, is given by $E = -(h^7/140)f^{vi}(\lambda)$, where $x_0 < \lambda < x_6$.

Illustrative Example 4.2. Evaluate by numerical integration (quadrature) $\int_0^1 \frac{dx}{1 + x^2}$ to six decimal places and hence find the value of π.

We compute the values of $y = 1/(1 + x^2)$ for $x = k/12, k = 0, 1, 2, \ldots,$ 12, and use (a) Simpson's one-third rule and (b) Weddle's rule to evaluate the integral. For the use of Simpson's one-third rule the range $(0, 1)$ is subdivided into six intervals: $(0, \frac{1}{6}), (\frac{1}{6}, \frac{2}{6}), \ldots, (\frac{5}{6}, 1)$, and for the application of Weddle's rule the range $(0, 1)$ is subdivided into two intervals: $(0, \frac{1}{2}), (\frac{1}{2}, 1)$.

The computations using all thirteen points are shown in the table.

x	$y = 1/(1 + x^2)$	Coefficients for	
		Simpson's rule	Weddle's rule
0	1.0000000	1	1
$\frac{1}{12}$	0.9931034	4	5
$\frac{2}{12}$	0.9729730	2	1
$\frac{3}{12}$	0.9411765	4	6
$\frac{4}{12}$	0.9000000	2	1
$\frac{5}{12}$	0.8520710	4	5
$\frac{6}{12}$	0.8000000	2	2
$\frac{7}{12}$	0.7461140	4	5
$\frac{8}{12}$	0.6923077	2	1
$\frac{9}{12}$	0.6400000	4	6
$\frac{10}{12}$	0.5901639	2	1
$\frac{11}{12}$	0.5433962	4	5
1	0.5000000	1	1

The value of the integral from Simpson's one-third rule turns out to be

$$I_S = \tfrac{1}{3} \times \tfrac{1}{12}[1.0000000 + 4(0.9931034) + 2(0.9729730)$$
$$+ 4(0.9411765) + \cdots + 0.5000000]$$
$$= 0.7853982,$$

and its value from Weddle's rule is

$$I_W = \tfrac{3}{10} \times \tfrac{1}{12}[1.000000 + 5(0.9931034) + 0.9729730$$
$$+ 6(0.9411765) + 0.9000000 + 5(0.8520710)$$
$$+ 2(0.8000000) + \cdots\cdots + 0.5000000] = 0.7853982.$$

The two values agree to seven decimal places.

The value of the integral is known to be $\pi/4$. This gives

$$\pi = 4(0.7853982) = 3.1415928,$$

which is in excess of the correct value by one unit in the seventh decimal place.

General Formula for Quadrature. If the $n + 1$ arguments x_i ($i = 0$, $1, 2, \ldots, n$) are not necessarily equispaced, by replacing the integrand by Lagrange's formula 2.1.2, we have

(4.2.4) $$\int_a^b y \, dx = \sum_{i=0}^{n} W_i y_i + E,$$

where E is the error term, and $W_i = \int_a^b L_i(x) \, dx$, $L_i(x)$ being given by 2.1.2.

Gauss's Formula. By choosing the $n + 1$ values of the argument $x_0, x_1, \ldots, x_n$ properly, the error term E in formula 4.2.4 can be made to vanish so long as $f(x)$ is a polynomial of degree at most $2n + 1$ in x. This gives

$$(4.2.5) \qquad \int_a^b f(x) \, dx = (b - a) \sum_{i=0}^n W_i g(t_i) + E,$$

where E is the error term, $g(x) = f[a + (b - a)x]$,

$$W_i = \int_0^1 \frac{(t - t_0)(t - t_1) \cdots (t - t_{i-1})(t - t_{i+1}) \cdots (t - t_n)}{(t_i - t_0)(t_i - t_1) \cdots (t_i - t_{i-1})(t_i - t_{i+1}) \cdots (t_i - t_n)} \, dt,$$

and $t_0, t_1, \ldots, t_n$ are the $n + 1$ roots of the equation $\phi_{n+1}(t) = 0$, where $\phi_n(t)$ is the Legendre polynomial of degree n in t, defined by

$$(4.2.6) \qquad \phi_n(t) = \sum_{k=0}^n (-1)^k \binom{n}{k} \binom{n + k}{k} t^k.$$

The values of t_i and W_i $(i = 0, 1, \ldots, n)$ for $n = 1, 2,$ and 3 are tabulated below for ready reference:

n	i	t_i	W_i
1	0	0.2113249	0.5000000
	1	0.7886751	0.5000000
2	0	0.1127017	0.2777778
	1	0.5000000	0.4444444
	2	0.8872983	0.2777778
3	0	0.0694318	0.1739274
	1	0.3300095	0.3260726
	2	0.6699905	0.3260726
	3	0.9305682	0.1739274

4.3 SUMMATION

We wish to evaluate the sum $S = \sum_{i=0}^n y_i$, where $y_i = f(x_i)$, $x_i = x_0 + ih$ $(i = 0, 1, 2, \ldots n)$, $x_0 = a$, $x_n = b$.

The Euler–Maclaurin Formula. When the function $f(x)$ is readily integrable and also differentiable, we use

$$(4.3.1) \quad S = \sum_{i=0}^n y_i = \frac{1}{h} \int_a^b f(x) \, dx + \tfrac{1}{2}(y_0 + y_n) + \frac{h}{12}[f'(b) - f'(a)]$$

$$- \frac{h^3}{720}[f'''(b) - f'''(a)] + \frac{h^5}{30240}[f^{\mathrm{v}}(b) - f^{\mathrm{v}}(a)] - \cdots.$$

Gregory's Formula. If the derivatives are difficult to evaluate and higher-order differences are negligible, we use the following form involving differences:

$$(4.3.2) \quad S = \sum_{i=0}^{n} y_i = \frac{1}{h} \int_a^b f(x)\, dx + \tfrac{1}{2}(y_0 + y_n)$$

$$+ \tfrac{1}{12}(\Delta y_{n-1} - \Delta y_0) + \tfrac{1}{24}(\Delta^2 y_{n-2} + \Delta^2 y_0)$$

$$+ \tfrac{19}{720}(\Delta^3 y_{n-3} - \Delta^3 y_0) - \tfrac{3}{160}(\Delta^4 y_{n-4} + \Delta^4 y_0) + \cdots.$$

Illustrative Example 4.3. Evaluate $S = \sum_{x=50}^{75} 1/x^2$ to seven places of decimals.

Here $f(x) = 1/x^2$, $n = 25$, $x_0 = 50$, $x_n = 75$, and $h = 1$. Also $\int f(x)\, dx = -1/x$, $f'(x) = -2/x^3$, $f'''(x) = -24/x^5$, $f^v(x) = -720/x^7$. Using the Euler–Maclaurin formula 4.3.1, we thus have

$$S = \left(\frac{1}{50} - \frac{1}{75}\right) + \frac{1}{2}\left(\frac{1}{50^2} + \frac{1}{75^2}\right) + \frac{1}{12}\left(\frac{2}{50^3} - \frac{2}{75^3}\right)$$

$$- \frac{1}{720}\left(\frac{24}{50^5} - \frac{24}{75^5}\right) + \frac{1}{30,240}\left(\frac{720}{50^7} - \frac{720}{75^7}\right) + \cdots$$

$$= 0.0069565.$$

4.4 EXERCISES

4.1. Find the differential coefficient of the following tabulated functions $f(t)$ of t at $t = 3.5, 4$, and 4.5.

t	0	1	2	3	4	5
$f(t)$	13.1623	18.8730	24.4721	30.0000	35.4772	40.9169

4.2. The following table gives the vertical distance $y(t)$ in feet of a projectile from the point of observation at different points of time t measured in seconds. Estimate the vertical components of the velocity and the acceleration of the projectile at the following times: $t = 0.25, 0.5$.

t	0	0.1	0.2	0.3	0.4	0.5	0.6
$y(t)$	0	107	211	312	382	451	487

4.3. Find the value of x for which the following tabulated function $f(x)$ is a minimum:

x	1.2	1.3	1.4	1.5	1.6	1.7
$f(x)$	81.82	79.75	78.73	78.62	79.35	80.36

4.4. Evaluate by quadrature $\int_0^1 (1 - x^2)^{1/2}\, dx$ and hence find the value of π correct to five decimal places.

4.5. Evaluate by quadrature $\log_e 2 = \int_1^2 (dx/x)$ to seven decimal places.

4.6. Find by quadrature the value of

$$\frac{1}{n^{\frac{1}{2}} B(\frac{1}{2}, \frac{1}{2}n)} \int_0^{1.96} \left(1 + \frac{t^2}{n}\right)^{-\frac{1}{2}(n+1)} dt$$

correct to four decimal places for $n = 10, 20,$ and 30.

4.7. Find, to four decimal places, the value of

$$\sum_{x=25}^{49} (2x + 1)^{-2}.$$

CHAPTER 5

Matrix Calculations

5.0 DEFINITIONS AND NOTATIONS

A matrix A of order $m \times n$ is an array of mn elements in m rows and n columns, the elements being, usually, numbers real or complex. Denoting by a_{ij} the element at the (i, j)th position, we can write the matrix A as

$$
A = ((a_{ij})) = \begin{bmatrix} a_{11} & a_{12} & \cdots & a_{1n} \\ a_{21} & a_{22} & \cdots & a_{2n} \\ \cdots & \cdots & \cdots & \cdots \\ a_{m1} & a_{m2} & \cdots & a_{mn} \end{bmatrix}.
$$

When $m = n$, the matrix is a *square* matrix of order $n \times n$ or simply n. A matrix which has a single row of n elements is a *row vector*, and one with a single column of m elements is a *column vector*. A square matrix A of order n is *symmetric* if $a_{ij} = a_{ji}$ for all i and j. A symmetric matrix with all elements real numbers is a real *symmetric* matrix.

The positions $(1, 1)$, $(2, 2)$, ..., (n, n) in a square matrix of order n define a *diagonal* of the matrix. A square matrix which has ones in the diagonal positions and zeros in the off-diagonal positions is called a *unit* or *identity* matrix and will be denoted by I.

The matrix A', called the *transpose* of A, has at its (i, j)th position the element a_{ji} of A, for all i and j. Thus, if A has m rows and n columns, A' will have n rows and m columns.

Multiplication of A by a scalar c is defined as

$$
cA = \begin{bmatrix} ca_{11} & ca_{12} & \cdots & ca_{1n} \\ ca_{21} & ca_{22} & \cdots & ca_{2n} \\ \cdots & \cdots & \cdots & \cdots \\ ca_{m1} & ca_{m2} & \cdots & ca_{mn} \end{bmatrix}.
$$

44

The sum $A + B$ of two matrices is defined only if they have the same number of rows and the same number of columns:

$$A + B = \begin{bmatrix} a_{11} + b_{11} & a_{12} + b_{12} & \cdots & a_{1n} + b_{1n} \\ a_{21} + b_{21} & a_{22} + b_{22} & \cdots & a_{2n} + b_{2n} \\ \cdots & \cdots & \cdots & \cdots \\ a_{m1} + b_{m1} & a_{2m} + b_{m2} & \cdots & a_{mn} + b_{mn} \end{bmatrix}$$

The product AC of two matrices $A = ((a_{ij}))$ of order $m \times n$ and $C = ((c_{ij}))$ of order $n \times r$ is defined only if the number of columns of A is the same as the number of rows of C. The product matrix AC is, then, of order $m \times r$.

$$AC = \begin{bmatrix} a_{11}c_{11} + a_{12}c_{21} + & \cdots & + a_{1n}c_{n1} & \cdots & a_{11}c_{1r} + a_{12}c_{2r} + & \cdots & + a_{1n}c_{nr} \\ a_{21}c_{11} + a_{22}c_{21} + & \cdots & + a_{2n}c_{n1} & \cdots & a_{21}c_{1r} + a_{22}c_{2r} + & \cdots & + a_{2n}c_{nr} \\ \cdots & & & & \cdots & & \\ a_{m1}c_{11} + a_{m2}c_{21} + & \cdots & + a_{mn}c_{n1} & \cdots & a_{m1}c_{1r} + a_{m2}c_{2r} + & \cdots & + a_{mn}c_{nr} \end{bmatrix}$$

The associative laws for addition and multiplication and the distributive law hold, provided the matrices are conformable for addition and multiplication. However, the commutative law does not hold in general. Thus

Associative laws: $(A + B) + C = A + (B + C)$; $(AB)C = ABC$,

Distributive law: $A(B + C) = AB + AC$,

But $\qquad\qquad AB \neq BA$, in general.

The rules for forming the transpose of the sum and the product of matrices are

$$(A + B)' = A' + B', \qquad (AB)' = B'A'.$$

The *determinant*, defined only for a square matrix, is a function of the elements of the matrix. The determinant of $A = ((a_{ij}))$, denoted by $|A|$, is defined as

$$|A| = \Sigma \pm a_{1i_1} a_{2i_2} \cdots a_{ni_n},$$

where the summation extends over all the $n!$ permutations $i_1, i_2, \ldots, i_n$ of the integers $1, 2, \ldots, n$. The sign before a summand is $+$ $(-)$ if an even (odd) number of interchanges is required to permute $1, 2, \ldots, n$ into $i_1, i_2, \ldots, i_n$.

A square matrix is called *singular* if its determinant is zero. Otherwise, it is *non-singular*.

Every *non-singular* matrix A has an *inverse* matrix denoted by A^{-1}, such that $AA^{-1} = A^{-1}A = I$.

The expression $\sum_{i=1}^{n} \sum_{j=1}^{n} a_{ij} x_i x_j$ is called a *quadratic form* in n variables $x_1, x_2, \ldots, x_n$. The coefficients $a_{ij} = a_{ji}$ are the elements of a symmetric matrix A. A convenient notation for a quadratic form is $x'Ax$, where x' is the row vector $(x_1, x_2, \ldots, x_n)$ and x, its transpose, is the column vector.

A real quadratic form $x'Ax$ is said to be *positive definite* (or *negative definite*) if it is positive (or negative) for every set of real values $x_1, x_2, \ldots,$ x_n other than the set $x_1 = x_2 = \cdots = x_n = 0$. A quadratic form which is never negative but which assumes zero value for some non-null values of $x_1, x_2, \ldots, x_n$ is called *positive semidefinite*. The matrix associated with a positive definite (negative definite) quadratic form is called *positive definite* (negative definite).

The *characteristic polynomial* of a square matrix A is the determinant of the matrix

$$A - \lambda I = \begin{bmatrix} a_{11} - \lambda & a_{12} & \cdots & a_{1n} \\ a_{21} & a_{22} - \lambda & \cdots & a_{2n} \\ \cdots & \cdots & \cdots & \cdots \\ a_{n1} & a_{n2} & \cdots & a_{nn} - \lambda \end{bmatrix}.$$

The roots of the polynomial equation

$$P_n(\lambda) = |A - \lambda I| = 0$$

are called the *latent roots* of A. Let λ_1 be a root of the equation just given, and $x' = (x_1, x_2, \ldots, x_n)$ be a vector such that

$$x'A = \lambda_1 x'.$$

Then x' is called a *latent vector* corresponding to the latent root λ_1.

A *submatrix* or a *minor* of a matrix A is a matrix obtained from A by any one of the following operations: (i) crossing out only certain rows of A, (ii) crossing out only certain columns of A, (iii) crossing out certain rows and columns of A.

The *rank* of a matrix is defined as the largest integer p for which it has a non-singular square minor with p rows.

5.1   RESOLUTION INTO TRIANGULAR FACTORS

A matrix T is said to be upper (lower) triangular in form if all its elements below (above) the principal diagonal are zeros. Since such matrices are easy to manipulate computationally, the first step in most computational procedures involving a matrix A is to resolve it as a product of a lower triangular matrix L and an upper triangular matrix U:

(5.1.1) $$A_0 = LU,$$

where A_0 either is the original matrix A or is derived from it by a permutation of the rows and of the columns. We will now describe two methods for carrying out this resolution.

Pivotal Condensation. Let A be an $m \times n$ matrix:

$$A = \begin{bmatrix} a_{11} & a_{12} & a_{13} & a_{14} & \cdots & a_{1n} \\ a_{21} & a_{22} & a_{23} & a_{24} & \cdots & a_{2n} \\ a_{31} & a_{32} & a_{33} & a_{34} & \cdots & a_{3n} \\ a_{41} & a_{42} & a_{43} & a_{44} & \cdots & a_{4n} \\ \cdots & \cdots & \cdots & \cdots & \cdots & \cdots \\ a_{m1} & a_{m2} & a_{m3} & a_{m4} & \cdots & a_{mn} \end{bmatrix}.$$

From this the matrix

(5.1.2) $$A^* = \begin{bmatrix} l_{11} & u_{12} & u_{13} & u_{14} & \cdots & u_{1n} \\ l_{21} & l_{22} & u_{23} & u_{24} & \cdots & u_{2n} \\ l_{31} & l_{32} & l_{33} & u_{34} & \cdots & u_{3n} \\ l_{41} & l_{42} & l_{43} & l_{44} & \cdots & u_{4n} \\ \cdots & \cdots & \cdots & \cdots & \cdots & \cdots \\ l_{m1} & l_{m2} & l_{m3} & l_{m4} & \cdots & l_{mn} \end{bmatrix}$$

is obtained by the following sequence of operations.

INITIAL STEP. Find the sum of each row of A and enter this as an extra column; that is, compute

$$a_{i,n+1} = \sum_{j=1}^{n} a_{ij} \qquad (i = 1, 2, \ldots, m)$$

STEP 1a. Fill in the first column of A^* by the first column of A, that is, take

$$l_{i1} = a_{i1} \qquad (i = 1, 2, \ldots, m).$$

STEP 1b. Fill in the rest of the first row of A^* by

$$u_{1j} = a_{1j}/a_{11} \qquad (j = 2, 3, \ldots, n+1).$$

Note. It is assumed that $a_{11} \neq 0$; otherwise permute the rows and columns of A to make the first diagonal entry non-zero.

STEP 1c. Check that

$$1 + \sum_{j=2}^{n} u_{1j} = u_{1,n+1}.$$

STEP 2a. Fill in the rest of the second column of A^* by

$$l_{i2} = a_{i2} - b_{i1}u_{12} \qquad (i = 2, 3, \ldots, m).$$

STEP 2*b*. Fill in the rest of the second row of A^* by

$$u_{2j} = (a_{2j} - l_{21}a_{1j})/l_{22} \qquad (j = 3, 4, \ldots, n + 1).$$

Note. It is assumed that $l_{22} \neq 0$; otherwise permute rows and columns to make this element non-zero.

STEP 2*c*. Check that

$$1 + \sum_{j=3}^{n} u_{2j} = u_{2,n+1}.$$

STEP 3*a*. Fill in the rest of the third column of A^* by

$$l_{i3} = a_{i3} - l_{i1}u_{13} - l_{i2}u_{23} \qquad (i = 3, 4, \ldots, m).$$

STEP 3*b*. Fill in the rest of the third row of A^* by

$$u_{3j} = (a_{3j} - l_{31}u_{1j} - l_{32}u_{2j})/l_{33} \qquad (j = 4, 5, \ldots, n + 1).$$

Note. Prior permutation of rows and columns to ensure $l_{33} \neq 0$ is taken for granted.

STEP 3*c*. Check that

$$1 + \sum_{j=4}^{n} u_{3j} = u_{3,n+1}.$$

STEP 4*a*. Fill in the rest of the fourth column of A^* by

$$l_{i4} = a_{i4} - l_{i1}u_{14} - l_{i2}u_{24} - l_{i3}u_{34} \qquad (i = 4, 5, \ldots, m).$$

STEP 4*b*. Fill in the rest of the fourth row of A^* by

$$u_{4j} = (a_{4j} - l_{41}u_{1j} - l_{42}u_{2j} - l_{43}u_{3j})/l_{44} \qquad (j = 5, 6, \ldots, n + 1).$$

STEP 4*c*. Check that

$$1 + \sum_{j=5}^{n} u_{4j} = u_{4,n+1}.$$

Computations are carried on in this way until the whole of matrix A^* is filled. The general formulae for the elements of A^* are

$$l_{ip} = a_{ip} - \sum_{t=1}^{p-1} l_{it}u_{tp} \qquad (i = p, p + 1, \ldots, m),$$

$$u_{pj} = \left(a_{pj} - \sum_{t=1}^{p-1} l_{pt}u_{tj}\right)\Big/ l_{pp} \qquad (j = p + 1, p + 2, \ldots, n + 1),$$

with the check that

$$1 + \sum_{j=p+1}^{n} u_{pj} = u_{j,n+1}.$$

Then if we write

$$
L = \begin{bmatrix}
l_{11} & 0 & 0 & \cdots & 0 \\
l_{21} & l_{22} & 0 & \cdots & 0 \\
l_{31} & l_{32} & l_{33} & \cdots & 0 \\
\cdots & \cdots & \cdots & \cdots & \cdots \\
l_{m1} & l_{m2} & l_{m3} & \cdots & \cdots
\end{bmatrix}
\quad \text{and} \quad
U = \begin{bmatrix}
1 & u_{12} & u_{13} & \cdots & u_{1n} \\
0 & 1 & u_{23} & \cdots & u_{2n} \\
0 & 0 & 1 & \cdots & u_{3n} \\
\cdots & \cdots & \cdots & \cdots & \cdots \\
\cdots & \cdots & \cdots & \cdots & \cdots
\end{bmatrix}
$$

we have the resolution $A = LU$.

Illustrative Example 5.1. By the method of pivotal condensation resolve the matrix

$$
A = \begin{bmatrix}
2.286 & 8.000 & 5.333 & 3.596 \\
0.35 & 1.25 & 0.45 & 0.466 \\
1.0 & 1.0 & 1.0 & 0.667
\end{bmatrix}
$$

into triangular factors of the form $A = LU$, where L is a lower triangular matrix and U an upper triangular matrix with unit diagonal elements.

First, the sum of each row is computed and entered as an additional column of A; we thus get the matrix:

				Sum
2.286	8.000	5.333	3.596	19.215
0.350	1.250	0.450	0.466	2.516
1.000	1.000	1.000	0.667	3.667

The next step is to write the first column as such unaltered and then fill in the other elements of the first row by dividing the corresponding original elements by the pivotal 2.286. At the end of these operations, the worksheet looks like this:

```
2.286   3.49956   2.33290   1.57305   8.40551
0.350
1.000
```

where, for instance, 3.49956 is obtained as 8.000/2.286. The check is

$$
1 + 3.49956 + 2.33290 + 1.57305 = 8.40551 = \frac{19.215}{2.286}.
$$

Then the other elements of the second column are filled in as follows. The first entry is $1.250 - (0.350)(3.49956) = 0.025154$, and the second is $1.000 - (1.000)(3.49956) = -2.49956$. Then the other elements in the second row are obtained by the same operations as for the elements in the second column but followed by an extra operation of division by the pivotal element 0.025154. Thus the first entry is $[0.450 - (0.350)(2.33290)]/ 0.025154 = -14.57084$, and so on. The check is $1 + (-14.57084) + (-3.36199) = -16.93283$. At the end of these operations, the worksheet looks like this:

2.286	3.49956	2.33290	1.57305	8.40551
0.350	0.025154	−14.57084	−3.36199	−16.93283
1.000	−2.49956			

Finally, the last element of the third column is computed as $1.000 - (1.000)(2.33290) - (-2.49956)(-14.57084) = -37.75359$. The other elements of the third row are then obtained by similar operations followed by division by the pivotal element -37.75359. Thus $[0.667 - (1.000)(1.57305) - (-2.49956)(-3.36199)]/(-37.75359) = 0.24659$ and so on. The check is $1 + 0.24659 = 1.24659$. At the end of all these computations, the worksheet looks like this:

TRIANGULAR RESOLUTION BY PIVOTAL CONDENSATION

2.286	3.49956	2.33290	1.57305	8.40551
0.350	0.025154	−14.57084	−3.36199	−16.93283
1.000	−2.49956	−37.75359	0.24659	1.24659

We thus have $A = LU$, where

$$L = \begin{bmatrix} 2.286 & 0 & 0 \\ 0.350 & 0.025154 & 0 \\ 1.000 & -2.49956 & -37.75359 \end{bmatrix},$$

$$U = \begin{bmatrix} 1 & 3.49956 & 2.33290 & 1.57305 \\ 0 & 1 & -14.57084 & -3.36199 \\ 0 & 0 & 1 & 0.24659 \end{bmatrix}.$$

Illustrative Example 5.2. By the method of pivotal condensation, resolve the symmetric matrix A whose elements on and above the principal diagonal are as follows:

984.500	284.030	−4,591.900	−3,920.050
	212.769	−2,763.000	−1,688.140
		43,690.000	33,466.500
			150,843.000

into triangular factors of the form $A = LU$, where L is a lower triangular matrix and U an upper triangular matrix with unit diagonal elements.

The same technique as used in illustrative example 5.1 is used here again, but because the matrix is symmetric the elements in the rows can be obtained by dividing the corresponding elements in the columns by the pivotal elements. We thus obtain the following:

PIVOTAL CONDENSATION OF A SYMMETRIC MATRIX

				Sum: check
984.500	284.030	−4,591.900	−3,920.050	−7,243.420
	212.769	−2,763.000	−1,688.140	−3,954.341
		43,690.000	33,466.500	69,801.600
			150,843.000	178,701.310
984.500	0.28850178	−4.66419502	−3.98176759	−7.3574606
284.030	130.82584	−10.99346031	−4.25908674	−14.2525472
−4591.900	−1438.22868	6461.37298	1.40172710	2.4017271
−3920.050	−557.19860	9057.08162	120,165.55882	1.00000000

From this we get:

$$L = \begin{bmatrix} 984.500 & 0 & 0 & 0 \\ 284.030 & 130.82584 & 0 & 0 \\ -4591.900 & -1438.22868 & 6461.37298 & 0 \\ -3920.050 & -557.19860 & 9057.08162 & 120,165.55882 \end{bmatrix},$$

and

$$U = \begin{bmatrix} 1 & 0.28850178 & -4.66419502 & -3.98176739 \\ 0 & 1 & -10.99346031 & -4.25908674 \\ 0 & 0 & 1 & 1.40172710 \\ 0 & 0 & 0 & 1 \end{bmatrix}.$$

Square-Root Method. If the $n \times n$ matrix $A = ((a_{ij}))$ is symmetric and positive-definite or positive-semidefinite, it can be factorized as

(5.1.3) $A = LL',$

where $L = ((l_{ij}))$ is a lower triangular matrix and L' is the transpose of L. (If the matrix A is positive-semidefinite, it may be necessary to permute its rows and columns before such a resolution.)

To find the elements of L, the computational steps are as follows.

INITIAL STEP. Find the sum of each column of A and enter it as an extra row, that is, compute:

$$a_{n+1,j} = \sum_{i=1}^{n} a_{ij} \qquad (j = 1, 2, \ldots, n).$$

STEP 1. Fill in the first column of L by

$$l_{11} = \sqrt{a_{11}}, \quad l_{i1} = a_{i1}/l_{11} \qquad (i = 2, 3, \ldots, n + 1).$$

Check that

$$\sum_{i=1}^{n} l_{i1} = l_{n+1,1}.$$

STEP 2. Fill in the second column of L by

$$l_{12} = 0, \quad l_{22} = \sqrt{a_{22} - l_{21}^2}, \quad l_{i2} = (a_{i2} - l_{i1}l_{21})/l_{22} \quad (i = 3, 4, \ldots, n + 1).$$

Check that

$$\sum_{i=2}^{n} l_{i2} = l_{n+1,2}.$$

STEP 3. Fill in the third column of L by

$$l_{13} = l_{23} = 0, \quad l_{33} = \sqrt{a_{33} - l_{31}^2 - l_{32}^2},$$

$$l_{i3} = (a_{i3} - l_{i1}l_{31} - l_{i2}l_{32})/l_{33} \qquad (i = 4, 5, \ldots, n + 1).$$

Check that

$$\sum_{i=3}^{n} l_{i3} = l_{n+1,3}.$$

STEP 4. Fill in the fourth column of L by

$$l_{14} = l_{24} = l_{34} = 0, \quad l_{44} = \sqrt{a_{44} - l_{41}^2 - l_{42}^2 - l_{43}^2},$$

$$l_{i4} = (a_{i4} - l_{i1}l_{41} - l_{i2}l_{42} - l_{i3}l_{43})/l_{44} \qquad (i = 5, 6, \ldots, n + 1).$$

Check that

$$\sum_{i=4}^{n} l_{i4} = l_{n+1,4}.$$

Continue this process until all the elements of L are obtained. The general formulae for the elements of L are

$$l_{ij} = 0 \quad \text{if } i < j,$$

$$l_{jj} = \sqrt{a_{jj} - \sum_{t=1}^{j-1} l_{jt}^2},$$

$$l_{ij} = \left(a_{ij} - \sum_{t=1}^{j-1} l_{it}l_{jt}\right) \bigg/ l_{jj} \qquad (i = j + 1, j + 2, \ldots, n + 1),$$

with the check that

$$\sum_{i=j}^{n} l_{ij} = l_{n+1,j}.$$

Illustrative Example 5.3. Resolve the positive definite matrix A whose elements on the principal diagonal and below are as follows:

15.129

23.860   54.756

1.793   3.633   18.225

0.998   3.5111   21.122   60.516

into triangular factors: $A = LL'$, where L is a lower triangular matrix.

An additional row, each element of which is the sum of all the elements in the corresponding column of A, is first appended to the matrix A. This row has elements

41.780,   85.760,   44.773,   86.147

The elements of L on and below the principal diagonal are then computed as follows. The first element is $l_{11} = \sqrt{15.129} = 3.88960$, and its reciprocal, $1/l_{11} = 0.247095713$, is written by its side. The other elements of the first column of A are then multiplied by $1/l_{11}$ to give the other elements of the first column of L, for example, $l_{21} = 23.860 \times 0.257095713 = 6.13430$. The check is provided by $3.88960 + 6.13430 + 0.46097 + 0.25658 = 10.74145$. Next l_{22} is obtained as $l_{22} = \sqrt{54.716 - (6.13430)^2} = 4.13840$. The next entry l_{32} is obtained as $l_{32} = [3.633 - (6.13430)(0.46097)]/4.13840 = 0.19459$. The following entry is

$$l_{42} = [3.5111 - (6.13430)(0.25658)]/4.13840 = 0.46807,$$

and so on. Having completed the second column, we carry out the check: $4.13840 + 0.19459 + 0.46807 = 4.80106$.

The diagonal entry of the third column is then obtained as $l_{33} = \sqrt{18.225 - (0.46097)^2 - (0.19459)^2} = 4.23965$. The next entry in the same column is $l_{43} = [21.122 - (0.46097)(0.25658) - (0.19459)(0.46807)]/4.23965 = 4.93263$. The entry l_{53} is similarly computed, and we have the check: $4.23965 + 4.93263 = 9.17228$. Finally, the last diagonal entry is computed as $l_{44} = \sqrt{60.516 - (0.25658)^2 - (0.46807)^2 - (4.93263)^2} = 5.99168$. The only other entry in this column is

$$l_{54} = [86.147 - (0.25658)(10.74145) - (0.46807)(4.80106)$$
$$- (4.93263)(9.17228)]/5.99168 = 5.99168,$$

which agrees with l_{44} as a check.

The details are as follows:

SQUARE-ROOT METHOD OF TRIANGULAR RESOLUTION

	15.129			
	23.860	54.756		
	1.793	3.633	18.225	
	0.998	3.511	21.122	60.516
Sum	41.780	85.760	44.773	86.147
	3.88960			
	6.13430	4.13840		
	0.46097	0.19459	4.23965	
	0.25658	0.46807	4.93263	5.99168
Sum	10.74145	4.80106	9.17228	5.99168

5.2 SOLUTION OF LINEAR EQUATIONS

Consider the set of m simultaneous linear equations in n unknowns $x_1, x_2, \ldots, x_n$:

$$a_{11}x_1 + a_{12}x_2 + \cdots + a_{1n}x_n = c_1,$$
$$a_{21}x_1 + a_{22}x_2 + \cdots + a_{2n}x_2 = c_2,$$
$$\cdots \quad \cdots \quad \cdots \quad \cdots \quad \cdots$$
$$a_{m1}x_1 + a_{m2}x_2 + \cdots + a_{mn}x_n = c_m,$$

where a_{ij} and c_i $(i = 1, 2, \ldots, m; \ j = 1, 2, \ldots, n)$ are given constants. Using matrix notations,

$$A = \begin{bmatrix} a_{11} & a_{12} & \cdots & a_{1n} \\ a_{21} & a_{22} & \cdots & a_{2n} \\ \cdots & \cdots & \cdots & \cdots \\ a_{m1} & a_{m2} & \cdots & a_{mn} \end{bmatrix} \quad \mathbf{c} = \begin{bmatrix} c_1 \\ c_2 \\ \cdots \\ c_m \end{bmatrix} \quad \mathbf{x} = \begin{bmatrix} x_1 \\ x_2 \\ \cdots \\ x_n \end{bmatrix}$$

these equations can be expressed in the condensed form: $A\mathbf{x} = \mathbf{c}$. Let r be the rank of the matrix A and $\bar{r}$ that of the augmented matrix $[A \mathbin{\vdots} \mathbf{c}]$ obtained by adding the column of $\mathbf{c}$ on the right of matrix A. Then it necessarily follows that $r \leq \min(m, n)$, $\bar{r} \leq \min(m, n + 1)$, and $r \leq \bar{r}$.

If $r < \bar{r}$, the equations are algebraically inconsistent and no solution exists.

Triangular Equations.   Linear equations of the form

$$d_1 = b_{11}x_1,$$
$$d_2 = b_{21}x_1 + b_{22}x_2,$$
$$d_3 = b_{31}x_1 + b_{32}x_2 + b_{33}x_3,$$
$$\cdots \quad \cdots \quad \cdots \quad \cdots$$
$$d_n = b_{n1}x_1 + b_{n2}x_2 + b_{n3}x_3 + \cdots + b_{nn}x_n,$$

or of the form

$$e_{11}x_1 + e_{12}x_2 + e_{13}x_3 + \cdots + e_{1n}x_n = f_1,$$
$$e_{22}x_2 + e_{23}x_3 + \cdots + e_{2n}x_n = f_2,$$
$$e_{33}x_3 + \cdots + e_{3n}x_n = f_3,$$
$$\cdots + e_{nn}x_n = f_n,$$

are called *triangular* equations because in each case the matrix of their coefficients is triangular. Such equations can be readily solved successively by substitution. For instance, in the first case we have

$$x_1 = d_1/b_{11},$$
$$x_2 = (d_2 - b_{21}x_1)/b_{22},$$
$$x_3 = (d_3 - b_{31}x_1 - b_{32}x_2)/b_{33},$$
$$\cdots \quad \cdots$$
$$x_n = (d_n - b_{n1}x_1 - b_{n2}x_2 - \cdots - b_{n,n-1}x_{n-1})/b_{nn}.$$

This is called *forward substitution.*

In the second case, we solve for x_n first, then for x_{n-1}, and so on, obtaining

$$x_n \quad = f_n/e_{nn},$$
$$x_{n-1} = (f_{n-1} - e_{n-1,n}x_n)/e_{n-1,n-1},$$
$$\cdots \quad \cdots$$
$$x_1 \quad = (f_1 - e_{1n}x_n - \cdots e_{12}x_2)/e_{11}.$$

This is known as *backward substitution.*

Pivotal Condensation Method.   To solve the equations $A\mathbf{x} = \mathbf{c}$, we can first resolve A into triangular factors $A = LU$, as in Section 5.1. Then we solve for $\mathbf{y}$ the triangular equations $L\mathbf{y} = \mathbf{c}$ by forward substitution. The required solution $\mathbf{x}$ is obtained from the triangular equations $U\mathbf{x} = \mathbf{y}$ by backward substitution. In practice, if the method of pivotal condensation is applied on the augmented matrix $[A \vdots \mathbf{c}]$, the last column gives $\mathbf{y}$ directly.

56   TECHNIQUES OF COMPUTATION

Illustrative Example 5.4.   Solve the equations

$$2.286x_1 + 8.000x_2 + 5.333x_3 = 3.596,$$
$$0.35x_1 + 1.25x_2 + 0.45x_3 = 0.466,$$
$$1.0x_1 + 1.0x_2 + 1.0x_3 = 0.667.$$

We take over from illustrative example 5.1 the triangular resolution of the matrix

2.286	8.000	5.333	3.596
0.35	1.25	0.45	0.466
1.0	1.0	1.0	0.667

The triangular equations to be solved are then

$$x_1 + 3.49956x_2 + 2.33290x_3 = 1.57305,$$
$$x_2 - 14.57084x_3 = -3.36199,$$
$$x_3 = 0.24659,$$

which are obtained from the elements of the matrix U in illustrative example 5.1.

By backward substitution we then obtain

$$x_3 = 0.24659,$$
$$x_2 = -3.36199 + 14.57084x_3 = 0.23103,$$
$$x_1 = 1.47305 - 2.33290x_3 - 3.49956x_2 = 0.18928.$$

The complete computational layout would be as follows:

SOLUTION of EQUATIONS BY PIVOTAL CONDENSATION

2.286	3.49956	2.33290	−1.57305	8.40551	$x_1 = 0.18928$
0.350	0.025154	−14.57084	−3.36199	−16.93283	$x_2 = 0.23103$
1.000	−2.49956	−37.75359	0.24659	1.24659	$x_3 = 0.24659$

Illustrative Example 5.5.   Solve the equations:

$$984.500\beta_1 + 284.030\beta_2 - 4591.90\beta_3 - 3920.05\beta_4 = 461.415,$$
$$284.030\beta_1 + 212.769\beta_2 - 2763.00\beta_3 - 1688.14\beta_4 = 334.456,$$
$$-4591.90\beta_1 - 2763.00\beta_2 + 46,390.0\beta_3 + 33,466.5\beta_4 = -3931.05,$$
$$-3920.05\beta_1 - 1688.14\beta_2 + 33,466.5\beta_3 + 150,843.0\beta_4 = 16,497.822.$$

The coefficients of the β's form a symmetric matrix A which has already been resolved into triangular factors $A = LU$ in illustrative example 5.2. Writing **c** for the column vector (461.415, 334.456, −3931.05, 16497.822), we can express the equations $A\boldsymbol{\beta} = \mathbf{c}$ as $LU\boldsymbol{\beta} = \mathbf{c}$. Then setting $U\boldsymbol{\beta} = \mathbf{y}$, we first solve for $\mathbf{y}$ from $L\mathbf{y} = \mathbf{c}$. These equations can be written out as

$$984.500y_1 = 461.415,$$
$$284.030y_1 + 130.82584y_2 = 334.456,$$
$$-4591.900y_1 - 1438.22868y_2 + 6461.37298y_3 = -3931.05,$$
$$-3920.050y_1 - 557.19860y_2$$
$$+ 9057.08162y_3 + 120{,}165.55882y_4 = 16{,}497.822,$$

and solving these by the method of forward substitution we find $y_1 = 0.46867953$, $y_2 = 1.53896929$, $y_3 = 0.06724102$, $y_4 = 0.15464975$. Finally we solve the equations $U\boldsymbol{\beta} = \mathbf{y}$, which can be written out as:

$$\beta_1 + 0.28850178\beta_2 - 4.66419502\beta_3 - 3.98176739\beta_4 = 0.46867953,$$
$$\beta_2 - 10.99346031\beta_3 - 4.25908674\beta_4 = 1.53896929,$$
$$\beta_3 + 1.40172710\beta_4 = 0.06724102,$$
$$\beta_4 = 0.15464975.$$

Solving these equations by the method of backward substitution, we obtain $\beta_4 = 0.15465$, $\beta_3 = -0.14954$, $\beta_2 = 0.55372$, $\beta_1 = 0.22725$. In actual practice, the equations are solved by applying the method of pivotal condensation on the matrix $[A \vdots \mathbf{c}]$. The details are shown in the table on p. 58.

Square-Root Method. If the matrix of coefficients A is symmetric and positive-definite (or positive-semidefinite) we may resolve A into factors $A = LL'$, where L is a lower triangular matrix as in Section 5.1. Then the equations $A\mathbf{x} = \mathbf{c}$ are solved in two stages: first for $\mathbf{y}$ from the triangular equations $L\mathbf{y} = \mathbf{c}$ by forward substitution, and then for $\mathbf{x}$ from the triangular equations $L'\mathbf{x} = \mathbf{y}$ by backward substitution. In practice, if the square-root method is applied on the augmented matrix $\begin{bmatrix} A \\ \hline \mathbf{c}' \end{bmatrix}$ obtained by adding the row $\mathbf{c}'$ at the bottom of A, the last row gives the elements of $\mathbf{y}$ directly.

Illustrative Example 5.6. Solve the equations:

$$15.129\beta_1 + 23.860\beta_2 + 1.793\beta_3 + 0.998\beta_4 = 4.583,$$
$$23.860\beta_1 + 54.756\beta_2 + 3.635\beta_3 + 3.511\beta_4 = 10.091,$$
$$1.793\beta_1 + 3.633\beta_2 + 18.225\beta_3 + 21.122\beta_4 = 29.156,$$
$$0.998\beta_1 + 3.511\beta_2 + 21.122\beta_3 + 60.516\beta_4 = 60.173.$$

Denoting the equations in the form $A\boldsymbol{\beta} = \mathbf{c}$, where $\mathbf{c}' = (4.583, 10.091, 29.156, 60.173)$, we note that the matrix of coefficients A is positive-definite

SOLUTION OF EQUATIONS WITH SYMMETRIC COEFFICIENTS BY PIVOTAL CONDENSATION

					Sum: check
984.500	284.030	-4,591.900	-3,920.050	461.415	-6,782.005
	212.769	-2,763.000	-1,688.140	334.456	-3,619.885
		43,690.000	33,466.500	-3,931.050	65,870.550
			150,843.000	16,497.822	195,199.132

					Sum: check	
984.500	0.28850178	-4.66419502	-3.98176739	0.46867953	-6.88878110	$0.22725 = \beta_1$
284.030	130.82584	-10.99346031	-4.15908674	1.53896929	-12.71357776	$0.55372 = \beta_2$
-4,591.900	-1,438.22868	6,461.37298	1.40172710	0.06724102	2.46896812	$-0.14954 = \beta_3$
-3,920.050	-557.19860	9,057.08162	120,165.55882	0.15464975	1.15464975	$0.15465 = \beta_4$

and has already been factorized as $A = LL'$ in illustrative example 5.3. We take over the matrix L from there. Noting that the equations $A\beta = c$ can be written as $LL'\beta = c$, we set $L'\beta = y$ and solve for y from the equations $Ly = c$.

Written out, this gives:

$$3.88960y_1 \qquad\qquad\qquad\qquad\qquad\qquad = 4.583,$$
$$6.13430y_1 + 4.13840y_2 \qquad\qquad\qquad\qquad = 10.091,$$
$$0.46097y_1 + 0.19459y_2 + 4.23965y_3 \qquad\qquad = 29.156,$$
$$0.25658y_1 + 0.46807y_2 + 4.93263y_3 + 5.99168y_4 = 60.173.$$

Solving by forward substitution, we get $y_1 = 1.17827$, $y_2 = 0.69185$, $y_3 = 6.71712$, $y_4 = 4.40841$. Next we find β by solving the equations $L'\beta = y$, shown in detail as follows:

$$3.88960\beta_1 + 6.13430\beta_2 + 0.46097\beta_3 + 0.25658\beta_4 = 1.17827,$$
$$4.13840\beta_2 + 0.19459\beta_3 + 0.46807\beta_4 = 0.69185,$$
$$4.23965\beta_3 + 4.93263\beta_4 = 6.71712,$$
$$5.99168\beta_4 = 4.40841.$$

Solving these by backward substitution, we obtain $\beta_4 = 0.73576$, $\beta_3 = 0.72834$, $\beta_2 = 0.04971$, $\beta_1 = 0.08968$.

In actual practice, the solutions are obtained by applying the square-root method on the matrix $\left[\dfrac{A}{c'}\right]$. The layout is as follows:

SOLUTION OF EQUATIONS BY THE SQUARE-ROOT METHOD

	15.129			
	23.860	54.756		
	1.793	3.633	18.225	
	0.998	3.511	21.122	60.516
	4.583	10.091	29.156	60.173
Sum	46.363	95.851	73.929	146.320
	3.88960			
	6.13430	4.13840		
	0.46097	0.19459	4.23965	
	0.25658	0.46807	4.93263	5.99168
	1.17827	0.69185	6.71712	4.40841
Sum: check	11.91972	5.49291	15.88940	10.40009
	$\beta_1 = 0.08968$	$\beta_2 = 0.04971$	$\beta_3 = 0.72834$	$\beta_4 = 0.73576$

Iteration. In this process, the linear equations $A\mathbf{x} = \mathbf{c}$ are first brought into the form

$$
\begin{aligned}
x_1 &= \beta_1 &&- \beta_{12}x_2 - \beta_{13}x_3 - \cdots - \beta_{1n}x_n, \\
x_2 &= \beta_2 - \beta_{21}x_1 && \cdots \quad - \beta_{23}x_3 - \cdots - \beta_{2n}x_n, \\
x_3 &= \beta_3 - \beta_{31}x_1 - \beta_{32}x_2 && \cdots \quad - \cdots - \beta_{3n}x_n, \\
&\cdots \qquad \cdots \qquad \cdots && \cdots \qquad \cdots \quad \cdots \\
x_n &= \beta_n - \beta_{n1}x_1 - \beta_{n2}x_2 - \beta_{n3}x_3 - \cdots && \cdots,
\end{aligned}
$$

where $\beta_i = c_i/a_{ii}$ and $\beta_{ij} = a_{ij}/a_{ii}$. The equations may have to be suitably arranged to ensure that all the a_{ii}'s are non-zero. Then, starting with an approximate solution $[x_1^{(1)}, x_2^{(1)}, \ldots, x_n^{(1)}]$, we derive a second approximation $[x_1^{(2)}, x_2^{(2)}, x_3^{(2)}, \ldots, x_n^{(2)}]$ as follows:

$$
\begin{aligned}
x_1^{(2)} &= \beta_1 &&- \beta_{12}x_2^{(1)} - \beta_{13}x_3^{(1)} \cdots - \beta_{1n}x_n^{(1)}, \\
x_2^{(2)} &= \beta_2 - \beta_{21}x_1^{(2)} && - \beta_{23}x_3^{(1)} \cdots - \beta_{2n}x_n^{(1)}, \\
x_3^{(2)} &= \beta_3 - \beta_{31}x_1^{(2)} - \beta_{32}x_2^{(2)} - && \cdots \quad \cdots - \beta_{3n}x_n^{(1)}, \\
&\cdots \quad \cdots \qquad \cdots && \cdots \qquad \cdots \quad \cdots \\
x_n^{(2)} &= \beta_n - \beta_{n1}x_1^{(2)} - \beta_{n2}x_2^{(2)} - \beta_{n3}x_3^{(2)} \cdots && \cdots.
\end{aligned}
$$

This process is continued to derive successively better and better approximations. It works if certain convergence conditions hold. It is difficult to check them initially.

5.3 EVALUATION OF DETERMINANTS

To evaluate the determinant of a square matrix A of order n one possibility is to apply the method of pivotal condensation to bring it into the form A^* shown by matrix 5.1.2. Then

$$(5.3.1) \qquad |A^*| = u_{11}u_{22} \cdots u_{nn}.$$

If A is positive-definite and resolved into triangular factors $A = LL'$ as given by 5.1.3, then

$$(5.3.2) \qquad |A^*| = l_{11}^2 l_{22}^2 \cdots l_{nn}^2,$$

where l_{ii}'s are the diagonal elements of the matrix L.

Partitioned Determinants. If the square matrix A is partitioned in the form

$$
A = \left[\begin{array}{c:c} P & Q \\ \hdashline R & S \end{array}\right],
$$

where P is a square and non-singular matrix, then

$$(5.3.3) \qquad |A| = |P| \; |S - RP^{-1}Q|.$$

This can be made use of in evaluating determinants when the matrix P is easy to invert. On the other hand, if S is square and non-singular, then

(5.3.4) $$|A| = |S| \, |P - QS^{-1}R|,$$

and this can be used if S is easier to invert than P.

Illustrative Example 5.7. Evaluate the determinant:

$$D = \begin{vmatrix} 2.286 & 8.000 & 5.333 \\ 0.35 & 1.25 & 0.45 \\ 1.0 & 1.0 & 1.0 \end{vmatrix}.$$

We take over from illustrative example 5.1 the pivotal condensation:

2.286	3.49956	2.33290
0.35	0.025154	-14.57084
1.0	-2.49956	-37.74359

(omitting the fourth column). Hence the determinant is given by the product of the pivotal elements:

$$D = (2.286)(0.025154)(-37.75359) = -2.170909.$$

Illustrative Example 5.8. Evaluate the determinant

$$D = \begin{vmatrix} 15.129 & 23.860 & 1.793 & 0.998 \\ 23.860 & 54.756 & 3.633 & 3.511 \\ 1.793 & 3.633 & 18.225 & 21.122 \\ 0.998 & 3.511 & 21.122 & 60.516 \end{vmatrix}.$$

Writing A for the matrix, we take over from illustrative example 5.3 the resolution $A = LL'$. The principal diagonal elements of L are $l_{11} = 3.88960$, $l_{22} = 4.13840$, $l_{33} = 4.23965$, $l_{44} = 5.99168$. Hence

$$D = l_{11}{}^2 l_{22}{}^2 l_{33}{}^2 l_{44}{}^2 = 167,198.37.$$

5.4 INVERSION

Use of Triangular Factorization. To find the inverse X of a non-singular square matrix A of order n, we make use of the identities

(5.4.1) $$A = LU, \qquad LY = I, \qquad UX = Y,$$

where $L = ((l_{ij}))$ and $U = ((u_{ij}))$ are the triangular factors of A obtained as in Section 5.1, and I is the identity matrix of order n. Thus X is obtained in three stages: first A is resolved into triangular factors $A = LU$, next the matrix Y is obtained from the equation $LY = I$, and finally X is obtained from UX. Note that for each column of Y the equations are triangular and can be solved by forward substitution, and, similarly, for each column of X the equations are triangular and can be solved by backward substitution.

Thus we have for the first column of Y

$$y_{11} = \frac{1}{l_{11}},$$

$$y_{21} = -\frac{l_{21}y_{11}}{l_{22}},$$

$$y_{31} = -\frac{l_{31}y_{11} + l_{32}y_{21}}{l_{33}},$$

$$\cdots \qquad \cdots$$

$$y_{n1} = -\frac{l_{n1}y_{11} + l_{n2}y_{21} + \cdots + l_{n,n-1}y_{n-1,1}}{l_{nn}}.$$

Similarly, for the second column of Y we have

$$y_{12} = 0,$$

$$y_{22} = \frac{1}{l_{22}},$$

$$y_{32} = -\frac{l_{32}y_{22}}{l_{33}},$$

$$\cdots \qquad \cdots$$

$$y_{n2} = -\frac{l_{n2}y_{22} + l_{n3}y_{32} + \cdots + l_{n,n-1}y_{n-1,2}}{l_{nn}},$$

and so on. The general formulae are

$$y_{ij} = 0 \qquad\qquad \text{for } i = 1, 2, \ldots, j-1,$$

$$y_{jj} = \frac{1}{l_{jj}},$$

$$y_{ij} = -\frac{\sum_{t=j}^{i-1} l_{it}y_{tj}}{l_{ii}} \qquad \text{for } i = j+1, j+2, \ldots, n.$$

Having obtained the elements of Y, we find the elements of $X = ((x_{ij}))$ as follows.

The last row of X is obtained first as

$$x_{nj} = y_{nj} \qquad (j = 1, 2, \ldots n).$$

Then, the second row from the bottom is obtained as

$$x_{n-1,j} = y_{n-1,j} - u_{n-1,n}y_{n,j} \qquad (j = 1, 2, \ldots, n).$$

Then the third row from the bottom is

$$x_{n-2,j} = y_{n-2,j} - u_{n-2,n-1}y_{n-1,j} - u_{n-2,n}x_{nj} \qquad (j = 1, 2, \ldots, n),$$

and so on.

Illustrative Example 5.9. Find the inverse of the symmetric matrix A whose elements on and below the principal diagonal are

984.50

284.03   212.769

−4591.90   −2763.00   43,690

−3920.05   −1688.14   33,466.50   150,843

We take over from illustrative example 5.2 the resolution $A = LU$. If X is the required inverse, then X satisfies $LUX = I$. Writing $UX = Y$, we have for Y the equation $LY = I$, so that Y is the inverse of L. We thus get

$$Y = \begin{bmatrix} 0.00101574 & 0 & 0 & 0 \\ -0.00220524 & 0.00764375 & 0 & 0 \\ 0.00023100 & 0.00170141 & 0.00015477 & 0 \\ 0.00000550 & -0.00009279 & -0.00001166 & 0.00000832 \end{bmatrix}.$$

The inverse X is then obtained from $UX = Y$. The elements on and below the principal diagonal of the symmetric matrix X thus turn out to be

$$X = 10^{-6} \begin{bmatrix} 2000.37 & & & \\ 272.905 & 27,382.9 & & \\ 223.289 & 1831.49 & 171.117 & \\ 5.499 & -92.795 & -11.665 & 8.322 \end{bmatrix}.$$

64   TECHNIQUES OF COMPUTATION

In case the matrix A is positive-definite, an alternative way to obtain the inverse X would be to use the identities

(5.4.2) $\qquad A = LL', \qquad LY = I, \qquad X = Y'Y.$

Illustrative Example 5.10. Find the inverse of the positive-definite matrix:

$$A = \begin{bmatrix} 15.129 & 23.860 & 1.793 & 0.998 \\ 23.860 & 54.756 & 3.633 & 3.511 \\ 1.793 & 3.633 & 18.225 & 21.122 \\ 0.998 & 3.511 & 21.122 & 60.516 \end{bmatrix}$$

by the square-root method.

We use the triangular factorization already obtained in illustrative example 5.3: $A = LL'$, where L is:

3.88960	0	0	0
6.13430	4.13840	0	0
0.46097	0.19459	4.23965	0
0.25658	0.46807	4.93263	5.99168

By forward substitution we get $Y = L^{-1}$ as

0.25710	0	0	0
−0.38109	0.24164	0	0
−0.01046	−0.01109	0.23587	0
0.02738	−0.00975	−0.19418	0.16690

From this we get by multiplication $A = Y'Y$ whose elements in the diagonal and below are

0.21219			
−0.09224	0.05861		
−0.00778	0.00072	0.09334	
0.00457	−0.00163	−0.03241	0.02786

Inverse of Partitioned Matrices. If the square matrix A is partitioned in the form

$$A = \begin{bmatrix} P & Q \\ \hline R & S \end{bmatrix},$$

where P is a square matrix, then the inverse of the matrix A can also be similarly partitioned as

$$A^{-1} = \left[\begin{array}{c:c} W & X \\ \hdashline Y & Z \end{array}\right].$$

The component matrices can be obtained by equating the product to the identity matrix. Thus, if P is non-singular,

(5.4.3)
$$W = P^{-1} - XRP^{-1},$$
$$X = -P^{-1}QZ,$$
$$Y = -ZRP^{-1},$$
$$Z = (S - RP^{-1}Q)^{-1}.$$

The inversion of a matrix of bigger order is thus reduced to the inversion of two matrices each of smaller order and a number of matrix multiplications.

Illustrative Example 5.11. Find the inverse of the symmetric matrix A in illustrative example 5.10 by partitioning it into two by two matrices.

To find the inverse A^{-1}, we write A in the form of a partitioned matrix

$$A = \left[\begin{array}{c:c} P & Q \\ \hdashline R & S \end{array}\right],$$

where

$$P = \begin{bmatrix} 15.129 & 23.860 \\ 23.860 & 54.756 \end{bmatrix},$$

$$Q = \begin{bmatrix} 1.793 & 0.998 \\ 3.633 & 3.511 \end{bmatrix}, \quad R = Q',$$

$$S = \begin{bmatrix} 18.225 & 21.122 \\ 21.122 & 60.516 \end{bmatrix}.$$

Then

$$A^{-1} = \left[\begin{array}{c:c} W & X \\ \hdashline Y & Z \end{array}\right], \quad Y = X',$$

where

$$Z = (S - Q'P^{-1}Q)^{-1},$$
$$Y = -Z(Q'P^{-1}),$$
$$W = P^{-1} - Y'Q'P^{-1}.$$

So we compute successively

$$P^{-1} = \begin{bmatrix} 0.211328330 & -0.092086602 \\ -0.092086602 & 0.058389698 \end{bmatrix},$$

$$P^{-1}Q = \begin{bmatrix} 0.044361071 & -0.112410386 \\ 0.047018495 & 0.113103801 \end{bmatrix},$$

$$Q'P^{-1}Q = \begin{bmatrix} 0.250357593 & 0.209354287 \\ 0.209354285 & 0.284921880 \end{bmatrix},$$

$$S - Q'P^{-1}Q = \begin{bmatrix} 17.974642407 & 20.912645713 \\ 20.912645715 & 60.231078120 \end{bmatrix},$$

$$Z = (S - Q'P^{-1}Q)^{-1} = \begin{bmatrix} 0.093339072 & -0.032407970 \\ & 0.027854996 \end{bmatrix},$$

$$Y = -Z(P^{-1}Q)' = \begin{bmatrix} -0.007783614 & -0.000723198 \\ 0.004568843 & -0.001626732 \end{bmatrix},$$

$$Y'(P^{-1}Q)' = \begin{bmatrix} -0.000858875 & 0.000150780 \\ 0.000150780 & -0.000217993 \end{bmatrix},$$

$$W = P^{-1} - Y'(P^{-1}Q)' = \begin{bmatrix} 0.212187205 & -0.092237382 \\ & 0.058607691 \end{bmatrix}.$$

Thus we obtain

$$A^{-1} = \begin{bmatrix} 0.2121872 & -0.0922374 & -0.0077836 & 0.0045688 \\ -0.0922374 & 0.0586077 & -0.0007232 & -0.0016267 \\ -0.0077836 & -0.0007232 & 0.0933391 & -0.0324080 \\ 0.0045688 & -0.0016267 & -0.0324080 & 0.0278550 \end{bmatrix}.$$

This agrees with the inverse already found in illustrative example 5.10.

Iteration. If X_0 is an approximation to the inverse $X = A^{-1}$ of the matrix A, then, writing

$$E_0 = I - AX_0,$$

we have $A^{-1} = X_0(I - E_0)^{-1}$. But $(I - E_0)^{-1} = I + E_0 + E_0^2(I - E_0)^{-1}$. If X_0 is a fairly close approximation to X, the term $E_0^2(I - E_0)^{-1}$ can be neglected. A better approximation X_1 to X is

(5.4.4) $$X_1 = X_0(I + E_0).$$

5.5 EVALUATION OF LATENT ROOTS AND VECTORS

Direct Method. If all the latent roots and latent vectors of a square matrix of order n are required, the direct method is to evaluate the characteristic polynomial

$$(5.5.1) \qquad P_n(\lambda) = |A - \lambda I|$$
$$= (-1)^n(\lambda^n + c_1\lambda^{n-1} + c_2\lambda^{n-2} + \cdots + c_n),$$

where the coefficients are given by

$$c_1 = -\operatorname{tr} A,$$
$$c_2 = \operatorname{tr}_2 A,$$
$$(5.5.2) \qquad c_3 = -\operatorname{tr}_3 A,$$
$$\cdots \qquad \cdots$$
$$c_n = (-1)^n |A|,$$

where $\operatorname{tr} A$ denotes the sum of all the diagonal elements of A and $\operatorname{tr}_k A$ denotes the sum of all the $\binom{n}{k}$ principal minors of order k of the matrix A. The latent roots $\lambda_1, \lambda_2, \ldots, \lambda_n$ are then obtained as the roots of the polynomial equation

$$(5.5.3) \qquad P_n(\lambda) = 0.$$

To obtain a latent vector $\mathbf{x}$ corresponding to a latent root λ, we solve for the column vector $\mathbf{x}$ the simultaneous linear equations

$$(5.5.4) \qquad A\mathbf{x} = \lambda\mathbf{x}.$$

In actual computation, we make use of the fact that the latent roots of the matrix A^2 are the squares of the latent roots of the matrix A. Thus, to find a polynomial equation whose roots are, say, the $N = 2^p$th powers of the required latent roots, we simply compute the matrix $B = A^N$ by successive squaring and then evaluate the characteristic polynomial of the matrix B. If the order n of the matrix B is small, to obtain its characteristic polynomial the simplest method is to evaluate the determinant $|B - \lambda I|$ for $n + 1$ suitably chosen values of λ and obtain the polynomial $Q_n(\lambda)$ passing through these $n + 1$ points by means of an interpolation formula. Since the roots of $Q_n(\lambda) = 0$ are well separated out, these being the Nth powers of the roots of $P_n(\lambda)$, we can obtain all the latent roots by Graeffe's method (Section 3.2).

Dominant Latent Root of Real Symmetric Matrix. Let A be a real symmetric matrix of order n. All its latent roots are real, and we shall assume that there is just one latent root λ which has the largest absolute value and that every other latent root is smaller than λ in absolute value. λ_{max} is also called the dominant latent root.

If only the value of λ_{max} is required, we can make use of the result that, for any positive integer N,

$$\left(\frac{1}{n} \operatorname{tr} A^N\right)^{1/N} \leq \lambda_{max} \leq (\operatorname{tr} A^N)^{1/N}.$$

so that for large N

(5.5.5) $\lambda_{max} \sim (\operatorname{tr} A^N)^{1/N}.$

It is convenient to take $N = 2^p$ and get A^N by successive squaring of $A, A^2, A^4, \ldots$, etc. The method just described is rather laborious because it requires quite a number of matrix multiplications. Another disadvantage is that it does not yield the corresponding latent vector.

The following method is advantageous, as successive squaring of matrices is replaced by multiplication of the matrix by a vector and also the method gives simultaneously the dominant latent root as well as the corresponding latent vector. The principle used is that, if $\mathbf{x}_0$ is an arbitrary column vector of n elements and if the sequences of column vectors $\mathbf{x}_1, \mathbf{x}_2, \ldots$, etc., is defined recursively as $\mathbf{x}_{m+1} = A\mathbf{x}_m$, for sufficiently large N we obtain $\mathbf{x}_{N+1} \doteq \lambda_{max}\mathbf{x}_N$. Then the ratio of corresponding elements of $\mathbf{x}_{N+1}$ and $\mathbf{x}_N$ gives λ_{max}, and $\mathbf{x}_{N+1}$ is itself the latent vector corresponding to λ_{max}. The method fails if at any stage $\mathbf{x}_m$ becomes the latent vector corresponding to some latent root other than the dominant one. If $\lambda_{max} > 1$ the elements of $\mathbf{x}_N$ increase very rapidly, and if $\lambda_{max} < 1$ these elements decrease very rapidly with N. In actual computation, therefore, to keep the elements bounded it is convenient to work instead with the sequence of vectors $\mathbf{y}_{m+1} = k_m A\mathbf{y}_m$, where k_m is some suitably chosen constant.

For the computation of the dominant latent root and the corresponding latent vector of a symmetric matrix A, the following is a convenient procedure. By successive squaring raise A to a high power 2^p and, if necessary, pre- and postmultiply by a diagonal matrix Δ with diagonal elements ± 1 to get $B = \Delta A^{2^p} \Delta$ with most, if not all, elements positive. Let

$$B = \begin{bmatrix} b_{11} & b_{12} & \cdots & b_{1n} \\ b_{21} & b_{22} & \cdots & b_{2n} \\ \cdots & \cdots & \cdots & \cdots \\ b_{n1} & b_{n2} & \cdots & b_{nn} \end{bmatrix},$$

where $b_{ij} = b_{ji}$.

Compute column sums $c_j = \sum_{i=1}^{n} b_{ij}$, $j = 1, 2, \ldots, n$, and the grand total $G = \sum_{j=1}^{n} c_j$. Let $x_{0j} = c_j/\sqrt{G}$; then $\mathbf{x}_0 = (x_{01}, x_{02}, \ldots, x_{0n})$ is a first approximation to the latent vector, and $\mu_0 = \sum_{j=1}^{n} x_{0j}^2$ is a first approximation to the dominant latent root of B. Then compute

$$x_{11} = \frac{b_{11}x_{01} + b_{12}x_{02} + \cdots + b_{1n}x_{0n}}{\mu_0},$$

$$\mu_{01} = \mu_0 - x_{01}^2 + x_{11}^2,$$

$$x_{12} = \frac{b_{21}x_{11} + b_{22}x_{02} + \cdots + b_{2n}x_{0n}}{\mu_{01}},$$

$$\mu_{02} = \mu_{01} - x_{02}^2 + x_{12}^2,$$

$$x_{13} = \frac{b_{31}x_{11} + b_{32}x_{12} + b_{33}x_{03} + \cdots + b_{3n}x_{0n}}{\mu_{02}},$$

$$\mu_{03} = \mu_{02} - x_{03}^2 + x_{13}^2,$$

and so on, correcting at each stage one additional element of the vector and the sum of squares of the elements.

Then $\mathbf{x}_1 = (x_{11}, x_{12}, \ldots, x_{1n})$ is a second approximation to the latent vector, and $\mu_1 = \mu_{0n}$ is a second approximation to the dominant latent root of B. Starting with $\mathbf{x}_1$ and μ_1 and repeating the same cycle of operations, we find the third approximations $\mathbf{x}_2$, μ_2, and so on until the results stabilize. The latent root of A is the 2^pth root of that of B.

Illustrative Example 5.12. Find the largest latent root and the associated normalized latent vector of the symmetric matrix whose elements on the principal diagonal and above are as follows:

2.296	0.067	−0.567	0.709	−0.991
	0.499	0.113	0.311	−0.158
		0.417	0.070	0.270
			1.472	−0.503
				1.295

Denoting the above matrix by A, we obtain on successive squaring the matrix A^8, which contains some negative elements. On pre- and post-multiplication of A^8 by the diagonal matrix $\Delta = \text{diag}(1, 1, -1, 1, -1)$, we get the symmetric matrix $B = \Delta A^8 \Delta$ with all elements positive, whose elements on and above the principal diagonal are as follows:

11,016.7662	1147.1820	2513.3019	5852.2300	6896.6806
	93.4232	260.9773	612.2019	718.7350
		573.9219	1333.0442	1572.9588
			3111.2697	3665.1330
				4317.8141

The column totals are 27,426.1607, 2832.5194, 6254.2041, 14,573.8788, and 17,171.3215, respectively, and the grand total $G = 68,258.0845$. Dividing the column totals by $\sqrt{G} = 261.262482$, we obtain the vector $\mathbf{x}_0$ with elements 104.975504, 10.841662, 23.938393, 55.782517, 65.724406 as a first approximation to the latent vector, and the sum of squares of these elements, $\mu_0 = (104.975504)^2 + \cdots + (65.724406)^2 = 19,141.831481$, as the first approximation to the maximum latent root of B.

We now multiply the first row of B by the vector $\mathbf{x}_0$ and divide the result by μ_0 to find $[(104.975504)(11,016.7662) + \cdots + (65.724406)(6896.6806)]/$ $19,141.831481 = 104.944227$, which is now taken as an improved value for the first element of the latent vector. The sum of squares has then to be corrected to $\mu_{01} = 19,141.831481 - (104.975504)^2 + (104.944227)^2 = 19,135.265822$, which is the second approximation to the latent root. We then take the improved vector $\mathbf{x}_{01}$, whose elements are 104.944227, 10.841662, 23.938393, 55.782517, 65.724406, multiply the second row of the matrix B by $\mathbf{x}_{01}$, and divide the result by μ_{01} to get

$$\frac{(104.944227)(1147.1820) + \cdots + (65.724406)(6896.6806)}{19,135.265822} = 10.924278,$$

which is to be taken as an improved value for the second element of the latent vector. The sum of squares has then to be corrected to $\mu_{02} = 19,135.265822 - (10.841662)^2 + (10.924278)^2 = 19,137.064037$, and this is our next improved value for the latent root. We then multiply the third row of the matrix B by the vector $\mathbf{x}_{02}$ with elements 104.944227, 10.924278, 23.938393, 55.782517, 65.724406 and divide the result by μ_{02} to get 23.937247, which is the improved value for the third element of the latent vector. Then the sum of squares is corrected accordingly. Proceeding in this way, after five steps we obtain the vector $\mathbf{x}_1 = \mathbf{x}_{05}$ with elements 104.944227, 10.924278, 23.937247, 55.766194, 65.713859 and with sum of squares of elements equal to $\mu_1 = \mu_{05} = 19,133.802083$. This completes the first cycle of computations.

We then start with the approximations x_1 to the latent vector and μ_1 to the maximum latent root of B and proceed exactly as before, until after five operations the second cycle is completed. These cycles are continued until the results stabilize. The computations are generally arranged as shown in the table.

COMPUTATION OF LATENT ROOT AND VECTOR

Cycle					
1	104.944227	10.924278	23.937247	55.766194	65.713859
	19,135.265822	19,137.064037	19,137.009172	19,135.188362	19,133.802083
2	104.966266	10.923263	23.936410	55.764215	65.708782
	19,138.428300	19,138.406125	19,138.366055	19,138.145336	19,137.478103
3	104.956185	10.924139	23.938302	55.768433	65.712565
	19,135.361875	19,135.381013	19,135.471592	19,135.942037	19,136.439204
4	104.959034	10.923660	23.937273	55.766239	65.711207
	19,137.037252	19,137.026787	19,136.977523	19,136.732816	19,136.554343
5	104.958719	10.923817	23.937613	55.766923	65.711462
	19,136.488220	19,136.491650	19,136.507927	19,136.584216	19,136.617729
6	104.958545	10.923791	23.937552	55.766821	65.711493
	19,136.581203	19,136.580635	19,136.577715	19,136.566339	19,136.570413
7	104.958674	10.923786	23.937541	55.766794	65.711446
	19,136.597492	19,136.597383	19,136.596856	19,136.593845	19,136.594239

We therefore obtain 19,136.59 as the value of the dominant latent root of $R = \Delta A^8 \Delta$. But the dominant latent root of B is λ_{max}^8, where λ_{max} is the dominant latent root of A. Thus $\lambda_{max}^8 = 19,136.59$, and therefore $\lambda_{max} = 3.42952$. The latent vector of A is obtained by postmultiplying the latent vector of B by Δ; this gives 104.958674, 10.923786, -23.937541, 55.766794, -65.711446. Dividing each element of this vector by $\lambda^4 = 138.335064$, we find the normalized latent vector:

$$0.75873, \quad 0.07897, \quad -0.17304, \quad 0.40313, \quad -0.47502.$$

On postmultiplying this vector by the matrix A and dividing each element by $\lambda = 3.42952$, we get the vector

$$0.75871, \quad 0.07905, \quad -0.17305, \quad 0.40318, \quad -0.47500.$$

This agrees with the latent vector to four places of decimals.

5.6 EXERCISES

5.1. Find the volume and the length of the major axis of the hyperellipsoid defined by

$$\sum_{i,j=1}^{5} a_{ij} x_i x_j \leq 7,$$

where the matrix $A \equiv ((a_{ij}))$ is as follows:

$$
\begin{array}{ccccc}
1.000 & 0.313 & 0.280 & 0.182 & 0.166 \\
0.313 & 1.000 & 0.652 & 0.554 & 0.615 \\
0.280 & 0.652 & 1.000 & 0.747 & 0.693 \\
0.182 & 0.554 & 0.747 & 1.000 & 0.774 \\
0.166 & 0.615 & 0.693 & 0.774 & 1.000
\end{array}
$$

5.2. Solve for $x' = (x_1, x_2, x_3, x_4, x_5)$ the set of simultaneous linear equations

$$x'A = c',$$

where $c' = (0.495, 0.650, 0.803, 0.804, 0.812)$, and A is the matrix in exercise 5.1.

5.3. Find the inverse of the matrix A in exercise 5.1.

5.4. Using a suitable method, find the inverse of the matrix

$$
\begin{array}{ccc}
1.000 & 0.243 & 0.266 \\
0.243 & 1.000 & 0.628 \\
0.266 & 0.628 & 1.000
\end{array}
$$

Use the inverse obtained to compute the inverse of the following extended matrix:

$$
\begin{array}{ccccc}
1.000 & 0.243 & 0.266 & 0.307 & 0.156 \\
0.243 & 1.000 & 0.628 & 0.553 & 0.305 \\
0.266 & 0.628 & 1.000 & 0.489 & 0.212 \\
0.307 & 0.553 & 0.489 & 1.000 & 0.165 \\
0.156 & 0.305 & 0.212 & 0.165 & 1.000
\end{array}
$$

5.5. The following table gives the fraction q_x expected to burn out in 1 year's time among all fluorescent tubes x years old:

x	0	1	2	3
q_x	0.1200	0.4545	0.7917	1.0000

An industrial establishment starts with 1000 new tubes and replaces all burnt-out tubes by new ones at the end of the year, so that the total number of tubes remains the same (1000) but the age composition changes from year to year. Let $n_{x,t}$ be the number of tubes of age x at the end of the tth year, and let

$$N_t' = (n_{0,t}, n_{1,t}, n_{2,t}, n_{3,t}).$$

Show that
$$N'_{t+1} = N'_t A,$$
where A is the matrix

0.1200	0.8800	0	0
0.4545	0	0.5455	0
0.7917	0	0	0.2083
1.0000	0	0	0

Find the age composition of the fluorescent tubes at the end of (a) 5 years and (b) 100 years.

PART II

Descriptive Methods

CHAPTER 1

Presentation of Statistical Data

1.1 STATISTICAL DATA

Data in numerical form are needed in different fields of human activity. Scientists require data to formulate or confirm scientific theory. Businessmen and administrators need them to arrive at decisions. Statistics is mainly concerned with the collection of data relevant to a problem, their proper interpretation, and their presentation to the ultimate user.

Statistical Population. Statistical data arise out of observations on characteristics of individuals. The term *individual* in statistics is used in a general sense. For instance, when the data consist of hourly temperature records, each hour is an individual. Or, when the relationship between the stature of a father and that of his eldest son is under investigation, the father–son pair is the individual on whom two characteristics are observed. In a statistical investigation, the interest usually lies in the assessment of the general magnitude and the study of variation with respect to one or more characteristics relating to individuals belonging to a group. The group of individuals under study is called a *population*. In most problems, the identification or arrangement of individuals in the population is not relevant.

Qualitative and Quantitative Characteristics. A characteristic of an individual may be qualitative or quantitative. A qualitative characteristic is called an *attribute*. With respect to an attribute, the individuals of a population are divided into different classes or categories which may or may not admit grading. For example, with respect to the attribute eye color, an individual may belong to one of these categories: blue, gray, green, black, etc., which are not graded. But with respect to intellectual ability an individual may be classified in one of, say, three graded categories: superior, average, and inferior. A quantitative characteristic is called a *variable*. A variable may be *discrete*, taking only a number of distinct values, or *continuous*, in which case any value in a certain range is possible.

77

The number of children born to a couple is an example of a discrete variable, since it can only be 0, 1, 2, or some other integer. On the other hand, the stature of man is a continuous variable; it can be anywhere between, say, 120 cm and 220 cm. However, because of limitations of the fineness of measuring instruments, observations can be recorded only as integral multiples of a certain unit, however small, and thereby they take discrete forms in practice, Stature, for instance, would be recorded to, say, the nearest millimeter.

Data obtained on a single characteristic of the individuals are said to be *univariate;* if obtained on more than one characteristic, *multivariate.*

Complete Enumeration and Sampling. In an investigation, a statistician may himself organize the collection of data or he may use data compiled by other agencies. If information is collected from every individual of the population, the inquiry is known as *complete enumeration.* Considerations of cost, time, and problems of organization sometimes make complete enumeration impracticable. Information is then collected from a sample of selected individuals of the population. This is known as *sampling.* Statistical methods are available for drawing valid inference about the population on the basis of properly selected samples. Inferences of this type necessarily have a certain amount of uncertainty, but the magnitude of this uncertainty can be numerically assessed through the calculus of probability.

There are various methods for observing characteristics on individuals selected for an investigation. One method is to use investigators to interview the individuals; or if the individuals are not persons, the statistician or his agents make measurements or note attributes. The information obtained is recorded on specially prepared data sheets called *schedules.* In another method, the individual himself supplies the information by recording his answers to a *questionnaire* sent to him by mail or otherwise. The framing of schedules or questionnaires for use in an investigation is a skilled job, requiring careful planning. Questions, or the description of items in a schedule, should be precisely worded, free from vagueness or ambiguity. Instructions regarding concepts, definitions, units, coverage, methods of observation, etc., may be given in the body of the questionnaire or schedule itself if, convenient; or separate instruction sheets may be prepared. The arrangement of the items in a questionnaire or schedule has to be thought out carefully, taking into account probable psychological reactions of the informant and also the needs for mechanical processing of data. Sometimes, by including one or two extra items of information, it is possible to provide checks on the internal consistency of the primary data.

Information for an investigation may also be compiled from primary data already collected, as, for example, published official statistics or meteorological data.

After the data are collected, they are scrutinized, edited, arranged, and then statistically analyzed. Final results are published in the form of reports.

1.2 SCRUTINY OF DATA

The Need for Scrutiny. The results of a statistical investigation are likely to be affected by different types of errors. If the investigation is based on a sample, the results will depend on the particular sample chosen; usually a different result will be obtained if a different sample is selected. This variation in the results from sample to sample is known as *sampling fluctuation.* Though it is unavoidable, its magnitude can be ascertained by using the calculus of probability. An altogether different type of error may arise from inaccuracies in the primary returns coming in at different stages of compilation. In any investigation of some size, the data are seldom collected by a single investigator. It is known from experience that data collected by different investigators, from the same informant, usually differ. This discrepancy can arise because the psychological reaction of an informant to different investigators is different or because investigators differ in their interpretation of the items in the questionnaire or schedule and the concepts and definitions used therein.

Sometimes there may be genuine omissions in recording the information collected. On other occasions, in order to guard against loss, multiple copies of primary records are prepared and at this stage copying errors may creep in. Also, when derived figures like totals, ratios, or indices are compiled, there may be mistakes in computation. Moreover, the possibility of dishonest manipulation of data by investigators cannot be overlooked. For all these reasons, it is essential that primary data should be "cross-examined" for genuineness before statistical analysis is undertaken. Also, after the analysis is over, final results should be carefully checked against the results of other comparable investigations whenever available before presenting them to the ultimate user. Such checks come under the scope of scrutiny of data.

Methods of Scrutiny. In organizing any statistical investigation we have to consider carefully the possible sources of inaccuracies in the primary returns or derived statistics and accordingly provide for necessary checks and scrutiny at the proper stages. Once a mistake is detected, we should always try to locate its source and take necessary corrective actions so that it does not recur. But such effective actions can be taken only if the mistakes are detected early at the time of compilation. Hence provisions should be made for verification of primary returns on the basis of at least sample checks when data are being compiled.

Some mistakes will inevitably arise, even though extreme care is taken at the time of compilation. Some principles of scrutiny for the detection of such mistakes, when compilation is complete, will now be discussed.

If multiple sets of primary returns are available, they should be compared among themselves and also against the original set, if available.

When observations on the same characteristic of a number of individuals are recorded, any observation which deviates too much from the rest is called an *outlying* observation (or *outlier*). Statistical tests are available to decide whether an outlier is too rare to be acceptable without further examination.

A study of associated characteristics often helps in detecting suspicious observations. For instance, among a list of statures of adult males, an observation of 6 ft may not be rare; however, if the corresponding weight recorded is only 100 lb, the figures would appear to be extremely doubtful. Cross classification of the data by a number of associated characteristics is thus a very useful tool in scrutiny work.

Just as a large deviation from the general trend is unusual, much too close agreement also arouses suspicion in some cases. An interesting example is given by Philip and Haldane. In commenting upon the results of a genetical experiment in which observations agreed too closely with theory, they say, "So good a general agreement with theory would be obtained by chance once in 3.5×10^{22} trials; that is to say, if every member of the human race conducted a set of experiments of this type daily, they might reasonably hope for such a success once in fifty thousand million years. There are two alternates to the hypothesis of chance. One is that a wholly new type of biological regulation has been unwittingly discovered . . . . The other is that the author has consciously or unconsciously adjusted his observations to fit his theory."

Statistical returns should also be checked for constant errors of rounding off, specially if these are obtained from readings on crude measuring instruments. In a population census, for example, informants have a noticeable preference for reporting ages which are multiples of five or two.

The numerical accuracy of derived figures should be checked by duplicate computation.

Final results of statistical investigations should always be compared with results of similar investigations, and differences, if any, should be explained.

1.3 PRESENTATION OF DATA

Tabular Presentation. A statistical table is a convenient way of presenting numerical information, so that essential comparisons are brought out by suitable placement of relevant figures near one another. It is a two-way arrangement of data in rows and columns against classified headings.

Every table has broadly five parts:

1. TITLE. The title is placed at the top of the table and gives an explicit but brief description of the contents. The title should also preferably indicate the coverage and the extent of the information, the period to which it relates, the mode of collection of information, and the units of measurement if not described elsewhere. If the title is too long, part of this description may be presented as a *headnote* below the title. A table number is prefixed to the title where there is more than one table.

2. COLUMN CAPTION. Since it is easier for the eye to compare entries in a row, usually the more important way of classification is arranged columnwise. The characteristic with respect to which the columns are classified is described in a general heading for all columns. If there is a subclassification, groups of columns in the same subclass are placed together under a proper caption called the *spanner head*, which comes below the general heading for the columns. Captions for individual columns are placed below this spanner head and at the top of the respective columns. The columns themselves are arranged either in order of importance or in an alphabetical or time sequence.

3. STUB OR ROW CAPTION. The rows representing the classes with respect to other characteristics are similarly arranged and described by captions on the left-hand corner of the corresponding rows. The characteristics with respect to which the rows are classified are described by means of a *stubhead*. Subclassification of rows is emphasized by sectionalization of the table by means of horizontal rules or spacing.

4. BODY. The set of entries in the appropriate cells of the table, together with totals, subtotals, etc., forms the body of the table.

5. FOOTNOTE. The source of the information is generally cited at the bottom of the table.

Illustrative Example 1.1. The essential parts of a statistical table are shown in Table 1.1, which is taken from *Current Population Reports*, Series P-20, No. 77, published by the U.S. Department of Commerce, Bureau of the Census.

Graphic Presentation. In statistical diagrams, numerical magnitudes are represented by geometrical dimensions like length, angle, area, and volume. Statistical data so presented in the form of graphs and charts easily attract attention, and the visual comparison and interpretation provided are likely to leave a more striking impression on the mind than most other forms of presentation. But only a limited set of facts can be presented in a graph, and magnitudes can be shown only approximately.

TABLE 1.1   *Title*

Headnote

PERSONS 14 YEARS OLD AND OVER IN THE UNITED STATES, BY YEARS OF SCHOOL COMPLETED, BY AGE AND SEX: 1957

(In thousands; as of March)

General column heading · *Spanner head* · *Column caption* · *Body* · *Stub head* · *Row caption*

Age and sex	Total 14 yr and over	None	Elementary school			High school		College		School years not reported
			1–4 yr	5–7 yr	8 yr	1–3 yr	4 yr	1–3 yr	4 yr or more	
Total	119,333	2,377	6,739	14,842	20,567	25,544	30,710	8,952	7,637	1,965
14–17 yr	9,877	31	150	1,850	2,569	5,122	98	16	...	41
18–24 yr	13,826	98	276	786	888	3,471	5,780	1,951	465	111
25–44 yr	46,550	406	1,482	3,933	5,492	9,747	16,758	4,036	4,245	451
45 yr and over	49,080	1,842	4,831	8,273	11,618	7,204	8,074	2,949	2,927	1,362
Male	57,470	1,206	3,734	7,603	10,244	12,025	12,541	4,433	4,572	1,112
14–17 yr	4,981	18	97	1,082	1,296	2,432	27	8	...	21
18–24 yr	6,281	45	170	409	426	1,590	2,284	1,078	213	66
25–44 yr	22,637	205	854	2,054	2,838	4,738	6,929	2,067	2,680	272
45 yr and over	23,571	938	2,613	4,058	5,684	3,265	3,301	1,280	1,679	753
Female	61,863	1,171	3,005	7,239	10,323	13,519	18,169	4,519	3,065	853
14–17 yr	4,896	13	53	668	1,273	2,690	71	8	...	20
18–24 yr	7,545	53	106	462	462	1,881	3,496	873	252	45
25–44 yr	23,913	201	628	1,879	2,654	5,009	9,829	1,969	1,565	179
45 yr and over	25,509	904	2,218	4,215	5,934	3,939	4,773	1,669	1,248	609

Years of school completed

Footnote

Source: U.S. Department of Commerce, Bureau of the Census, *Current Population Reports*, Series P-20, No. 77.

Statisticians also use graphs and charts as a means of discovering regularity in the data, as a guide to further analysis, and sometimes even as an aid to finer computation.

Every graph or chart has a *caption* or a title which is a concise description of what it portrays. A brief note called the *legend* is usually added at a corner to explain the symbols used, the axes and the scales chosen, and other relevant information to make the graph self-explanatory. The source of the data represented in the graph should always be indicated.

A few of the important types of diagrams will be described.

RECTILINEAR CHART. On this chart the two coordinates of a point measured along two perpendicular axes X and Y from a fixed point called the *origin* are taken to represent numerical values of two characteristics of an individual. Usually, the X axis represents a quantitative classification such as time, age, or some other characteristic. The graduation marks on the axes, the origin, and the characteristic represented along a particular axis should be written neatly on the graph. Different but related series of data classified by the same characteristic may be plotted on the same graph, and by proper arrangement, shading, etc., the totals or differences between the series may be easily indicated. Sometimes, scales other than the arithmetic scale (logarithm, square-root, etc.) are used for one or both axes to obtain a simple relationship between the two variables.

Illustrative Example 1.2. Table 1.2 gives the death rates per thousand for the male and female populations in India for the years 1941–50.

TABLE 1.2

DEATH RATE PER THOUSAND IN INDIA BY SEX, 1941–50

Year	Male	Female	Year	Male	Female
1941	22.0	21.6	1946	18.7	17.8
1942	21.5	21.0	1947	20.0	19.4
1943	24.2	23.1	1948	17.4	16.6
1944	24.5	23.7	1949	16.1	15.4
1945	21.9	21.2	1950	16.4	15.6

Source: *Statistical Abstract of India*, 1952–53.

A graphical representation of these data is given in Chart 1.1.

PIE CHART. A pie chart is a circle divided into different sectors, with angles at the center proportional to different components of a total.

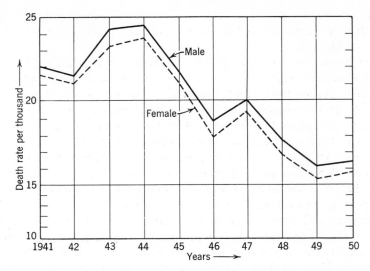

Chart 1.1   Death rate per thousand in India by sex, 1941–50.

Illustrative Example 1.3.   Table 1.3 gives the sectoral components of the national income of the United States in 1947.

TABLE 1.3

NATIONAL INCOME IN THE UNITED STATES, 1947, BY SECTORS

Sector	Income (million dollars)
Agriculture, forestry, fisheries, mining	23,321
Construction and manufacturing	70,448
Wholesale and retail trade	37,531
Finance, insurance, real estate	16,479
Transporation, communication, utilities	16,784
Services	18,831
Government and government enterprises	18,687
Total	202,081

The relative contributions of the different sectors can be represented in a pie chart as shown in Chart 1.2. For example, the contribution of "agriculture, forestry, fisheries, mining" is 23,321/202,081 = 11.54%. In

Chart 1.2   National income in the United States, 1947, by sectors.

the pie chart therefore this sector subtends an angle of 41°33′ at the center, which is 11.54% of 360°.

BAR CHART.   In a bar chart, quantities are represented by areas or lengths of vertical or horizontal bars.   There are many different forms of bar charts.   Sometimes a single bar is divided into different sections (having different shadings) with lengths proportional to the magnitudes of different components.   Again, vertical or horizontal bars placed along an axis are sometimes used to represent the numerical values associated with different groups of a classification.   If the data are classified by two characteristics, bars are drawn with heights adjusted according to one characteristic; each bar may be divided into sections according to the other classification.

Illustrative Example 1.4.   Table 1.4 gives for the United States the values (in million dollars) of the exports and imports for the years 1930, 1935, 1940, and 1945.

The same data can be graphically represented in a bar chart, as shown in Chart 1.3.

TABLE 1.4

VALUE OF EXPORTS AND IMPORTS FOR THE UNITED STATES, 1930–45

	Value of Exports (million dollars)			Value of imports (million dollars)		
Year	To foreign countries	To U.S. territories	Total	From foreign countries	From U.S. territories	Total
1930	3,771	253	4,024	2,930	358	3,288
1935	2,227	236	2,463	1,938	320	2,258
1940	3,926	376	4,302	2,522	316	2,838
1945	9,756	511	10,267	4,085	310	4,394

In addition, pictorial diagrams and statistical maps are also used to represent statistical data. A statistical map shows quantitative information on a geographical basis. In a pictorial diagram, a unit is represented by a suitable picture, and the number or size of pictures is varied to show different magnitudes.

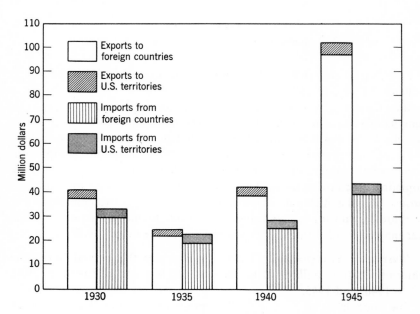

Chart 1.3   Value of exports and imports for the United States, 1930–45.

1.4 EXERCISES

Scrutiny of Data

1.1. Table 1.5 shows the average size and composition of 1374 families by monthly income groups in a town. Check the figures in the different columns of the table and copy the table after correcting the errors.

TABLE 1.5

COMPOSITION OF FAMILIES

| Monthly income groups | No. of families | Average size of families | No. of persons in all the families | | | | |
| | | | Adult | | Child | | |
			Male	Female	Male	Female	Total
I	31	2.03	17	17	10	8	63
II	135	30.8	176	164	74	63	477
III	207	4.36	307	266	169	160	902
IV	190	4.53	335	303	197	196	1031
V	153	5.82	293	256	179	153	890
VI	116	6.14	270	218	128	96	712
VII	94	7.37	272	207	131	128	693
VIII	79	8.04	224	178	135	89	635
IX	51	8.51	150	112	98	74	434
X	53	8.92	166	140	93	74	473
XI	108	9.07	369	288	186	155	980
XII	47	10.11	189	131	71	87	478
XIII	34	11.32	158	99	69	59	385
XIV	56	13.54	328	210	98	122	758

1.2. Scrutinize the following data carefully for any inconsistencies:

The total number of candidates who appeared for the Bachelor of Science (Honors) examination with statistics as the main subject and mathematics as the subsidiary subject during the last fifteen years in a university was 694, of whom 119 were girls. Out of these 176, including 37 girls, failed in both subjects. The number of candidates earning Honors in statistics was 84, but unfortunately 24 of them failed in mathematics. Of the candidates 229 boys and 55 girls failed in statistics. The number failing in mathematics was 261, of whom 47 were girls. The number of boys passing in both subjects (without getting Honors in statistics) was 270.

1.3. Table 1.6 is an extract from a record of anthropometric measurements on adult males. Rewrite the table after careful scrutiny and write a short note on the nature of the defects detected.

TABLE 1.6

ANTHROPOMETRIC MEASUREMENTS

Serial no.	Nasal length	Total facial length	Upper facial length	Stature	Sitting height	Weight
1	51	112	52	161	85	8.0
2	50	117	60	158	82	7.5
3	48	115	60	154	80	6.2
4	050	136	49	164	85	8.0
5	47	108	61	155	84	7.2
6	47	108	59	157	84	6.1
7	51	98	55	148	76	6.2
8	44	110	58	164	86	7.3
9	46	12	60	159	34	7.2
10	50	114	60	162	86	6.6
11	053	120	64	160	84	6.3
12	050	120	62	163	88	7.6
13	1.8	4.3	2.2	60.00	...	78
14	2.0	4.4	2.4	65.40	...	100
15	2.1	4.3	2.5	64.10	...	94
16	2.0	4.8	2.6	65.40	...	108
17	1.8	4.3	2.4	64.00	...	104
18	2.0	4.4	2.0	63.31	...	106
19	2.0	9.5	2.4	63.10	...	100
20	1.9	4.5	2.4	64.13	...	164

Preparation of tables

1.4. The following is an account of the accidents, due to four different causes, resulting in deaths or injuries to passengers in five different railways (*A, B, C, D, E*) in a particular year. Present the information in a suitable tabular form and find out the total number of accidents in the five railways due to the four causes.

In *A* 12 people were killed and an equal number were injured, while in *B* and *C* only 10 and 4 people, respectively, were injured and none killed. In *D* as many as 39 people were injured and 28 killed, while in *E* 9 people were killed and 10 injured. All of these accidents were due to "falling between trains and platforms."

Deaths and accidents caused by "crossing of the lines at stations" were not as numerous. In *E*, however, 6 people were injured and 5 killed, while in *C* and *D* only 4 and 2 people were killed and 2 and 1 injured, respectively. Railway *A* had only 1 injury and 3 deaths.

"Closing of carriage doors" resulted in serious injuries but happily no deaths. Thirty-three people were injured in *C*, 2 in *E*, and 4 in *A*.

The largest number of accidents, however, happened because of "falling or jumping out of running trains." As many as 218, 202, 115, 101, and 74 injuries happened in railways *C*, *E*, *B*, *D*, and *A*, respectively, while the deaths due to the same cause in these railways were respectively 35, 37, 26, 30, and 27.

1.5. Table 1.7 gives the sex (male or female), the blood group (A, B, AB, or O), and the ability (+) or inability (−) to taste a chemical compound (PTC) of 40 individuals investigated in a genetical study.

TABLE 1.7

SEX, BLOOD GROUP, AND TASTE REACTION TO
PTC OF 40 INDIVIDUALS

Serial no.	Sex	Blood group	Taste reaction to PTC	Serial no.	Sex	Blood group	Taste reaction to PTC
1	male	AB	+	21	female	A	+
2	female	AB	+	22	male	O	+
3	male	B	+	23	male	O	−
4	female	B	+	24	male	O	−
5	male	B	−	25	female	O	−
6	male	A	+	26	male	B	+
7	male	A	−	27	male	B	+
8	female	A	+	28	female	O	+
9	male	A	+	29	female	O	+
10	female	O	+	30	female		
11	female	O	+	31	female	A	+
12	female	O	+	32	male	A	+
13	male	O	+	33	female	O	+
14	female	A	+	34	female	O	+
15	male	A	−	35	female	A	+
16	male	B	−	36	female	O	+
17	male	B	+	37	male	O	+
18	female	A	+	38	male	O	+
19	male	AB	−	39	male	A	−
20	female	O	+	40	female	B	−

TABLE 1.8

A General Report on Attendance and Performance in Class Exercises

No. of lectures			No. of practical exercises			Exercises attended			All exercises		
Total	Present	% attended	Total	Present	% attended	Total marks	Marks secured	%	Total marks	Marks secured	% mark secured
146	125	86	50	44	88	440	$287\frac{1}{2}$	65	500	$287\frac{1}{2}$	58
	136	93		47	94	470	329	70		329	66
	137	94		49	98	490	290	59		290	58
	106	73		44	88	440	278	63		278	56
	127	87		41	82	410	$276\frac{1}{2}$	67		$276\frac{1}{2}$	55
	142	97		50	100	500	$320\frac{1}{2}$	64		$320\frac{1}{2}$	64
	142	97		47	94	470	$345\frac{1}{2}$	74		$345\frac{1}{2}$	69
	144	99		50	100	500	341	68		341	68
	135	92		45	90	450	313	70		313	63
	128	88		43	86	430	285	66		285	57
	135	92		47	94	470	$276\frac{1}{2}$	59		$276\frac{1}{2}$	55
	131	90		49	98	490	$319\frac{1}{2}$	65		$319\frac{1}{2}$	64
	143	98		50	100	500	$311\frac{1}{2}$	62		$311\frac{1}{2}$	62
	114	78		40	80	400	265	66		265	53
	138	95		44	88	440	$300\frac{1}{2}$	68		$300\frac{1}{2}$	60
	133	91		49	98	490	$316\frac{1}{2}$	65		$316\frac{1}{2}$	63
	113	77		48	96	480	$322\frac{1}{2}$	67		$322\frac{1}{2}$	65
	129	88		44	88	440	$290\frac{1}{2}$	66		$290\frac{1}{2}$	58

Summarize the information in another table, with a suitable title, column and row headings, and other essential details to make the table self-explanatory.

1.6. All the students of five colleges in a big city were medically examined for the occurrence of tonsilitis. The age, sex, and economic status of the student (whether totally or partly dependent on parents for finances or self-supporting) were noted, as was the state where the student was born.

Prepare a blank tabular layout in which the results of the investigation could be presented in a summary form.

1.7. Table 1.8 gives the statistics of attendance and performance in class exercises of eighteen trainees in a certain institution. Give your critical comments on the method of presentation and prepare an improved version of the table.

Graphical presentation

1.8. Table 1.9 shows the production of electricity in the U.S. and the U.S.S.R. Represent the data graphically to compare the absolute and relative increases in production.

TABLE 1.9

PRODUCTION OF ELECTRICITY IN THE U.S.
AND U.S.S.R., 1952–58

Year	Production of electricity (million kwh)	
	U.S.A.	U.S.S.R.
1952	38,588	9,926
53	42,847	11,194
54	45,387	12,558
55	52,417	14,185
56	57,016	15,975
57	59,696	17,457
58	60,363	19,400

Source: *U.N. Monthly Bulletin of Statistics.*

1.9. Table 1.10 gives for India the values of imports and exports of merchandise, in millions of rupees (1 U.S. dollar = 7.50 Indian rupees, approximately) for the years 1948–49 to 1952–53. Represent the data graphically and comment on the essential features.

TABLE 1.10

VALUE OF IMPORTS AND EXPORTS (IN MILLION RUPEES) FOR
INDIA, 1948–49 TO 1952–53

Item	1948–49	1949–50	1950–51	1951–52	1952–53
Imports					
Foreign merchandise	5,589	6,174	5,812	8,749	6,355
Exports					
Indian merchandise	4,210	4,721	5,790	7,018	5,538
Foreign merchandise	73	133	278	139	57
Total	4,283	4,853	6,068	7,157	5,595

Source: *Statistical Abstract of India*, 1952–53.

1.10. Table 1.11 gives the estimated populations and the national incomes in 1957, together with currency conversion factors, of several countries. Represent the data in a suitable graphical form so as to bring out the differences in national income per capita.

TABLE 1.11

POPULATION AND NATIONAL INCOME OF SEVERAL COUNTRIES, 1957

Country	Population (millions)	National income	Currency conversion factor (U.S. dollar per unit of national currency)
Canada	16.6	23,860 million dollars (Canadian)	1.04
France	44.1	15,680 thousand million francs	0.0020
West Germany	51.5	160.3 thousand million Deutsch marks	0.24
India	392.4	113.6 thousand million rupees (Indian)	0.21
Japan	90.9	8251.6 thousand million yens	0.0028
Switzerland	5.1	27,280 million francs (Swiss)	0.23
United Kingdom	51.5	17,578 million pounds (sterling)	2.80
United States	171.9	366.5 thousand million dollars (U.S.)	1.00

Source: *U.N. Monthly Bulletin of Statistics.*

1.11. Table 1.12 gives the volume (in millions of passenger-miles) of domestic intercity passenger traffic in the United States, by type of transportation, for the years 1950–57.

TABLE 1.12

INTERCITY PASSENGER TRAFFIC IN THE UNITED STATES
(IN MILLION PASSENGER MILES), 1950–57

Year	Total traffic	Rail-roads	Commercial motor carriers	Private auto-mobiles	Inland water-ways	Airways
1950	473,022	32,481	26,436	402,843	1,190	10,072
1951	534,782	35,306	27,418	457,787	1,333	12,938
1952	573,345	34,710	28,704	495,547	1,396	14,988
1953	608,769	32,261	28,397	529,194	1,487	17,430
1954	625,113	29,467	25,614	548,763	1,701	19,568
1955	664,510	28,695	25,519	585,817	1,738	22,741
1956	698,895	28,610	25,189	617,713	1,800	25,523
1957	719,236	26,251	24,998	637,755	1,930	28,302

Source: *Statistical Abstract of the United States*, 1959.

Make a suitable graphical presentation of the data in order to find out the essential features.

CHAPTER 2

Condensation of Univariate Data

2.1 PREPARATION OF FREQUENCY TABLES

When observations, discrete or continuous, are available on a single characteristic of a large number of individuals, often it becomes necessary to condense the data as far as possible without losing any information of interest. If the identity of the individual on whom a particular observation is taken is not relevant, nor the order in which the observations arise, then the first step of condensation is to divide the observed range of the variable into a suitable number of *class intervals* and to record the number of observations falling in each class. This number is called the *frequency* of the class. A table showing the distribution of the frequencies in the different classes is called a *frequency table*.

Choice of Class Intervals. In the choice of the number, width (size), and limits of the class intervals to be used in forming a frequency table, we should be guided by the following considerations.

Class intervals of equal width facilitate later computations.

If too many classes are used, some irregularities may enter because of fluctuations of sampling; some classes may even be empty. If too few classes are used, much information is lost. Ordinarily eight to fifteen classes, depending on the volume of observations, may be adequate. Class limits should be fixed after a careful consideration of the nature of rounding-off errors in the observations: whether they are rounded off to the nearest unit or expressed in terms of completed units with fractions neglected. A recorded value x rounded off by the first rule really stands for an observation which may be anywhere in the interval $(x - \frac{1}{2}, x + \frac{1}{2})$. On the other hand, if x is rounded off by the second rule, it really stands for an observation in the interval $(x, x + 1)$.

Class intervals should be non-overlapping. There should not be any ambiguity about the category to which a class limit belongs.

If observations are subject to bias caused by preference for particular

94

digits like 0, 5, or some of the even digits, so that the frequency of measurements ending with the preferred digits is unduly high, it is better to use class intervals in which the preferred digits are the central points.

Illustrative Example 2.1. The scores in English of 250 candidates selected at random from among those appearing at a certain examination are given in Table 2.1. Prepare a frequency distribution.

TABLE 2.1

SCORES IN ENGLISH OF 250 CANDIDATES

32	47	41	51	41	30	39	18	48	53
54	32	31	46	15	37	32	56	42	48
38	26	50	40	38	42	35	22	62	51
44	21	45	31	37	41	44	18	37	47
68	41	30	52	52	60	42	38	38	34
61	53	48	21	28	49	42	36	41	29
30	33	37	35	39	37	38	40	32	49
43	32	24	38	38	22	41	50	17	46
46	50	26	15	23	42	25	52	38	46
41	38	40	37	40	48	45	30	28	31
40	33	42	36	51	42	56	44	34	38
31	51	45	41	50	53	50	32	45	48
40	43	40	34	34	44	38	58	49	28
40	45	19	24	34	47	37	33	37	36
36	32	61	30	44	43	50	31	38	35
46	40	32	34	44	54	35	39	31	48
48	50	43	55	43	39	41	48	53	34
32	31	42	34	34	32	33	24	43	39
40	50	27	47	34	44	34	33	47	42
17	42	57	35	38	17	33	46	36	23
48	50	31	58	33	44	26	29	31	37
47	55	57	37	31	54	42	45	37	43
37	52	47	46	44	50	44	38	42	19
52	45	23	41	47	33	42	24	48	39
48	44	61	38	38	44	38	43	40	48

Here, the maximum score is 68 and the minimum 15, so that the range is $68 - 15 = 53$. We may use a class interval of width 5, so that the total number of classes will be 11. Since scores are presumably rounded off to the nearest integer, a score of 15 means a score between 14.5 and 15.5.

So the classes chosen are 14.5–19.5, 19.5–24.5, . . . , 64.5–69.5. The frequencies in the different class intervals are recorded by putting a tally mark in the appropriate class for each observation. To facilitate counting, tallies are arranged in groups of five. The frequency table thus obtained is shown as Table 2.2.

TABLE 2.2

FREQUENCY DISTRIBUTION OF SCORES IN ENGLISH

Class limits	Tally marks	Frequency	Relative frequency
14.5–19.5	洙 ////	9	0.036
19.5–24.5	洙 洙 /	11	0.044
24.5–29.5	洙 洙	10	0.040
29.5–34.5	洙 洙 洙 洙 洙 洙 洙 洙 ////	44	0.176
34.5–39.5	洙 洙 洙 洙 洙 洙 洙 洙 洙	45	0.180
39.5–44.5	洙 洙 洙 洙 洙 洙 洙 洙 洙 洙 洙 ////	54	0.216
44.5–49.5	洙 洙 洙 洙 洙 洙 洙 //	37	0.148
49.5–54.5	洙 洙 洙 洙 洙 /	26	0.104
54.5–59.5	洙 ///	8	0.032
59.5–64.5	洙	5	0.020
64.5–69.5	/	1	0.004
	Total	250	1.000

Graphical Representation of a Frequency Distribution

HISTOGRAM. A frequency distribution in which f_i is the frequency in the class interval (a_i, a_{i+1}) can be represented graphically by a system of contiguous rectangles in which a rectangle with the class interval (a_i, a_{i+1}) as base and the *relative frequency* $p_i = f_i/N$ (N being the total number of observations) as area represents the ith class frequency. This diagram is called a *histogram*.

FREQUENCY POLYGON. If the characteristic is a discrete variate with possible values $x_1, x_2, . . . , x_k$ $(x_1 < x_2 < \cdots < x_k)$ and the relative frequency for x_i is p_i, then a graphical representation of the frequency distribution is obtained by plotting the points $A_i = (x_i, p_i)$ and joining the pairs of points $(A_1, A_2), (A_2, A_3), . . . , (A_{k-1}, A_k)$ successively by straight lines. The diagram so obtained is called a *frequency polygon*.

OGIVE. A graph showing against each value of x the relative frequency (proportion) $F(x)$ of individuals with the characteristic less than or equal to x is called an *ogive* (less-than type). The function $F(x)$ is called the *cumulative frequency distribution function*. Similarly the graph showing the relative frequency $G(x) = 1 - F(x)$ of observations greater than x against x is called an ogive of the greater-than type.

Illustrative Example 2.2. Draw the histogram (see Chart 2.1) and the ogive (less-than type) for the frequency distribution of scores obtained in illustrative example 2.1.

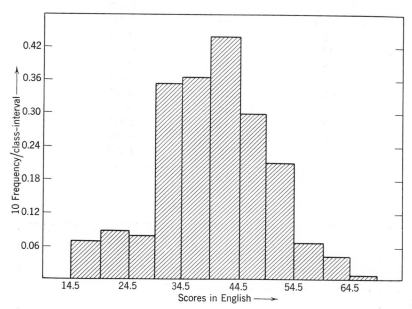

Chart 2.1   Histogram of the frequency distribution of scores in English.

To draw the ogive (less-than type) we first prepare the cumulative frequency distribution as shown in Table 2.3.

The ogive is given as Chart 2.2.

FREQUENCY CURVE.   For a continuous variate it is often convenient to approximate the cumulative frequency distribution function by a continuous function which is differentiable everywhere and can be expressed as

$$F(x) = \int_{-\infty}^{x} f(t)\, dt.$$

In this case the function $f(x)$ is called its *frequency density function*; if it is continuous, the curve $y = f(x)$ is called the *frequency curve*. The frequency curve is said to be *symmetric* about the point c if, for every value of x, $f(x - c) = f(c - x)$, and c is said to be the center of symmetry. An

TABLE 2.3

CUMULATIVE FREQUENCY DISTRIBUTION OF SCORES

Upper limit of class	Cumulative frequency	Cumulative relative frequency
14.5	0	0.000
19.5	9	0.036
24.5	20	0.080
29.5	30	0.120
34.5	74	0.296
39.5	119	0.476
44.5	173	0.692
49.5	210	0.840
54.5	236	0.944
59.5	244	0.976
64.5	249	0.996
69.5	250	1.000

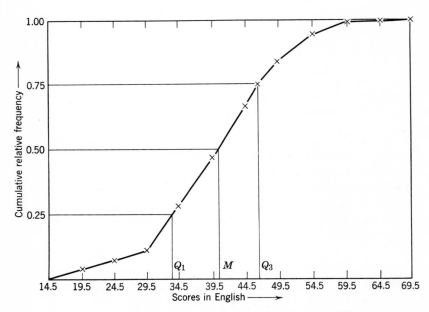

Chart 2.2   Ogive of the distribution of scores in English.

asymmetric frequency curve is said to be positively or negatively *skew* according to whether the longer tail of the curve is on the right-hand or the left-hand side, respectively.

Random Variables. Suppose that an individual is chosen from a population in such a way that any member of the population is equally likely to have been chosen. Let X be the value of the characteristic for the selected individual; then the magnitude of X depends upon which particular individual is chosen and X is said to be a *random variable*. Let x be a given constant. Suppose that the process of choosing an individual is repeated a large number of times under identical conditions. It is then expected that in a proportion $P(x)$ of cases the value of X will be less than or equal to x, where $P(x)$ is the relative frequency of individuals in the population with the characteristic less than or equal to x. $P(x)$ is said to be the cumulative probability distribution function of the random variable X, and we write

$$\text{Prob }(X \leq x) = P(x).$$

If the characteristic is discrete, that is, it takes only a finite or countably infinite number of values x_i, $i = 1, 2, \ldots$, then the probability that the random variable X takes on the value x_i will be denoted by

$$\text{Prob }(X = x_i) = p_i,$$

where p_i is the relative frequency of x_i in the population. The random variable X in such cases will be said to be discrete.

A random variable X is said to be absolutely continuous if its cumulative probability distribution function $P(x)$ is differentiable everywhere and can be expressed as

$$P(x) = \int_{-\infty}^{x} f(t) \, dt,$$

in which case $f(x)$ is called the *probability density function*, or simply the *density function*, of x. This is a somewhat intuitive approach to the concept of random variables; the calculus of probability is described in Chapter 1 of Part III.

2.2 SUMMARY MEASURES

A set of observations on a certain characteristic, whether in the form of a frequency distribution or not, can often be effectively described by means of a few summary measures. We will discuss a number of such commonly used summary measures.

Notation. The symbol $\mathcal{M}$ will be used to denote the *arithmetic mean*. Thus, if $x_1, x_2, \ldots, x_N$ are N observations on a characteristic X, and $g(x)$

is a given function of x, we have

$$\mathcal{M}[g(X)] = \frac{1}{N}\sum_{i=1}^{N} g(x_i).$$

On the other hand, if the observations are grouped into a frequency distribution with k class intervals, and if the frequency in the ith class interval (a_i, a_{i+1}) is f_i, $\sum_{i=1}^{k} f_i = N$, then, on the assumption that observations are concentrated at the midpoints $\bar{a}_i = \frac{1}{2}(a_i + a_{i+1})$ of the classes, we obtain

$$\mathcal{M}[g(X)] = \frac{1}{N}\sum_{i=1}^{k} g(\bar{a}_i)f_i.$$

When there is a continuous probability density function $f(x)$, this equation reduces to

$$\mathcal{M}[g(X)] = \int g(x)f(x)\,dx,$$

integration being over the entire range of X.

Measures of Location. A single representative value for a set of observations on a characteristic X is called a *measure of location.* Some measures of location commonly used will now be described.

ARITHMETIC MEAN. $\mu = \mathcal{M}(X).$

Two other measures of location used if the characteristic X takes only positive values are as follows.

GEOMETRIC MEAN. $G = \text{antilog}\,\mathcal{M}(\log X) = \sqrt[N]{\prod_{i=1}^{N} x_i}.$

HARMONIC MEAN. $H = \dfrac{1}{\mathcal{M}(1/X)}.$

The arithmetic mean is the most commonly used measure of location. For a symmetric distribution it coincides with the center of symmetry. The geometric mean is useful in averaging a sequence of ratios and for highly positively skew distributions.

Illustrative Example 2.3. The radii of five circular sockets (in centimeters) are 2.03, 1.98, 2.24, 2.17, 2.08. Find the arithmetic mean, $\bar{x}$, of this sample.

Writing x for the measured radius, we have $\Sigma x = 10.50$ and $N = 5$; hence the arithmetic mean is $\bar{x} = \Sigma x/N = 2.10$ cm.

Illustrative Example 2.4. For four consecutive years, the ratios of the volume of production of a factory in a given year to that in the preceding year were $x_1 = 102.1$, $x_2 = 107.6$, $x_3 = 112.5$, and $x_4 = 125.4$, respectively. Find a suitable average of these ratios.

If production were growing at a constant rate, the common ratio being G, we would then have $G^4 = x_1 x_2 x_3 x_4$, so that, in a case like this, the geometric mean is the appropriate measure of location. Thus

$G =$ antilog $[\frac{1}{4}(\log 102.1 + \log 107.6 + \log 112.5 + \log 125.4)]$

$\quad =$ antilog $[\frac{1}{4}(2.0090257 + 2.0318123 + 2.0511525 + 2.0622058)]$

$\quad =$ antilog 2.0385491

$\quad = 109.28.$

Illustrative Example 2.5. A motor car traveled 3 consecutive miles, the first mile at $x_1 = 35$ miles per hour (mph), the second at $x_2 = 48$ mph, and the third at $x_3 = 40$ mph. Find the average speed of the car in miles per hour.

Here the total distance of 3 miles is covered in $(1/x_1) + (1/x_2) + (1/x_3)$ hours, so that the required average speed is

$$H = \frac{3}{\dfrac{1}{x_1} + \dfrac{1}{x_2} + \dfrac{1}{x_3}}$$

which is the harmonic mean of the given speeds. Thus

$$\frac{1}{H} = \frac{1}{3}\left(\frac{1}{35} + \frac{1}{48} + \frac{1}{40}\right) = 0.0244$$

and therefore $H = 41.0$ mph.

FRACTILES. For a given number p, $0 < p < 1$, the fractile $\tilde{x}(p)$ is defined as the smallest number x for which the cumulative frequency distribution function $F(x) \geq p$. Specially important are:

Median: $M = \tilde{x}(\frac{1}{2})$.

Quartiles: First quartile, $Q_1 = \tilde{x}(\frac{1}{4})$; third quartile, $Q_3 = \tilde{x}(\frac{3}{4})$.

Percentiles: rth percentile, $\tilde{x}(r/100)$, $r = 1, 2, \ldots, 99$.

For continuous variables, fractiles are usually obtained from the cumulative frequency distribution function by linear interpolation. When observations are arranged in ascending order, the median is the middle-most value in an odd number of observations and the smaller of the two middle values when the number of observations is even. It is therefore not greatly affected by extreme values, which may be in error.

Illustrative Example 2.6. Find the median and the first and third quartiles of the frequency distribution of scores obtained in illustrative example 2.1.

From the cumulative frequency distribution, it is found that the relative frequency below 29.5 is 0.120 and that below 34.5 is 0.296. Since below the first quartile Q_1 the relative frequency is 0.25, we have by linear interpolation

$$Q_1 = 29.6 + (34.5 - 29.5) \times \frac{0.25 - 0.120}{0.296 - 0.120}$$

$$= 33.19.$$

Similarly, the median M is obtained as

$$M = 39.5 + (44.5 - 39.5) \times \frac{0.50 - 0.476}{0.692 - 0.476}$$

$$= 40.06,$$

and the third quartile Q_3 is given by

$$Q_3 = 44.5 + (49.5 - 44.5) \times \frac{0.75 - 0.692}{0.840 - 0.692}$$

$$= 46.46.$$

These values can also be read off directly from the ogive drawn in illustrative example 2.2.

MODE. The value of the characteristic which has the maximum frequency is called the *mode*. For a continuous variate the mode is defined as that value of x for which the density function $f(x)$ is maximum. To obtain the mode M_0 from a frequency distribution with equal class intervals the approximate formula

(2.2.1) $$M_0 = l - \frac{h(f_0 - f_{-1})}{f_1 - 2f_0 + f_{-1}}$$

may be used, where l is the lower limit of the class with the maximum frequency, f_0 is the frequency in this class, f_{-1} and f_1 are the frequencies in the classes just preceding and succeeding this class, and h is the width of the class intervals. This formula is obtained on the assumption that the density function is a quadratic parabola in the range covered by these three classes.

Illustrative Example 2.7. To find the mode of the frequency distribution obtained in illustrative example 2.1, we note that the frequency in the modal class (39.5–44.5) is $f_0 = 54$, and the frequencies in the two adjacent classes are $f_{-1} = 45$ and $f_1 = 37$. Hence, using formula 2.2.1, we obtain

$$M_0 = 39.5 - \frac{5 \times (54 - 45)}{37 - 2 \times 54 + 45} = 41.23.$$

Measures of Dispersion. Sometimes it is necessary to obtain a summary measure for the variation or scatter of the observations on a certain characteristic.

If the observations $x_1, x_2, \ldots, x_N$ on a characteristic X are not grouped, the most obvious measure of dispersion is the

RANGE. $R = x_{max} - x_{min}$, where x_{max} and x_{min} represent respectively the maximum and minimum values of x in the set of observations. One disadvantage is that this measure may be affected if the extreme observations are not reliable.

The most commonly used measure of dispersion is the

VARIANCE. $V(X) = \sigma^2 = \mathcal{M}[(X - \mu)^2] = \mu_2$, where μ is the arithmetic mean.

The positive square root of the variance is called the

STANDARD DEVIATION. $\sigma = +\sqrt{\mu_2}$.

The ratio of the standard deviation to the arithmetic mean is called the

COEFFICIENT OF VARIATION. $V = 100 \dfrac{\sigma}{\mu} \%$.

Another measure used is the

MEAN DEVIATION ABOUT A GIVEN POINT c. $\Delta = \mathcal{M}[|X - c|]$.

Illustrative Example 2.8. The radii of five circular sockets (in centimeters) are 2.03, 1.98, 2.24, 2.17, 2.08. Find the range, variance, standard deviation, mean deviation about the median, and coefficient of variation.

Since the smallest observation is 1.98 and the largest is 2.24, the range $= 2.24 - 1.98 = 0.26$ cm.

Writing x for the radius, we have, from illustrative example 2.3, $\bar{x} = (1/n)\Sigma x = 2.10$. The deviations from the mean, $x - \bar{x}$, are -0.07, $-0.12, 0.14, 0.07, -0.02$, respectively. Hence

$$\text{Variance} = \frac{1}{n}\Sigma (x - \bar{x})^2$$
$$= \tfrac{1}{5}(0.0049 + 0.0144 + 0.0196 + 0.0049 + 0.0004)$$
$$= 0.00884.$$

Therefore the standard deviation $= +\sqrt{0.00884} = 0.094$. The median of these observations is $M = 2.08$. The absolute values of the deviation from the median, $|x - M|$, are 0.05, 0.10, 0.16, 0.09, 0.00, respectively. Consequently, the mean deviation about the median is

$$\frac{1}{n}\Sigma |x - M| = \tfrac{1}{5}(0.05 + 0.10 + 0.16 + 0.09 + 0.00) = 0.08.$$

CONCENTRATION RATIO. This measure of dispersion is commonly used for economic variables like income and consumption. Let x be a variable which takes only positive values, and let T be the total of all the variate values in the population. For a given number x, let $P(x)$ be the proportion of individuals in the population with variate values not exceeding x. Let $T(x)$ be the total of their variate values, and $Q(x) = T(x)/T$ the proportion of the total which can be attributed to these individuals. The graph showing $Q(x)$ against $P(x)$ (for various values of x) is called the *concentration curve*. Let A be the area bounded by the concentration curve and the equiangular line $Q = P$; then the concentration ratio is defined as $\delta = 2A$. Obviously $0 \leq \delta \leq 1$, and the larger the value of δ, the greater is the disparity between the individuals.

If, in addition to the two terminal points, $(0, 0)$ and $(1, 1)$, n other points (P_i, Q_i), $i = 1, 2, \ldots, n$, where $P_i = P(x_i)$ and $Q_i = Q(x_i)$, $x_1 < x_2 < x_3 < \cdots < x_n$ on the concentration curve, are empirically determined, the concentration ratio can be approximately evaluated by using the trapezoidal rule for quadrature. This gives

(2.2.2)

$$\delta = P_1 Q_2 + P_2(Q_3 - Q_1) + P_3(Q_4 - Q_2) + \cdots + P_n(1 - Q_{n-1}) - Q_n.$$

Illustrative Example 2.9. Table 2.4 gives the distribution of monthly expenditure per person in rupees (1 U.S. dollar = 7.50 Indian rupees, approximately) in rural India for the period from October 1953 to March 1954.

TABLE 2.4

DISTRIBUTION OF MONTHLY EXPENDITURE PER PERSON IN RURAL INDIA, OCTOBER 1953–MARCH 1954

Monthly expenditure (rupees) per person	Percentage distribution of persons p	Average monthly expenditure per person (rupees) a
0–8	15.47	6.20
8–11	17.80	9.63
11–13	12.04	11.92
13–15	10.31	13.96
15–18	10.83	16.21
18–21	8.75	19.06
21–24	6.94	22.26
24–28	5.77	26.06
28–34	4.82	30.53
34–43	3.73	36.89
43–55	1.97	48.98
55 and above	1.57	89.05

Source: *National Sample Survey*, Report No. 20, India.

From this table, we get the values of $P(x)$ and $Q(x)$ shown in Table 2.5. Column (1) gives the upper limits of the classes; columns (2) and (3) are copied from Table 2.4; other computations are presented in columns (4)

TABLE 2.5

COMPUTATIONS FOR DRAWING THE CONCENTRATION CURVE

x	p	a	$t = p \times a$	Cumulative total of $T(x)$	$Q(x) =$ $T(x)/T$	Cumulative total of $p \div 100$ $P(x)$
(1)	(2)	(3)	(4)	(5)	(6)	(7)
8	15.47	6.20	95.9140	95.9140	0.0557	0.1547
11	17.80	9.63	171.4140	267.3280	0.1552	0.3327
13	12.04	11.92	143.5168	410.8448	0.2384	0.4531
15	10.31	13.96	143.9276	554.7724	0.3220	0.5562
18	10.83	16.21	175.5543	730.3267	0.4239	0.6645
21	8.75	19.06	166.7750	897.1017	0.5207	0.7520
24	6.94	22.26	154.4844	1051.5861	0.6103	0.8214
28	5.77	26.06	150.3662	1201.9523	0.6976	0.8791
34	4.82	30.53	147.1546	1349.1069	0.7830	0.9273
43	3.73	36.89	137.5997	1486.7066	0.8629	0.9646
55	1.97	48.98	96.4906	1583.1972	0.9189	0.9843
...	1.57	89.05	139.8085	$T = 1723.0057$	1.0000	1.0000

through (7). The concentration curve is shown as Chart 2.3. The concentration ratio is

$$\delta = P_1 Q_2 + P_2(Q_3 - Q_1) + \cdots + P_{11}(1 - Q_{10}) - Q_{11}$$
$$= 0.1547 \times 0.1552 + 0.3327(0.2384 - 0.0557) + \cdots$$
$$+ 0.9843(1 - 0.8629) - 0.9189$$
$$= 0.333.$$

SEMI-INTERQUARTILE RANGE. This measure is defined as half the difference of the third and the first quartiles: $\frac{1}{2}(Q_3 - Q_1)$.

Moments. The moments of a variable X are defined as follows:

*r*TH MOMENT ABOUT A GIVEN POINT c.

$$\mu_r' = \mathcal{M}[(X - c)^r], \qquad r = 1, 2, \ldots .$$

More useful are the central moments, which are the moments about the arithmetic mean, defined as follows:

*r*TH CENTRAL MOMENT. $\mu_r = \mathcal{M}[(X - m)^r]$, where $m = \mathcal{M}(X)$.

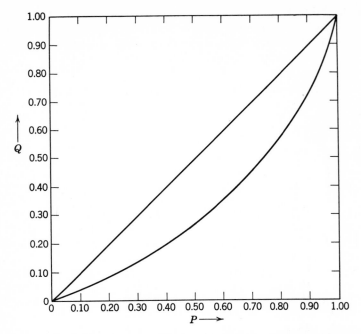

Chart 2.3   Concentration curve for the distribution of monthly expenditure per person in rural India, 1953–54. *P*: Proportion of persons having monthly expenditure of *x* or less. *Q*: Proportion of total expenditure enjoyed by persons having monthly expenditure of *x* or less.

The relation between a moment about the mean and the moments about any given point is

(2.2.3)
$$\mu_r = \sum_{t=0}^{r} (-1)^t \binom{r}{t} \mu'_{r-t} \mu'^t_1.$$

BETA COEFFICIENTS.   The coefficients β_1 and β_2, defined by

$$\beta_1 = \frac{\mu_3^2}{\mu_2^3} = \alpha_3^2 \quad \text{and} \quad \beta_2 = \frac{\mu_4}{\mu_2^2} = \alpha_4,$$

are useful in describing the shape of frequency curves. The coefficient β_1 or equivalently $\alpha_3 = \mu_3/\mu_2^{3/2}$ (square root of β_1 with the same sign as μ_3) is a measure of *skewness* (asymmetry). For a symmetric distribution, $\beta_1 = 0$. The distribution is (generally) positively or negatively skew according as μ_3 is positive or negative. The coefficient β_2 or equivalently $\beta_2 - 3$ is a measure of *kurtosis* (peakedness). If $\beta_2 < 3$, the distribution is said to be *platykurtic*; if $\beta_2 > 3$, it is said to be *leptokurtic*.

Computation of Central Moments. The labor in computing moments may sometimes be reduced by a suitable change of origin and scale. Let $U = (X - a)/b$ be the transformed variable. The first step is to compute the moments of U about zero: $q_r = \mathcal{M}[U^r]$, $r = 1, 2, 3, \ldots$.

The first four moments are then computed as follows.

MEAN.

(2.2.4)
$$\mu = a + bq_1.$$

CENTRAL MOMENTS.

$$\mu_2 = b^2(q_2 - q_1{}^2),$$
$$\mu_3 = b^3(q_3 - 3q_2q_1 + 2q_1{}^3),$$
$$\mu_4 = b^4(q_4 - 4q_3q_1 + 6q_2q_1{}^2 - 3q_1{}^4).$$

CHARLIER'S CHECK. A check on the computation is obtained from the identity:

(2.2.5)
$$T_r = S_r + \binom{r}{1}S_{r-1} + \binom{r}{2}S_{r-2} + \cdots + S_0,$$

where $T_r = \Sigma f_i(u_i + 1)^r$ and $S_r = \Sigma f_i u_i{}^r$, $r = 1, 2, \ldots$; $S_0 = N$.

For a frequency distribution with equal class intervals we should take the midpoint of some class as the value for a and the width of the class interval as b, and use the above procedure.

AN ALTERNATIVE SUMMATION METHOD. In this procedure the classes are arranged in increasing order and their frequencies are denoted by $f_1, f_2, \ldots, f_k$, say. Then we compute the cumulative frequencies from below: $g_k = f_k$; $g_{k-1} = f_k + f_{k-1}$; $g_1 = f_k + f_{k-1} + \cdots + f_1 = N$. This procedure is applied on the g's to get $h_k = g_k$; $h_{k-1} = g_k + g_{k-1}$; $\ldots h_1 = g_k + \cdots + g_1 = N_1$. Repeating this operation three times, we obtain N_2, N_3, and N_4. Then the first four moments are obtained from the formulae (2.2.4), by putting

$$q_1 = \frac{N_1}{N},$$

$$q_2 = \frac{2N_2 - N_1}{N},$$

(2.2.6)

$$q_3 = \frac{6N_3 - 6N_2 + N_1}{N},$$

$$q_4 = \frac{24N_4 - 36N_3 + 14N_2 - N_1}{N},$$

where b is the width of the class interval and a is equal to the midpoint of the first class interval *minus b*.

SHEPPARD'S CORRECTIONS FOR GROUPING.   If the frequency distribution is grouped into a number of classes of equal width b and the central moments μ_r are computed by using the midpoints of the classes as variate values, and the distribution seems to be such that the corresponding frequency curve has a high degree of contact at both ends, then the corrected central moments $\bar{\mu}_r$ are computed by the formulae

$$\bar{\mu}_1 = \mu_1 = 0,$$

(2.2.7)
$$\bar{\mu}_2 = \mu_2 - \tfrac{1}{12}b^2,$$

$$\bar{\mu}_3 = \mu_3,$$

$$\bar{\mu}_4 = \mu_4 - \tfrac{1}{2}b^2\mu_2 + \tfrac{7}{240}b^4.$$

Cumulants.   The cumulants k_r of order r $(r = 1, 2, 3, \ldots)$ are defined by the formal Taylor expansion:

(2.2.8) $\ln \left(1 + \mu_1't + \mu_2' \dfrac{t^2}{2!} + \mu_3' \dfrac{t^3}{3!} + \cdots \right)$

$$= k_1 t + k_2 \frac{t^2}{2!} + k_3 \frac{t^3}{3!} + \cdots,$$

where the μ_j''s are moments about zero.

In particular:

(2.2.9) $k_1 = \mu_1'; \quad k_2 = \mu_2; \quad k_3 = \mu_3; \quad k_4 = \mu_4 - 3\mu_2^2,$

where the μ_j's are the central moments.

Illustrative Example 2.10.   Compute the mean, the standard deviation, and the β_1 and β_2 coefficients of the frequency distribution of scores obtained in illustrative example 2.1.

To obtain these measures, the first four moments are computed as shown in Table 2.6.

The transformation used in these computations is $u = (x - a)/b$, where x is the original score, $a = 42$, and $b = 5 = h$ (the width of a class). The accuracy of the computations is confirmed by Charlier's check, as follows:

$T_1 = S_1 + S_0$: $136 = -114 + 250,$

$T_2 = S_2 + 2S_1 + S_0$: $1052 = 1030 - 288 + 250,$

$T_3 = S_3 + 3S_2 + 3S_1 + S_0$: $1408 = -1590 + 3090 - 342 + 250,$

$T_4 = S_4 + 4S_3 + 6S_2 + 4S_1 + S_0$:

$12,620 = 13,006 - 6360 + 6180 - 456 + 250.$

TABLE 2.6

COMPUTATION OF MOMENTS OF THE DISTRIBUTION OF SCORES IN ENGLISH

Midvalue of class x	$u = \dfrac{x-42}{5}$	f	fu	$f(u+1)$	fu^2	$f(u+1)^2$	fu^3	$f(u+1)^3$	fu^4	$f(u+1)^4$
17	-5	9	-45	-36	225	144	-1125	-576	5625	2304
22	-4	11	-44	-33	176	99	-704	-297	2816	891
27	-3	10	-30	-20	90	40	-270	-80	810	160
32	-2	44	-88	-44	176	44	-352	-44	704	44
37	-1	45	-45	0	43	0	-45	0	45	0
42	0	54	0	54	0	54	0	54	0	54
47	1	37	37	74	37	148	37	296	37	592
52	2	26	52	78	104	234	208	702	416	2106
57	3	8	24	32	72	128	216	512	648	2048
62	4	5	20	25	80	125	320	625	1280	3125
67	5	1	5	6	25	36	125	216	625	1296
Total		250	-114	136	1030	1052	-1590	1408	13,006	12,620
Notation		$N = S_0$	S_1	T_1	S_2	T_2	S_3	T_3	S_4	T_4

The crude moments are next computed as follows:

$$q_1 = \frac{\sum fu}{N} = -0.456, \qquad q_2 = \frac{\sum fu^2}{N} = 4.12,$$

$$q_3 = \frac{\sum fu^3}{N} = -6.36, \quad \text{and} \quad q_4 = \frac{\sum fu^4}{N} = 52.024.$$

The mean $\bar{x}$ is then given by

$$\bar{x} = a + bq_1 = 42 + 5(-0.456) = 39.72.$$

The central moments of the sample are obtained as follows:

$$m_2 = b^2(q_2 - q_1^2) = 25(4.12 - 0.207936) = 97.8016,$$
$$s = \sqrt{m_2} = 9.8894,$$
$$m_3 = b^3(q_3 - 3q_2q_1 + 2q_1^3)$$
$$= 125(-6.36 + 5.63616 - 0.189638) = -114.18475,$$
$$m_4 = b^4(q_4 - 4q_3q_1 + 6q_2q_1^2 - 3q_1^4)$$
$$= 625(52.024 - 11.60064 + 5.140176 - 0.129711)$$
$$= 28,396.140625.$$

The values of the β_1 and β_2 coefficients are then computed:

$$\beta_1 = \frac{m_3^2}{m_2^3} = 0.013937 \quad \text{and} \quad \beta_2 = \frac{m_4}{m_2^2} = 2.968707.$$

To correct for the effect of grouping on the moments, Sheppard's corrections are applied as follows: $\bar{m}_2 = m_2 - (b^2/12) = 95.7183$, $\bar{m}_3 = m_3$, $\bar{m}_4 = m_4 - (b^2/2)m_2 + \frac{7}{240}b^4 = 27,191.849792.$

TABLE 2.7

COMPUTATION OF MOMENTS (SUMMATION METHOD)

		Cumulative frequencies from below			
	Frequency	First	Second	Third	Fourth
	9	$N = 250$	$N_1 = 1,386$	$N_2 = 5,024$	$N_3 = 14,566$
	11	241	1,136	3,638	9,542
	10	230	895	2,502	5,904
	44	220	665	1,607	3,402
	45	176	445	942	1,795
	54	131	269	497	853
	37	77	138	228	356
	26	40	61	90	128
	8	14	21	29	38
	5	6	7	8	9
	1	1	1	1	1
Total (check)	$N = 250$	$N_1 = 1,386$	$N_2 = 5,024$	$N_3 = 14,566$	$N_4 = 36,594$

After correction:

$$\bar{s} = \sqrt{\bar{m}_2} = 9.7836, \quad \bar{\beta}_1 = \frac{\bar{m}_3{}^2}{\bar{m}_2{}^3} = 0.0149, \text{ and } \bar{\beta}_2 = \frac{\bar{m}_4}{\bar{m}_2{}^2} = 2.968.$$

Alternatively, we may use the summation method (Table 2.7).

$$q_1 = \frac{N_1}{N} = 5.544, \quad q_2 = \frac{2N_2 - N_1}{N} = 34.648,$$

$$q_3 = \frac{6N_3 - 6N_2 + N_1}{N} = 234.552,$$

$$q_4 = \frac{24N_4 - 36N_3 + 14N_2 - N_1}{N} = 1691.320,$$

and

$$a = 12 \quad \text{and} \quad b = 5.$$

If we now use formulae 2.2.4 the moments obtained are the same as before.

2.3 INDEX NUMBERS

An index number is a single measure of changes (over time or place) in a group of related variables. It is generally expressed as a percentage. Index numbers are commonly used to indicate the change in the level of prices, in the volume of production, etc., at different points of time. For example, if prices of consumer goods in 1960 were on an average 1.25 times the prices in 1955, this is expressed by saying that the consumer price index number for 1960 is 125 (base 1950 = 100).

A number of formulae for computing index numbers of prices are discussed below. In these formulae p_{i0} and q_{i0} denote respectively the price and the quantity (produced, marketed, or consumed) of the ith commodity in the base period (0), and p_{i1} and q_{i1} the corresponding figures for the current period, that is, the period to be compared (1). The price relatives are defined by $r_i = p_{i1}/p_{i0}$. The summation Σ extends over all the n commodities included in the index. For weighted averages, w_i denotes a suitably chosen weight for the ith commodity.

Average of Price Relatives

ARITHMETIC MEAN

$$\text{Simple:} \quad I = 100 \frac{\Sigma r_i}{n}.$$

$$\text{Weighted:} \quad I = 100 \frac{\Sigma w_i r_i}{\Sigma w_i}.$$

GEOMETRIC MEAN

$$\text{Simple:} \quad I = 100 \text{ antilog} \left(\frac{1}{n} \sum \log r_i\right).$$

$$\text{Weighted:} \quad I = 100 \text{ antilog} \frac{\sum w_i \log r_i}{\sum w_i}.$$

Aggregative Index Numbers. These are named after the authors who first proposed them.

LASPEYRES. $\quad I_L = 100 \dfrac{\sum p_{i1} q_{i0}}{\sum p_{i0} q_{i0}}.$

This can be expressed as a weighted arithmetic mean of the price relatives with the base period values $p_{i0} q_{i0}$ as weights.

PAASCHE. $\quad I_P = 100 \dfrac{\sum p_{i1} q_{i1}}{\sum p_{i0} q_{i1}}.$

FISHER. $\quad I_F = \sqrt{I_L \cdot I_P}.$

EDGEWORTH–MARSHALL. $\quad I_{EM} = 100 \dfrac{\sum p_{i1}(q_{i0} + q_{i1})}{\sum p_{i0}(q_{i0} + q_{i1})}.$

An index number of wholesale prices is usually computed as a weighted geometric mean of price relatives, the weights being the quantity or the value of commodities marketed, produced, or consumed.

An index number of cost of living (consumer price index number) is computed as a weighted arithmetic mean of price relatives, where the weights are proportional to the expenditures on different commodities by average households and the price quotations are taken from the consumer's market, that is, are the retail sale prices.

An index number of the business activity of a country is computed as a weighted arithmetic mean of indices of industrial, agricultural, and mineral production, of foreign and inland trade, and of financial activities, weights being suitably chosen.

Illustrative Example 2.11. Table 2.8 gives the farmer's prices and quantities produced of a number of grains in the United States of America for the years 1950 and 1955. Shown below is the use of various formulae in computing an index number of farmer's prices of grains in 1955 with 1950 as base = 100.

By direct computation we obtain

$$\sum p_0 q_0 = 8183.52, \quad \sum p_1 q_0 = 7265.92,$$
$$\sum p_0 q_1 = 8523.76, \quad \sum p_1 q_1 = 7526.60.$$

TABLE 2.8

QUANTITIES PRODUCED AND FARMER'S PRICES OF GRAINS IN THE UNITED STATES, 1950 AND 1955

Grains (1)	Quantity produced				Farmer's price (dollars)			Conversion factor (6)
	Unit (2)	1950 q_0 (3.1)	1955 q_1 (3.2)	Unit (4)	1950 p_0 (5.1)	1955 p_1 (5.2)		
Wheat	million bushels	1019	935	bushel	2.00	1.98	1 bushel = 60 lb	
Rye	million bushels	21	29	bushel	1.32	1.06	1 bushel = 50 lb	
Rice	million bags	39	56	bag	5.09	4.80	1 bag = 100 lb	
Buckwheat	million bushels	4	2	bushel	1.11	1.17	1 bushel = 50 lb	
Corn	million bushels	2764	2884	bushel	1.53	1.34	1 bushel = 50 lb	
Oats	million bushels	1369	1503	bushel	0.79	0.60	1 bushel = 32 lb	
Barley	million bushels	304	401	bushel	1.18	0.92	1 bushel = 48 lb	
Sorghums	million bushels	234	243	bushel	1.05	0.98	1 bushel = 50 lb	

Source: U.S. Agricultural Statistics, 1957.

From these values, we can compute the aggregative indices:

Laspeyres index: $I_L = 100 \dfrac{\sum p_1 q_0}{\sum p_0 q_0} = 88.8\%.$

Paasche index: $I_P = 100 \dfrac{\sum p_1 q_1}{\sum p_0 q_1} = 88.3\%.$

Edgeworth–Marshall index:

$$I_{EM} = 100 \frac{\sum p_1(q_0 + q_1)}{\sum p_0(q_0 + q_1)} = 100 \frac{\sum p_1 q_0 + \sum p_1 q_1}{\sum p_0 q_0 + \sum p_1 q_1} = 88.5\%.$$

Fisher index: $I_F = \sqrt{I_L \cdot I_P} = 88.5\%.$

We may also compute an index number by taking the weighted (i) arithmetic mean or (ii) geometric mean of the price relatives, the weights being the quantities produced in 1950, all measured in pounds. The computational details are shown in Table 2.9.

TABLE 2.9

INDEX NUMBER OF FARMER'S PRICES OF GRAINS:
WEIGHTED AVERAGE OF PRICE RELATIVES

Grain	Quantity produced in 1950 (million lb) w	Price relative $r = p_1/p_0$ (%)	$\log r$
(1)	(2)	(3)	(4)
Wheat	61,140	99.000	1.9956352
Rye	1,176	80.303	1.9047318
Rice	3,900	94.303	1.9745255
Buckwheat	200	105.405	2.0228612
Corn	138,200	87.582	1.9424149
Oats	43,808	75.949	1.8805221
Barley	14,592	77.966	1.8919053
Sorghums	11,700	93.333	1.9700352

Thus we obtain the weighted means:
Weighted arithmetic mean of price relatives:

$$\frac{\sum wr}{\sum w} = \frac{24{,}196{,}841}{274{,}716}$$

$$= 88.1\%.$$

TABLE 2.10

CONSTRUCTION OF INDEX NUMBER OF COST OF LIVING

Base 1939 = 100.

1 U.S. dollar = 7.50 rupees approx.

Item	Percentage of total expenditure spent on the item	Unit	Prices (rupees)		Price relative for Jan. 1949
			1939	Jan. 1949	$r = p_1/p_0$
	w		p_0	p_1	(%)
(1)	(2)	(3)	(4.1)	(4.2)	(5) = (4.2)/(4.1)
Food					
Rice	15.41	kg	0.14	0.50	357.14
Rice products	0.61	kg	0.14	1.13	807.14
Wheat products	4.53	kg	0.13	0.53	407.69
Pulses	2.89	kg	0.18	0.60	333.33
Fish	6.09	kg	0.57	1.99	349.13
Meat	2.08	kg	0.60	2.75	458.33
Eggs	0.38	20	0.53	1.85	349.06
Milk	4.80	kg	0.19	0.79	415.79
Butter	2.60	kg	1.59	5.25	330.19
Oil	4.72	kg	0.48	2.14	445.83
Potatoes	3.48	kg	0.12	0.50	416.67
Other vegetables	5.74	kg	0.10	0.35	350.00
Salt	0.42	kg	0.06	0.09	150.00
Spices	1.62	kg	0.60	2.74	456.67
Sugar	2.30	kg	0.29	0.70	241.38
Tea	4.71	kg	0.69	2.76	400.00
Rent and tax	9.81	...	...	...	110.00[a]
Fuel and light					
Coal	3.46	50 kg	0.38	1.69	444.7
Other fuels	3.18	...	...	...	364.65[a]
Clothing	6.43	...	...	...	472.64[a]
Miscellaneous					
Liquor	2.56	...	...	...	250.00[a]
Toiletries	1.13	...	...	...	300.00[a]
Education	1.83	...	...	...	150.00[a]
Medicine	1.89	...	...	...	250.00[a]
Others	7.33	...	...	...	300.00[a]

[a] Price relatives indirectly estimated.

Weighted geometric mean of price relatives:

$$\text{antilog} \left(\sum w \log r / \sum w \right)$$

$$= \text{antilog} \ (533{,}838.076/274{,}716)$$

$$= \text{antilog} \ 1.9432362$$

$$= 87.7\%.$$

Illustrative Example 2.12. From the preceding data relating to middle-class citizens of Calcutta, we can compute a cost of living index for January 1949, with 1939 as base $= 100$, as shown in Table 2.10 (p. 115). Column (5) of the table gives the price relatives $r = p_1/p_0$ expressed as percentages. The index number is obtained as a weighted average of these price relatives, the weights w being the percentage of total expenditure spent on the items. Thus

$$I = \frac{\sum wr}{\sum w} = 344.19\%.$$

2.4 EXERCISES

Preparation of Frequency Tables

2.1. In an experiment a coin was tossed 800 times, and each time the side coming up—head H or tail T—was noted. The results, arranged in consecutive sets of five tosses, are given in Table 2.11.

Prepare a frequency distribution of the number of heads H in consecutive sets of five tosses.

TABLE 2.11

RESULTS OF 800 SUCCESSIVE THROWS OF COIN:
HEAD H, TAIL T

TTTHT	THHHT	HTHHH	TTHTT	TTHTH	THHTT	TTHHH	HHTTT
HHHTH	HTHHH	TTHTH	THHHT	HTTTH	THHTT	HHHTT	THTHT
HTTTH	TTHHH	TTTHT	HTHTH	HTTTH	THTHT	HTHHH	HTTHT
HHTTT	HTTHT	HTTTH	THHTT	HTHTH	TTHHT	TTHTH	THTTH
TTHHT	HHTHH	THHTH	HHHHH	TTTTH	TTHTT	HHTTH	THTHH
HTTHH	THTTH	TTHTH	TTTHT	HHTTT	TTTTH	HHHHH	THHHT
TTHTH	THTHH	HHTHH	THTTH	HTTTT	HHHHH	TTHHT	TTTHH
TTTHH	TTHHH	THHTH	THHTT	THHHH	TTTHT	HTHTT	TTHHH
THTHH	HHHHT	TTTTH	HTTHT	THTHT	THHHH	HTTHT	TTHHT
THHHT	TTHHT	THTHT	THTHH	HTHHH	HHHHT	THTTH	HHTTT
THHHH	THHHT	TTTTH	HHTTH	THTTH	HHHTH	THTHT	THTHH
THHHT	HHTHT	HHTTT	HHTHH	THHHT	HTHHH	THHHT	THHTT
THTTH	THTHH	HTHTT	HHTTH	HTHHT	TTHHT	TTTHT	THTTT
HHHHT	HHHTH	HHHTT	HHTTH	THHHH	THTTT	HTTHH	THHHH
HHHHT	TTTTH	HHHTT	TTTTH	HHHTH	HTHTT	HHTHT	THTTH
HHHTT	HHTTT	HTHHT	TTTHT	TTHHT	THTHT	TTTHH	HTHTT
TTHTH	HHTTH	TTTTT	THTTT	HHHTT	TTHTH	HTTTT	TTHHH
TTHTH	HHTHT	THTTT	TTHTT	TTHHT	THTTH	HHHTT	HHTTT
HHTTT	HTHHT	TTTHT	TTHHT	THTHT	TTTHH	THTHT	THHHT
HHTHH	THHHH	HTTTT	HHHTT	THTTT	HHHTH	HHTTT	HHHHT

2.2. In an experiment four cards were drawn from a thoroughly shuffled full pack, and the number of spades among these was noted. The cards were then put back in the pack, and the experiment was repeated 200 times. The results are given in Table 2.12. Prepare a frequency distribution of the number of spades in sets of four cards.

TABLE 2.12

NUMBER OF SPADES IN 200 SUCCESSIVE SETS OF FOUR CARDS

20112	11211	11020	10101	20100	11022	11110	01012
10120	00101	00111	10112	10021	10101	23011	00111
00301	00114	10100	11110	11100	22111	11100	10100
11011	00120	01211	20111	30012	02000	01201	20111
11200	11210	03212	01011	01111	21220	00010	21200

2.3. From the data given in exercise 2.1, proceed horizontally from left to right and count the number of heads (H) between two consecutive tails (T). Prepare a frequency distribution of these numbers.

TABLE 2.13

HEMOCYTOMETER COUNT OF RED BLOOD CELLS

2	1	5	0	2	2	1	3	1	4	4	2	3	2	2	1
5	5	2	1	3	5	2	1	5	5	1	2	2	4	2	1
2	2	1	2	3	2	4	3	4	3	4	1	1	0	0	3
1	4	3	2	2	2	2	2	4	3	2	2	3	2	1	
3	3	1	4	0	2	3	5	2	4	3	3	5	2	5	3
1	1	4	5	3	1	0	1	3	2	1	4	3	3	2	4
5	4	1	1	2	3	7	3	3	3	3	3	2	0	4	0
2	5	0	1	4	2	3	2	3	1	2	3	3	4	3	1
3	2	3	2	3	2	0	1	3	3	4	2	3	0	1	3
3	1	1	5	3	6	5	4	3	3	4	2	2	2	2	1
5	3	0	2	1	3	2	2	3	4	2	3	2	4	3	3
1	1	2	3	2	1	5	2	4	2	2	1	3	3	2	1
1	3	2	1	5	3	7	4	3	2	4	1	2	3	5	2
4	2	1	5	4	2	5	1	2	2	2	4	1	2	3	2
1	3	3	2	3	1	2	4	3	4	4	8	6	5	0	1
4	4	2	1	3	5	3	2	2	1	2	2	3	2	3	4
3	5	2	1	3	3	1	1	3	2	5	4	4	4	4	4
3	1	1	3	1	0	2	2	2	2	2	1	5	3	2	6
0	5	2	0	2	3	4	0	5	1	2	1	1	0	3	4
3	2	2	1	3	3	2	4	2	6	6	1	4	5	2	2
4	2	3	1	0	2	1	2	3	6	2	1	1	2	1	3
4	6	5	7	1	4	2	4	4	1	1	1	2	3	6	4
3	3	2	5	1	2	3	1	3	5	2	3	3	6	2	1
2	2	2	1	2	6	2	0	2	1	0	3	1	1	3	2
5	3	2	3	2	0	0	3	4	3	4	0	2	0	5	1

2.4. From the data given in exercise 2.1, proceed vertically with the first two consecutive columns and count separately the four different types of doublets—(1) HH, (2) HT, (3) TH, and (4) TT—among the twenty pairs in these two columns. Repeat this operation for the next two columns and so on. Finally obtain the frequencies of the four types of doublets in the whole set of 400 such doublets.

2.5. Take a set of 100 consecutive two-digit numbers from a table of random sampling numbers and count how many times 00 occurs in this set. Take 200 such sets, and prepare a frequency distribution of the number of 00's in these sets.

2.6. Table 2.13 (p. 117) gives the hemocytometer count of red blood corpuscles in four hundred square cells, each of area 0.0025 sq mm, obtained by a technician. Prepare a frequency table of the number of red blood corpuscles per square cell.

2.7. Table 2.14 gives the scores in a psychological test of 213 candidates for admission into a technical institution. Prepare a frequency distribution.

TABLE 2.14

SCORES ON A PSYCHOLOGICAL TEST

63	57	53	62	70	35	53	52	69	82
50	83	40	74	66	36	51	48	42	52
53	69	50	38	66	53	56	41	65	47
52	46	50	58	61	50	48	65	41	69
67	49	61	60	71	45	68	68	51	77
35	43	50	57	82	62	66	38	70	56
40	45	78	64	44	52	56	37	63	56
41	43	62	55	83	51	56	46	62	59
39	36	33	51	86	48	49	44	39	83
42	56	41	36	62	60	38	56	57	62
47	55	36	84	48	41	58	47	53	47
34	61	45	67	41	69	31	71	54	65
49	65	71	82	40	63	66	70	54	78
42	49	52	61	51	46	40	45	65	54
44	60	43	66	50	69	42	51	57	30
53	60	45	79	45	45	71	40	79	42
54	68	43	66	92	79	53	71	49	59
36	32	69	60	61	45	52	64	65	57
58	47	61	57	35	53	52	46	63	57
55	57	51	73	77	69	41	57	46	71
50	53	60	73	43	47	52	67	77	85
65	60	80							

TABLE 2.15

Yields of Brown Sasson (in $\frac{1}{8}$ oz Obtained) from Different Plots of Size 5' × 5'

116	114	112	112	110	110	110	116	96	88	104	102	92	94	92	86	100	100
86	86	90	78	88	82	96	84	74	72	68	64	80	90	90	92	88	94
106	84	80	88	90	94	100	70	84	92	78	86	106	106	90	98	80	78
98	102	92	100	84	84	106	82	94	108	100	104	110	74	64	66	98	78
112	100	100	84	86	98	108	94	94	100	100	82	108	96	76	80	104	106
78	100	84	94	82	110	100	96	84	90	88	88	98	106	92	94	88	84
80	98	102	76	94	96	110	90	88	90	88	78	108	68	122	92	92	102
80	96	92	62	104	104	100	106	84	90	108	88	92	90	70	90	90	96
52	80	104	84	104	96	108	96	102	98	108	96	98	78	88	108	82	98
72	76	82	82	58	68	78	72	82	94	80	78	84	82	78	92	84	99
82	64	70	68	88	72	84	92	90	92	76	66	80	78	90	86	62	92
124	100	110	86	92	104	122	88	96	94	126	96	116	106	98	108	104	106
108	96	100	76	92	86	114	94	118	80	82	82	94	92	82	90	82	110
82	104	116	104	108	108	104	114	104	98	104	104	104	104	108	108	114	104
86	94	100	96	86	112	116	98	116	90	82	106	96	106	110	108	104	102
98	108	110	92	88	110	96	106	108	82	110	100	112	108	106	94	114	116
110	92	108	88	82	100	96	116	108	100	94	118	94	88	98	98	96	90
104	120	104	92	104	128	124	100	112	98	108	98	104	98	84	98	94	76

Source: Optimum size and shape of plots for *Brassica* experiments in the Punjab, *Sankhya*, Vol. 6.

2.8. A uniformity trial on brown sasson (an oilseed) was conducted in a square plot 90′ × 90′ divided into 324 square cells, each 5′ × 5′. Table 2.15 (p. 119) gives the arrangement of the cells and the corresponding yields in $\frac{1}{8}$ oz.

Obtain the frequency distribution of the yields in the following classes: 52–57, 58–63, 64–69, . . . , etc.

TABLE 2.16

AGE DISTRIBUTION OF MALES IN UTTAR PRADESH
(10% SAMPLE COUNT OF 1951 CENSUS)

x = Age in years last birthday.
$(SP)_x$ = Sample count of males aged x.

x	$(SP)_x$	x	$(SP)_x$	x	$(SP)_x$
0	107,424	25	117,858	50	91,679
1	76,744	26	41,422	51	12,738
2	78,724	27	30,422	52	21,043
3	84,421	28	55,395	53	11,111
4	81,750	29	20,872	54	14,382
5	97,802	30	120,596	55	49,909
6	85,958	31	20,320	56	12,001
7	74,475	32	53,688	57	8,709
8	93,492	33	20,729	58	14,798
9	67,312	34	26,110	59	7,786
10	113,538	35	104,649	60	52,803
11	64,075	36	36,544	61	6,680
12	106,883	37	19,461	62	10,089
13	58,541	38	31,258	63	5,431
14	75,331	39	16,813	64	6,449
15	72,013	40	114,674	65	23,528
16	69,324	41	16,344	66	3,736
17	39,933	42	32,316	67	3,440
18	78,277	43	15,716	68	4,399
19	32,957	44	18,707	69	2,899
20	89,716	45	89,639	70	21,395
21	33,548	46	17,280	Residual	39,820
22	63,562	47	13,919	Total	3,314,140
23	28,772	48	24,222		
24	44,589	49	11,200		

Source: *Census of India*, Paper No. 3, 1954; Age Tables, 1951 Census.

2.9. Table 2.16 (p. 120) gives the age distribution of males in Uttar Pradesh (a state in India), as obtained in a 10% sample from the census returns of 1951.

Represent the data graphically and write a note on the peculiarities observed. Prepare a frequency distribution, choosing appropriate class intervals of equal width.

2.10. Take a page of two-digit random numbers. Write down 4000 successive two-digit random numbers (proceeding horizontally from left to right), and arrange these in consecutive sets of four.

(a) Prepare a frequency distribution of the two-digit random numbers in the following classes: 00–04, 05–09, 10–14, . . . , 90–94, 95–99.

(b) Compute the average of each set of four numbers. Arrange these averages in sets of four. Prepare the frequency distribution of the average, using the same classes as before, and draw the histogram for the frequency distribution.

(c) Compute the grand average of each set of four averages. This gives the average of 16 numbers. Prepare the frequency distribution of the average of 16 in the same classes, and draw the histogram for the frequency distribution.

2.11. Using the material collected in exercise 2.9 (two-digit random numbers arranged in hundred sets of four), write down the values of the maximum M, the minimum m, and the range R ($R = M - m$) for each set of four two-digit numbers.

Using suitable class intervals, obtain the frequency distributions of (a) the maximum M, (b) the minimum m, and (c) the range R.

2.12. Table 2.17 shows the diastolic blood pressures (in millimeters of mercury) of candidates for life insurance, taken by different medical examiners. Examine the nature of "digit preference" in the records, and prepare a frequency distribution in not more than six groups, choosing the class intervals suitably to minimize the bias due to digit preference.

Graphical presentation of frequency distributions

2.13.–2.24. For each of the frequency distributions obtained in exercises 2.1–2.12, draw (a) the histogram (for continuous variables) or frequency polygon (for discrete variables) and (b) the ogive (less-than type).

2.25.–2.35. For each of the frequency distributions given below, draw (a) the histogram (for continuous variables) or the frequency polygon (for discrete variables) and (b) the ogive (less-than type).

2.25. During World War II, to study the characteristics of flying bomb hits, the city of London was divided into 576 cells of ¼ sq km each, and the frequency distribution of the number of hits shown in Table 2.18 was obtained.

TABLE 2.17

DISTRIBUTION OF CANDIDATES FOR LIFE INSURANCE
BY DIASTOLIC BLOOD PRESSURE

Blood pressure (mm)	Frequency	Blood pressure (mm)	Frequency
60	5	78	20
61	...	79	1
62	1	80	80
63	...	81	...
64	1	82	12
65	8	83	1
66	1	84	10
67	...	85	15
68	2	86	8
69	...	87	...
70	24	88	8
71	...	89	...
72	5	90	16
73	...	91	...
74	7	92	1
75	25	93	...
76	12	94	1
77	...	95	2

TABLE 2.18

DISTRIBUTION OF CELLS ACCORDING TO THE NUMBER
OF FLYING BOMB HITS

No. of hits x	No. of cells with x hits
0	229
1	211
2	93
3	35
4	7
5	1
Total	576

Source: R. D. Clarke, An application of the Poisson distribution, *Journal of the Institute of Actuaries*, Vol. 72.

2.26. Table 2.19 gives the counts of the number of European red mites on apple leaves (Garman's data). On a certain date, 25 apple leaves were selected at random from each of six McIntosh trees in a single orchard receiving the same spray treatment, and the number of adult females was counted on each leaf. The frequency distribution of the mites on the 150 leaves is given in Table 2.19.

TABLE 2.19

COUNTS OF RED MITES ON APPLE LEAVES

No. of mites per leaf	No. of leaves observed
0	70
1	38
2	17
3	10
4	9
5	3
6	2
7	1
8 or more	0
Total	150

Source: C. I. Bliss and R. A. Fisher, Fitting the negative binomial distribution to biological data, *Biometrics*, Vol. 9.

2.27. Table 2.20 gives the hemocytometer distribution count of yeast cells (Student's data).

TABLE 2.20

COUNT OF YEAST CELLS PER SQUARE

No. of cells	Frequency
0	213
1	128
2	37
3	18
4	3
5	1
Total	400

Source: C. I. Bliss and R. A. Fisher, Fitting the negative binomial distribution to biological data, *Biometrics*, Vol. 9.

2.28. Table 2.21 gives the frequency distribution of the number of albino children in families of five children including at least one albino child (Pearson's data).

TABLE 2.21

ALBINO CHILDREN IN FAMILIES OF FIVE CHILDREN

No. of albinos in family	No. of families
1	25
2	23
3	10
4	1
5	1
Total	60

Source: J. B. S. Haldane, The estimation of the frequencies of recessive conditions in man, *Annals of Eugenics*, Vol. 8.

2.29. Table 2.22 gives the frequency distribution of the number of dust nuclei in a small volume of air that fell onto a stage in a chamber containing moisture and filtered air (Scrase's data). It is suspected that a number of zero counts were wrongly rejected on the ground that the apparatus was not working.

TABLE 2.22

FREQUENCY DISTRIBUTION OF NUMBER OF DUST NUCLEI

No. of dust nuclei	Frequency
0	23
1	56
2	88
3	95
4	73
5	40
6	17
7	5
8	3
Total	400

Source: P. G. Moore, A note on truncated Poisson distributions, *Biometrics*, Vol. 10, p. 402.

2.30. Table 2.23 shows the distributions of rural Indian couples by the number of children, as obtained by the National Sample Survey.

2.31. Table 2.24 gives the age distribution of males and females in the United States in 1950.

TABLE 2.23

FREQUENCY DISTRIBUTION OF NUMBER OF CHILDREN
PER COUPLE (ALL INDIA: RURAL)

No. of children	Frequency of couples (%)	No. of children	Frequency of couples (%)
0	27.78	7	4.68
1	14.18	8	3.77
2	11.68	9	1.51
3	10.54	10	0.79
4	9.92	11	0.60
5	8.06	12	0.17
6	6.25	13 and above	0.07

Source: A. K. Dasgupta, M. M. Mazumdar, R. K. Som, and S. N. Mitra, Couple fertility, *Sankhya*, Vol. 16.

TABLE 2.24

AGE DISTRIBUTION OF U.S. MALES AND FEMALES,
1950

Age last birthday	Population (thousands)	
	Male	Female
0–4	8236	7927
5–9	6715	6485
10–14	5660	5459
15–19	5311	5305
20–24	5606	5876
25–29	5972	6270
30–34	5625	5892
35–39	5518	5729
40–44	5070	5134
45–49	4526	4544
50–54	4129	4144
55–59	3630	3605
60–64	3038	3022
65–69	2425	2578
70–74	1629	1783
75 and above	1744	2111

Source: *Statistical Abstract of the United States*, 1959.

2.32. Table 2.25 gives the frequency distribution of scores in English obtained by students who passed in the subject (i.e., scored 36 or more) in a School Leaving Certificate (SLC) examination.

TABLE 2.25

FREQUENCY DISTRIBUTION OF SCORES IN ENGLISH
IN SLC EXAMINATION

Score	Frequency
36–40	441
41–45	397
46–50	333
51–55	186
56–60	107
61–65	38
66–70	14
71–75	4
76–80	2
Total	1522

2.33. In an experimental sampling scheme, 700 samples were drawn from a certain population and a statistic T was calculated from each sample. The frequency distribution is shown in Table 2.26.

TABLE 2.26

FREQUENCY DISTRIBUTION OF A STATISTIC T

Class interval	Frequency
0–2	9
2–4	49
4–6	104
6–8	137
8–10	118
10–12	112
12–14	75
14–16	36
16–18	33
18–20	10
20–22	7
22–24	5
24–26	3
26–28	2
Total	700

2.34. One thousand shots were fired from a battery gun at the central horizontal line of a target 50 ft long and 11 ft high. All the shots hit the target, and their distribution in 11 horizontal strips of width 1 ft each is given in Table 2.27.

TABLE 2.27

DISTRIBUTION OF SHOTS IN HORIZONTAL STRIPS

Strip no.	No. of shots
1	1
2	4
3	10
4	89
5	190
6	212
7	204
8	193
9	79
10	16
11	2
Total	1000

2.35. Table 2.28 gives the distribution, for the year 1950, of families (an unattached individual being counted as a family) in the United States, classified by income level.

TABLE 2.28

INCOME DISTRIBUTION IN THE UNITED STATES, 1950

Income before taxes (dollars)	No. of families (thousands)	Income before taxes (dollars)	No. of families (thousands)
Under 1,000	3,861	7,500–9,999	2,758
1,000–1,999	7,464	10,000–14,999	1,536
2,000–2,999	8,091	15,000–19,999	414
3,000–3,999	8,586	20,000–24,999	218
4,000–4,999	7,054	25,000–49,999	294
5,000–5,999	4,694	50,000 and	84
6,000–7,499	3,836	over	
		Total	48,890

Source: *Statistical Abstract of the United States*, 1959.

Measures of location and dispersion

2.36. A chemical compound containing 12.5% of iron was given to two technicians *A* and *B* for chemical analysis. *A* made 15 determinations, and *B* 10 determinations, of the percentage of iron. Their results are given in Table 2.29.

TABLE 2.29

DETERMINATIONS OF THE PERCENTAGE OF IRON IN
A COMPOUND BY TWO TECHNICIANS

Determinations by *A*			Determinations by *B*	
12.46	12.43	12.77	12.05	12.33
11.89	12.12	12.33	12.22	12.45
12.76	11.85	12.56	12.45	12.39
11.95	12.24	12.65	11.97	12.37
12.77	12.28	12.12	12.21	12.65

Find separately for *A* and *B* (a) the arithmetic mean and the median, (b) the range, (c) the standard deviation, (d) the mean deviation about the median, and (e) the coefficient of variation of the determinations.

2.37. Find the geometric mean of the following numbers: 102.6, 103.5, 108.7, 121.4, 119.2.

2.38. The speeds of a train in different sections (of equal length) of a journey were 35, 50, 48, 54, 60, 55, and 40 miles per hour, respectively. Find the average speed.

2.39. The means and the standard deviations of the weekly wages of two groups of industrial workers are given in Table 2.30.

TABLE 2.30

MEAN AND STANDARD DEVIATION OF WEEKLY WAGES

Group	No. of workers	Weekly wages (dollars)	
		Mean	Standard deviation
1	230	82.42	18.67
2	346	85.13	17.29

Find the mean and the standard deviation of the weekly wages of the 230 + 346 = 576 workers taken together.

2.40.–2.42. From the data given in exercises 2.6–2.8 compute (a) the arithmetic mean, (b) the median, (c) the range, and (d) the variance.

2.43. For the U.S. income distribution given in exercise 2.35, draw the concentration curve and compute the concentration ratio.

Moments

2.44.–2.78. For each of the frequency distributions prepared or given in exercises 2.1–2.35, compute the following:

(a) The median, the quartiles, and the 5th and the 95th percentiles.

(b) The arithmetic mean, variance, standard deviation, and coefficient of variation.

(c) The first four central moments and the β_1 and β_2 coefficients. Recompute these values, using Sheppard's corrections wherever applicable. Compare the variances obtained in exercises 2.40–2.42 from ungrouped data with those obtained from the frequency distributions (with and without Sheppard's corrections).

(d) For continuous distributions, obtain the mode.

2.79. The moment coefficients of a frequency distribution based on 100 observations were calculated as follows:

$$\text{Mean} \quad = \quad 9.36758,$$
$$\text{Variance} = 19.35396$$
$$\beta_1 \qquad = \quad 0.73474, \quad (\mu_3 \text{ positive}),$$
$$\beta_2 \qquad = \quad 4.05433.$$

Later it was discovered that an observation 2.9 was misread as 9.2. Calculate the above moments correctly.

2.80. Examine the following results of a piece of computation for internal consistency:

$$N = 100,$$
$$\Sigma x = -114, \qquad \Sigma x^2 = 1030, \qquad \Sigma x^3 = -1590, \qquad \Sigma x^4 = 1424.$$

2.81. The mean and the standard deviation of the statures of 1000 army recruits were reported as 69.5 in. and 1.3 in. respectively. Among the recruits there were 207 with stature more than 72 in. and 51 with stature less than 66 in.

Show that the data are inconsistent.

Index numbers

2.82. Table 2.31 gives the average retail prices in dollars of selected food articles in the United States for an average month in 1955 and for March 1959.

TABLE 2.31

RETAIL PRICES OF SELECTED FOOD ARTICLES

Commodity	Unit	Retail prices	
		1955	Mar. 1959
Cereals and bakery products			
Wheat flour	lb	0.11	0.11
Corn meal	lb	0.13	0.13
Bread	lb	0.18	0.20
Meat, poultry, fish			
Round steak	lb	0.90	1.07
Chuck roast	lb	0.50	0.65
Hamburger	lb	0.40	0.55
Pork chops	lb	0.79	0.82
Sliced bacon	lb	0.66	0.68
Whole ham	lb	0.61	0.64
Lamb leg	lb	0.68	0.74

Commodity	Unit	Retail prices	
		1955	Mar. 1959
Fruits and vegetables, fresh			
Bananas	lb	0.17	0.17
Oranges	doz	0.53	0.61
Grapefruit	each	0.10	0.12
Potatoes	lb	0.06	0.05
Onions	lb	0.08	0.16
Lettuce	head	0.16	0.17
Cabbage	lb	0.08	0.09
Vegetables, canned			
Green peas	lb	0.22	0.21
Tomatoes	lb	0.15	0.16

Frankfurters	lb	0.53	0.65
Chickens, fryers, ready-to-cook	lb	0.57	0.44
Dairy products			
Fresh milk	qt	0.23	0.25
Butter	lb	0.71	0.74
Cheese	lb	0.58	0.58
Fruits and vegetables, frozen			
Strawberries	10 oz	0.31	0.26
Orange juice	6 oz	0.18	0.25
Green peas	10 oz	0.20	0.20
Fruits and vegetables, dried			
Prunes	lb	0.34	0.40
Beans	lb	0.16	0.17
Other foods			
Coffee	lb	0.93	0.80
Lard	lb	0.21	0.21
Salad dressing	pt	0.35	0.38
Sugar	lb	0.10	0.11
Eggs, grade A, large	doz	0.61	0.54

Source: *Statistical Abstract of the United States, 1959.*

Compute an index number of retail prices of the selected food articles
for March 1959, taking an average month in 1955 as base = 100, and
using (a) the arithmetic mean and (b) the geometric mean of the price
relatives.

2.83. Table 2.32 gives, for India, the weights of various commodities

TABLE 2.32

INDEX NUMBER OF WHOLESALE PRICES IN INDIA
Base 1939 = 100

Groups and commodities	Weights for commodities in each group	Weights for different groups	Index number of prices — Average week in 1950	Index number of prices — Week ending Apr 14, 1956
Food		31		
Cereals	59		471.9	459
Pulses	8		449.9	351
Others	33		315.3	236
Industrial raw material		18		
Fibres	53		475.8	459
Oil seeds	30		662.3	524
Minerals	10		351.6	444
Others	7		389.4	395
Semimanufactures		17		
Leather	8		354.2	410
Mineral oil	13		193.8	208
Vegetable oil	16		685.2	510
Cotton yarn	35		411.1	455
Metals	18		176.8	282
Oil cakes	5		471.8	418
Others	5		308.1	362
Manufactures		30		
Textile products	64		401.6	409
Metal products	17		267.9	371
Other finished products	19		273.5	286
Miscellaneous		4	681.5	496.5

Source: *Index Number of Wholesale Prices in India*, 1956.

and the average indices of their wholesale prices for the year 1950, as well as those for the week ending April 14, 1956, with 1939 prices as base.

Compute an index of wholesale prices for each group of commodities, as well as for all commodities pooled together, for the week ending April 14, 1956, with the year 1950 as base.

2.84. Using the data given in Table 2.33 and taking the ratios of the indices as price relatives, compute an index number of the cost of living (consumer price index) for the year 1959 with the year 1958 as base.

TABLE 2.33

ALL-CITY AVERAGE CONSUMER PRICE INDICES IN THE
UNITED STATES, 1958 AND 1959
Base 1947–49 = 100

	Relative importance		Index	
Group of commodities	Total	Within group	1959	1958
Food	29.84	100		
A. Food at home		84.72	115.9	118.8
Cereals and bakery products		10.33	134.2	133.1
Meats, poultry, and fish		25.79	110.7	115.1
Dairy products		14.02	114.3	113.5
Fruits and vegetables		15.25	125.1	127.1
Other foods at home		19.33	106.1	112.4
B. Restaurant meals		15.28	131.6	128.6
Housing	32.19		129.2	127.7
Apparel	9.41		107.9	107.0
Transportation	11.33		146.3	140.5
Medical care	4.78		150.8	144.6
Personal care	2.12		131.2	128.6
Reading and recreation	5.32		118.6	116.7
Other goods and services	5.01		129.7	127.2

Source: *Techniques of Preparing Major BLS* [Bureau of Labor Statistics] *Statistical Series*, B.L.S. Bulletin 1168 (1954).

2.85. Using the data given in Table 2.34, and taking the ratios of the price indices as price relatives, compute a wholesale price index for the United States in 1959 with 1958 = 100 as base.

TABLE 2.34

WHOLESALE PRICE INDEX FOR THE UNITED STATES, 1958 AND 1959

Base 1947–49 = 100

	Relative importance		Index	
Group	Total	Within group	1959	1958
Farm products	14.6	100.0	89.1	94.9
Fresh and dried produce	1.3	8.9	102.7	112.0
Grains	2.1	14.6	77.3	79.5
Livestock and poultry	5.2	35.6	85.1	92.9
Plant and animal fibers	1.3	9.1	98.2	101.5
Fluid milk	2.0	13.6	94.4	94.6
Eggs	0.9	6.2	65.6	81.7
Hay and seeds	0.9	5.8	76.6	76.9
Other	0.9	6.2	132.6	140.4
Processed foods	15.4		107.0	110.9
Textiles and apparel	9.8		95.0	93.5
Hides, skins, and leather products	2.1		114.3	100.6
Fuel, power, light materials	8.7		112.7	112.7
Chemicals and products	5.3		109.9	110.4
Rubber and products	1.6		114.7	145.0
Lumber and wood products	2.6		125.8	117.7
Pulp, paper, and products	3.4		132.2	131.0
Metals and metal products	11.7		153.6	150.4
Machinery and motive products	14.1		153.0	149.8
Furniture and household durables	3.9		123.4	123.2
Non-metallic minerals	1.4		137.7	136.0
Tobacco manufactures and bottled beverages	2.4		131.4	128.2
Miscellaneous	3.0		94.5	94.2

Source: *U.S. Monthly Labor Review*, September 1960.

CHAPTER 3

Standard Discrete Distributions

3.1 PROBLEMS OF SPECIFICATION AND ESTIMATION

An effective summarization of an observed frequency distribution is achieved if it is possible to describe it by a simple mathematical formula, involving a few constants. There are thus two types of problems. First, one has to decide on the form of the function. This is known as the problem of *specification*. Sometimes, this can be solved from theoretical considerations of how the frequency distribution is generated. Most often, however, the form is specified empirically by choosing one which appears to fit the data reasonably well, out of a number of standard forms.

Once the form of the function is decided, the next problem is to evaluate the unknown constants (or parameters), as they are called, occurring in the function. This is known as the problem of *estimation*. There is an elaborate statistical theory for estimation of parameters from observations. This is briefly discussed in Chapter 3 of Part III. For the present, however, if a parameter is looked upon as a particular characteristic of the theoretical frequency distribution represented by the mathematical function, then the corresponding characteristic of the observed frequency distribution will be taken as an estimate for the parameter.

The deviations of the observed frequency distribution from the mathematical function may be looked upon either as fluctuations of sampling when the observed frequency distribution is based on a sample, or as errors of graduation when it is based on a complete enumeration of the population.

We will now describe a number of standard discrete distributions. Some standard continuous distributions are discussed in Chapter 4.

For each probability distribution, the mean, the variance, and the β_1 and β_2 coefficients are given. A list of publications which contain tables of the cumulative distribution function is also given.

135

3.2 BINOMIAL DISTRIBUTION

The probability distribution of the number of successes X in n independent trials in each of which the probability of success is p, given by

$$(3.2.1) \quad \text{Prob}\,(X = x) = b(x, p, n) = \binom{n}{x} p^x (1 - p)^{n-x},$$

$$x = 0, 1, 2, \ldots, n,$$

is known as the binomial distribution.

The mean, the variance, and the β_1 and β_2 coefficients for this distribution are

$$\mathcal{M}(X) = np,$$
$$V(X) = np(1 - p),$$

$$(3.2.2) \qquad \beta_1(X) = \frac{(1 - 2p)^2}{np(1 - p)},$$

$$\beta_2(X) = 3 + \frac{1 - 6p(1 - p)}{np(1 - p)}.$$

The cumulative distribution can be computed from *Tables of Incomplete Beta Function*, edited by K. Pearson, by using the relation

$$B(x, p, n) = \sum_{r=0}^{x} b(r, p, n)$$

$$(3.2.3) \qquad = I_{1-p}(n - x, x + 1),$$

where

$$I_x(u, v) = \frac{1}{B(u, v)} \int_0^x t^{u-1}(1 - t)^{v-1}\, dt$$

is the incomplete beta function ratio.

For large n, if p is not too small, we may use the approximation

$$(3.2.4) \quad \text{Prob}\,(\alpha < X \le \beta) = B(\beta, p, n) - B(\alpha, p, n) \doteq \phi(\beta^*) - \phi(\alpha^*),$$

where

$$\phi(x) = \int_{-\infty}^{x} \frac{1}{\sqrt{2\pi}} e^{-\frac{1}{2}t^2}\, dt$$

is called the normal probability integral and

$$x^* = \frac{(x + \frac{1}{2} - np)}{\sqrt{np(1 - p)}},$$

in the sense that the percentage error of approximation tends to zero with n provided that both $(\alpha + \frac{1}{2} - np)^3/[np(1 - p)]^2$ and $(\beta + \frac{1}{2} - np)^3/[np(1 - p)]^2$ tend to zero with n.

Another approximation useful when n is large but p is small is obtained from the Poisson limit:

$$(3.2.5) \qquad \lim_{\substack{n \to \infty \\ np=\mu}} b(x, p, n) = p(x, \mu) = \frac{e^{-\mu}\mu^x}{x!} .$$

The binomial distribution is tabulated in the following publications.

H. G. ROMIG, 50–100 *Binomial Tables.* These tables, published by John Wiley & Sons, 1953, give values of $b(x, p, n)$ and $B(x, p, n)$ for $p = 0.01$ (0.01) 0.50 and $n = 50$ (5) 100.

Tables of Binomial Probabilities, Applied Mathematics, Series 6. These tables, published by the National Bureau of Standards, U.S. Department of Commerce, 1950, give values of $b(x, p, n)$ for $n = 2$ (1) 49, $p = 0.01$ (0.01) 0.50.

E. S. PEARSON and H. O. HARTLEY, *Biometrika Tables for Statisticians,* Vol. I. Table 37 of these tables, published by the Cambridge University Press, 1958, gives individual terms of binomial distributions for $n = 5$ (5) 30, and $p = 0.01, 0.02$ (0.02) 0.10 (0.01) 0.50.

Tables of the Cumulative Binomial Probability Distribution by the Staff of the Computation Laboratory, Harvard University Press, 1955.

If $\bar{x}$ is the average number of successes in N sets of n trials each, then p is estimated by

$$(3.2.6) \qquad \hat{p} = \frac{\bar{x}}{n} .$$

Illustrative Example 3.1. An experiment consists in throwing 12 dice and counting fives and sixes as success. $N = 23,306$ such experiments were conducted; the frequency distribution of the number of successes observed is given in Table 3.1. Fit a binomial distribution.

TABLE 3.1

NUMBER OF SUCCESSES IN THROWING 12 DICE

No. of successes	Frequency	No. of successes	Frequency
0	185	7	1,331
1	1,149	8	403
2	3,265	9	105
3	5,475	10	14
4	6,114	11	4
5	5,194	12	0
6	3,067	Total	26,306

The binomial distribution to be fitted to the given frequency distribution is $P(X = x) = \binom{12}{x}p^x q^{12-x}$, where $q = 1 - p$. Theoretically we would expect $p = \frac{1}{3}$, and by computing the expected frequencies we could examine whether the data are in agreement with this hypothetical value of p. We are, however, estimating p from the data by equating $\bar{x}$, the sample mean, to its expected value $12p$. The computations are shown in the form of Table 3.2. We compute $p^x q^{12-x}$ by using the formula $p^x q^{12-x} = q^{12}r^x$, where $r = p/q$, and by successive multiplication by r. The expected frequency is given by $f_e = 26{,}306 \cdot \binom{12}{x} \cdot p^x q^{12-x}$.

TABLE 3.2
FITTING A BINOMIAL DISTRIBUTION

No. of successes x	Observed frequency f	fx	$\binom{12}{x}$	$p^x q^{12-x}$	Expected frequency f_e
0	185	0	1	$712{,}305 \times 10^{-8}$	187.38
1	1,149	1,149	12	363,195	1,146.52
2	3,265	6,530	66	185,189	3,215.25
3	5,475	16,425	220	94,426	5,464.70
4	6,114	24,456	495	48,147	6,269.35
5	5,194	25,970	792	24,550	5,114.65
6	3,067	18,402	924	12,518	3,042.55
7	1,331	9,317	792	6,383	1,329.74
8	403	3,224	495	3,225	423.76
9	105	945	220	1,600	96.02
10	14	140	66	846	14.68
11	4	44	12	431	1.37
12	0	0	1	220	0.05
Total	26,306	106,602			26,306.20

$$\bar{x} = 106{,}602/26{,}306 = 4.052384,$$
$$p = 4.052384/12 = 0.337699,$$
$$q = 1 - p = 0.662301,$$
$$12 \log q = 12 \times \bar{1}.8210555 = \bar{3}.8526660 = 7.8526660 - 10,$$
$$q^{12} = 0.00712305,$$
$$r = p/q = 0.5098875$$

Illustrative Example 3.2. What is the probability that in 100 throws of an unbiased coin the number of heads obtained will be between 45 and 60?

Writing X for the number of heads obtained in $n = 100$ throws, we are here interested in computing $P = \text{Prob} \, (44 < X \leq 60)$. Here p, the probability of getting a head in a single throw, is assumed to equal $\frac{1}{2}$. Using formula 3.2.4, we have $\alpha = 44$, $\beta = 60$, and therefore

$$\beta^* = \frac{\beta + \frac{1}{2} - np}{\sqrt{np(1 - p)}} = 2.1 \quad \text{and} \quad \alpha^* = \frac{\alpha + \frac{1}{2} - np}{\sqrt{np(1 - p)}} = -1.1.$$

From tables of the normal probability integral, we obtain $\phi(\beta^*) = 0.98214$, $\phi(\alpha^*) = 0.13567$. Thus

$$P \doteq \phi(\beta^*) - \phi(\alpha^*) = 0.84647.$$

Illustrative Example 3.3. The probability of a manufactured article being defective is $p = 0.01$. What is the probability that in a lot of $n = 200$ manufactured articles there will be no defectives?

Here $n = 200$, $p = 0.01$, and we are interested in computing $b(0, n, p)$. Since n is large, p is small, and $\mu = np = 2$ is only moderately large, we use formula 3.2.5. Thus

$$b(0, 200, 0.01) \sim p(0, 2) = e^{-2} = 0.13534.$$

Truncated Binomial Distribution. The probability distribution

$$(3.2.7) \quad \text{Prob} \, (X = x) = \frac{\binom{n}{x} p^x (1 - p)^{n-x}}{1 - (1 - p)^n}, \quad x = 1, 2, \ldots, n,$$

is known as the truncated binomial distribution, truncated below $x = 1$. This is the conditional distribution of the number of successes when it is known that there are no failures. The parameter p is estimated by equating the mean $\bar{x}$ in a sample of N to the mean of the population given by

$$(3.2.8) \qquad \mathcal{M}(X) = \frac{np}{1 - (1 - p)^n}.$$

3.3 POISSON DISTRIBUTION

The probability distribution

$$(3.3.1) \quad \text{Prob} \, (X = x) = p(x, \mu) = \frac{e^{-\mu} \mu^x}{x!}, \quad x = 0, 1, 2, \ldots, \infty,$$

obtained as a limit of the binomial distribution as $n \to \infty$ and $np = \mu$, is known as the Poisson distribution. The mean, the variance, and the β_1 and β_2 coefficients are given by

$$\mathcal{M}(X) = V(X) = \mu,$$

(3.3.2)
$$\beta_1(X) = \frac{1}{\mu},$$

$$\beta_2(X) = 3 + \frac{1}{\mu}.$$

The cumulative distribution can be computed from *Tables of Incomplete Gamma Function*, edited by K. Pearson, by using the relation

(3.3.3) $$P(x, \mu) = \sum_{r=0}^{x} p(r, \mu) = \frac{1}{\Gamma(x+1)} \int_{\mu}^{\infty} e^{-t} t^x \, dt.$$

The following tables of Poisson distribution are useful.

E. C. MOLINA, *Poisson's Exponential Binomial Limit*, published by Van Nostrand, 1949. This gives values of $p(x, \mu)$ and $1 - P(x, \mu)$ for $\mu = 0.001 \ (0.0001) \ 0.01 \ (0.01) \ 0.3 \ (0.1) \ 15 \ (1) \ 100$.

T. KITAGAWA, *Tables of Poisson Distribution*, published by Baifukan Co., Tokyo, 1952.

Tables of the Individual and Cumulative Terms of Poisson Distribution, General Electric Co., published by Van Nostrand, 1962.

E. S. PEARSON and H. O. HARTLEY, *Biometrika Tables for Statisticians*, Vol. I, published by Cambridge University Press, 1958. Table 39 gives values of $p(x, \mu)$, for $\mu = 0.1 \ (0.1) \ 15.0$. Table 7 gives values of $P(x, \mu)$ for $\mu = 0.0005 \ (0.0005) \ 0.005 \ (0.005) \ 0.05 \ (0.05) \ 1.0 \ (0.1) \ 5.0 \ (0.25) \ 10.0 \ 20 \ (1) \ 67$.

For large μ, we have the normal approximation

(3.3.4) $$\text{Prob} \ (\alpha < X \le \beta) = P(\beta, \mu) \doteqdot \phi(\beta^*) - \phi(\alpha^*),$$

where

$$\phi(x) = \int_{-\infty}^{x} \frac{1}{\sqrt{2\pi}} e^{-\frac{1}{2}t^2} \, dt$$

and

$$x^* = \frac{x + \frac{1}{2} - \mu}{\sqrt{\mu}}$$

in the sense that the percentage error in the approximation tends to zero with μ provided that both $(\alpha + \frac{1}{2} - \mu)^3/\mu^2$ and $(\beta + \frac{1}{2} - \mu)^3/\mu^2$ tend to zero with μ.

The arithmetic mean $\bar{x}$ in a sample of N from a Poisson population provides an estimate of the parameter μ.

Illustrative Example 3.4. Table 3.3 gives the frequency distribution of the number of red blood corpuscles (rbc) per cell of a hemocytometer. Fit a Poisson distribution to the data.

TABLE 3.3

FREQUENCY DISTRIBUTION OF RED BLOOD CORPUSCLES

No. of rbc x	No. of cells f
0	143
1	156
2	68
3	27
4	5
5	1
Total	400

The mean of the distribution is

$$\bar{x} = \frac{\sum xf}{\sum f} = \frac{398}{400} = 0.995,$$

which is to be taken as the estimate for the parameter μ of the Poisson distribution. Thus

$$\mu = 0.995,$$

$$\log e^{-\mu} = -\mu \times 0.4342945 = \bar{1}.5678770 = 9.5678770 - 10,$$

and

$$e^{-\mu} = 0.369724.$$

The theoretical probabilities

$$p_x = \frac{e^{-\mu}\mu^x}{x!}$$

for $x = 0, 1, 2, 3, \ldots$ are then computed by starting with $e^{-\mu}$ and multiplying successively by $\mu, \mu/2, \mu/3, \ldots$, etc. The expected frequencies are obtained by multiplying the probabilities by $n = 400$. The computations are shown in Table 3.4.

TABLE 3.4

FITTING A POISSON DISTRIBUTION

$$n = 400, \quad \mu = 0.995$$

No. of rbc x	Observed frequency f	fx	Probability $P_x = e^{-\mu}\mu^x/x!$	Expected frequency np_x
0	143	0	0.36972	147.89
1	156	156	0.36788	147.15
2	68	136	0.18302	73.21
3	27	81	0.06070	24.28
4	5	20	0.01510	6.04
5	1	5	0.00300	1.20
Above 5	0	0	0.00058	0.23
Total	400	398	1.00000	400.00

Truncated Poisson Distribution. The probability distribution

$$(3.3.5) \qquad \text{Prob}\,(X = x) = \frac{\mu^x}{(e^\mu - 1)x!}, \quad x = 1, 2, \ldots$$

is called the truncated Poisson distribution, truncated below $x = 1$. The parameter μ is estimated from a sample of N by equating the sample mean $\bar{x}$ to the mean in the population, which is

$$(3.3.6) \qquad \mathcal{M}(X) = \frac{\mu}{1 - e^{-\mu}}.$$

3.4 OTHER DISCRETE DISTRIBUTIONS

Negative Binomial Distribution. The probability distribution

$$(3.4.1) \quad \text{Prob}\,(X = x) = y(x, k, p) = \frac{\Gamma(k + x)}{x!\,\Gamma(k)}\, p^k(1 - p)^x,$$

$$x = 0, 1, 2, \ldots, \infty,$$

is known as the negative binomial distribution. If x is a given positive integer and $X + k$ is the number of independent trials required to get k successes when the probability of success in a single trial is p, then the random variable X has the probability distribution shown in 3.4.1.

PASCAL DISTRIBUTION. If $k = 1$, the distribution is known as the Pascal distribution.

When the negative binomial distribution is taken as a descriptive model, k is usually regarded as an unknown positive-valued parameter, not necessarily integral. This distribution arises as a compound of Poisson distributions $p(x, \mu)$ when the parameter μ behaves as a random variable with density

(3.4.2)
$$\frac{p^k}{\Gamma(k)} e^{-p\mu}\mu^{k-1}, \qquad 0 \le \mu < \infty,$$

where p and k are unknown positive parameters. The mean, the variance, and the β_1 and β_2 coefficients for this distribution are

(3.4.3)
$$\mathcal{M}(X) = \frac{k(1 - p)}{p},$$

$$V(X) = \frac{k(1 - p)}{p^2},$$

$$\beta_1(X) = \frac{p(2 - p)}{k(1 - p)},$$

$$\beta_2(X) = 3 + \frac{p^2}{k(1 - p)} + \frac{6}{p},$$

respectively.

The cumulative distribution can be obtained from *Tables of Incomplete Beta Function*, edited by Karl Pearson, by means of the relationship

(3.4.4)
$$Y(x, k, p) = \sum_{r=0}^{x} y(r, k, p) = I_p(k, x + 1),$$

where

$$I_w(u, v) = \frac{1}{B(u, v)} \int_0^w t^{u-1}(1 - t)^{v-1}\, dt$$

is the incomplete beta function ratio.

If $\bar{x}$ and m_2 are the mean and the variance based on a sample of N from a negative binomial distribution, the parameters k and p can be estimated by equating them to the mean and the variance in the population:

(3.4.5)
$$\bar{x} = \frac{k(1 - p)}{p},$$

$$m_2 = \frac{k(1 - p)}{p^2},$$

which gives

(3.4.6)
$$p = \frac{\bar{x}}{m_2},$$

$$k = \frac{\bar{x}^2}{m_2 - \bar{x}}.$$

If k is a known positive integer, the parameter p is estimated from equation 3.4.5 alone as

$$(3.4.7) \qquad\qquad p = \frac{k}{\bar{x} - k}.$$

Logarithmic Series Distribution. The probability distribution given by

$$(3.4.8) \quad \text{Prob}\,(\,X = x) = \frac{\theta^x}{-x \log (1 - \theta)}, \qquad x = 1, 2, \ldots, \infty,$$

where θ is a positive-valued parameter, is known as the logarithmic series distribution. The mean and the variance of this distribution are given by

$$(3.4.9) \qquad \mathscr{M}(X) = \frac{\theta}{-(1 - \theta) \log (1 - \theta)},$$

$$V(X) = \frac{\theta}{-(1 - \theta)^2 \log (1 - \theta)},$$

respectively. The parameter θ is estimated from a sample of N by equating the arithmetic mean $\bar{x}$ in the sample to the population mean:

$$(3.4.10) \qquad\qquad \bar{x} = \frac{\theta}{-(1 - \theta) \log (1 - \theta)}.$$

Hypergeometric Distribution.   If a sample of n is drawn without replacement from a population of N individuals among which there are M individuals possessing a certain attribute, then the probability distribution of X, the number of individuals in the sample possessing that attribute, is given by

$$\text{Prob}\,(\,X = x) = h(x, n, M, N)$$

$$(3.4.11) \qquad\qquad = \frac{\binom{M}{x}\binom{N - M}{n - x}}{\binom{N}{n}}.$$

This is known as the hypergeometric distribution. The mean and the variance for this distribution are given by

$$\mathscr{M}(x) = \frac{nM}{N},$$

$$(3.4.12)$$

$$V(X) = \frac{nM(N - M)(N - n)}{N^2(N - 1)},$$

respectively.

Compound Binomial Distribution. If the parameter p of the binomial distribution $b(x, p, n)$ behaves as a random variable with the density function

(3.4.13) $$\frac{1}{B(\alpha, \beta)} p^{\alpha-1}(1 - p)^{\beta-1}, \qquad 0 \le p \le 1,$$

where α and β are positive-valued parameters, then the probability distribution of the number of successes X in n trials is given by

(3.4.14) $$\text{Prob}\,(X = x) = \frac{\binom{n}{x} B(\alpha + x, n + \beta - x)}{B(\alpha, \beta)},$$

$$x = 0, 1, 2, \ldots, n.$$

The mean and the variance of this distribution are given respectively by

(3.4.15)
$$\mathscr{M}(X) = \frac{n\alpha}{\alpha + \beta},$$
$$V(X) = \frac{n\alpha\beta}{(\alpha + \beta)(\alpha + \beta + 1)}\left(1 + \frac{n}{\alpha + \beta}\right).$$

Compound Poisson Distribution (Neyman's Type A Contagious Distribution). If the parameter μ of the Poisson distribution $p(x, \mu)$ behaves like a random variable with probability distribution

(3.4.16) $$\text{Prob}\,(\mu = kc) = \frac{e^{-\lambda}\lambda^k}{k!}, \qquad k = 0, 1, 2, \ldots, \infty,$$

where λ and c are positive-valued parameters, then the resulting probability distribution

(3.4.17) $$\text{Prob}\,(X = x) = \frac{e^{-\lambda}c^x}{x!} \sum_{k=0}^{\infty}(e^{-c}\lambda)^k$$

is known as Neyman's type A contagious distribution.

The mean and the variance of this distribution are

(3.4.18) $$\mathscr{M}(X) = c\lambda,$$
$$V(X) = c(1 + c)\lambda,$$

respectively.

3.5 EXERCISES

Binomial distribution

3.1–3.3. To each of the frequency distributions in exercises 2.1, 2.2, and 2.5, fit a binomial distribution, using (a) the estimated value and (b) the theoretical value for the proportion. Compare the observed and the theoretical frequencies.

3.4. Compare the accuracy of the normal approximation to the binomial distribution:

$$\sum_{x=0}^{r} \binom{n}{x} p^x (1 - p)^{n-x} \sim \int_{-\infty}^{r*} \frac{1}{\sqrt{2\pi}} e^{-\frac{1}{2}x^2} dx,$$

where

$$r* = \frac{r + \frac{1}{2} - np}{\sqrt{np(1 - p)}}$$

for $p = 0.2 \,(0.2)\, 0.8$ and the following values of n and r:

n	r
5	2
10	2, 4
20	2, 4, 8, 10
50	2, 5, 10, 15, 20, 25

3.5. Compute the probability of x successes in n independent trials when the probability of success in each single trial is p, using (a) the exact binomial expression and (b) the Poisson approximation to the binomial for $x = 0, 1, 2, \ldots$ and the following values of n and p:

n	p		
10	0.1	(0.1)	0.4
20	0.05	(0.05)	0.20
50	0.02	(0.02)	0.08
100	0.01	(0.01)	0.04

Give your comments.

3.6. A farmer sells bean seeds in packets of 100 and agrees to refund the price if the number of seeds germinating from a packet is less than 75. He knows from experience that on an average 80% of his seeds germinate and that it costs him $2.00 for a packet of seeds. How should he fix the price of a packet so as to ensure an average profit of 25%?

3.7. Two different plans for examining a large number N of blood samples for a certain disease are proposed. (a) Each sample is to be tested separately, in which case N tests are required. (b) A portion from each of k samples is to be pooled and analyzed together. If the result is negative, this one test suffices for the k samples. If the result is positive, the remaining portions of each of the k samples are to be examined separately so that a total of $k + 1$ tests is required for the k samples.

Assume that the probability p that a sample of blood will be positive is the same for all samples and regard the drawing of the different samples as statistically independent.

Compute the expected value of the number of tests necessary under plan (b) and determine k so as to minimize this for each of the following values of p: 0.01, 0.02 (0.02) 0.10 (0.05) 0.25.

Find the maximum percentage saving attainable in the number of tests by using plan (b) instead of plan (a) in each of the above cases.

Source: R. Dorfman, The detection of defective members of large populations, *Annals of Mathematical Statistics*, Vol. 14 (1943).

3.8. A company sells its products to a distributor in lots of a large number of individual articles. Since a fraction of the articles produced might be defective, the distributor inspects a sample of articles from each lot before accepting it. His rule is to take a sample of n articles with replacement from the lot and to accept the lot only if the sample contains no more than r defectives.

Find the probability $F(n, r, p)$ that a lot will be accepted when the proportion of defectives in it is p. Using tables of the binomial probability distribution, determine n and r to satisfy as nearly as possible the equations

$$F(n, r, 0.02) = 0.90,$$
$$F(n, r, 0.10) = 0.05.$$

Plot $F(n, r, p)$ against p for these values of n and r.

3.9. Fit a truncated binomial distribution to the frequency distribution in exercise 2.28.

Poisson distribution

3.10–3.13. To each of the frequency distributions in exercises 2.5, 2.6, 2.25, and 2.27 fit a Poisson distribution. Compare the observed and the theoretical frequencies.

3.14. When the first proof of 200 pages of an encyclopedia of 5000 pages was read, the distribution of printing mistakes was found to be as shown in Table 3.5.

TABLE 3.5

FREQUENCY DISTRIBUTION OF NUMBER
OF MISPRINTS IN A PAGE

No. of misprints on page	Frequency
0	112
1	63
2	20
3	3
4	1
5	1
Total	200

Fit a Poisson law to the frequency distribution of printing mistakes. Estimate the total cost of correcting the first proof of the whole encyclopedia by using the information given in Table 3.6.

TABLE 3.6

COST OF DETECTION AND CORRECTION OF MISPRINTS

No. of misprints on page	Cost of detection and correction (dollars) per page
0	0.10
1	0.16
2	0.23
3	0.29
4	0.34
5 or more	0.36

3.15. A telephone exchange A is to connect 2000 subscribers to a nearby exchange B. Since it is too expensive to install 2000 trunklines from A to B, it is decided to make the number N of lines so large that during a busy hour, on an average, only one out of every 100 calls would fail to find an idle trunkline immediately at its disposal.

Determine N, on the assumption that during a busy hour of the day, on an average, each subscriber requires a trunkline to B for 1 minute.

Would it be cheaper to divide the 2000 subscribers into two groups of 1000 each and install two separate groups of trunklines from A to B?

Source: W. Feller, *Introduction to Probability Theory and Its Applications*, Vol. I, John Wiley & Sons, New York, 1957.

3.16. Fit a truncated Poisson distribution to the frequency distribution in exercise 2.29, omitting the zero counts.

Other discrete distributions

3.17. Fit a hypergeometric distribution to the data in exercise 2.2 and compare the observed and theoretical frequencies.

3.18. Fit a Pascal distribution to the data in exercise 2.3, using (a) the estimated value and (b) the theoretical value of the proportion.

3.19–3.20. Fit a negative binomial distribution to each of the frequency distributions in exercises 2.26 and 2.27. Compare the observed and the theoretical frequencies.

3.21. Fit Neyman's contagious distribution of type A to the data in exercise 2.27. Compare the observed and the theoretical frequencies.

3.22. According to Lotka, in the United States the relative frequency p_n of families having exactly n children is given by

$$p_0 = \frac{1 - (1 + \alpha)p}{1 - p}, \qquad p_n = \alpha p^n \quad \text{for } n \geq 1,$$

where α and p are parameters.

Assuming that this law holds for India, fit this distribution to the distribution shown in Table 2.23, p. 125.

CHAPTER 4

Standard Continuous Distributions

4.1 UNIFORM DISTRIBUTION

A random variable X is said to have a uniform or rectangular distribution in the interval (α, β) if its density function is

$$(4.1.1) \qquad f(x, \alpha, \beta) = \frac{1}{\beta - \alpha}, \qquad \alpha \le x \le \beta.$$

The mean, the variance, and the values of β_1 and β_2 coefficients for this distribution are

$$\mathcal{M}(X) = \frac{\alpha + \beta}{2},$$

$$(4.1.2) \qquad V(X) = \frac{(\beta - \alpha)^2}{12},$$

$$\beta_1(X) = 0,$$

$$\beta_2(X) = 1.8,$$

respectively. The cumulative distribution function is

$$(4.1.3) \qquad \text{Prob}\,(X \le x) = \frac{x - \alpha}{\beta - \alpha}, \quad \text{for } \alpha \le x \le \beta.$$

If α and β are unknown parameters, they are estimated respectively by the smallest and the largest observations in the sample.

4.2 NORMAL DISTRIBUTION

A random variable X is said to have the normal distribution if its probability density function is of the form

$$(4.2.1) \quad f(x, \mu, \sigma) = \frac{1}{\sigma\sqrt{2\pi}} \exp\left[-\frac{1}{2}\left(\frac{x - \mu}{\sigma}\right)^2\right], \qquad -\infty < x < \infty,$$

where μ and σ are parameters $-\infty < \mu < \infty, 0 < \sigma < \infty$.

For this distribution, the mean, the variance, and the β_1 and β_2 co-efficients are as follows:

(4.2.2) $\mathcal{M}(X) = \mu, \quad V(X) = \sigma^2, \quad \beta_1(X) = 0, \quad \beta_2(X) = 3.$

The distribution is symmetric about the mean. The probability density function and the cumulative distribution function can be computed from the relations

(4.2.3) $$f(x, \mu, \sigma) = \frac{1}{\sigma}\, \phi\!\left(\frac{x - \mu}{\sigma}\right)$$

and

(4.2.4) $$\text{Prob}\,(X \leq x) = F(x, \mu, \sigma) = \Phi\!\left(\frac{x - \mu}{\sigma}\right),$$

where

(4.2.5) $$\phi(x) = \frac{1}{\sqrt{2\pi}}\, e^{-\frac{1}{2}x^2}$$

is the probability density function for the normal distribution standardized to mean zero and variance unity, and

(4.2.6) $$\Phi(x) = \int_{-\infty}^{x} \phi(t)\, dt$$

is the cumulative distribution function of the standardized normal distribution.

The ordinates $\phi(x)$ and the areas $\Phi(x)$ of the standardized normal distribution have been extensively tabulated. Some of the easily available tables are as follows.

Biometrika Tables for Statisticians. Table 1 in this publication gives values of $Z = \phi(x)$ and $P = \Phi(x)$ to seven places of decimals for non-negative values of x at intervals of 0.01. For negative x, the relations

(4.2.7) $$\phi(-x) = \phi(x)$$

and

(4.2.8) $$\Phi(-x) = 1 - \Phi(x)$$

are used.

Tables 4 and 5 of *Biometrika Tables* give the values of x and $\phi(x)$ for specified values of $P = 0.000\ (0.001)\ 1$.

R. A. FISHER and F. YATES, *Statistical Tables for Biological, Agricultural, and Medical Research.* Table 1 gives the values of x for specified values of $2\Phi(-x) = 0.00\ (0.01)\ 0.99$. Table II gives the values of $\phi(x)$ for $x = 0.00\ (0.01)\ 3.0\ (0.1)\ 3.9$. Table VIII gives the values of the normal probability integral $\Phi(x)$ for $x = 0.00\ (0.1)\ 4.99$.

Illustrative Example 4.1. Fit a normal distribution to the frequency distribution of scores in illustrative example 2.1.

Since the values of β_1 and β_2 coefficients for this distribution computed in illustrative example 2.10 are close to 0 and 3, respectively, we are justified in fitting a normal distribution. The mean of the distribution is $\mu = 39.72$, and the value of the standard deviation after applying Sheppard's correction for grouping is $\sigma = 9.724$. The details of fitting the normal distribution with these parameters are shown in Table 4.1. Since the theoretical

TABLE 4.1

FITTING A NORMAL DISTRIBUTION

$n = 250, \quad \mu = 39.72, \quad \sigma = 9.784$

Class limit x	Observed frequency f	$u = \dfrac{x - \mu}{\sigma}$	$P(u)$	ΔP	Expected frequency $n\,\Delta P$
$-\infty$	...	$-\infty$	0.0	...	...
19.5	9	-2.0666	0.0193871	0.0193871	4.85
24.5	11	-1.5556	0.0599040	0.0405169	10.13
29.5	10	-1.0446	0.1481070	0.0882030	22.05
34.5	44	-0.5335	0.2968459	0.1487389	37.18
39.5	45	-0.0225	0.4910246	0.1941787	48.54
44.5	54	$+0.4886$	0.6874365	0.1964119	49.10
49.5	37	0.9996	0.8412474	0.1538109	38.45
54.5	26	1.5106	0.9345543	0.0933069	23.33
59.5	8	2.0217	0.9783956	0.0438413	10.96
64.5	5	2.5327	0.9943402	0.0159446	3.98
$+\infty$	1	$+\infty$	1.0	0.0056598	1.41
Total	250			1.0	249.98

distribution extends from $-\infty$ to $+\infty$, the lower limit of the first class is taken as $-\infty$ and the upper limit for the last class as $+\infty$. The values of $P(u)$ are obtained by linear interpolation from Table 1 of *Biometrika Tables* for positive values of u. For negative values of u use is made of the identity $P(-u) = 1 - P(u)$. The column for ΔP gives the first differences of the column for P.

Truncated Normal Distribution. If the normal distribution is truncated below c, the probability density function is given by

$$(4.2.9) \qquad f^*(x; \mu, \sigma, c) = \frac{\dfrac{1}{\sigma}\,\phi\!\left(\dfrac{x - \mu}{\sigma}\right)}{1 - \Phi\!\left(\dfrac{c - \mu}{\sigma}\right)}, \qquad c \le x < \infty.$$

The mean and the variance of this distribution are

(4.2.10)
$$\mathcal{M}(X) = \mu + \sigma\theta,$$
$$V(X) = \sigma^2(1 + c^*\theta - \theta^2),$$

respectively, where

(4.2.11)
$$c^* = \frac{c - \mu}{\sigma}$$

and

(4.2.12)
$$\theta = \frac{\phi(c^*)}{1 - \Phi(c^*)}.$$

Log-Normal Distribution. A random variable X is said to follow the log-normal distribution if

(4.2.13)
$$Y = \log(X - \alpha)$$

follows the normal distribution.

If logarithms are taken to the base e, the moments of the distribution can be computed from the relation

(4.2.14)
$$\mathcal{M}(X - \alpha)^t = \exp(t\mu + \tfrac{1}{2}t^2\sigma^2).$$

Gram–Charlier Type A Series Expansion. Under certain conditions, the probability density function $f(x)$ of a random variable X with mean zero can be expressed as

(4.2.15)
$$f(x) = \sum_{j=0}^{\infty} c_j H_j(x)\,\phi(x),$$

where $\phi(x)$ is the probability density function of the standardized normal distribution, $H_j(x)$ is the Tchebycheff–Hermite polynomial of degree j in x, defined by

(4.2.16)
$$(-1)^j \frac{d^j}{dx^j}\phi(x) = H_j(x)\,\phi(x)$$

and

(4.2.17)
$$c_j = \frac{1}{j!}\int_{-\infty}^{\infty} H_j(x)f(x)\,dx.$$

The values of $H_j(x)$ and c_j for $j = 0, 1, 2, 3,$ and 4 are given in Table 4.2, where

$$\mu_j = \mathcal{M}(X^j), \qquad j = 2, 3, 4, \ldots.$$

If term by term integration is possible, the cumulative distribution function is given by

(4.2.18)
$$\text{Prob}(X \le x) = \Phi(x) - \sum_{j=2}^{\infty} c_j H_{j-1}(x)\,\phi(x),$$

TABLE 4.2
TCHEBYCHEFF–HERMITE POLYNOMIALS

j	$H_j(x)$	c_j
0	1	1
1	x	0
2	$x^2 \quad -1$	$\frac{1}{2}(\mu_2 - 1)$
3	$x^3 \quad -3x$	$\frac{1}{6}\mu_3$
4	$x^4 \quad -6x^2 \quad +3$	$\frac{1}{24}(\mu_4 - 6\mu_2 + 3)$

where $\Phi(x)$ is the cumulative distribution function of the standardized normal distribution. In practice, only the first few terms of the series expansion are generally used.

Normalization. Let X be a random variable whose cumulative distribution function is $F(x)$. Let $\lambda = \lambda(x)$ be defined by

$$(4.2.19) \qquad \int_{-\infty}^{\lambda} \frac{1}{\sqrt{2\pi}} e^{-\frac{1}{2}t^2} \, dt = F(x).$$

Then $\lambda(X)$ follows the normal distribution with mean zero and variance unity. The transformation $\lambda(x)$ is called normalization.

Suppose that the cumulative distribution function of X involves a positive integer index n. Let the rth cumulant of X be denoted by K_r, and suppose that constants μ and σ^2 are so chosen that

$$\rho_1 = \frac{K_1 - \mu}{\sigma} = 0(n^{-\frac{1}{2}}),$$

$$(4.2.20) \qquad \rho_2 = \frac{K_2 - \sigma^2}{\sigma^2} = 0(n^{-1}),$$

$$\rho_r = \frac{K_r}{\sigma^r} = 0(n^{1-\frac{1}{2}r}), \quad \text{for } r = 2, 3, 4, \ldots.$$

Then we have approximately:

$$(4.2.21) \quad x - \lambda = \rho_1 + \tfrac{1}{6}\rho_3(x^2 - 1) + \tfrac{1}{2}\rho_2 x - \tfrac{1}{3}\rho_1\rho_3 x + \tfrac{1}{24}\rho_4(x^3 - 3x)$$
$$- \tfrac{1}{36}\rho_3^2(4x^3 - 7x) - \tfrac{1}{2}\rho_1\rho_2 + \tfrac{1}{6}\rho_1^2\rho_3 - \tfrac{1}{12}\rho_2\rho_3(5x^2 - 3)$$
$$- \tfrac{1}{8}\rho_1\rho_2(x^2 - 1) + \tfrac{1}{120}\rho_5(x_4 - 6x^2 + 3) + \tfrac{1}{36}\rho_1\rho_3^2(12x^2 - 7)$$
$$- \tfrac{1}{144}\rho_3\rho_4(11x^4 - 42x^2 + 15) + \tfrac{1}{648}\rho_3^3(69x^4 - 187x + 52) - \tfrac{3}{8}\rho_2^2 x$$
$$+ \tfrac{5}{6}\rho_1\rho_2\rho_3 x + \tfrac{1}{8}\rho_1^2\rho_4 x - \tfrac{1}{48}\rho_2\rho_4(7x^3 - 15x)$$
$$- \tfrac{1}{30}\rho_1\rho_5(x^3 - x) + \tfrac{1}{720}\rho_6(x^5 - 10x^3 + 15x) - \tfrac{1}{3}\rho_1^2\rho_3^2 x$$
$$+ \tfrac{1}{72}\rho_2\rho_3^2(36x^3 - 49x) - \tfrac{1}{384}\rho_4^2(5x^5 - 32x^3 + 35x)$$
$$+ \tfrac{1}{36}\rho_1\rho_3\rho_4(11x^3 - 21x) - \tfrac{1}{360}\rho_3\rho_5(7x^5 - 48x^3 + 51x)$$
$$- \tfrac{1}{324}\rho_1\rho_3^3(138x^3 - 187x) + \tfrac{1}{864}\rho_3^2\rho_4(111x^5 - 547x^3 + 456x)$$
$$- \tfrac{1}{7776}\rho_3^4(948x^5 - 3628x^3 + 2473x)$$

to order n^{-2}. An alternative expression for x in terms of λ is

$$x - \lambda = \rho_1 + \tfrac{1}{6}\rho_3(\lambda^2 - 1) + \tfrac{1}{2}\rho_2\lambda + \tfrac{1}{24}\rho_4(\lambda^3 - 3\lambda) - \tfrac{1}{36}\rho_3^2(2\lambda^3 - 5\lambda)$$
$$- \tfrac{1}{6}\rho_2\rho_3(\lambda^2 - 1) + \tfrac{1}{120}\rho_5(\lambda^4 - 6\lambda^2 + 3) - \tfrac{1}{24}\rho_3\rho_4(\lambda^4 - 5\lambda^2 + 2)$$
$$+ \tfrac{1}{324}\rho_3^3(12\lambda^4 - 53\lambda^2 + 17) - \tfrac{1}{8}\rho_2^2\lambda - \tfrac{1}{16}\rho_2\rho_4(\lambda^3 - 3\lambda)$$
$$+ \tfrac{1}{720}\rho_6(\lambda^5 - 10\lambda^3 + 15\lambda) + \tfrac{1}{72}\rho_2\rho_3^2(10\lambda^3 - 25\lambda)$$
$$- \tfrac{1}{384}\rho_4^2(3\lambda^5 - 24\lambda^3 + 29\lambda) - \tfrac{1}{180}\rho_3\rho_5(2\lambda^5 - 17\lambda^3 + 21\lambda)$$
$$+ \tfrac{1}{288}\rho_3^2\rho_4(14\lambda^5 - 103\lambda^3 + 107\lambda) - \tfrac{1}{7776}\rho_3^4(252\lambda^5 - 1688\lambda^3 + 1511\lambda).$$

4.3 PEARSONIAN SYSTEM OF DISTRIBUTIONS

Karl Pearson introduced a system of distribution whereby the probability density function $y = f(x)$ satisfies the differential equation

$$(4.3.1) \qquad \frac{dy}{dx} = \frac{y(x + a)}{b_0 + b_1 x + b_2 x^2},$$

where a, b_0, b_1, and b_2 are parameters. The type of curve depends on the value of the criterion $K = b_1^2/4b_0b_2$, which can be expressed in terms of the moment coefficients of the distribution as

$$(4.3.2) \qquad K = \frac{\beta_1(\beta_2 + 3)^2}{4(4\beta_2 - 3\beta_1)(2\beta_2 - 3\beta_1 - 6)}.$$

The values of the parameters can also be expressed in terms of the first four moments of the distribution.

To graduate an observed frequency distribution by a Pearsonian curve, the first step is to compute the first four moments of the observed distribution. We can then evaluate K, which in turn determines the type of the curve; alternatively, the values of (β_1, β_2) may be plotted in the diagram provided by Pearson (Table 43 in *Biometrika Tables*), from which the type of the curve can be read off directly. When the type of the curve has been specified, the parameters involved can be estimated from the equations connecting them with the first four moments of the distribution, for which sample values are substituted. This is known as the *method of moments*.

Some of the important types of curves belonging to the Pearsonian system will now be described.

Type I. If $K < 0$, we obtain

$$(4.3.3) \qquad y = y_0\left(1 + \frac{x}{a_1}\right)^{m_1}\left(1 - \frac{x}{a_2}\right)^{m_2}, \qquad -a_1 \leq x \leq a_2,$$

with origin at the mode of the distribution. The parameters are estimated from the equations

$$y_0 = \frac{a_1{}^{m_1}a_2{}^{m_2}}{(a_1 + a_2)^{m_1+m_2+1}} \frac{\Gamma(m_1 + m_2 + 2)}{\Gamma(m_1 + 1)\Gamma(m_2 + 1)},$$

$$m_1 + m_2 + 2 = r = \frac{6(\beta_2 - \beta_1 - 1)}{6 + 3\beta_1 - 2\beta_2},$$

$$(m_1 + 1)(m_2 + 1) = \epsilon = r^2 \bigg/ \left[4 + \tfrac{1}{4}\beta_1 \frac{(r + 2)^2}{r + 1}\right],$$

(4.3.4)

$$(a_1 + a_2)^2 = \frac{\mu_2(r + 1)r^2}{\epsilon},$$

$$\frac{m_1}{a_1} = \frac{m_2}{a_2},$$

$$\text{Mode} = \text{Mean} - \frac{1}{2}\frac{\mu_3}{\mu_2} \cdot \frac{r + 2}{r - 2}.$$

The cumulative distribution function can be obtained from *Tables of Incomplete Beta Function*, edited by K. Pearson, by using the relations

(4.3.5) $$\operatorname{Prob}(X \le x) = \int_{-a_1}^{x} y\, dx = I_{x^*}(m_1 + 1, m_2 + 1),$$

where $x^* = (x + a_1)/(a_1 + a_2)$, and

$$I_x(p, q) = \frac{1}{B(p, q)} \int_0^x t^{p-1}(1 - t)^{q-1}\, dt$$

is the incomplete beta function ratio.

Type II. If $\beta_1 = 0$ and $\beta_2 < 3$, we get the probability density function

(4.3.6) $$y = y_0\left(1 - \frac{x^2}{a^2}\right)^m, \qquad -a \le x \le a,$$

with origin at the mean of the distribution. The parameters are estimated from the equations:

$$y_0 = \frac{1}{a}\frac{\Gamma(m + \tfrac{3}{2})}{\sqrt{\pi}\Gamma(m + 1)},$$

(4.3.7) $$m = \frac{5\beta_2 - 9}{6 - 2\beta_2},$$

$$a^2 = \frac{2\mu_2\beta_2}{3 - \beta_2}.$$

The cumulative distribution function can be obtained from *Tables of Incomplete Beta Function* by using the relationship

(4.3.8) $$\text{Prob} \left(| X | < x \right) = \int_{-x}^{x} y \, dx = I_{x^*}(m + 1, \tfrac{1}{2}),$$

where $x^* = x^2/a^2$.

Type III. If $2\beta_2 - 3\beta_1 - 6 = 0$, we obtain the probability density function

(4.3.9) $$y = y_0 e^{-\gamma x} \left(1 + \frac{x}{a} \right)^p, \qquad -a \leq x < \infty,$$

with origin at the mode of the distribution. The parameters can be estimated from the equations

(4.3.10)

$$y_0 = \frac{a^{-1} e^{-p} p^{p+1}}{\Gamma(p + 1)},$$

$$a = \frac{p}{\gamma} = \frac{4}{\beta_1} - 1,$$

$$\gamma = \frac{2\mu_2}{\mu_3},$$

$$\text{Mode} = \text{mean} - \frac{1}{\gamma}.$$

The cumulative distribution function can be obtained from *Tables of Incomplete Gamma Function*, edited by K. Pearson, as follows:

(4.3.11) $$\text{Prob} \left(X \leq x \right) = \int_{-a}^{x} y \, dx = \frac{1}{\Gamma(p + 1)} \int_{0}^{x^*} e^{-t} t^p \, dt,$$

where $x^* = \gamma(a + x)$.

Type IV. If $0 < K < 1$, we obtain

(4.3.12) $$y = y_0 \left(1 + \frac{x^2}{a^2} \right)^{-m} \exp \left[-\nu \tan^{-1} \frac{x}{a} \right], \qquad -\infty < x < \infty,$$

with origin at the mode of the distribution.

The constant y_0 is obtained from the relation

(4.3.13) $$y_0 = \frac{1}{F(2m - 2, \nu)},$$

where

$$F(m, \nu) = \int_{-\pi/2}^{\pi/2} (\cos \theta)^m e^{-\nu \theta} \, d\theta$$

is tabulated in *Tables for Statisticians and Biometricians*, Part I, edited by K. Pearson, Third Edition, Cambridge University Press, 1930.

The parameters m, ν, and a are estimated from the relations

$$2m - 2 = r = \frac{6(\beta_2 - \beta_1 - 1)}{2\beta_2 - 3\beta_1 - 6}$$

(4.3.14)
$$= r(r - 2)\sqrt{\frac{\beta_1}{k}},$$

and
$$a = \sqrt{\frac{k\mu_2}{16}},$$

where
$$k = 16(r - 1) - \beta_1(r - 2)^2.$$

The cumulative distribution function can be obtained from tabulated integrals in *Tables for Statisticians and Biometricians*, Part I, or by quadrature.

Type V. If $K = 1$, we find

(4.3.15)
$$y = y_0 x^{-p} e^{-\nu/x}, \qquad 0 \leq x < \infty,$$

with origin at the start of the curve,

$$y_0 = \frac{\nu^{p-1}}{\Gamma(p - 1)},$$

(4.3.16)
$$p = 4 + \frac{8 + 4\sqrt{\beta_1 + 4}}{\beta_1},$$

$$\nu = (p - 2)\sqrt{\mu_2(p - 3)},$$

and

(4.3.17) $$\text{Prob}\,(X \leq x) = \int_0^x y \, dx = 1 - \frac{1}{\Gamma(p - 1)} \int_0^{x^*} e^{-t} t^{p-2} \, dt,$$

where $x^* = \nu/x$.

The special form with $\nu = 0$ is called the *Pareto distribution*.

Type VI. If $K > 1$, we get

(4.3.18)
$$y = y_0(x - a)^{q_2} x^{-q_1}, \qquad a \leq x < \infty,$$

with origin at a distance a before the start of the curve, and

$$y_0 = a^{q_1 - q_2 - 1} \frac{\Gamma(q_1)}{\Gamma(q_2 + 1)\Gamma(q_1 - q_2 - 1)}.$$

q_2 and $-q_1$ are given by

(4.3.19)
$$\frac{r - 2}{2} \pm \frac{r(r + 2)}{2} \sqrt{\frac{\beta_1}{\beta_1(r + 2)^2 + 16(r + 1)}},$$

where

$$r = 6(\beta_2 - \beta_1 - 1)/(6 + 3\beta_1 - 2\beta_2),$$

$$a = \tfrac{1}{2}\sqrt{\mu_2}\,\sqrt{\beta_1(r + 2)^2 + 16(r + 1)}.$$

Then

$$\text{Prob}\,(X \le x) = \int_{-a}^{x} y\,dx = I_{x^*}(q_2 + 1, q_1 - q_2 - 1),$$

where $x^* = 1 - a/x$.

Type VII. If $\beta_1 = 0$, $\beta_2 > 3$, we get

$$(4.3.20) \qquad y = y_0\left(1 + \frac{x^2}{a^2}\right)^{-m}, \qquad -\infty < x < \infty,$$

with origin at the mean of the distribution.

The parameters are estimated from the relations

$$(4.3.21) \qquad \begin{aligned} y_0 &= \frac{\Gamma(m)}{a\sqrt{\pi}\,\Gamma(m - \frac{1}{2})}, \\ m &= \frac{5\beta_2 - 9}{2\beta_2 - 6}, \\ a^2 &= \frac{2\mu_2\beta_2}{\beta_2 - 3}. \end{aligned}$$

The cumulative distribution can be computed from *Tables of Incomplete Beta Function* by using the relation

$$(4.3.22) \qquad \text{Prob}\,(-x \le X \le x) = \int_{-x}^{x} y\,dx = I_{x^*}(m - \tfrac{1}{2}, \tfrac{1}{2}),$$

where $x^* = a^2/(a^2 + x^2)$.

Illustrative Example 4.2. In an experimental sampling scheme, 342 samples were drawn from a certain population and a statistic T was calculated from each sample. The frequency distribution of T is given in Table 4.3. Fit an appropriate Pearsonian type of distribution.

TABLE 4.3

FREQUENCY DISTRIBUTION OF A STATISTIC T

Class interval	Frequency	Class interval	Frequency
0–2	4	14–16	14
2–4	23	16–18	18
4–6	51	18–20	3
6–8	69	20–22	4
8–10	59	22–24	3
10–12	57	24–26	1
12–14	35	26–28	1
		Total	342

The moments of this distribution are as follows: mean $= 9.36758$, $\mu_2 = 19.35396$, $\mu_3 = 72.98265$, and $\mu_4 = 1518.64$, so that $\beta_1 = 0.73474$ and $\beta_2 = 4.05433$. By plotting (β_1, β_2) on the chart relating the type of Pearson frequency curve to the values of (β_1, β_2) in Table 43 of *Biometrika Tables*, it is found that the appropriate curve is of Type III. The equation to the curve is

$$y = y_0\left(1 + \frac{x}{a}\right)^p e^{-\gamma x}$$

with origin at the mode.

The parameters are estimated as follows:

$$p = \frac{4}{\beta_1} - 1 = 4.44410,$$

$$\gamma = \frac{2\mu_2}{\mu_3} = 0.53037,$$

$$a = \frac{p}{\gamma} = 8.37924,$$

$$\text{Mode} = \text{mean} - \frac{\mu_3}{2\mu_2} = 7.48210,$$

$$y_0 = \frac{a^{-1}e^{-p}p^{p+1}}{\Gamma(p+1)},$$

$$\log y_0 = \bar{2}.9934675,$$

which is computed by using the relation $\Gamma(p+1) = p\Gamma(p)$ and obtaining the value of $\log \Gamma(1.4441)$ by interpolation in Table 52 of *Biometrika Tables*.

The expected frequencies can be computed either by direct quadrature or by interpolation in *Tables of Incomplete Gamma Function*.

TABLE 4.4

COMPUTATION OF EXPECTED FREQUENCIES FROM A
TYPE III CURVE

X	$x = X$ − mode	$1 + \dfrac{x}{a}$	$\log\left(1 + \dfrac{x}{a}\right)$	$\log y$	y	$P = \frac{1}{3} \times$ $(y_0 + 4y_1 + y_2)$	Expected frequency nP
...	...	...	...	...	...	...	...
6	−1.4821	0.82312	$\bar{1}.9154632$	$\bar{2}.9591596$	0.0910248		
7	−0.4821	0.94246	$\bar{1}.9742629$	$\bar{2}.9901347$	0.0977540	0.1932496	66.09
8	+0.5179	1.06181	0.0260468	$\bar{2}.9899307$	0.0977081		
9	1.5179	1.18115	0.0723052	$\bar{2}.9651708$	0.0922934	0.1833914	62.72
10	2.5179	1.30049	0.1141070	$\bar{2}.9206054$	0.0832924		
...	...	...	...	...	...	...	...

The layout for computing the expected frequencies by quadrature using Simpson's one-third rule is shown in Table 4.4. The details of computation of frequencies in the classes 6–8 and 8–10 are presented; other frequencies can be computed in the same way.

The expected frequencies in all the cells thus computed are as follows: 3.76, 24.50, 52.09, 66.09, 62.72, 49.46, 34.32, 21.68, 12.75, 7.09, 3.77, 1.93, 0.96, and 0.46, respectively.

4.4 DISTRIBUTIONS OCCURRING IN SAMPLING THEORY

A number of probability density functions belonging to the Pearsonian system are listed separately below, because of their special importance in the theory of sampling.

t Distribution.   A random variable is said to follow the *t* distribution with *n* degrees of freedom if its probability density function is

$$(4.4.1) \qquad \frac{1}{\sqrt{n}B(\frac{1}{2}, \frac{1}{2}n)}\left(1 + \frac{x^2}{n}\right)^{-(n+1)/2}, \qquad -\infty < x < \infty.$$

The cumulative distribution function of the *t* distribution is tabulated for $n = 1$ (1) 24, 30, 40, 60, 120, ∞ in Table 9 of *Biometrika Tables*. Percentage points of the *t* distribution are given in Table 12 of *Biometrika Tables* and Table 3 of *Statistical Tables for Biological, Agricultural, and Medical Research*.

Chi-Square Distribution.   A random variable is said to have the chi-square distribution with *n* degrees of freedom if its probability density function is

$$(4.4.2) \qquad \frac{1}{2^{n/2}\Gamma(n/2)}\, e^{-\frac{1}{2}x} x^{\frac{1}{2}n-1}, \qquad 0 \leqq x < \infty.$$

The cumulative distribution function of the chi-square distribution is given in Table 7 in *Biometrika Tables* for $n = 1$ (1) 30 (2) 70. Percentage points of chi-square distribution are given in Table 8 of *Biometrika Tables* for $n = 1$ (1) 30 (10) 100 and in Table 4 of *Statistical Tables for Biological, Agricultural, and Medical Research* for $n = 1$ (1) 30.

Variance Ratio or F Distribution.   The probability density function for this distribution is

$$(4.4.3) \qquad \frac{(m/n)^{\frac{1}{2}m}}{B(\frac{1}{2}m, \frac{1}{2}n)} \frac{x^{\frac{1}{2}m-1}}{\left(1 + \frac{m}{n}x\right)^{\frac{1}{2}(m+n)}}, \qquad 0 \leq x < \infty.$$

Percentage points of this distribution are tabulated in Table 18 of *Biometrika Tables* for $m = 1$ (1) 10, 12, 15, 20, 24, 30, 40, 60, 120, ∞ and

$n = 1\ (1)\ 30, 40, 60, 120, \infty$ and Table 5 of *Statistical Tables for Biological
Agricultural, and Medical Research* for $m = 1\ (1)\ 8,\ 12,\ 24,\ \infty$ and $n = 1\ (1)\ 30, 40, 60, 120, \infty$.

Beta Distribution. A random variable X is said to have the beta distribution with m and n degrees of freedom if its probability density function is

$$(4.4.4) \qquad \frac{1}{B(\tfrac{1}{2}m,\ \tfrac{1}{2}n)}\, x^{\tfrac{1}{2}m-1}(1 - x)^{\tfrac{1}{2}n-1}, \qquad 0 \le x \le 1.$$

The cumulative distribution function can be obtained from *Tables of
Incomplete Beta Function.* Percentage points are tabulated in Table 16
of *Biometrika Tables* for $m = 1\ (1)\ 10,\ 12,\ 15,\ 20,\ 24,\ 30,\ 40,\ 60,\ 120$ and
$n = 1\ (1)\ 30, 40, 60, 120, \infty$.

If X follows the beta distribution with m and n degrees of freedom, then
the random variable

$$(4.4.5) \qquad\qquad Y = \frac{n}{m}\frac{X}{1 - X}$$

follows the variance-ratio (F) distribution with m and n degrees of freedom.

4.5 MIXTURE OF DISTRIBUTIONS

If $g_n(x)$, $n = 0, 1, 2, \ldots$, is a sequence of probability density functions
and if N is a random variable defined over the integers with probability
distribution

$$(4.5.1) \qquad\qquad \text{Prob}\ (N = n) = p_n, \qquad n = 0, 1, 2, \ldots,$$

then the probability density function

$$(4.5.2) \qquad\qquad g(x) = \mathscr{M} g_N(x) = \sum_{n=0}^{\infty} p_n g_n(x)$$

is said to be a mixture of distributions $g_n(x)$ and p_n.

Three distributions of this type arising in the theory of sampling will
now be discussed.

Non-central Chi-Square Distribution. A random variable is said to
have the non-central chi-square distribution with n degrees of freedom and
a non-centrality parameter δ^2 if its probability density function is

$$(4.5.3) \qquad \sum_{j=0}^{\infty} p(j,\ \tfrac{1}{2}\delta^2)\, f(x,\ n + 2j), \qquad 0 \le x < \infty,$$

where $p(j,\ \tfrac{1}{2}\delta^2) = e^{-\tfrac{1}{2}\delta^2}(\tfrac{1}{2}\delta^2)^j/j!$ is the Poisson probability, and $f(x, n + 2j)$
is the probability density function of the chi-square distribution with

$n + 2j$ degrees of freedom. A non-central chi-square distribution is thus a mixture of a sequence of chi-square distributions and a Poisson distribution.

Non-central Beta Distribution of Type I. A random variable is said to follow the non-central beta distribution Type I with m and n degrees of freedom and non-centrality parameter $\frac{1}{2}\delta^2$ if its probability density function is

$$(4.5.4) \qquad \sum_{j=0}^{\infty} p(j, \tfrac{1}{2}\delta^2)g(x, m + 2j, n), \qquad 0 \le x \le 1,$$

where $p(j, \frac{1}{2}\delta^2)$ is as defined above and $g(x, m + 2j, n)$ is the probability density function of the beta distribution with $m + 2j$ and n degrees of freedom. A non-central beta distribution of Type I is thus a mixture of a sequence of beta distributions and a Poisson distribution.

Non-central Beta Distribution of Type II. A random variable is said to have the non-central beta distribution of Type II with parameters $m, n, p,$ and θ if its probability density function is

$$(4.5.5) \qquad \sum_{j=0}^{\infty} y(\tfrac{1}{2}p, j, \theta)f(x, m + 2j, n), \qquad 0 \le x \le 1,$$

where

$$y(\tfrac{1}{2}p, j, \theta) = \frac{\Gamma(\tfrac{1}{2}p + j)}{j!\,\Gamma(\tfrac{1}{2}p)} \theta^{\frac{1}{2}p}(1 - \theta)^j$$

is the negative binomial probability distribution, θ is a parameter with a range of values between 0 and 1, and $g(x, m + 2j, n)$ is the probability density function of the beta distribution with $m + 2j$ and n degrees of freedom.

A non-central beta distribution of Type II is thus a mixture of a sequence of beta distributions and a negative binomial distribution.

4.6 EXERCISES

Normal distribution

4.1–4.4. Fit a normal distribution to each of the frequency distributions in exercises 2.7, 2.8, 2.10(b), and 2.10(c). Compare the observed and the theoretical frequencies.

4.5. Fit a truncated normal distribution to the data in exercise 2.32.

4.6. Fit a log normal distribution to the data in exercise 2.35.

4.7. In an examination, a candidate fails if he scores less than 400, gets an ordinary passing grade if his score is between 400 and 500, and wins honors if he scores 500 or more. In one year, the percentages of failures, ordinary passes, and passes with honors were respectively 23, 62, and 15%.

Assuming normality of the distribution of scores, find the mean and the standard deviation of the scores of (a) all candidates and (b) candidates passing with honors.

4.8. From extensive optometric data, it was found that the distribution of interpupillary distance of adult males was sensibly normal with mean 64.90 mm and standard deviation 3.81 mm. A company manufacturing optical instruments plans to produce the following standard types of field glasses:

Type	A	B	C	D	E
Distance between eyepieces (mm)	54	58	62	66	70

Assuming that persons having interpupillary distance differing by not more than 2 mm from the distance between the eyepieces of a field glass have no difficulty in using it, estimate how many of each type of field glass should be manufactured in a lot of 10,000.

4.9. An industrialist finds that 20% of his manufactured articles fail to pass the specified minimum quality level. The quality characteristic is normally distributed with a coefficient of variation of 30%. The manufacturer wants to ensure that 95% of articles manufactured pass the specification level, which he can attain either by increasing the mean level of quality or by reducing the variation in the quality.

Find which way will be profitable to him if the cost in increasing the mean level by 1% is twice the cost of reducing variation by 1%.

4.10. The breaking strength of a manufactured product is normally distributed with mean 100 and standard deviation 20. Every piece manufactured is tested for a breaking strength of 75, and the articles that stand the test are put for sale.

Find the percentage of rejection and the mean and the standard deviation of the breaking strength of pieces put for sale.

4.11. Under suitable conditions a gunner from a bomber tries to hit a square target of side 250 ft with the center of the target just below the plane. The errors of the gunner along axes parallel to the sides of the target are supposed to be independent and normally distributed with the center of the target as mean and 400 ft standard deviation.

Find the probability (a) that the target will be hit at the first attempt and (b) that the target will be hit at least once in ten attempts.

4.12. A machine fixes caps on bottles by applying an average torque of 8 units with a standard deviation of 1 unit. The bottles can stand a torque of 10 units on an average with a standard deviation of 2 units.

Assuming normality and independence of the distribution, estimate the percentage of breakage.

4.13–4.14. Find the first four terms in the Gram–Charlier series expansion of each of the distributions in exercises 2.10(b) and 2.10(c), using the theoretical moments:

$$\text{Mean} = 50, \quad \text{variance} = \frac{10,000}{12n}, \quad \beta_1 = 0, \quad \text{and} \quad \beta_2 = 3 - \frac{1.2}{n},$$

where n is the size of the sample from which the means are computed.

4.15. For the Gram-Charlier type of frequency curve with only the first four terms:

$$f(x) = \frac{1}{\sqrt{2\pi}} e^{-\frac{1}{2}x^2} \left[1 + \frac{K_3}{6} (x^3 - 3x) + \frac{K_4}{24} (x^4 - 6x^2 + 3) \right],$$

$$-\infty < x < \infty$$

show that the probability integral can be expressed in the form

$$\int_{-\infty}^{x} f(t)\, dt = F(x) + K_3 F_3(x) + K_4 F_4(x)$$

and prepare a table showing the values of $F(x)$, $F_3(x)$, and $F_4(x)$ for $x = -2.0\ (0.5)\ 2.0$.

Pearsonian systems

4.16–4.25. Fit appropriate Pearsonian frequency curves to the distributions in exercises 2.10(b), 2.10(c), 2.11(a), 2.11(b), 2.11(c), 2.31 (separately for males and females), 2.33, 2.34, and 2.35.

4.26. The tth moment about the origin of a sampling distribution of statistic L_1 used to examine the equality of the variances of k normal populations on the basis of a sample of size n from each is given by

$$\mu_t' = E(L_1^t) = k^t \frac{\Gamma\left(\frac{k(n-1)}{2}\right)}{\Gamma\left(\frac{k(n-1)}{2} + t\right)} \left[\frac{\Gamma\left(\frac{n-1}{2} + \frac{t}{k}\right)}{\Gamma\left(\frac{n-1}{2}\right)} \right]^k.$$

Using the first four moments, fit an appropriate Pearsonian type of frequency curve to the sampling distribution of L_1 for the case $n = 21$, $k = 4$. Using this frequency curve, determine a value L_0 such that

$$\text{Prob}\ (L_1 \leq L_0) = 0.05.$$

4.27–4.30. Sketch the following frequency curves:

Normal: $\dfrac{1}{\sqrt{2\pi}}\,e^{-\frac{1}{2}x^2}, \quad -\infty < x < \infty.$

Gamma: $\dfrac{\alpha^{\frac{1}{2}\alpha^2}}{\Gamma(\alpha^2)}\,(x+\alpha)^{\alpha^2-1}e^{-\alpha(x+\alpha)}, \quad -\infty \le x < \infty.$

(Sketch this for $\alpha = 2.5$.)

Beta: $\dfrac{\beta}{B(p,\,q)}\,(\alpha+\beta x)^{p-1}(1-\alpha-\beta x)^{q-1}, \quad -\alpha/\beta \le x \le (1-\alpha)/\beta,$

where $\alpha = p/(p+q)$, $\beta^2 = \alpha(1-\alpha)/(p+q+1)$, $p, q > 0$.
(Sketch this for $p = 1.7$ and $q = 3.2$.)

Gram–Charlier (with first four terms only:

$$\frac{1}{2\pi}\,e^{-\frac{1}{2}x^2}\left[1 + \frac{K_3}{6}(x^3 - 3x) + \frac{K_4}{24}(x^4 - 6x^2 + 3)\right], \quad -\infty < x < \infty.$$

(Sketch this for $K_3 = 1.0$ and $K_4 = 0.5$.)

4.31. The moments about the origin of the distribution of the correlation coefficient r computed from a sample of size n from bivariate normal population in which the value of the correlation coefficient is ρ are given by

$$\mu_1' = \frac{q_n}{q_{n-1}}\left[1 + \frac{1^2}{n+1}\frac{\rho^2}{2} + \frac{1^2\cdot 3^2}{1\cdot 2(n+1)(n+3)}\frac{\rho^4}{4} + \frac{1^2\cdot 3^2\cdot 5^2}{1\cdot 2\cdot 3\cdot(n+1)(n+3)(n+5)}\frac{\rho^6}{8} + \cdots\right],$$

$$\mu_2' = 1 - \frac{q_n}{q_{n-2}}(1-\rho^2)\left[1 + \frac{2^2}{n+1}\frac{\rho^2}{2} + \frac{2^2\cdot 4^2}{1\cdot 2(n+1)(n+3)}\frac{\rho^4}{4} + \frac{2^2\cdot 4^2\cdot 6^2}{1\cdot 2\cdot 3(n+1)(n+3)(n+5)}\frac{\rho^6}{8} + \cdots\right],$$

$$\mu_3' = \mu_1' - (1-\rho^2)\frac{q_{n+2}}{q_{n-1}}\frac{n-2}{n-1} \times \left[1 + \frac{3^2}{n+3}\frac{\rho^2}{2} + \frac{3^2\cdot 5^2}{1\cdot 2\cdot(n+3)(n+5)}\frac{\rho^4}{4} + \frac{3^2\cdot 5^2\cdot 7^2}{1\cdot 2\cdot 3\cdot(n+3)(n+5)(n+7)}\frac{\rho^6}{8} + \cdots\right],$$

$$\mu_4' = 2\mu_2' - 1 + \frac{n(n-2)}{n^2-1}\left[1 + \frac{4^2}{n+3}\frac{\rho^2}{2} + \frac{4^2\cdot 6^2}{1\cdot 2\cdot(n+3)(n+5)}\frac{\rho^4}{4} + \frac{4^2\cdot 6^2\cdot 8^2}{1\cdot 2\cdot 3\cdot(n+3)(n+5)(n+7)}\frac{\rho^6}{8} + \cdots\right],$$

where
$$q_n = \int_0^{\pi/2} (\sin t)^{n-1} \, dt.$$

Fit an appropriate Pearsonian curve to the distribution of r when $n = 25$ and $\rho = 0.6$. The values of q_n for $n = 20$ to $n = 29$ are given below.

n	q_n	n	q_n
20	0.283773	25	0.253181
21	0.276770	26	0.248169
22	0.270260	27	0.243444
23	0.264189	28	0.238978
24	0.258510	29	0.234749

4.32. Table 4.5 gives the distribution of life (t) in hours of 337 electronic tubes of a certain manufacturing company. Assuming that the frequency density function of the length of life is of the exponential type: $\frac{1}{\theta} e^{-t/\theta}$, estimate the parameter θ from the given data. Compare the observed and the expected frequencies.

Find the number of electronic tubes likely to burn away within 80 hours of their life and also the average life of these tubes.

TABLE 4.5

DISTRIBUTION OF LIFE OF 337 ELECTRONIC TUBES

Life (hours)	Observed frequency
0–50	100
50–100	68
100–150	48
150–200	31
200–300	42
300–400	21
400–600	27
Total	337

Miscellaneous

4.33–4.34. The frequency density function $f_n(x)$ for the distribution of the mean of a sample of size n from a rectangular distribution is given by

$$f_n(x) = \frac{n^n}{(n-1)!}\left[x^{n-1} - \binom{n}{1}\left(x - \frac{1}{n}\right)^{n-1} + \binom{n}{2}\left(x - \frac{2}{n}\right)^{n-1} - \cdots \right]$$

for $0 < x < 1$, where the summation is continued as long as $x - (r/n)$ $(r = 0, 1, 2, \ldots)$ is positive.

Fit this curve to the data in exercises 2.10(b) and 2.10(c). Compare the observed and the expected frequencies.

4.35. The frequency density function $f_n(x)$ for the distribution of the range of a sample of size n from a rectangular population in the interval $(0,1)$ is given by

$$f_n(x) = n(n-1)x^{n-2}(1-x) \quad \text{for} \quad 0 < x < 1.$$

Fit this curve to the data in exercise 2.11 and compare the observed and the expected frequencies.

4.36. Pareto found that in many countries, for persons having income above a certain level, the distribution of income is characterized by the law: $\log P = \alpha - \gamma \log I$, where P is the proportion of persons having income above I, and α and γ are parameters. The constant γ is known as Pareto's constant, and Pareto's computations gave $\gamma = 1.5$ approximately in most cases.

TABLE 4.6

STATISTICS OF INDIVIDUAL SALARIES ASSESSED, 1955

Annual salary (rupees)	Frequency	Annual salary (rupees)	Frequency
Below 4,200	16,361	40,001–55,000	1,178
4,201–5,000	43,498	55,001–70,000	312
5,001–8,400	60,032	70,001–85,000	127
8,401–10,000	19,835	85,001–100,000	60
10,001–15,000	17,583	100,001–150,000	89
15,001–25,000	8,550	150,001–200,000	34
25,001–40,000	3,779	200,001 and above	12

Table 4.6 gives the frequency distribution of annual salaries of individuals in rupees obtained from *Indian Income Tax Returns* (1955). (1 U.S. dollar = 7.50 Indian rupees approximately.)

Plot the data, using a suitable scale, and find out whether Pareto's law will give an adequate fit over the entire range of the observed distribution. If not, try to fit the law in a suitable range.

CHAPTER 5

Bivariate Data:
Regression and Correlation

5.1 BIVARIATE DISTRIBUTION

Sometimes statistical data consist of observations on two different characteristics of each individual in a population. Consider, for example, the stature and weight of each person in a group, or the temperature and humidity on each day of a month. If the two variables are denoted by X and Y, the cumulative distribution function $F(x, y)$ is the relative frequency of individuals in the population with $X \leq x$ and $Y \leq y$.

If both variables take discrete values, X taking the discrete values x and Y taking the discrete values y with relative frequencies to be denoted by $f(x, y)$, then

$$(5.1.1) \qquad F(x, y) = \sum_{t \leq x} \sum_{u \leq y} f(t, u).$$

On the other hand, the cumulative distribution is said to be continuous if $F(x, y)$ is continuous everywhere and if the joint frequency density function defined by

$$(5.1.2) \qquad f(x, y) = \frac{\partial^2 F(x, y)}{\partial x \, \partial y}$$

exists and is continuous (almost) everywhere. We then have

$$F(x, y) = \int_{-\infty}^{x} \int_{-\infty}^{y} f(t, u) \, dt \, du.$$

Marginal and Conditional Distribution. In the discrete case, the relative frequency $f_1(x)$ of individuals with X taking a specified value x, no matter what value Y takes, is given by

$$(5.1.3) \qquad f_1(x) = \sum_{y} f(x, y),$$

the summation being over all values of y. This is called the *marginal distribution* of X. In the continuous case, the marginal frequency density function $f_1(x)$ of X is similarly defined by

$$(5.1.4) \qquad f_1(x) = \int_{-\infty}^{\infty} f(x, y)\, dy.$$

If $f_1(x)$ is positive, the *conditional frequency distribution*, or *density function*, in the continuous case, of Y, given that X has the value x, is defined by

$$(5.1.5) \qquad g_2(y \mid x) = \frac{f(x, y)}{f_1(x)}.$$

The marginal distribution (or density) $f_2(y)$ of Y and the conditional distribution (or density) $g_1(x \mid y)$ of X, given that $Y = y$, are similarly defined.

The variable Y is said to be *statistically independent* of the random variable X if the conditional distribution of Y for a given value x of X does not involve x. Statistical independence is a symmetric relationship: if Y is statistically independent of X, then X is also statistically independent of Y. A necessary and sufficient condition for statistical independence of X and Y is that

$$(5.1.6) \qquad f(x, y) = f_1(x) \cdot f_2(y)$$

for all x and y.

Regression and Correlation.   If $h(x, y)$ is a given function of x and y, the arithmetic mean of the variable $h(X, Y)$ is defined by

$$\mathscr{M}[h(X, Y)] = \sum_x \sum_y h(x, y) f(x, y)$$

in the discrete case, the summation being over all values of x and y. Summing first over all values of y for a fixed value of x, we have

$$(5.1.7) \qquad \mathscr{M}[h(X, Y)] = \sum_x h^*(x) f_1(x) = \mathscr{M} h^*(X),$$

where $h^*(x) = \sum_y h(x, y) g_2(y \mid x)$ is called the *conditional mean* of $h(X, Y)$, given that $X = x$. We shall denote this conditional mean by

$$h^*(x) = \mathscr{M}[h(X, Y) \mid X = x].$$

In the continuous case, the arithmetic mean is given by

$$(5.1.8) \qquad \mathscr{M} h(X, Y) = \int_{-\infty}^{\infty} \int_{-\infty}^{\infty} h(x, y) f(x, y)\, dx\, dy$$

$$= \int_{-\infty}^{\infty} h^*(x) f_1(x)\, dx = \mathscr{M} h^*(X),$$

where $h^*(x)$, the conditional mean of $h(X, Y)$, given that $X = x$, is obtained from

$$h^*(x) = \mathscr{M}[h(X, Y) \mid X = x] = \int_{-\infty}^{\infty} h(x, y)\, g_2(y \mid x)\, dy.$$

In particular, the conditional mean of Y, given that $X = x$,

(5.1.9) $$\mu(x) = \mathscr{M}(Y \mid X = x),$$

regarded as a function of x, is called the *regression function* of Y on X.

The variance of the conditional distribution of Y for a fixed value x of X is given by

(5.1.10) $$V(Y \mid X = x) = \mathscr{M}[(Y - \mu(x))^2 \mid X = x],$$

and if this is free of x, the conditional distribution of Y is said to be *homoscedastic*. The arithmetic mean of the conditional variance is called the *residual variance of* y.

The *bivariate moments* about the origin are defined by

(5.1.11) $$\mu_{rs}' = \mathscr{M}(X^r Y^s), \qquad r, s = 1, 2, \ldots,$$

and the central moments about the respective means by

(5.1.12) $$\mu_{rs} = \mathscr{M}[(X - \mu_{10}')^r (Y - \mu_{01}')^s], \qquad r, s = 1, 2, \ldots.$$

In particular, μ_{11} is called the *covariance* of X and Y, and

(5.1.13) $$\rho = \frac{\mu_{11}}{\sqrt{\mu_{20}\mu_{02}}}$$

is called the *product moment coefficient of correlation* between X and Y. The coefficient ρ always lies between -1 and $+1$. A measure of the strength of dependence of Y on X is the *correlation ratio* η, defined by

(5.1.14) $$\eta^2 = \frac{V[\mu(X)]}{V(Y)} = 1 - \frac{\mathscr{M}V(Y \mid X)}{V(Y)},$$

where $\mu(x)$ is the regression function of Y on X.

5.2 LEAST-SQUARES APPROXIMATION TO REGRESSION FUNCTIONS

Linear Approximation. Sometimes it is convenient to approximate the regression function $\mu(x)$ by means of a linear function $\phi(x) = \alpha + \beta x$, the coefficients α and β being chosen to minimize $L = \mathscr{M}[\mu(X) - \phi(X)]^2$. This gives

(5.2.1) $$\alpha = \mu_{01}' - \beta\mu_{10}'; \qquad \beta = \frac{\mu_{11}}{\mu_{20}},$$

and β is then called the *coefficient of* (linear) *regression* of Y on X. The *residual mean square* of Y about $\phi(X)$ is

$$\mathcal{M}[Y - \phi(X)]^2 = (1 - \rho^2)V(Y).$$

Illustrative Example 5.1. Table 5.1 gives, for each of 40 jute plants, the weight in decagrams of the plant x and the weight of the fiber extracted from the plant y. The problem is to build up a formula for predicting y on the basis of x.

TABLE 5.1

WEIGHT OF PLANT AND OF FIBER OF 40 JUTE PLANTS

Weight (decagm) of		Weight (decagm) of		Weight (decagm) of		Weight (decagm) of	
plant	fiber	plant	fiber	plant	fiber	plant	fiber
x	y	x	y	x	y	x	y
93	6.8	51	3.8	46	3.3	37	2.8
89	6.3	87	6.0	35	2.7	36	2.3
112	7.0	81	6.4	30	2.1	47	3.5
8	0.6	47	3.0	8	0.5	33	2.5
93	6.5	54	3.9	23	1.4	102	7.0
11	0.7	48	3.4	33	2.7	17	1.3
16	0.7	33	4.1	18	1.7	59	4.5
32	2.9	68	5.1	70	5.3	87	6.0
31	2.7	106	7.0	87	6.2	62	4.2
37	3.0	56	4.4	74	11.5	54	3.9

Here we have $\Sigma x = 2111$, $\Sigma y = 159.7$, $\Sigma x^2 = 144{,}461$, $\Sigma y^2 = 846.75$, $\Sigma xy = 10{,}766.9$, and the number of observations, n, is 40. Hence we obtain the following means and corrected sums of squares and products:

$$\mu_{10}' = \bar{x} = \Sigma x/n = 52.775, \quad \mu_{01}' = \bar{y} = \Sigma y/n = 3.9925,$$

$$n\mu_{20} = S_{xx} = \Sigma x^2 - (\Sigma x)^2/n = 33{,}052.975,$$

$$n\mu_{02} = S_{yy} = \Sigma y^2 - (\Sigma y)^2/n = 209.148,$$

$$n\mu_{11} = S_{xy} = \Sigma xy - (\Sigma x)(\Sigma y)/n = 2338.733.$$

The best linear formula for predicting y on the basis of x is $y = a + bx$, where

$$b = S_{xy}/S_{xx} = 0.070757,$$

$$a = \bar{y} - b\bar{x} = 0.25830.$$

The product-moment coefficient of correlation is

$$r = \frac{S_{xy}}{\sqrt{S_{xx}S_{yy}}} = 0.8895.$$

The residual sum of squares about the straight line is

$$\Sigma y^2 - a\Sigma y - b\Sigma xy = S_{yy} - bS_{xy} = 43.666.$$

Polynomial Approximation. In general, the regression function $\mu(x)$ may be approximated by a polynomial

(5.2.2) $$\phi(x) = \beta_0 + \beta_1 x + \beta_2 x^2 + \cdots + \beta_m x^m$$

of the mth degree in x, the coefficients $\beta_0, \beta_1, \ldots, \beta_m$ being chosen so as to minimize $L = E[\mu(X) - \phi(X)]^2$, the average squared deviation of $\phi(x)$ from $\mu(x)$. The coefficients thus are obtained by solving the linear equations

(5.2.3) $\mu_{r1}' = \beta_0\mu_{r0}' + \beta_1\mu_{r+1,0}' + \cdots + \beta_m\mu_{r+m,0}',$ $r = 0, 1, 2, \ldots, m.$

The mth degree correlation coefficient ρ_m of Y on X is then defined as the positive square root of

(5.2.4)

$$\rho_m{}^2 = \frac{V[\phi(X)]}{V(Y)}$$

$$= \frac{\sum\limits_{t=0}^{m} \beta_t\mu_{t1}'}{V(Y)}.$$

In particular, $\rho_1 = |\rho|$, and

(5.2.5) $$1 \geq \eta^2 \geq \cdots \geq \rho_{m+1}^2 \geq \rho_m{}^2 \geq \cdots \geq \rho_1{}^2$$

holds. A necessary and sufficient condition that the regression function $\mu(x)$ of Y on X is a polynomial of the mth degree in x is that m is the smallest integer for which $\rho_m{}^2 = \eta^2$ holds.

Orthogonal Polynomials. Fitting of polynomial regression functions is facilitated through the use of orthogonal polynomials. An mth-degree regression function of Y on X can be written in the form

(5.2.6) $$\phi(x) = \alpha_0 + \alpha_1\phi_1(x) + \alpha_2\phi_2(x) + \cdots + \alpha_m\phi_m(x),$$

where $\phi_t(x)$'s are mutually orthogonal polynomials, $\phi_t(x)$ being of degree t in x, and

(5.2.7) $$\mathcal{M}[\phi_t(X)\phi_u(X)] = 0 \quad \text{for} \quad t \neq u.$$

Then

(5.2.8) $$\alpha_t = \frac{\mathcal{M}[Y\phi_t(X)]}{\mathcal{M}[\phi_t(X)]^2},$$

and the residual mean square is given by

(5.2.9) $$\mathcal{M}[Y - \phi(X)]^2 = V(Y) - \sum_{t=1}^{m}\alpha_t\mathcal{M}[Y\phi_t(X)].$$

If x takes N equidistant values $x_i = x_0 + hi$, $i = 1, 2, \ldots, N$ with equal frequencies, the algebraic expressions for $\phi_t(x)$ for $t = 1, 2, \ldots, 6$ and $N = 3 \ (1) \ 52$, as well as the numerical values of $\phi_t(x_i)$ and $\sum_{i=1}^{N} [\phi_t(x_i)]^2$, can be obtained from Table 47 of *Biometrika Tables*. See Chapter 7 for details.

Illustrative Example 5.2.   In continuation of illustrative example 5.1, let us examine whether, by using a quadratic formula, the efficiency of prediction is increased.   From Table 5.1, we get $n = 40$, $\Sigma x = 2111$, $\Sigma y = 159.7$, $\Sigma x^2 = 144{,}461$, $\Sigma y^2 = 846.75$, $\Sigma xy = 10{,}766.9$, $\Sigma x^2 y = 837{,}717.7$, $\Sigma x^3 = 11{,}440{,}487$, $\Sigma x^4 = 987{,}598{,}205$.

Writing the prediction equation as

$$\phi(x) = b_0 + b_1 x + b_2 x^2,$$

the b's are then obtained from equations 5.2.3, which may be written as

$$\Sigma y x^j = b_0 \Sigma x^j + b_1 \Sigma x^{j+1} + b_2 \Sigma x^{j+2}, \qquad j = 0, 1, 2.$$

This gives:

$$159.7 = \qquad 40 b_0 + \qquad 2{,}111 b_1 + \qquad 144{,}461 b_2,$$
$$10{,}766.9 = \quad 2{,}111 b_0 + \qquad 144{,}461 b_1 + \quad 11{,}440{,}487 b_2,$$
$$837{,}717.7 = 144{,}461 b_0 + 11{,}440{,}487 b_1 + 987{,}598{,}205 b_2.$$

Solving these equations by methods described in Chapter 5 of Part I, we have

$$b_0 = -0.637813, \quad b_1 = 0.112441, \quad b_2 = -0.000361.$$

The residual sum of squares about the second-degree parabola is

$$\Sigma y^2 - b_0 \Sigma y - b_1 \Sigma xy - b_2 \Sigma x^2 y = 40.384.$$

The reduction in the residual sum of squares by fitting a second-degree parabola instead of a straight line (illustrative example 5.1) is not great. The second-degree coefficient of correlation r_2 is given by

$$r_2^2 = \frac{b_0 \Sigma y + b_1 \Sigma xy + b_2 \Sigma x^2 y}{\Sigma y^2 - (1/n)(\Sigma y)^2} = 0.80691,$$

so that $r_2 = 0.8983$, which is slightly larger than the value of the coefficient of correlation ($r = 0.8895$) obtained in illustrative example 5.1.

5.3   COMPUTATION OF REGRESSION AND CORRELATION FROM A BIVARIATE FREQUENCY TABLE

Bivariate data are usually condensed into what are known as bivariate frequency tables or correlation tables. The range of each variate is divided into a number of class intervals, and the frequency f_{ij} in the cell determined by the ith class interval of the first variate and the jth class interval of the second variate is obtained. For each variate, it is convenient to have class intervals of equal width. Choice of class limits and number of class intervals are based on considerations like those for univariate data.

The method of computation of the regression function, correlation coefficient, correlation ratio, etc., from a bivariate frequency table is illustrated below. Consider a bivariate frequency table with p classes for the first variate X and q classes for the second variate Y. Let f_{ij} denote the frequency in the (i, j)th cell, that is, the number of observations with X lying between $x_i \pm \frac{1}{2}h$ and Y lying between $y_j \pm \frac{1}{2}k$. Thus x_i is the midpoint or class mark for the ith class interval for X, and y_j that for the jth class interval for Y; h is the uniform width of the class intervals for X, and k that for Y. A transformation $u_i = (x_i - x_0)/h$ and $v_j = (y_j - y_0)/k$ with properly chosen values of x_0 and y_0 is first made. We then compute (see illustrative example 5.3 for a layout of the computation) the following:

Marginal
frequencies: $\qquad f_{i0} = \sum_j f_{ij}, \qquad f_{0j} = \sum_i f_{ij}.$

Sums: $\qquad T_u = \sum_i u_i f_{i0}, \qquad T_v = \sum_j v_j f_{0j}.$

Sums of
squares: $\qquad T_{uu} = \sum_i u_i^2 f_{i0}, \qquad T_{vv} = \sum_j v_j^2 f_{0j}.$

Row and
column sums: $\qquad V_i = \sum_j v_j f_{ij}, \qquad U_j = \sum_i u_i f_{ij}.$

Check: $\qquad T_v = \sum_i V_i, \qquad T_u = \sum_j U_j.$

Sum of
products: $\qquad T_{uv} = \sum_i u_i V_i = \sum_j v_j U_j.$

Writing N for the total frequency, $N = \sum_i \sum_j f_{ij}$, we next compute

$$\bar{u} = T_u/N, \qquad \bar{v} = T_v/N,$$

$$S_{uu} = T_{uu} - T_u^2/N, \qquad S_{uv} = T_{uv} - T_u T_v/N, \qquad S_{vv} = T_{vv} - T_v^2/N.$$

Then means, variances, and covariance of X and Y are given by

Means: $\qquad \bar{X} = x_0 + h\bar{u}, \qquad \bar{Y} = y_0 + k\bar{v}.$

Variances
and covariance: $\quad s_{XX} = h^2 S_{uu}/N, \qquad s_{XY} = hk S_{uv}/N,$

$$s_{YY} = k^2 S_{vv}/N.$$

The least-squares linear regression function of Y on X is $a + bX$, where

$$b = \frac{(k/h)S_{uv}}{S_{uu}} \quad \text{and} \quad a = \bar{Y} - b\bar{X}.$$

The product-moment coefficient of correlation r is given by

$$r = \frac{S_{uv}}{\sqrt{S_{uu}S_{vv}}}.$$

The correlation ratio η of Y on X is given by

$$\eta^2 = \frac{\sum_i (V_i^2/f_{i0}) - T_v^2/N}{S_{vv}}.$$

Polynomial regression functions can also be computed in a similar manner.

Illustrative Example 5.3. Table 5.2 gives the frequency distribution of yield y of dry bark in ounces and the age x in years of 157 *Cinchona* plants. Obtain the least-squares linear regression equation of y on x, the coefficient of correlation, and the correlation ratio of y on x.

TABLE 5.2

AGE AND YIELD OF DRY BARK OF *Cinchona* PLANTS

Age (years) x	Yield (ounces) y					
	4–7	8–11	12–15	16–19	20–23	24–27
3–4	2					
5–6	3	6	6	1		
7–8	3	7	10	5		
9–10		8	15	10	10	
11–12			12	19	15	5
13–14			2	4	10	4

The computations required for this problem are shown in Table 5.3 and below the table.

Here

$$u = \frac{x - x_0}{h}, \qquad v = \frac{y - y_0}{k},$$

TABLE 5.3
Computation of Regression and Correlation

x	u	$y=$ 5.5	9.5	13.5	17.5	21.5	25.5	f_{i0}	$u_i f_{i0}$	$u_i^2 f_{i0}$	$V_i = \sum_j v_j f_{ij}$	$u_i V_i$	V_i^2/f_{i0}
	$v=$	-2	-1	0	1	2	3						
3.5	-2	2						2	-4	8	-4	8	8.0000
5.5	-1	3	6	6	1			16	-16	16	11	11	7.5625
7.5	0	3	7	10	5			25	0	0	-8	0	2.5600
9.5	1		8	15	10	10		43	43	43	22	22	11.2558
11.5	2			12	19	15	5	51	102	204	64	128	80.3137
13.5	3			2	4	10	4	20	60	180	36	108	64.8000
f_{0j}		8	21	45	39	35	9	157	185	451	99	277	174.4920
$v_j f_{0j}$		-16	-21	0	39	70	27	99					
$V_j^2 f_{0j}$		32	21	0	39	140	81	313					
$U_j = \sum_i u_i f_{ij}$		-7	2	39	59	70	22	185					
$U_j v_j$		14	-2	0	59	140	66	277					

Checks

where $x_0 = 7.5$, $h = 2$, $y_0 = 13.5$, and $k = 4$. From Table 5.3 we get
$N = 157$, $T_u = 185$, $T_v = 99$, $T_{uu} = 451$, $T_{uv} = 277$, $T_{vv} = 313$, so that

$$\bar{u} = T_u/N = 1.1783, \qquad \bar{v} = T_v/N = 0.6306,$$

$$S_{uu} = T_{uu} - T_u^2/N = 233.0145, \qquad S_{uv} = T_uT_v/N = 160.3483,$$

$$S_{vv} = T_{vv} - T_v^2/N = 250.5706.$$

Then

$$\bar{x} = x_0 + h\bar{u} = 9.8566, \qquad \bar{y} = y_0 + k\bar{v} = 16.0224,$$

$$b = \frac{(k/h)S_{uv}}{S_{uu}} = 1.3762, \qquad a = \bar{y} - b\bar{x} = 2.4576.$$

The least-squares linear regression equation of y on x is thus

$$2.4576 + 1.3762x.$$

The coefficient of correlation r between y and x is

$$r = \frac{S_{uv}}{\sqrt{S_{uu}S_{vv}}} = 0.6636.$$

The correlation ratio η of y on x is given by

$$\eta^2 = \frac{\sum (V_i^2/f_{i0}) - T_v^2/N}{S_{vv}} = 0.44723,$$

so that $\eta = 0.6687$.

5.4 BIVARIATE NORMAL DISTRIBUTION

Two variables X and Y are said to have the bivariate normal distribution
if their joint frequency density function is

$$(5.4.1) \qquad\qquad f(x, y) = ce^{-\frac{1}{2}Q},$$

where $1/c = 2\pi\sigma_1\sigma_2\sqrt{1 - \rho^2}$, and

$$Q = \frac{1}{1 - \rho^2}\left[\left(\frac{x - \mu_1}{\sigma_1}\right)^2 - 2\rho\left(\frac{x - \mu_1}{\sigma_1}\right)\left(\frac{y - \mu_2}{\sigma_2}\right) + \left(\frac{y - \mu_2}{\sigma_2}\right)^2\right],$$

where μ_1, μ_2, σ_1, σ_2, and ρ are parameters, $-\infty < \mu_1, \mu_2 < \infty$, $0 < \sigma_1$, $\sigma_2 < \infty$, $-1 < \rho < 1$. Here $\mathcal{M}(X) = \mu_1$, $\mathcal{M}(Y) = \mu_2$, $V(X) = \sigma_1^2$, $V(Y) = \sigma_2^2$, and the product-moment coefficient of correlation between X and Y is ρ. The random variables X and Y are statistically independent if and only if $\rho = 0$.

The marginal distribution of each of the random variables is normal, and the conditional distribution of Y, given that $X = x$, is normal with conditional expectation

(5.4.2) $$\mathcal{M}(Y \mid X = x) = \alpha + \beta x$$

and conditional variance

(5.4.3) $$V(Y \mid X = x) = \sigma_2{}^2(1 - \rho^2),$$

where $\alpha = \mu_2 - \beta\mu_1$ and $\beta = \rho\sigma_2/\sigma_1$. The regression is thus linear, and the conditional distributions are homoscedastic. Similarly, the conditional distribution of X, given that $Y = y$, is also normal and homoscedastic and the regression is linear.

In general, for any two fixed numbers l and m, the linear function $Z = lX + mY$ is distributed normally with

(5.4.4) $$\mathcal{M}(Z) = l\mu_1 + m\mu_2; \qquad V(Z) = l^2\sigma_1{}^2 + m^2\sigma_2{}^2 + 2ml\rho\sigma_1\sigma_2.$$

The joint cumulative distribution function is given by

(5.4.5) $$\text{Prob}\,(X < x,\, Y \le y) = \psi\left(\frac{\mu_1 - x}{\sigma_1},\, \frac{\mu_2 - y}{\sigma_2},\, \rho\right).$$

Here

(5.4.6) $$\psi(x, y, \rho) = \int_x^\infty \int_y^\infty \varphi(t, u, \rho)\, dt\, du,$$

where

$$\varphi(x, y, \rho) = \frac{1}{2\pi\sqrt{1 - \rho^2}} \exp\left[-\frac{1}{2(1 - \rho^2)}(x^2 + y^2 - 2\rho xy)\right]$$

is the joint frequency density function of a bivariate normal distribution when each of the two random variables is standardized to mean zero and variance unity. It can be shown that

(5.4.7) $$\psi(x, y, \rho) = \alpha(x)\alpha(y) + \phi(x)\phi(y) \sum_{m=0}^{\infty} \frac{\rho^{m+1}}{(m+1)!} H_m(x)H_m(y),$$

where $\phi(x) = (1/\sqrt{2\pi})e^{-\frac{1}{2}x^2}$ is the standard normal density, $\alpha(x) = \int_x^\infty \phi(t)\, dt$ is the normal probability integral, and $H_m(x)$ is the Tchebycheff–Hermite polynomial of degree m as defined by 4.2.16.

Defining tetrachoric functions by

(5.4.8) $$\tau_0(x) = \alpha(x); \qquad \tau_m(x) = \frac{1}{\sqrt{m!}} H_{m-1}(x)\phi(x), \qquad m = 1, 2, \ldots,$$

we obtain

(5.4.9) $$\psi(x, y, \rho) = \sum_{m=0}^{\infty} \rho^m \cdot \tau_m(x)\tau_m(y).$$

Short tables of $\psi(x, y, \rho)$ and $\tau_m(x)$ are available in *Tables for Statisticians and Biometricians*, Part II, edited by K. Pearson. In particular,

(5.4.10) $$\psi(0, 0, \rho) = \frac{1}{4} + \frac{1}{2\pi} \sin^{-1} \rho.$$

5.5   OTHER MEASURES OF CORRELATION

A few other measures of correlation which are useful when quantitative measurements are not available on all the individuals, or if available are not reliable, will now be described.

Rank Correlation. If n individuals are ranked with respect to two characters and there is no tie, then the following measures of correlation are available.

SPEARMAN'S COEFFICIENT OF RANK CORRELATION.

(5.5.1) $$\rho = 1 - \frac{6 \sum d_i^2}{n(n-1)},$$

where d_i = the difference in the ranks of the ith individual with respect to the two characters. This is simply the product-moment coefficient of correlation between the ranks.

KENDALL'S COEFFICIENT OF RANK CORRELATION.

(5.5.2) $$\tau = \frac{4P}{n(n-1)} - 1,$$

where $P = r_1 + r_2 + \cdots + r_n$, and r_i is the number of persons having greater rank in both the characters than the ith individual.

COEFFICIENT OF CONCORDANCE.   This is a measure of agreement of m judges in ranking n individuals and is given by

(5.5.3) $$W = \frac{12S}{m^2 n(n^2 - 1)},$$

where $S = \Sigma T_i^2 - \frac{1}{4}nm^2(n+1)^2$, T_i being the total of the ranks awarded to the ith individual by all the judges, there being no tie.

Point-Biserial Correlation. The product-moment correlation coefficient between two variates one of which takes only two values is called point-biserial correlation.

Tetrachoric Correlation. Consider the frequencies in four cells obtained by dichotomizing two variates X, Y following a bivariate normal distribution with the coefficient of correlation ρ, as shown in the table below:

X Y	$X \le L$	$X > L$	Total
$Y > M$	a	b	$a + b$
$Y \le M$	c	d	$c + d$
Total	$a + c$	$b + d$	$N = a + b + c + d$

To estimate ρ from such a table, determine h and k from the equations:

$$\Phi(h) = \frac{a + c}{N} ; \qquad \Phi(k) = \frac{c + d}{N} ,$$

where

$$\Phi(x) = \int_{-\infty}^{x} \frac{1}{\sqrt{2\pi}} e^{-\frac{1}{2}t^2} dt$$

Then solve for ρ the equation

$$(5.5.4) \qquad \frac{b}{N} = \sum_{m=0}^{\infty} \tau_m(h)\tau_m(k)\rho^m,$$

where $\tau_m(x)$ is a tetrachoric function defined by 5.4.8.

Grade Correlation. The grade of an individual A with respect to a characteristic X is defined as the proportion of individuals in the population with characteristic values not exceeding that of A. If ξ and η are the grades of an individual with respect to the characteristics X and Y, the product-moment coefficient of correlation between ξ and η is called the grade correlation. It is denoted by ρ_g. If X, Y have a bivariate normal distribution with the coefficient of correlation ρ, then

$$(5.5.5) \qquad \rho_g = \frac{6}{\pi} \sin^{-1}\left(\frac{\rho}{2}\right).$$

Illustrative Example 5.4. Eight students were ranked with respect to ntellectual ability by two teachers A and B as given below (arranged in order of ranks given by A):

A	1	2	3	4	5	6	7	8
B	3	1	6	2	7	5	4	8

To measure to what extent the teachers agree, we compute Spearman's rank correlation coefficient as follows. The rank differences $d\,(= A - B)$ are -2, 1, -3, 2, -2, 1, 3, 0 so that $\Sigma\, d^2 = 32$. Here $n = 8$, and from 5.5.1 we obtain $\rho = 0.619$.

Alternatively we may compute Kendall's rank correlation coefficient. In the B series we have five higher ranks following 3, six higher ranks following 1, two higher ranks following 6, and so on. Thus $P = r_1 + r_2 + \cdots + \cdots + r_8 = 5 + 6 + 2 + 4 + 1 + 1 + 1 + 0 = 20$. Then from 5.5.2 we find $\tau = 0.429$.

5.6 EXERCISES

Preparation of bivariate frequency tables

5.1. A person Z was asked to draw 100 straight lines each 2 in. in length with an ungraduated straightedge. The lines drawn were then measured to the nearest $\frac{1}{40}$ mm independently by two other persons X and Y. The results in centimeters are given in Table 5.4.

Denote by x and y the lengths of a line as measured by X and Y, respectively. Plot the points (x, y). This is called a *scatter diagram.*

Prepare a bivariate frequency table in about 10 × 10 classes.

5.2. Table 5.5 gives the bivariate frequency distribution of the stature in inches of father and son, in 17 × 20 classes. If an observation coincided with class limits common to a number of cells, equal fractional frequencies adding to unity were allocated to each one of these cells. This explains the occurrence of fractional frequencies in the table.

Prepare a condensed bivariate frequency table, using about one fourth as many cells.

5.3. Table 5.6 gives the age in years, the stature in centimeters, and the weight in pounds of a number of male persons of the caste Kāyastha of the district of Dacca in East Pakistan.

Plot scatter diagrams and prepare bivariate frequency tables separately for the three pairs of variates (age × stature, age × weight, stature × weight).

5.4–5.6. For each of the bivariate frequency distributions obtained in exercises 5.1–5.3, (a) draw the histograms for all the marginal and conditional frequency distributions and examine whether they are similar in shape, (b) compute the means of each of the conditional distributions and draw the regression curves, and (c) compute the variances of each of the conditional distributions and examine whether the distributions are homoscedastic.

Regression and correlation from ungrouped data

5.7–5.8. For the data given in the tables, (a) draw the scatter diagram, (b) fit the regression line of Y on X, (c) compute the coefficient of correlation, and (d) compute the residual sum of squares of Y.

5.7. Table 5.7 gives the abrasion loss and the hardness of 30 specimens of synthetic rubber.

TABLE 5.4

LENGTHS OF 200 LINES MEASURED BY TWO PERSONS

Length (cm) as measured by		Length (cm) as measured by		Length (cm) as measured by		Length (cm) as measured by	
X	Y	X	Y	X	Y	X	Y
5.425	5.450	4.950	4.950	5.350	5.275	4.725	4.700
4.850	4.800	4.800	4.850	4.950	4.925	5.250	5.250
5.225	5.200	5.500	5.445	5.600	5.625	5.075	5.050
5.375	5.350	5.500	5.500	4.550	4.550	4.150	4.200
5.350	5.450	4.925	4.875	4.550	4.650	5.200	5.150
4.900	4.900	4.850	4.950	4.325	5.275	4.250	4.200
5.175	5.150	4.550	4.525	4.500	4.475	5.200	5.175
4.925	4.950	5.725	5.725	4.375	4.850	4.475	4.450
5.625	5.600	4.875	4.850	4.700	4.700	5.000	5.025
5.325	5.250	4.625	4.675	5.350	5.375	5.025	5.000
4.900	4.950	5.025	5.050	5.000	5.025	4.225	4.750
5.375	5.350	4.850	4.850	4.700	4.650	5.425	5.425
4.450	4.450	4.925	4.800	4.575	4.600	4.250	4.200
4.925	4.900	4.350	4.475	5.150	5.175	4.700	4.750
4.500	4.550	4.600	4.650	4.675	4.725	4.375	4.400
4.975	4.900	5.000	5.000	5.200	5.250	4.325	4.350
4.750	4.750	5.725	5.725	4.900	4.875	4.825	4.825
4.850	4.850	4.650	4.675	5.125	5.175	4.400	4.450
4.675	5.200	5.325	5.425	4.450	4.475	5.150	5.125
5.550	5.550	5.275	5.250	4.875	4.850	4.825	4.800
5.450	5.500	5.350	5.325	4.125	4.250	4.950	4.875
5.195	5.150	5.100	5.125	5.325	5.450	4.650	4.675
5.350	5.325	4.800	4.775	5.175	5.150	4.775	4.750
5.450	5.450	5.300	5.300	4.575	4.550	5.125	5.150
5.225	5.225	5.225	5.225	4.900	4.900	5.375	5.650

TABLE 5.5

Frequency Distribution of Statures of Fathers and Sons

Stature of son	Stature of father																	Total
	58.5–59.5	59.5–60.5	60.5–61.5	61.5–62.5	62.5–63.5	63.5–64.5	64.5–65.5	65.5–66.5	66.5–67.5	67.5–68.5	68.5–69.5	69.5–70.5	70.5–71.5	71.5–72.5	72.5–73.5	73.5–74.5	74.5–75.5	
59.5–60.5	⋮	⋮	⋮	⋮	0.50	0.50	1	⋮	⋮	⋮	⋮	⋮	⋮	⋮	⋮	⋮	⋮	2.0
60.5–61.5	⋮	⋮	⋮	⋮	0.50	0.50	⋮	0.25	0.50	1.25	⋮	⋮	⋮	⋮	⋮	⋮	⋮	1.5
61.5–62.5	⋮	0.25	0.25	⋮	⋮	1	0.25	0.25	2.75	1.25	⋮	⋮	⋮	⋮	⋮	⋮	⋮	3.5
62.5–63.5	⋮	0.25	0.25	2.25	2	2	4	5	3	1.25	1.50	⋮	0.25	⋮	⋮	⋮	⋮	20.5
63.5–64.5	1	⋮	0.50	3.75	3	4.25	13.50	9.25	7.50	5.50	3.50	0.75	1.25	⋮	⋮	⋮	⋮	38.5
64.5–65.5	2	1	0.50	2	3.25	9.50	10	10.75	17.50	16	5.25	2.50	⋮	1	⋮	⋮	⋮	61.5
65.5–66.5	⋮	0.50	1	2.25	5.25	9.50	19.75	16.75	25.75	19.50	12.50	3.25	3.25	0.50	1	⋮	⋮	89.5
66.5–67.5	⋮	1.50	2	3.50	5.25	13.75	10.25	26.50	31.50	23.50	29.50	13.75	8.50	9.50	2.25	⋮	⋮	148.0
67.5–68.5	⋮	⋮	2	7	3.50	10	12.75	24.25	16	19.50	29	13.25	8.50	9.50	2.25	⋮	1	173.5
68.5–69.5	⋮	1	⋮	5.25	5	⋮	5.75	18.25	11.75	19	22.50	21.50	10	6.25	3.50	1.50	1	149.5
69.5–70.5	⋮	⋮	⋮	1	2.50	⋮	5	18.75	10.75	19.50	14.75	19.50	14.50	8	3.50	1	1	128.0
70.5–71.5	⋮	⋮	⋮	⋮	3.25	⋮	3	8.75	7	19	10.75	20.75	10.75	8.50	5	0.50	⋮	108.0
71.5–72.5	⋮	⋮	⋮	⋮	0.25	⋮	⋮	1.25	2.50	7.75	6.50	11.25	10	6.25	2.75	0.50	0.50	63.0
72.5–73.5	⋮	⋮	⋮	⋮	⋮	1	0.75	0.75	⋮	7.50	6.50	6	7.50	3.25	3.25	0.50	2	42.0
73.5–74.5	⋮	⋮	⋮	⋮	⋮	⋮	1.50	1.50	⋮	5.25	2.25	2.50	6.50	3.25	3.25	⋮	⋮	29.0
74.5–75.5	⋮	⋮	⋮	⋮	⋮	⋮	⋮	⋮	⋮	1	2	⋮	2.50	0.75	1.75	0.50	⋮	8.5
75.5–76.5	⋮	⋮	⋮	⋮	⋮	⋮	⋮	⋮	⋮	1.25	0.25	⋮	0.50	1	⋮	⋮	⋮	4.0
76.5–77.5	⋮	⋮	⋮	⋮	⋮	⋮	⋮	⋮	⋮	1.25	0.25	1	⋮	⋮	1.50	⋮	⋮	4.0
77.5–78.5	⋮	⋮	⋮	⋮	⋮	⋮	⋮	⋮	⋮	⋮	1	1	⋮	0.25	0.75	⋮	⋮	3.0
78.5–79.5	⋮	⋮	⋮	⋮	⋮	⋮	⋮	⋮	⋮	⋮	⋮	⋮	⋮	0.25	0.25	⋮	⋮	0.5
Total	3	3.5	8	17	33.5	61.5	95.5	142	137.5	154	141.5	116	78	49	28.5	4	5.5	1078

Source: K. Pearson, *Early Statistical Papers*, Cambridge University Press, 1948.

TABLE 5.6

AGE, STATURE, AND WEIGHT OF KĀYASTHA MALES OF DACCA

Age (years)	Stature (cm)	Weight (lb)	Age (years)	Stature (cm)	Weight (lb)
11	146	83	15	149	80
12	152	76	15	150	70
13	148	70	15	169	114
13	157	82	15	159	76
13	155	88	15	160	92
13	159	92	16	158	88
13	138	58	16	160	104
13	138	58	16	170	110
13	148	74	16	152	78
13	146	70	16	150	80
13	145	62	16	144	62
13	138	62	16	145	80
13	146	70	16	163	86
14	158	106	17	155	98
14	168	88	17	172	154
14	153	78	17	156	86
14	159	76	18	164	102
14	146	68	18	166	116
14	157	80	18	168	102
14	142	64	18	168	102
14	162	98	18	153	82
14	154	82	18	155	82
14	154	80	18	172	106
14	152	70	18	145	84
14	154	88	18	158	88
15	162	95	18	164	94
15	161	98	18	173	106
15	154	98	18	170	110
15	171	105	18	156	92
15	164	100	18	170	112
15	158	94	18	172	112
15	163	108	19	160	90
15	166	92	19	160	93
15	149	80	19	154	76
15	156	84	19	169	109

TABLE 5.6 (*continued*)

Age (years)	Stature (cm)	Weight (lb)	Age (years)	Stature (cm)	Weight (lb)
19	159	115	23	159	109
19	155	88	23	161	112
19	168	116	23	166	94
19	169	100	23	162	99
19	169	92	23	166	96
19	166	92	23	166	132
20	158	79	23	155	92
20	163	91	24	165	98
20	151	102	24	164	130
20	165	114	24	163	116
20	169	131	24	179	118
20	158	102	24	172	144
20	166	96	24	168	112
20	162	92	24	163	98
20	160	112	24	163	101
21	169	108	24	155	84
21	160	88	24	159	91
21	169	98	24	154	100
22	171	102	24	160	94
22	172	92	24	162	110
22	169	124	24	159	106
22	163	84	24	167	108
22	169	116	25	170	106
22	163	126	25	158	106
22	163	127	25	158	94
22	155	82	25	160	104
22	159	90	25	174	118
22	156	98	25	159	88
22	159	100	25	157	84
23	163	86	25	150	84
23	155	96	25	166	106
23	172	124	25	166	90
23	154	91	25	160	96
23	162	94	25	172	107
23	160	107	25	168	106

TABLE 5.6 (*continued*)

Age (years)	Stature (cm)	Weight (lb)	Age (years)	Stature (cm)	Weight (lb)
25	168	114	30	165	102
25	174	118	30	174	114
25	161	90	30	161	100
26	165	120	30	154	88
26	168	116	30	154	90
26	162	94	30	161	96
26	165	94	30	178	178
26	170	106	30	164	112
26	164	110	30	161	92
26	165	108	30	164	94
26	165	106	30	147	96
26	172	100	30	173	103
27	164	86	30	156	94
27	158	122	30	173	98
27	171	128	30	146	70
27	161	90	30	161	92
27	153	76	30	161	118
28	159	104	30	169	112
28	161	98	30	158	100
28	164	114	31	168	118
28	163	106	32	167	94
28	154	88	32	154	98
28	156	98	32	174	96
28	166	96	32	168	114
28	169	131	32	173	152
28	166	106	33	154	94
28	172	116	35	158	106
28	167	94	35	153	78
28	156	102	35	169	114
28	167	115	35	157	90
28	166	116	35	157	91
28	159	89	35	166	118
29	163	98	35	163	110
29	156	112	35	164	90
30	163	102	35	162	84

TABLE 5.6 (*continued*)

Age (years)	Stature (cm)	Weight (lb)	Age (years)	Stature (cm)	Weight (lb)
35	161	102	42	172	112
35	173	141	42	168	130
35	166	128	45	158	90
37	168	104	45	167	98
38	146	78	48	163	136
38	167	90	48	170	166
38	166	120	48	164	135
39	173	162	54	161	94
40	163	110	56	159	90
40	182	208			

Source: D. N. Majumdar and C. R. Rao, Bengal anthropometric survey, 1945: a statistical study, *Sankhya*, Vol. 19.

TABLE 5.7

ABRASION LOSS AND HARDNESS OF
30 SPECIMENS OF SYNTHETIC RUBBER

Hardness X	Abrasion loss Y	Hardness X	Abrasion loss Y
45	372	68	196
55	206	75	128
61	175	83	97
66	154	88	64
71	136	59	249
71	112	71	219
81	55	80	186
86	45	82	155
53	221	89	114
60	166	51	341
64	164	59	340
68	113	65	283
79	182	74	267
81	32	81	215
56	228	86	148

Source: S. S. Wilks, *Elementary Statistical Analysis*. Princeton University Press, Princeton, 1948.

5.8. Table 5.8 gives the scores of 16 students on a psychological test X and an achievement test Y.

TABLE 5.8

SCORES OF 16 STUDENTS: X ON PSYCHOLOGICAL AND Y ON ACHIEVEMENT TEST

X	Y	X	Y
65	78	47	70
68	61	52	55
67	62	93	123
42	48	71	65
58	50	69	73
72	72	86	110
75	76	63	77
70	42	79	86

5.9. Table 5.9 gives, in rupees per month (1 U.S. dollar = 7.50 Indian rupees, approximately), the average expenditure E_f on food items for households at different levels of living and also their average expenditure E on all items. The data relate to the township of Faridabad in India for the period March–April, 1954.

Fit regression curves of the types (a) $E_f = \alpha + \beta E$ and (b) $\log E_f = \alpha + \beta \log E$, and examine graphically which gives a better fit.

TABLE 5.9

TOTAL EXPENDITURE AND EXPENDITURE ON FOOD PER MONTH

Level of monthly expenditure (rupees)	Expenditure (rupees) per month on	
	All items E	Food items E_f
8–25	20.62	16.32
26–50	39.57	29.31
51–75	63.42	47.53
76–100	87.77	62.60
101–125	110.38	70.89
126–150	137.56	84.41
151–200	173.13	102.77
201 and above	291.24	147.15

Source: Survey of Faridabad township, *Sankhya*, Vol. 15, p. 179.

5.10. The pressure p of a gas and its volume v are related by an equation of the type

$$pv^\gamma = R$$

In an experiment the pressure of the gas was kept fixed at certain levels and the corresponding volumes were observed; the results are shown in Table 5.10. Determine the values of γ and R by the method of least squares, using the logarithmic transformation $Y = \alpha + \beta X$, where $Y = \log v$, $X = \log p$, $\alpha = (\log R)/\gamma$, $\beta = -1/\gamma$.

TABLE 5.10

VOLUME v OF A GAS AT DIFFERENT PRESSURES p

p	1	2	3	4	5	6
v	1.63	0.99	0.74	0.64	0.53	0.45

5.11. In a hydrogenation experiment, castor oil and alcohol in the ratio 1:3 and a catalyst concentration of 2% of weight of oil were taken in a reaction vessel and charged with hydrogen until the pressure of 100 psi was reached. Heating was then started, and when a temperature of 70°C was attained, the sample was withdrawn from the vessel and was designated as the zero-hour sample. Subsequent samples were withdrawn at 0.5, 1.0, 1.5, 2.0, 3.0, 4.5, and 6.0 hours, respectively. The samples were freed of alcohol and catalyst and analyzed for iodine value by hundred grams of fat. Table 5.11 gives the results of the experiment.

TABLE 5.11

IODINE VALUE AT DIFFERENT HOURS

Time (hr)	0.0	0.5	1.0	1.5	2.0	3.0	4.5	6.0
Iodine value	75.9	66.9	54.4	29.3	16.9	9.1	3.6	1.3

Fit an appropriate mathematical law followed by iodine values as a function of time.

5.12. An experiment was carried out by an agricultural farm to determine the most economical dose of a certain fertilizer for cultivation of wheat. Table 5.12 shows the net profit y when a dose x (in suitable units) is used.

Fit an appropriate polynomial to describe the dependence of y on x. Determine the most economical dose (that is, the value of x for which y is a maximum) if any.

TABLE 5.12

NET PROFIT FROM DIFFERENT DOSES OF A FERTILIZER

Dose	x	0	1	2	3	4	5	6	7	8
Net profit	y	59	127	181	228	252	261	253	230	195

Regression and correlation from bivariate frequency tables

5.13–5.15. For each of the bivariate frequency tables obtained in exercises 5.1–5.3, compute (a) the two regression equations, (b) the two correlation ratios, and (c) the product-moment correlation coefficient.

5.16. Table 5.13 gives the distribution of 100 casts of steel by the percentage of iron in the form of pig iron X and the lime consumption in hundredweight per cast Y.

Obtain the linear regression equation of Y on X. Compute the coefficient of correlation and the correlation ratio of Y on X.

Estimate the lime consumption for a cast for which the percentage of iron in the form of pig iron is 35.

TABLE 5.13

FREQUENCY DISTRIBUTION OF PERCENTAGE OF
PIG IRON AND LIME CONSUMPTION

Lime consumption (cwt per case)	Pig iron (%)						
	20–24	25–29	30–34	35–39	40–44	45–49	50–54
100–124				1			
125–149		2	1	7	1		
150–174	1	1	6	6	1	2	2
175–199			6	12	3	6	5
200–224				3	8	11	3
225–249			1	1	2	3	1
250–274						1	1
275–299				1			
300–324						1	

Source: L. J. Tippett, *Technological Applications of Statistics*, John Wiley and Sons, 1950.

5.17. Table 5.14 gives the distribution of the length in centimeters X and the weight of dry fiber in grams Y of 350 jute plants.

Obtain an appropriate formula for predicting Y on the basis of X. Find the coefficient of correlation and also the correlation ratio of Y on X.

5.18. For the bivariate frequency distributions obtained in exercise 5.3, (a) draw the two regression lines for stature on age and for weight on age and determine at what age, if at all, growth stops in respect of stature and weight; (b) compute the means, variance, and covariance between stature

TABLE 5.14

LENGTH OF PLANT AND WEIGHT OF DRY FIBER OF 350 JUTE PLANTS

Length (cm)

Weight (gm)	106.5– 112.5	112.5– 118.5	118.5– 124.5	124.5– 130.5	130.5– 136.5	136.5– 142.5	142.5– 148.5	148.5– 154.5	154.5– 160.5	160.5– 166.5	166.5– 172.5	172.5– 178.5	178.5– 184.5	184.5– 190.5	190.5– 196.5	196.5– 202.5	202.5– 208.5	208.5– 214.5	Total
0.255–1.255	8	6	8	6	10	2	1	1		1									43
1.255–2.255	1		1	2	9	12	15	14	8	6									72
2.255–3.255		1		1		3	6	10	20	22	3	2							81
3.255–4.255						2	1	3	5	13	13	7	5	1	1				51
4.255–5.255							1		1	2	11	13	5	2	2	1		1	34
5.255–6.255									1	1	4	3	9	1	3		1		24
6.255–7.255						1					3			5	2	2			9
7.255–8.255										1	2	2	2	4	7	3			20
8.255–9.255												1		5		2	1		7
9.255–10.255														3					3
10.255–11.255														2	1				3
11.255–12.255														1	2	1			2
12.255–13.255															1				1
Total	9	7	9	9	19	20	23	28	35	46	36	28	23	25	18	12	2	1	350

and weight for each of the following age groups: 11–15, 16–20, 21–25, and 26–35, and compare them; (c) calculate the regression coefficients of weight on stature, draw the regression lines for each of these four age groups separately, and compare them.

Bivariate normal distribution

5.19. In a university examination the frequency distribution of marks in mathematics and physics was found to be bivariate normal with the following parameters:

	Mean	Standard deviation
Physics	60	6
Mathematics	65	8

with a correlation coefficient of 0.5.

(a) What percentage of students score more than 75 in both physics and mathematics?

(b) Among those who score 75 in physics what percentage score more than 75 in mathematics?

(c) Among those who score 75 in mathematics what percentage score more than 75 in physics?

(d) What percentage score more than 75 in either physics or mathematics?

(e) What percentage score more than 150 in the aggregate?

5.20. The following table gives the number of passes and failures in mathematics and physics in a certain university examination. On the assumption that scores in mathematics and physics are jointly normally distributed, estimate the coefficient of correlation between the scores in the two subjects.

		Mathematics		
		Pass	Fail	Total
Physics	Pass	2279	142	2421
	Fail	119	89	208
	Total	2398	231	2629

5.21. A producer of electric bulbs, in his desire to put only good ones for sale, rejects all bulbs for which a certain quality characteristic X is less than a certain constant c. It is known that X and the life of the bulb in hours Y are jointly normally distributed with the following parameters:

	X		Y
Mean	80		1100
Standard deviation	10		100
Correlation coefficient		0.60	

Prepare a table showing the proportion P and the average life L of bulbs put for sale for the following values of c: 60, 65, 70, 75, and 80.

5.22. Past experience at a certain university showed that the joint distribution of marks scored by students on a preliminary examination X and on a final examination Y was normal with the following parameters:

	Mean	Variance	Correlation
X	55.7	15.1	
Y	40.6	12.3	0.80

As the average performance on the final examination was not considered satisfactory, the authorities decided that in the future a number of poor students should be eliminated at the preliminary stage, so that the average at the final would be at least 50.

Determine a value k such that, by eliminating all students securing less than k on the preliminary examination, the authorities can achieve their objective. What percentage of students will be rejected at the preliminary stage?

5.23. The following statistics were obtained from a bivariate frequency distribution of yield of plants X and that of offsprings Y in suitable units.

	Mean	Variance	Correlation
X	55	15	
Y	42	12	0.75

If from the parent plants only the top 10% in respect to yield are selected and allowed to propagate, what will be the expected yield from their offsprings? You may assume the joint frequency distribution to be bivariate normal.

5.24. A large number of candidates for a job appeared for a written test. Candidates scoring 45 or more on the written test were called in for a personality test. The following statistics were computed from the data on score X on the written tests and score Y on the personality test.

	X		Y
Mean	65.8		53.4
Standard deviation	8.57		7.31
Correlation		0.632	

The mean and the standard deviation of the score X on the written test of *all* the candidates were:

$$\text{Mean} = 20.6, \qquad \text{Standard deviation} = 10.62$$

Assuming linearity of the regression of Y on X and homoscedasticity about the regression line over the whole range of X, find the regression equation of Y on X and the coefficient of correlation between Y and X in the population of *all* the candidates.

Coefficient of rank correlation

5.25. For the data on the scores of 16 students on psychological test X and achievement test Y given in exercise 5.8, obtain the ranks of the students in both these tests and calculate (a) Spearman's coefficient and (b) Kendall's coefficient of rank correlation.

5.26. Ten students were interviewed for a job by a panel of three judges A, B, and C who independently ranked the candidates in order of suitability for the job. The ranks awarded are given in Table 5.15.

TABLE 5.15

RANKS OF TEN STUDENTS AS AWARDED BY JUDGES A, B, AND C

A	B	C	A	B	C
7	6	8	5	3	5
10	9	7	2	1	4
1	2	1	4	4	2
8	7	6	3	5	3
6	8	9	9	10	10

Compute the coefficient of concordance and examine to what extent the judges agree among themselves.

CHAPTER 6

Multivariate Data:
Multiple Correlation and Regression

6.1 MULTIVARIATE DISTRIBUTION

Given the joint distribution of p variables ($p \geq 2$), the marginal distribution of q ($q < p$) of them, or the conditional distribution of r of them when s others among the rest ($r + s \leq p$) are fixed, is defined in exactly the same way as in the case of bivariate distributions. To be specific, consider $k + 1$ variables $X_0, X_1, \ldots, X_k$ with a continuous frequency density function $f(x_0, x_1, \ldots, x_k)$. Let $g(x_0 \mid x_1, x_2, \ldots, x_k)$ be the conditional frequency density function of X_0, given that $X_1 = x_1$, $X_2 = x_2, \ldots, X_k = x_k$. Thus

$$(6.1.1) \qquad g(x_0 \mid x_1, x_2, \ldots, x_k) = \frac{f(x_0, x_1, \ldots, x_k)}{\displaystyle\int_{-\infty}^{\infty} f(x_0, x_1, \ldots, x_k)\, dx_0},$$

The conditional arithmetic mean of X_0, given that $X_1 = x_1$, $X_2 = x_2, \ldots, X_k = x_k$, is given by

$$(6.1.2) \quad \mathcal{M}(X_0 \mid X_1 = x_1, X_2 = x_2, \ldots, X_k = x_k)$$

$$= \int_{-\infty}^{\infty} x_0 g(x_0 \mid x_1, \ldots, x_k)\, dx_0 = \mu(x_1, x_2, \ldots, x_k),$$

is known as the regression function of X_0 on $X_1, X_2, \ldots, X_k$.

Linear Regression. The best linear approximation

$$(6.1.3) \qquad \phi(x_1, x_2, \ldots, x_k) = \alpha + \beta_1 x_1 + \beta_2 x_2 + \cdots + \beta_k x_k$$

to $\mu(x_1, x_2, \ldots, x_k)$ in the sense of minimizing the mean square deviation $\mathcal{M}[\mu - \phi]^2$ is given by

$$(6.1.4) \qquad \alpha = \mu_0 - \beta_1 \mu_1 - \beta_2 \mu_2 - \cdots - \beta_k \mu_k,$$

Here the regression coefficients $\beta_1, \beta_2, \ldots, \beta_k$ are obtained by solving the simultaneous linear equations

(6.1.5) $\qquad \sigma_{i0} = \beta_1 \sigma_{i1} + \beta_2 \sigma_{i2} + \cdots + \beta_k \sigma_{ik}, \quad i = 1, 2, \ldots, k;$

where

(6.1.6) $\qquad \begin{aligned} &\mu_i = \mathcal{M}(X_i); \qquad \sigma_{ij} = \mathcal{M}(X_i - \mu_i)(X_j - \mu_j), \\ &i, j = 0, 1, \ldots, k. \end{aligned}$

The residual mean square of X_0 is given by

(6.1.7) $\qquad \begin{aligned} \sigma_{00*12\cdots k} &= \mathcal{M}(X_0 - \alpha - \beta_1 X_1 - \cdots - \beta_k X_k)^2 \\ &= \sigma_{00} - \beta_1 \sigma_{10} - \beta_2 \sigma_{20} - \cdots - \beta_k \sigma_{k0}. \end{aligned}$

The matrix $\Sigma \equiv ((\sigma_{ij}))$ $(i, j = 0, 1, \ldots, k)$ is known as the variance-covariance matrix or the *dispersion matrix* of the joint distribution of $X_0, X_1, \ldots, X_k$.

6.2 MULTIPLE AND PARTIAL CORRELATION COEFFICIENTS

The *multiple correlation coefficient* $\rho_{0*1.2\ldots k}$ of X_0 on $X_1, X_2, \ldots, X_k$ is defined as the product-moment correlation coefficient between X_0 and the linear regression function $\phi(X_1, X_2, \ldots, X_k)$ and turns out to be the positive square root of

(6.2.1) $\qquad \begin{aligned} \rho_{0*1.2\ldots k}^2 &\equiv \frac{V[\phi(X_1, X_2, \ldots, X_k)]}{V(X_0)} \\ &= \frac{\beta_1 \sigma_{10} + \beta_2 \sigma_{20} + \cdots + \beta_k \sigma_{k0}}{\sigma_{00}} \\ &= 1 - \frac{|\Sigma|}{\sigma_{00}|\Sigma_{00}|}, \end{aligned}$

where Σ_{ij} is the cofactor of σ_{ij} in Σ.

The difference

(6.2.2) $\qquad X_{0*1.2\ldots k} = X_0 - \phi(X_1, X_2, \ldots, X_k)$

is called the *residual* of X_0 after eliminating the linear effect of $X_1, X_2, \ldots, X_k$.

The *partial correlation coefficient* $\rho_{0.k*1.2\cdots(k-1)}$ between X_0 and X_k, eliminating the effect of $X_1, X_2, \ldots, X_{k-1}$, is defined as the product-moment coefficient of correlation between the residuals $X_{0*1.2\cdots(k-1)}$ and $X_{k*1.2\cdots(k-1)}$. This turns out to be

(6.2.3) $\qquad \rho_{0,k*1.2\cdots(k-1)} = \frac{(-1)^{k+1}|\Sigma_{0k}|}{\sqrt{|\Sigma_{00}||\Sigma_{kk}|}}.$

The following recurrence relations may be noted:

$$\rho_{0,2^*1} = \frac{\rho_{02} - \rho_{01}\rho_{12}}{\sqrt{1 - \rho_{01}^2}\sqrt{1 - \rho_{02}^2}},$$

$$\rho_{0,3^*1.2} = \frac{\rho_{0,3^*1} - \rho_{0,2^*1}\rho_{3,2^*1}}{\sqrt{1 - \rho_{0,2^*1}^2}\sqrt{1 - \rho_{3,2^*1}^2}},$$

and in general

(6.2.4) $$\rho_{0,k^*1.2\cdots(k-1)} = \frac{a - bc}{\sqrt{1 - b^2}\sqrt{1 - c^2}},$$

where

$$a = \rho_{0,k^*1.2\cdots(k-2)}, b = \rho_{0,(k-1)^*1.2\cdots(k-2)}, \text{ and } c = \rho_{k,k-1^*1.2\cdots(k-2)}.$$

The multiple correlation coefficient is connected with the partial correlation coefficients by the relation

(6.2.5) $$1 - \rho_{0^*1.2\ldots k}^2 = (1 - \rho_{0^*1.2\ldots(k-1)}^2)(1 - \rho_{0,k^*1.2\ldots(k-1)}^2),$$

so that

$$1 - \rho_{0^*1.2\ldots k}^2 = (1 - \rho_{01}^2)(1 - \rho_{0,2^*1}^2)(1 - \rho_{0,3^*1.2}^2)\cdots$$
$$\times (1 - \rho_{0,k^*1.2\ldots(k-1)}^2).$$

The relationship between the residual mean square and the multiple correlation coeffiicent is also important:

(6.2.6) $$\sigma_{00^*1.2\ldots k} = \sigma_{00}(1 - \rho_{0^*1.2\ldots k}^2).$$

6.3   COMPUTATION OF MULTIPLE AND PARTIAL CORRELATION AND REGRESSION

Let $x_{0r}, x_{1r}, \ldots, x_{kr}$ $(r = 1, 2, \ldots, n)$ be n independent observations on the $k + 1$ variates $X_0, X_1, \ldots, X_k$. Let

$$T_i = \sum_{r=1}^{n} x_{ir}, \qquad T_{ij} = \sum_{r=1}^{n} x_{ir}x_{jr}.$$

Then compute

(6.3.1)

$$\text{Mean: } \bar{x}_i = \frac{T_i}{n},$$

$$\text{Corrected sum of products: } S_{ij} = T_{ij} - \frac{T_iT_j}{n},$$

for $i, j = 0, 1, \ldots, k$.

Equation 6.1.5 may be written as

$$S_{i0} = b_1 S_{i1} + b_2 S_{i2} + \cdots + b_k S_{ik}, \qquad i = 1, 2, \ldots, k.$$

To solve this equation, it is convenient to use the method of pivotal condensation. Thus by pivotal condensation of the matrix

$$
\begin{matrix}
S_{11} & S_{12} & S_{13} & \cdots & S_{1k} & S_{10} \\
S_{21} & S_{22} & S_{23} & \cdots & S_{2k} & S_{20} \\
S_{31} & S_{32} & S_{33} & \cdots & S_{3k} & S_{30} \\
\cdots & \cdots & \cdots & \cdots & \cdots & \cdots \\
S_{k1} & S_{k2} & \cdots & \cdots & S_{kk} & S_{k0} \\
S_{01} & S_{02} & \cdots & \cdots & S_{0k} & S_{00}
\end{matrix}
$$

as described in Chapter 5 of Part I the following matrix is obtained:

$$
\begin{matrix}
S_{11} & t_{12} & t_{13} & \cdots & t_{1k} & t_{10} \\
S_{21} & S_{22}^{(1)} & t_{23} & \cdots & t_{2k} & t_{20} \\
S_{31} & S_{32}^{(1)} & S_{33}^{(2)} & \cdots & t_{3k} & t_{30} \\
\cdots & \cdots & \cdots & \cdots & \cdots & \cdots \\
S_{k1} & S_{k2}^{(1)} & S_{k3}^{(2)} & \cdots & S_{kk}^{(k-1)} & t_{k0} \\
S_{01} & S_{02}^{(1)} & S_{03}^{(2)} & \cdots & S_{0k}^{(k-1)} & S_{00}^{(k)}
\end{matrix}
$$

Then the least-squares multiple linear regression function of X_0 on X_1, $X_2, \ldots, X_k$ is

$$\phi = a + b_1 X_1 + b_2 X_2 + \cdots + b_k X_k,$$

where

(6.3.2) $$a = \bar{x}_0 - b_1 \bar{x}_1 - b_2 \bar{x}_2 - \cdots - b_k \bar{x}_k$$

and $b_1, b_2, \ldots, b_k$ are given by

(6.3.3)
$$
\begin{aligned}
b_k &= t_{k0}, \\
b_{k-1} &= t_{k-1,0} - b_k t_{k-1,k}, \\
\cdots & \quad \cdots \quad \cdots \\
b_1 &= t_{10} - b_k t_{1k} - \cdots - b_2 t_{12}.
\end{aligned}
$$

The multiple correlation coefficient of X_0 on $X_1, X_2, \ldots, X_k$ is the positive square root of

(6.3.4)
$$
\begin{aligned}
R_{0*12\ldots k}^2 &= \frac{b_1 S_{10} + b_2 S_{20} + \cdots + b_k S_{k0}}{S_{00}} \\
&= \frac{t_{10} S_{01} + t_{20} S_{02}^{(2)} + \cdots + t_{k0} S_{0k}^{(k-1)}}{S_{00}} \\
&= 1 - \frac{S_{00}^{(k)}}{S_{00}}.
\end{aligned}
$$

Note that from this computational scheme we can readily obtain the least-squares multiple linear regression of X_0 on $X_1, X_2, \ldots, X_m$ for any $m \le k$, as well as the corresponding multiple correlation coefficients. Thus:

$$R_{0*1}^2 = \frac{t_{10}S_{01}}{S_{00}},$$

(6.3.5)
$$R_{0*12}^2 = \frac{t_{10}S_{01} + t_{20}S_{02}}{S_{00}},$$

$$R_{0*123}^2 = \frac{t_{10}S_{01} + t_{20}S_{02} + t_{30}S_{03}}{S_{00}},$$

and so on. Similarly partial correlation coefficients eliminating the effect of X_1 alone, or of both X_1 and X_2, or of X_1, X_2, and X_3, etc., can be obtained. For instance, $r_{0,k*12\ldots k-1}$ is given by

(6.3.6)
$$r_{0,k*12\ldots(k-1)} = \frac{S_{0k}^{(k-1)}}{\sqrt{S_{00}^{(k-1)}S_{kk}^{(k-1)}}},$$

where

(6.3.7)
$$S_{00}^{(k-1)} = S_{00} - t_{10}S_{01} - t_{20}S_{02}^{(1)} - \cdots - t_{k-1,0}S_{0,k-1}^{(k-2)}$$
$$= S_{00}^{(k)} + t_{k0}S_k^{(k-1)}.$$

Illustrative Example 6.1. Table 6.1 gives the means and the corrected sum of products (SP) matrix for five variates: $x_1 =$ crude oil gravity (API), $x_2 =$ crude oil vapor pressure, $x_3 =$ crude oil 10% point (ASTM), $x_4 =$ gasoline end point, $x_0 =$ gasoline yield percentage, based on 32 samples of crude oil. The problem is to build up a linear formula for estimating the percentage of gasoline yield from crude oil x_0 on the basis of the other four characteristics, x_1, x_2, x_3, x_4, of the oil.

TABLE 6.1

MATRIX OF CORRECTED SUMS OF SQUARES AND PRODUCTS AND MEANS

	x_1	x_2	x_3	x_4	x_0	Mean
x_1	984.500	284.030	-4,591.900	-3,920.050	461.415	39.2500
x_2		212.769	-2,763.000	-1,688.140	334.456	4.18125
x_3			43,690.000	33,466.500	-3,931.050	241.500
x_4				150,843.000	16,497.822	332.094
x_0					3,564.070	19.6594

Source: N. H. Prater, Estimated gasoline yields from crudes, *Petroleum Refiner*, Vol. 35 [quoted by R. J. Hader and H. E. Grandage, Simple and multiple regression analyses, *Experimental Designs in Industry* (V. Chew, ed.), John Wiley & Sons, 1958].

To build up the least-squares linear prediction formula

$$a + b_1 x_1 + \cdots + b_4 x_4$$

for estimating x_0 on the basis of the other four characteristics, x_1, x_2, x_3, x_4, the normal equations to be solved are

$$984.500b_1 + 284.030b_2 - 4591.900b_3 - 3920.050b_4 = 461.415,$$
$$284.030b_1 + 212.769b_2 - 2763.000b_3 - 1688.140b_4 = 334.456,$$
$$-4591.900b_1 - 2763.000b_2 + 46,390.000b_3 + 33,466.500b_4 = -3931.050,$$
$$-3920.050b_1 - 1688.140b_2 + 33,466.500b_3 + 150,843.000b_4 = 16,497.822.$$

The coefficient matrix of these equations is the corrected sum of products matrix of the variables x_1, x_2, x_3, x_4. To solve these equations, the first method of pivotal condensation as described in Chapter 5 of Part I of this book, is used. The matrix of coefficients is first written down with a column of row sums appended. In the next step, the first column is copied as such, and the other positions in the first row are filled by dividing the second, third, ... elements in the first row of the original matrix by the first pivotal element, 984.500. Then the other elements of the second column are filled as follows. The first entry is

$$212.769 - (284.030)(0.28850178) = 130.82584.$$

Similarly, the next entry is

$$-2763.00 - (-4591.900)(0.28850178) = -1438.22868.$$

The second row is completed by putting in the entries of the second column, each divided by the pivotal element 130.82584. Proceeding in this manner, we ultimately reduce the matrix to triangular form. Agreement of the check and sum columns is examined at each stage. Finally, the solution is obtained by back substitution. The details of computation are shown in Table 6.2 and the following material.

The regression coefficients are thus $b_1 = 0.22725$, $b_2 = 0.55372$, $b_3 = -0.14954$, $b_4 = 0.15465$, and $a = \bar{x}_0 - b_1\bar{x}_1 - b_2\bar{x}_2 - b_3\bar{x}_3 - b_4\bar{x}_4 = -6.81983$.

The multiple correlation R_{0*1234} of x_0 on x_1, x_2, x_3, x_4 is given by

$$R_{0*1234}^2 = (b_1 S_{10} + b_2 S_{20} + b_3 S_{30} + b_4 S_{40})/S_{00}$$
$$= (t_{10} S_{10} + t_{20} S_{20}^{(1)} + t_{30} S_{30}^{(2)} + t_{40} S_{40}^{(3)})/S_{00}$$
$$= 3429.289/3654.070 = 0.96218,$$

so that

$$R_{0*1234} = \sqrt{(0.96218)} = 0.9809.$$

TABLE 6.2

Solution of Normal Equation by Pivotal Condensation

Row						Sum	Check
	984.500				461.415	−6782.005	0.22725 = b_1
	284.030	212.769			334.456	−3619.885	0.55372 = b_2
	−4591.900	−2763.000	43,690.000		−3931.050	65,870.550	−0.14954 = b_3
	−3920.050	−1688.140	33,466.500	150,843.000	16,497.822	195,199.132	0.15465 = b_4
(1)	984.500	0.28850178	−4.66419502	−3.98176739	0.46867953	−6.88878110	−6.88878110
(2)	284.030	130.82584	−10.99346031	−4.25908674	1.53896929	−12.71357776	−12.71357776
(3)	−4591.900	−1438.22868	6461.37298	1.40172710	0.06724102	2.46896812	2.46896812
(4)	−3920.050	−557.19860	9057.08162	120,165.55882	0.15464975	1.15464975	1.15464975
(5)	461.415	201.33695	434.46931	18,583.57333	18,749.13216		
(6)	−6782.005	−1663.26449	15,952.92390	138,749.13216			

The partial correlation coefficient $r_{04 \cdot 123}$ of x_0 and x_4, eliminating the effect of x_1, x_2, x_3, is given by

$$r_{04 \cdot 123} = \frac{S_{04}^{(3)}}{\sqrt{S_{00}^{(3)} S_{44}^{(3)}}}.$$

From the computation sheet we have directly $S_{04}^{(3)} = 18{,}583.5738$, $S_{44}^{(3)} = 120{,}165.5588$, and $S_{00}^{(3)} = S_{00} - t_{10}S_{10} - t_{20}S_{20}^{(1)} - t_{30}S_{30}^{(2)} = 3008.7487$. Hence, $r_{04 \cdot 123} = 0.3091$.

6.4 MULTIVARIATE NORMAL DISTRIBUTION

The random variables X_1, X_2, ..., X_p are said to have the p-variate normal distribution if their joint frequency density function is

(6.4.1) $f(x_1, x_2, \ldots, x_p) = ke^{-\frac{1}{2}Q}.$

Here

$$Q = \sum_{i=1}^{p} \sum_{j=1}^{p} \sigma^{ij}(x_i - \mu_i)(x_j - \mu_j) \quad \text{and} \quad 1/k = (2\pi)^{\frac{1}{2}p} |\sigma_{ij}|^{\frac{1}{2}},$$

where μ_i and σ_{ij} are parameters $(i, j = 1, 2, \ldots, p)$, $((\sigma_{ij}))$ is a symmetric positive definite matrix, $((\sigma^{ij})) = ((\sigma_{ij}))^{-1}$, and $|\sigma_{ij}|$ denotes the determinant of the matrix $((\sigma_{ij}))$. For this distribution

(6.4.2) $\mathcal{M}(X_i) = \mu_i, \qquad \mathcal{M}(X_i - \mu_i)(X_j - \mu_j) = \sigma_{ij}$

for $i, j = 1, 2, \ldots, p$.

Let us write the dispersion matrix $\Sigma = ((\sigma_{ij}))$ in the partitioned form

(6.4.3) $\Sigma = \begin{bmatrix} \Sigma_{11} & \Sigma_{12} \\ \Sigma_{21} & \Sigma_{22} \end{bmatrix},$

where Σ_{11} is a $q \times q$ matrix, being the dispersion matrix of the first q random variables X_1, X_2, ..., X_q $(q < p)$. The marginal distribution of X_1, X_2, ..., X_q is then a q-variate normal distribution with mean values μ_1, μ_2, ..., μ_q and dispersion matrix Σ_{11}. The conditional distribution of X_{q+1}, ..., X_p, given that $X_1 = x_1$, $X_2 = x_2$, ..., $X_q = x_q$, is again a $p - q$ variate normal distribution with conditional means given by

(6.4.4) $\mathcal{M}(X_j \mid X_1 = x_1, \ldots, X_q = x_q)$

$$= \alpha_j + \beta_{j1}x_1 + \beta_{j2}x_2 + \cdots + \beta_{jq}x_q,$$

$$j = q + 1, q + 2, \ldots, p,$$

where $\alpha_j = \mu_j - \beta_{j1}\mu_1 - \beta_{j2}\mu_2 - \cdots - \beta_{jq}\mu_q$, and

$$
(6.4.5) \qquad \begin{bmatrix} \beta_{q+1,1} & \beta_{q+1,2} & \cdots & \beta_{q+1,q} \\ \beta_{q+2,1} & \beta_{q+2,2} & \cdots & \beta_{q+2,q} \\ \cdots & \cdots & \cdots & \cdots \\ \beta_{p1} & \beta_{p2} & \cdots & \beta_{pq} \end{bmatrix} = B = \Sigma_{21}\Sigma_{11}^{-1}.
$$

The conditional dispersion matrix of $X_{p+1}, \ldots, X_q$, given that $X_1 = x_1, \ldots, X_p = x_p$, is

$$
(6.4.6) \qquad \Sigma_{22}{}^* = \Sigma_{22} - \Sigma_{21}\Sigma_{11}^{-1}\Sigma_{12}.
$$

If $Y_1, Y_2, \ldots, Y_m$ are m linear functions of the variables $X_1, X_2, \ldots, X_p$ with known coefficients:

$$
Y_j = c_{j1}X_1 + c_{j2}X_2 + \cdots + c_{jp}X_p, \qquad j = 1, 2, \ldots, m
$$

then the joint distribution of $Y_1, Y_2, \ldots, Y_m$ is m-variate normal, with means $\mathscr{M}(Y_j) = c_{j1}\mu_1 + c_{j2}\mu_2 + \cdots + c_{jp}\mu_p$ and dispersion matrix $C \Sigma C'$, where $C = ((c_{jt})), j = 1, 2, \ldots, m, t = 1, 2, \ldots, p$.

6.5 EXERCISES

6.1. Table 6.3 gives the sepal length, sepal width, petal length, and petal width in centimeters of 50 flowers of each of these three species: *Iris setosa, Iris versicolor, and Iris virginica.*

Compute the mean vector and the dispersion matrix of the four characteristics: sepal length, sepal width, petal length, and petal width, separately for each of the three species and compare them.

6.2. Table 6.4 shows measurements on height and weight made on sixteen pairs of twins of opposite sex, all of 10 years of age.
  (a) Calculate the means, variances, and covariances for these data and compare them.
  (b) Suppose that you are given the following measurements for a boy of 10: height 126 cm, weight 25.0 kg. Obtain an estimate for (i) the height and (ii) the weight of his twin sister.
  (c) Find the residual dispersion matrix of the height and weight of the twin sister, eliminating the parts due to regression on the height and the weight of her brother.

6.3. Table 6.5 gives the scores of 25 workers in a factory on three psychological tests X_1, X_2, and X_3 and also their efficiency index Y.
  (a) Obtain a linear prediction formula for the efficiency index Y in

TABLE 6.3

LENGTH AND WIDTH (IN CENTIMETERS) OF SEPALS AND
PETALS OF FLOWERS OF THREE DIFFERENT SPECIES OF *Iris*

Iris setosa

Sepal		Petal		Sepal		Petal	
Length	Width	Length	Width	Length	Width	Length	Width
5.1	3.5	1.4	0.2	5.0	3.0	1.6	0.2
4.9	3.0	1.4	0.2	5.0	3.4	1.6	0.4
4.7	3.2	1.3	0.2	5.2	3.5	1.5	0.2
4.6	3.1	1.5	0.2	5.2	3.4	1.4	0.2
5.0	3.6	1.4	0.2	4.7	3.2	1.6	0.2
5.4	3.9	1.7	0.4	4.8	3.1	1.6	0.2
4.6	3.4	1.4	0.3	5.4	3.4	1.5	0.4
5.0	3.4	1.5	0.2	5.2	4.1	1.5	0.1
4.4	2.9	1.4	0.2	5.5	4.2	1.4	0.2
4.9	3.1	1.5	0.1	4.9	3.1	1.5	0.2
5.4	3.7	1.5	0.2	5.0	3.2	1.2	0.2
4.8	3.4	1.6	0.2	5.5	3.5	1.3	0.2
4.8	3.0	1.4	0.1	4.9	3.6	1.4	0.1
4.3	3.0	1.1	0.1	4.4	3.0	1.3	0.2
5.8	4.0	1.2	0.2	5.1	3.4	1.5	0.2
5.7	4.4	1.5	0.4	5.0	3.5	1.3	0.3
5.4	3.9	1.3	0.4	4.5	2.3	1.3	0.3
5.1	3.5	1.4	0.3	4.4	3.2	1.3	0.2
5.7	3.8	1.7	0.3	5.0	3.5	1.6	0.6
5.1	3.8	1.5	0.3	5.1	3.8	1.9	0.4
5.4	3.4	1.7	0.2	4.8	3.0	1.4	0.3
5.1	3.7	1.5	0.4	5.1	3.8	1.6	0.2
4.6	3.6	1.0	0.2	4.6	3.2	1.4	0.2
5.1	3.3	1.7	0.5	5.3	3.7	1.5	0.2
4.8	3.4	1.9	0.2	5.0	3.3	1.4	0.2
			Iris versicolor				
7.0	3.2	4.7	1.4	6.6	3.0	4.4	1.4
6.4	3.2	4.5	1.5	6.8	2.8	4.8	1.4
6.9	3.1	4.9	1.5	6.7	3.0	5.0	1.7
5.5	2.3	4.0	1.3	6.0	2.9	4.5	1.5
6.5	2.8	4.6	1.5	5.7	2.6	3.5	1.0

TABLE 6.3 (*continued*)

Iris versicolor

Sepal		Petal		Sepal		Petal	
Length	Width	Length	Width	Length	Width	Length	Width
5.7	2.8	4.5	1.3	5.5	2.4	3.8	1.1
6.3	3.3	4.7	1.6	5.5	2.4	3.7	1.0
4.9	2.4	3.3	1.0	5.8	2.7	3.9	1.2
6.6	2.9	4.6	1.3	6.0	2.7	5.1	1.6
5.2	2.7	3.9	1.4	5.4	3.0	4.5	1.5
5.0	2.0	3.5	1.0	6.0	3.4	4.5	1.6
5.9	3.0	4.2	1.5	6.7	3.1	4.7	1.5
6.0	2.2	4.0	1.0	6.3	2.3	4.4	1.3
6.1	2.9	4.7	1.4	5.6	3.0	4.1	1.3
5.6	2.9	3.6	1.3	5.5	2.5	4.0	1.3
6.7	3.1	4.4	1.4	5.5	2.6	4.4	1.2
5.6	3.0	4.5	1.5	6.1	3.0	4.6	1.4
5.8	2.7	4.1	1.0	5.8	2.6	4.0	1.2
6.2	2.2	4.5	1.5	5.0	2.3	3.3	1.0
5.6	2.5	3.9	1.1	5.6	2.7	4.2	1.3
5.9	3.2	4.8	1.8	5.7	3.0	4.2	1.2
6.1	2.8	4.0	1.3	5.7	2.9	4.2	1.3
6.3	2.5	4.9	1.5	6.2	2.9	4.3	1.3
6.1	2.8	4.7	1.2	5.1	2.5	3.0	1.1
6.4	2.9	4.3	1.3	5.7	2.8	4.1	1.3
Iris virginica							
6.3	3.3	6.0	2.5	7.2	3.2	6.0	1.8
5.8	2.7	5.1	1.9	6.2	2.8	4.8	1.8
7.1	3.0	5.9	2.1	6.1	3.0	4.9	1.8
6.3	2.9	5.6	1.8	6.4	2.8	5.6	2.1
6.5	3.0	5.8	2.2	7.2	3.0	5.8	1.6
7.6	3.0	6.6	2.1	7.4	2.8	6.1	1.9
4.9	2.5	4.5	1.7	7.9	3.8	6.4	2.0
7.3	2.9	6.3	1.8	6.4	2.8	5.6	2.2
6.7	2.5	5.8	1.8	6.3	2.8	5.1	1.5
7.2	3.6	6.1	2.5	6.1	2.6	5.6	1.4

TABLE 6.3 (*continued*)
Iris virginica

Sepal		Petal		Sepal		Petal	
Length	Width	Length	Width	Length	Width	Length	Width
6.5	3.2	5.1	2.0	7.7	3.0	6.1	2.3
6.4	2.7	5.3	1.9	6.3	3.4	5.6	2.4
6.8	3.0	5.5	2.1	6.4	3.1	5.5	1.8
5.7	2.5	5.0	2.0	6.0	3.0	4.8	1.8
5.8	2.8	5.1	2.4	6.9	3.1	5.4	2.1
6.4	3.2	5.3	2.3	6.7	3.1	5.6	2.4
6.5	3.0	5.5	1.8	6.9	3.1	5.1	2.3
7.7	3.8	6.7	2.2	5.8	2.7	5.1	1.9
7.7	2.6	6.9	2.3	6.8	3.2	5.9	2.3
6.0	2.2	5.0	1.5	6.7	3.3	5.7	2.5
6.9	3.2	5.7	2.3	6.7	3.0	5.2	2.3
5.6	2.8	4.9	2.0	6.3	2.5	5.0	1.9
7.7	2.8	6.7	2.0	6.5	3.0	5.2	2.0
6.3	2.7	4.9	1.8	6.2	3.4	5.4	2.3
6.7	3.3	5.7	2.1	5.9	3.0	5.1	1.8

Source: R. A. Fisher, The use of multiple measurements in taxonomic problems, *Annals of Eugenics* (*London*), Vol. 7, p. 179.

TABLE 6.4
HEIGHT AND WEIGHT OF TWINS OF OPPOSITE SEX

Serial no. of twin	Male		Female	
	Height (cm)	Weight (kg)	Height (cm)	Weight (kg)
1	136	27.2	132	29.4
2	141	35.0	133	29.0
3	137	30.6	140	27.8
4	137	30.4	135	26.8
5	134	33.2	131	31.2
6	134	31.2	137	30.2
7	130	28.4	133	27.8
8	139	30.0	140	28.8
9	128	27.0	123	26.4
10	132	27.8	136	30.0
11	133	28.4	134	28.0
12	129	26.6	134	28.4
13	137	30.6	134	29.9
14	128	24.4	134	28.6
15	134	30.0	135	26.4
16	130	27.4	127	27.8

DESCRIPTIVE METHODS

TABLE 6.5

SCORES ON PSYCHOLOGICAL TESTS AND EFFICIENCY INDEX
OF 25 WORKERS

Serial no. of worker	Scores on psychological tests			Efficiency index
	X_1	X_2	X_3	Y
1	15	38	29	47
2	77	79	29	67
3	18	53	16	38
4	8	33	18	30
5	16	12	18	26
6	54	34	20	44
7	95	61	34	72
8	22	31	18	40
9	69	82	31	67
10	75	75	39	72
11	8	41	32	43
12	4	46	21	36
13	97	66	35	72
14	53	31	31	54
15	26	31	14	35
16	49	33	11	40
17	3	27	19	34
18	21	55	27	48
19	56	55	20	52
20	72	57	15	49
21	97	58	28	67
22	18	23	11	27
23	53	29	10	39
24	60	60	20	57
25	9	12	10	28

terms of the scores on psychological tests X_1, X_2, and X_3. Compute the multiple correlation coefficient of Y on X_1, X_2, and X_3. Examine, by computing the appropriate partial correlation coefficient, to what extent X_3 helps in prediction when X_1 and X_2 have already been included in the prediction equation.

(b) Five applicants for jobs were given the three psychological tests and their scores were as follows:

Applicant	Scores on psychological tests		
	X_1	X_2	X_3
1	83	49	29
2	36	75	22
3	63	49	36
4	74	80	15
5	25	67	41

Select the two who are expected to be the most efficient (as measured by the efficiency index).

6.4. Three important measurements from which the cranial capacity C may be predicted are the glabella-occipital length L, the maximum parietal breadth B, and the basiobregmatic height H'. The prediction formula suggested is

$$C = \alpha' L^{\beta_1} B^{\beta_2} H'^{\beta_3},$$

where α', β_1, β_2, and β_3 are parameters to be estimated. This can be written in the form

$$y = \alpha + \beta_1 x_1 + \beta_2 x_2 + \beta_3 x_3,$$

where

$$y = \log_{10} C, x_1 = \log_{10} L, x_2 = \log_{10} B, \text{ and } x_3 = \log_{10} H'.$$

The mean values and the corrected sums of squares and products of these characters, computed on the basis of measurements on the 86 male skulls from the Farringdon Street series, are given in Table 6.6.

Estimate the values of the four parameters: α', β_1, β_2, and β_3.

TABLE 6.6

MEANS AND CORRECTED SUMS OF SQUARES AND PRODUCTS

Character	Mean	Corrected sum of squares and products			
		x_1	x_2	x_3	y
x_1	2.2752	0.01875	0.00848	0.00684	0.03030
x_2	2.1523		0.02904	0.00878	0.04410
x_3	2.1128			0.02886	0.03629
y	3.1685				0.12692

Source: C. R. Rao, *Linear Statistical Inference and Its Applications*, John Wiley & Sons, 1965.

6.5. Table 6.7 gives the intercorrelations, means, and standard deviations of five tests administered to a group of 164 school boys in the Minnesota study of mechanical ability. The criterion C, called the "quality criterion," was a measure of the excellence of the mechanical work done by the boys.

From among the five tests, choose the "best" set of four tests for predicting C. Derive the linear prediction formula for this set of four tests. Also, find a measure of the loss in the accuracy of prediction incurred through the omission of the fifth test.

TABLE 6.7

MEANS, STANDARD DEVIATIONS, AND INTERCORRELATIONS

	Mean	Standard deviation	^aC	X_1	X_2	X_3	X_4	X_5
						Intercorrelation		
C	61.2	9.82	...	0.365	0.526	0.518	0.547	0.403
X_1	58.3	7.20		...	0.243	0.266	0.307	0.156
X_2	63.4	5.25			...	0.628	0.553	0.305
X_3	68.7	6.47		...	...	...	0.489	0.212
X_4	65.8	5.44		...	...	...	...	0.165
X_5	54.3	6.39		...	...	...	...	...

^{a} C—Quality criterion X_3—Mechanical operation questionnaire
   X_1—General knowledge X_4—Mechanical drawing
   X_2—Model construction X_5—Elementary scientific knowledge

6.6. Five thousand candidates appeared for a certain examination in which there were three tests: T_1, T_2, and T_3, the perfect mark in each test being 100. The means, standard deviations, and correlation coefficients of the scores obtained on these tests are given in Table 6.8. Assuming the scores in the three tests to be jointly normally distributed, find the number of candidates securing 50% or more in the aggregate.

TABLE 6.8

MEANS, STANDARD DEVIATIONS, AND INTERCORRELATIONS
OF SCORES ON THREE TESTS

Tests	Mean	Standard deviation	T_1	T_2	T_3
				Intercorrelation	
T_1	39.46	6.2	...	0.29	0.38
T_2	52.31	9.4	...	...	0.43
T_3	45.26	8.7	...	...	...

6.7. Examine for internal consistency the following correlation matrix obtained by a computer:

$$
\begin{array}{cccc}
1.00 & 0.46 & 0.59 & 0.81 \\
0.46 & 1.00 & 0.38 & 0.67 \\
0.59 & 0.38 & 1.00 & 0.98 \\
0.81 & 0.67 & 0.98 & 1.00
\end{array}
$$

CHAPTER 7

Analysis of Time Series

7.1 TIME SERIES

A collection of observations y_t on a characteristic at different points of time t, arranged historically, is called a time series. In analyzing a time series, it is customary to consider y_t as built up of one or more of the following components: (1) a long-term growth or decay, which is called the *trend:* Y_t, (2) *seasonal fluctuations* S_t, superimposed on the trend, which are generally short-term fluctuations of a recurring pattern, (3) *cyclical fluctuations* C_t which have longer periodicity, and (4) *irregular fluctuations* ϵ_t. One of the following two assumptions is usually made:

$$y_t = Y_t + S_t + C_t + \epsilon_t \qquad \text{Additive model}$$
$$y_t = Y_t \cdot S_t \cdot C_t \cdot \epsilon_t \qquad \text{Multiplicative model}$$

A number of methods for separating out these components of an observed time series are described in the following sections.

7.2 TREND

The first step in time series analysis is to plot the values of y_t against t on a graph paper. One of the following methods of determining the trend is then selected by visual inspection of the graph.

Free-Hand Smoothing. If irregular fluctuations are minor, a free-hand smooth curve may be drawn, passing as nearly as possible through the points (t, y_t). Trend values are then read off from this smooth curve.

The following method is better.

Moving Averages. If the observations y_t are equispaced, the method of moving averages can be used. Suppose that time is measured in suitable units so that the range of t can be taken as $1, 2, \ldots, N$. If the series shows cyclical fluctuations, the period r of the moving average is taken to be equal to or a multiple of the period of the cyclical fluctuations. If r is odd, $r = 2m + 1$, say, the moving totals $\Sigma_t = y_{t-m} + y_{t-m+1} + \cdots + y_t + \cdots + y_{t+m}$ are computed for all possible values of t, and then the moving averages A_t are obtained from $A_t = \Sigma_t/(2m+1)$. If r is even, $r = 2m$, say, the moving totals $S_{t-\frac{1}{2}} = y_{t-m} + y_{t-m+1} + \cdots + y_t + \cdots + y_{t+m-1}$ and $S_{t+\frac{1}{2}} = y_{t-m+1} + \cdots + y_t + \cdots + y_{t+m}$ are taken, and the centered moving averages A_t are obtained from $A_t = (S_{t-\frac{1}{2}} + S_{t+\frac{1}{2}})/4m$. The values A_t give the trend component of the series.

Illustrative Example 7.1. Determination of trend by the method of moving averages is illustrated in Table 7.1. Column 2 of the table gives the volume of production of wheat y in million bushels in the United States in 1866–1956. The graph of this data is shown in Chart 7.1 (p. 215). On examination of this graph, we decide to take 5 years as the period of the moving average. Column 3 gives the 5-year moving totals, and column 4 the moving averages A. For example, the total for the years 1866–70 is $170 + 211 + \cdots + 254 = 1171$, and the average is $1171/5 = 234.2$. These figures are shown in columns 3 and 4 respectively against the central year 1868. Chart 7.1 also shows these moving averages.

Polynomial Trend. If the graph looks like a polynomial in t of a certain degree, say m, and if the seasonal and cyclical components are ignored, under the additive model we have

$$(7.2.1) \qquad y_t = \beta_0 + \beta_1 t + \beta_2 t^2 + \cdots + \beta_m t^m + \epsilon_t,$$

where β_j's are coefficients to be determined from the data. The method commonly used for this purpose is the method of least squares, which says that the β_j's should be determined such that

$$\Lambda_m = \sum_t [y_t - (\beta_0 + \beta_1 t + \beta_2 t^2 + \cdots + \beta_m t^m)]^2$$

is a minimum. This gives the equations

$$(7.2.2) \quad T_j = \beta_0 S_j + \beta_1 S_{j+1} + \cdots + \beta_m S_{j+m}, \qquad j = 1, 2, \ldots, m,$$

where $T_j = \sum_t y_t t^j$ and $S_j = \sum_t t^j$. These $m + 1$ equations in the $m + 1$ unknowns $\beta_0, \beta_1, \ldots, \beta_m$ are solved, and if $(\hat{\beta}_0, \hat{\beta}_1, \ldots, \hat{\beta}_m)$ is a solution, the minimum value of Λ_m, which measures the extent of agreement between the mth-degree polynomial and the observed time series, is given by the residual sum of squares

$$(7.2.3) \qquad L_m = \sum_t y_t^2 - (\hat{\beta}_0 T_0 + \hat{\beta}_1 T_1 + \cdots + \hat{\beta}_m T_m).$$

In most cases, the time points are equispaced and we can take for t the integer values $1, 2, \ldots, N$, where N is the total number of observations. In such a case, the computational labor involved in fitting a polynomial is very greatly reduced by using orthogonal polynomials.

TABLE 7.1

WHEAT PRODUCTION IN THE UNITED STATES, 1866–1956,
ORIGINAL AND MOVING AVERAGES (IN MILLION BUSHELS)

Year	Production y	5-Year moving total	Moving average A	Year	Production y	5-Year moving total	Moving average A
1866	170			1911	618	3408	681.6
67	211			12	730	3621	724.2
68	246	1171	234.2	13	751	4005	801.0
69	290	1273	254.6	14	897	4022	804.4
70	254	1333	266.6	15	1009	3912	782.4
71	272	1409	281.8	16	635	4065	813.0
72	271	1475	295.0	17	620	4120	824.0
73	322	1535	307.0	18	904	3954	790.8
74	356	1572	314.4	19	952	4138	827.6
75	314	1697	339.4	20	843	4365	873.0
76	309	1824	364.8	21	819	4220	844.0
77	396	1927	385.4	22	847	4110	822.0
78	449	2115	423.0	23	759	3936	787.2
79	459	2212	442.4	24	842	3949	789.8
80	502	2368	473.6	25	669	3977	795.4
81	406	2358	471.6	26	832	4132	826.4
82	552	2470	494.0	27	875	4114	822.8
83	439	2368	473.6	28	914	4331	866.2
84	571	2476	495.2	29	824	4441	888.2
85	400	2415	483.0	30	886	4322	864.4
86	514	2400	480.0	31	942	3960	792.0
87	491	2333	466.6	32	756	3662	732.4
88	424	2382	476.4	33	552	3404	680.8
89	504	2546	509.2	34	526	3092	618.4
90	449	2667	533.4	35	628	3210	642.0
91	678	2749	549.8	36	630	3578	715.6
92	612	2787	557.4	37	874	3793	758.6
93	506	2880	576.0	38	920	3980	796.0
94	542	2725	545.0	39	741	4292	858.4
95	542	2719	543.8	40	815	4387	877.4
96	523	2981	596.2	41	942	4311	862.2
97	606	3094	618.8	42	969	4630	926.0
98	768	3151	630.2	43	844	4923	984.6
99	655	3391	678.2	44	1060	5133	1026.6
1900	599	3472	694.4	45	1108	5523	1104.6
01	763	3367	673.4	46	1152	5974	1194.8
02	687	3268	653.6	47	1359	6012	1202.4
03	663	3375	675.0	48	1295	5923	1184.6
04	556	3353	670.6	49	1098	5759	1151.8
05	706	3295	659.0	50	1019	5706	1141.2
06	741	3275	655.0	51	988	5584	1116.8
07	629	3403	680.6	52	1306	5470	1094.0
08	643	3322	664.4	53	1173	5386	1077.2
09	684	3199	639.8	54	984	5395	1079.0
10	625	3300	660.0	55	935		
				56	997		

214

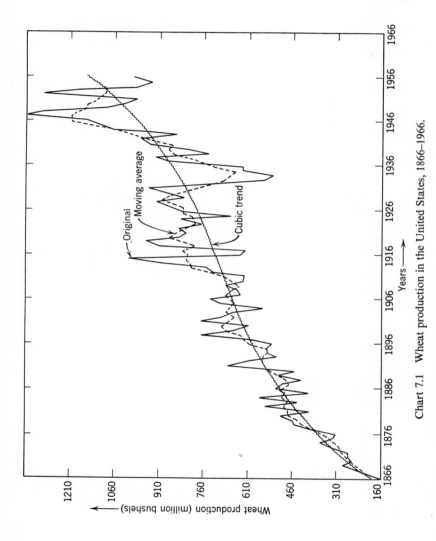

Chart 7.1 Wheat production in the United States, 1866–1966.

ORTHOGONAL POLYNOMIALS.   A set of polynomials $\phi_1(t)$, $\phi_2(t)$, $\phi_3(t)$, ...
where $\phi_j(t)$ is a polynomial of the jth degree in t, is said to be a set of
orthogonal polynomials if $\sum_t \phi_i(t)\phi_j(t) = 0$ for all i, j $(i \neq j)$. Writing the
model 7.2.1 in the form

(7.2.4) $y_t = \alpha_0 + \alpha_1\phi_1(t) + \alpha_2\phi_2(t) + \cdots + \alpha_m\phi_m(t) + \epsilon_t$,

the least-square estimates of the parameters α_j's are given by

(7.2.5) $$\hat{\alpha}_0 = \frac{1}{N}\sum_t y_t; \quad \hat{\alpha}_j = \frac{\sum_t y_t\phi_j(t)}{\sum_t (\phi_j(t))^2}, \qquad j = 1, 2, \ldots, m,$$

and the residual sum of squares is given by

(7.2.6) $$L_m = \sum y_t^2 - \left[\hat{\alpha}_0 \sum_t y_t + \hat{\alpha}_1 \sum y_t\phi_1(t) + \cdots + \hat{\alpha}_m \sum_t y_t\phi_m(t)\right].$$

Values of $\phi_j(t)$ are given by Fisher and Yates in *Statistical Tables for
Biological, Agricultural, and Medical Research* (Table XXIII) for $j = 1, 2,$
$3, 4, 5$; $t = 1, 2, \ldots, N$; and $N = 3, 4, \ldots, 75$.

Table 47 of *Biometrika Tables* gives values of $\phi_j(t)$ for $j = 1, 2, \ldots, 6$;
$t = 1, 2, \ldots, N$; and $N = 3, 4, \ldots, 52$. The values of $\sum_t (\phi_j(t))^2$ are
also tabulated. To express the orthogonal polynomials explicitly in terms
of t, we use the recurrence relations

$$\phi_j = \lambda_j\xi_j;$$

(7.2.7)

$$\xi_{j+1} = \xi_1\xi_j - \frac{j^2(N^2 - j^2)}{4(4j^2 - 1)}\xi_{j-1}; \quad \xi_0 = 1; \quad \xi_1 = t - \tfrac{1}{2}(N + 1),$$

where λ_j's are constants given in the above tables.

In particular, the first four orthogonal polynomials are given by

$$\phi_0 = 1, \qquad \phi_1 = \lambda_1 u, \qquad \text{where} \qquad u = t - \tfrac{1}{2}(N + 1),$$

$$\phi_2 = \lambda_2\left(u^2 - \frac{N^2 - 1}{12}\right),$$

(7.2.8)

$$\phi_3 = \lambda_3\left(u^3 - \frac{3N^2 - 7}{20}u\right),$$

$$\phi_4 = \lambda_4\left[u^4 - \frac{3N^2 - 13}{14}u^2 + \frac{3}{560}(N^2 - 1)(N^2 - 9)\right].$$

When it is not possible to decide beforehand on the degree m, the usual
practice is to fit successively polynomials of degrees one, two, three, ...,

etc., and compute $L_1, L_2, L_3, \ldots$ and so on, stopping at the mth stage if L_m is considered to be sufficiently small.

An alternative method for determining the degree of the polynomial is as follows.

VARIATE DIFFERENCE METHOD. In this method, we assume that the irregular components ϵ_t's are uncorrelated random variables, each with zero mean and a common variance σ^2. Then if we compute

$$(7.2.9) \qquad V_j = \frac{\sum (\Delta^j y_t)^2}{(N-j)\binom{2j}{j}} \quad \text{for } j = 1, 2, 3, \ldots,$$

where Δ^j denotes the jth-order difference operator and summation is over all available values, it can be shown that $\mathcal{M}(V_j) > \sigma^2$ for $j \leq m$ and $\mathcal{M}(V_j) = \sigma^2$ for $j > m$, where m is the degree of the polynomial. Therefore the required degree m is the smallest integer such that $V_{m+1}, V_{m+2}, \ldots$, etc., are equal, except for sampling fluctuations.

Illustrative Example 7.2. We shall fit a polynomial of appropriate degree to the wheat production data given in Table 7.1. To determine the degree of the polynomial, we first prepare a difference table, up to sixth-order differences, part of which is reproduced as Table 7.2.

TABLE 7.2

DIFFERENCE TABLE

Year	y	Δ_y	$\Delta_y{}^2$	$\Delta_y{}^3$	$\Delta_y{}^4$	$\Delta_y{}^5$	$\Delta_y{}^6$
1866	170						
		41					
67	211		−6				
		35		15			
68	246		9		−104		
		44		−89		327	
69	290		−80		223		−757
		−36		134		−430	
70	254		54		−207		781
		18		−73		351	
71	272		−19		144		−635
		−1		71		−284	
72	271		52		−140		434
		51		−69		150	
73	322		−17		10		−12

From this we get the following sums of squares of differences:

$$H_1 = \Sigma(\Delta_y)^2 = 1{,}243{,}149, \qquad H_2 = \Sigma(\Delta_y{}^2)^2 = 2{,}866{,}739,$$
$$H_3 = \Sigma(\Delta_y{}^3)^2 = 8{,}175{,}499,$$
$$H_4 = \Sigma(\Delta_y{}^4)^2 = 26{,}126{,}732, \qquad H_5 = \Sigma(\Delta_y{}^5)^2 = 88{,}827{,}739,$$
$$H_6 = \Sigma(\Delta_y{}^6)^2 = 313{,}978{,}227.$$

Here $N = 91$, and since $V_j = \dfrac{H_j}{(N - j)\binom{2j}{j}}$, we have

$$V_1 = \frac{H_1}{(N - 1) \times 2} = 6906.38, \qquad V_2 = \frac{H_2}{(N - 2) \times 6} = 5368.43,$$

$$V_3 = \frac{H_3}{(N - 3) \times 20} = 4645.17, \qquad V_4 = \frac{H_4}{(N - 4) \times 70} = 4290.10,$$

$$V_5 = \frac{H_5}{(N - 5) \times 252} = 4098.73, \qquad V_6 = \frac{H_6}{(N - 6) \times 924} = 3997.69.$$

We thus see that V_4, V_5, V_6 are more or less equal in magnitude. Consequently, we decide to fit a cubic $Y_t = b_0 + b_1 t + b_2 t^2 + b_3 t^3$. To simplify the computations, we take the middle year 1911 as the origin, so that the years 1866, 1867, . . . , 1956 are represented by $t = -45, -44, \ldots, +45$, respectively. We then have

$$T_0 = \Sigma y = 62{,}520, \qquad T_1 = \Sigma t y = 557{,}810,$$
$$T_2 = \Sigma t^2 y = 42{,}771{,}486, \qquad T_3 = \Sigma t^3 y = 737{,}722{,}556;$$
$$S_0 = N = 91, \qquad S_1 = \Sigma t = 0, \qquad S_2 = \Sigma t^2 = 62{,}790,$$
$$S_3 = \Sigma t^3 = 0, \qquad S_4 = \Sigma t^4 = 77{,}972{,}622, \qquad S_5 = \Sigma t^5 = 0,$$
$$S_6 = \Sigma t^6 = 115{,}250{,}964{,}270.$$

The values of the s_j's were obtained from *Biometrika Tables*. Equations 7.2.2 thus reduce to

$$T_0 = S_0 b_0 + \qquad\quad S_2 b_2,$$
$$T_1 = \qquad\quad S_2 b_1 + \qquad\quad S_4 b_3,$$
$$T_2 = S_2 b_0 + \qquad\quad S_4 b_2,$$
$$T_3 = S_4 b_0 + \qquad\quad S_6 b_2,$$

from which we get

$$b_0 = 694.348, \qquad b_1 = 5.84848, \qquad b_2 = -0.0106015,$$
$$b_3 = 0.00244424.$$

The fitted cubic is shown in Chart 7.1, together with the original series and the 5-year moving averages.

Illustrative Example 7.3. Table 7.3 gives the index number of the volume of production in a certain factory for the years 1948–59 with the year 1947

TABLE 7.3

INDEX NUMBER OF PRODUCTION IN A FACTORY, 1948–59
BASE 1947 = 100

Year	Index	Year	Index
1948	102.1	1954	126.1
49	108.1	55	124.9
50	112.0	56	124.1
51	113.6	57	124.6
52	115.7	58	127.0
53	120.9	59	125.6

as base = 100. Denoting the years 1948, 1949, 1950, ... by $t = 1, 2, 3, \ldots$, respectively, we show in Table 7.4 the details of fitting a polynomial of appropriate degree using orthogonal polynomials. The first column gives the values of the index number y. The values of the orthogonal polynomials $\phi_j(t)$, $j = 0, 1, 2, 3, 4$, are taken from *Biometrika Tables* (Table 47) for $N = 12$, as are the values of $\sum_t \phi_j^2(t)$. The values of $\sum y\phi_j$ are obtained next, and the coefficients a_j are evaluated as $a_j = \sum y\phi_j / \sum \phi_j^2$ $(j = 0, 1, 2, 3, 4)$. For instance, $a_3 = -19.5/5148 = -0.0037879$. The residual sum of squares R_j after fitting the jth-degree polynomial is computed as

$$R_j = \sum y^2 - a_0 \sum y\phi_0 - a_1 \sum y\phi_1 - \cdots - a_j \sum y\phi_j.$$

The residual sum of squares is not diminished appreciably by fitting a polynomial of degree higher than the second, R_2, R_3, and R_4 being of the order of 24.

The equation of the second-degree parabola is:

$$Y_t = a_0\phi_0 + a_1\phi_1 + a_2\phi_2 = 118.725 + 1.0526\phi_1 - 0.085390\phi_2.$$

To express this equation in terms of t or equivalently in terms of $u = t - 6.5$, we use equation 7.2.8 and get $\phi_1 = 2u$ and $\phi_2 = 3u^2 - 35.75$. Therefore

$$Y_t = 121.778 + 2.1052u - 0.25617u^2.$$

DESCRIPTIVE METHODS

TABLE 7.4
FITTING OF ORTHOGONAL POLYNOMIALS

Degree of polynomial		0	1	2	3	4
	j	ϕ_0	ϕ_1	ϕ_2	ϕ_3	ϕ_4
	y					
	102.1	1	−11	55	−33	33
	108.1	1	−9	25	3	−27
	112.0	1	−7	1	21	−33
	113.6	1	−5	−17	25	−13
	115.7	1	−3	−29	19	12
	120.9	1	−1	−35	7	28
	126.1	1	1	−35	−7	28
	124.9	1	3	−29	−19	12
	124.1	1	5	−17	−25	−13
	124.6	1	7	1	−21	−33
	127.0	1	9	25	−3	−27
	125.6	1	11	55	33	33
Sum of squares	169,893.83	12	= 572	= 12,012	= 5148	= 8008
$\sum y\phi_j$	1424.7		602.1	−1025.7	−19.5	71.7
a_j	118.725		1.0526	−0.085390	−0.0037879	0.0089536
Residual sum of squares		746.32	112.54	24.96	24.89	24.25

Other Mathematical Functions. In some situations, models of the type $\log y_t = \beta_0 + \beta_1 t + \beta_2 t^2 + \cdots + \beta_p t^p + \epsilon_t$ are appropriate. They may be fitted in the same way as shown above.

LOGISTIC CURVE. Among functions other than polynomials, the logistic curve is sometimes useful. It has an equation of the form:

$$(7.2.10) \qquad \frac{1}{Y_t} = \alpha + \beta \gamma^t,$$

where α, β, and γ are parameters to be estimated from the data. This curve is specially appropriate for a time series whose rate of growth starts from zero, gradually increases, reaches a maximum, and then falls down to zero. In order to find out whether the logistic is suitable for time series data, a graphical examination is necessary. The values of $\log \Delta(1/y_t)$ are to be plotted against the values of t, and this graph should be a straight line for a logistic curve. Alternatively, the points with coordinates $(1/y_t, 1/y_{t+1})$ should all lie on a straight line. The method of least squares in this case yields rather complicated equations, which have to be solved by an iterative process. A simpler method of estimation is to choose three equispaced observations, say y_0, y_k, and y_{2k}, and then equate $1/y_t = \alpha + \beta \gamma^t$ for $t = 0, k$, and $2k$. This gives the estimates

$$(7.2.11) \qquad \hat{\alpha} = \frac{1}{y_0} - \hat{\beta}; \qquad \hat{\beta} = \frac{d_1^2}{d_1 - d_2}; \qquad \hat{\gamma} = \left(\frac{d_2}{d_1}\right)^{1/k},$$

where $d_1 = (1/y_0) - (1/y_k)$, and $d_2 = (1/y_k) - (1/y_{2k})$.

If the observations are equispaced, an alternative method is to divide the series into three equal consecutive groups, omitting a few terminal observations if necessary. Writing $S_1 = \sum\limits_{t=1}^{k} (1/y_t)$, $S_2 = \sum\limits_{t=k+1}^{2k} (1/y_t)$, and $S_3 = \sum\limits_{t=2k+1}^{3k} (1/y_t)$ and equating these with their trend values, we get the following estimates:

$$\hat{\alpha} = \frac{1}{k}\left(S_1 - \frac{D_1^2}{D_1 - D_2}\right),$$

$$(7.2.12) \qquad \hat{\beta} = \frac{D_1^3}{(D_1 - D_2)^2}\left(\frac{1}{\hat{\gamma}} - 1\right),$$

$$\hat{\gamma} = \left(\frac{D_2}{D_1}\right)^{1/k},$$

where $D_1 = S_1 - S_2$ and $D_2 = S_2 - S_3$.

TABLE 7.5

POPULATION OF THE UNITED STATES, 1810–1950 (IN MILLIONS)

Year	Population	Year	Population
1810	7.24	1890	62.95
20	9.64	1900	76.00
30	12.87	10	91.97
40	17.07	20	105.71
50	23.19	30	122.78
60	31.44	40	131.67
70	38.56	50	150.70

TABLE 7.6

FITTING A LOGISTIC CURVE

Year	t	P_t	$1/P_t$	Trend value $1/(a + bc^t)$
1810	1	7.24	0.138122	7.11
20	2	9.64	0.103735	9.65
30	3	12.87	0.077700	13.02
40	4	17.07	0.058582	17.46
50	5	23.19	0.043122	23.20
			$S_1 = 0.421261$	
60	6	31.44	0.031807	30.51
70	7	38.56	0.025934	39.56
80	8	50.16	0.019936	50.45
90	9	62.95	0.015886	63.05
1900	10	76.00	0.013158	77.10
			$S_2 = 0.106721$	
10	11	91.97	0.010873	91.99
20	12	105.71	0.009460	107.02
30	13	122.78	0.008145	121.45
40	14	131.67	0.007594	134.66
50	15	150.70	0.006636	146.22
			$S_3 = 0.042708$	

In case least-squares estimates are required, the values of α, β, γ obtained by either of the two methods just described may be taken as the first approximation in the iterative procedure.

Illustrative Example 7.4. Table 7.5 (p. 222) gives the population in millions of the United States, 1810–1950. We fit a logistic curve

$$1/P_t = a + bc^t,$$

where P_t is the population at time t, the years 1810, 1820, . . . being represented by 1, 2, . . . , respectively. The computations are shown in Table 7.6 (p. 222), where the trend values are also presented.

We thus have $D_1 = S_1 - S_2 = 0.064013$, $D_2 = S_2 - S_3 = 0.314540$. Here $k = 5$, and we get $C^5 = 0.20351$, and so $C = 0.7273$.

$$b = \frac{D_1{}^3}{(D_1 - D_2)^2}\left(\frac{1}{C} - k\right) = 0.18589 \quad \text{and}$$

$$a = \frac{1}{k}\left(S_1 - \frac{D_1{}^2}{D_1 - D_2}\right) = 0.005272.$$

The equation of the logistic curve is thus

$$\frac{1}{P_t} = 0.005272 + 0.18589(0.7273)^t.$$

7.3 SEASONAL INDEX

Index numbers of seasonal variations are used to compare short-term periodic fluctuations like those between months or seasons in a year or between the days in a week. When we say, for instance, that the monthly index for January sales in a departmental store is 120, we mean that the sales in January are 120% of the average monthly sales in a year. Seasonal indices are computed on the assumption that the same seasonal pattern repeats over a number of years.

Two methods for computing index numbers of monthly variations will now be described. Index numbers of quarterly or weekly variations can be calculated in a similar manner with appropriate modifications.

Let y_{ij} denote the observation corresponding to the jth month of the ith year ($j = 1, 2, \ldots 12$; $i = 1, 2, \ldots$).

Ratios to Trend. The first step is to obtain the trend values Y_{ij} for each month by any one of the methods described in Section 7.2. The one most frequently used for this purpose is the method of centered 12-month moving averages. The next step is to compute the ratios $r_{ij} = y_{ij}/Y_{ij}$. Under the assumption that the model is multiplicative and that the cyclical fluctuations are absent, these ratios r_{ij} measure the seasonal component together with irregular fluctuations. For the jth month, a suitable measure of location of these ratios, say r_j = arithmetic mean or median of $(r_{1j}, r_{2j}, \ldots,$ etc.) is taken. The indices of monthly variations are then obtained by adjusting the r_j's to add to 1200. Thus if $f = 1200/\sum_{j=1}^{12} r_j$, the required indices are given by $s_j = fr_j$ ($j = 1, 2, \ldots, 12$).

Illustrative Example 7.5. Table 7.7 gives the monthly volumes of civil aviation traffic in billion passenger–kilometers in the United States, 1949–59. Indices of seasonal variation are computed below by using the method of moving averages.

The 12-month centered moving averages are presented in Table 7.8.

TABLE 7.7

CIVIL AVIATION TRAFFIC IN THE UNITED STATES, 1949–59
(IN BILLION PASSENGER-KILOMETERS)

Month	Year										
	1949	1950	1951	1952	1953	1954	1955	1956	1957	1958	1959
Jan.	0.92	0.99	1.46	1.74	2.10	2.34	2.93	3.30	3.78	4.12	4.19
Feb.	0.91	1.00	1.36	1.64	2.01	2.22	2.62	3.01	3.40	3.46	3.87
Mar.	1.12	1.19	1.72	1.90	2.34	2.51	3.04	3.51	4.04	4.06	4.65
Apr.	1.20	1.29	1.70	2.01	2.43	2.66	3.22	3.58	4.03	4.10	4.58
May	1.26	1.38	1.76	2.02	2.49	2.76	3.24	3.63	4.11	4.08	4.76
June	1.42	1.62	1.94	2.34	2.72	3.13	3.67	4.34	4.88	4.84	5.52
July	1.37	1.58	1.94	2.30	2.72	3.17	3.75	4.04	4.79	4.84	5.58
Aug.	1.34	1.62	2.01	2.42	2.79	2.98	3.70	4.27	4.98	5.13	5.84
Sept.	1.34	1.56	1.98	2.33	2.62	2.99	3.54	4.00	4.44	4.45	5.30
Oct.	1.26	1.52	1.89	2.27	2.49	2.86	3.38	3.82	4.14	4.30	4.92
Nov.	1.03	1.26	1.67	1.97	2.14	2.56	2.91	3.35	3.63	3.64	4.49
Dec.	1.01	1.42	1.73	2.08	2.34	2.84	3.18	3.59	4.07	3.68	4.83

Source: *U.N. Monthly Bulletin of Statistics.*

TABLE 7.8

TWELVE-MONTH CENTERED MOVING AVERAGES

Month	Year										
	1949	1950	1951	1952	1953	1954	1955	1956	1957	1958	1959
Jan.		1.24	1.59	1.92	2.31	2.58	3.03	3.50	3.97	4.23	4.50
Feb.		1.26	1.62	1.95	2.34	2.61	3.09	3.53	4.03	4.24	4.56
Mar.		1.28	1.66	1.98	2.37	2.63	3.14	3.58	4.08	4.24	4.62
Apr.		1.31	1.69	2.02	2.39	2.66	3.18	3.61	4.11	4.25	4.68
May		1.32	1.72	2.04	2.40	2.69	3.22	3.66	4.14	4.26	4.75
June		1.35	1.75	2.07	2.42	2.73	3.25	3.69	4.17	4.24	4.83
July	1.18	1.39	1.78	2.10	2.44	2.78	3.28	3.72	4.20	4.23	
Aug.	1.19	1.42	1.80	2.13	2.46	2.82	3.31	3.76	4.22	4.25	
Sept.	1.20	1.46	1.82	2.16	2.48	2.86	3.35	3.80	4.22	4.29	
Oct.	1.20	1.50	1.84	2.20	2.49	2.90	3.38	3.84	4.23	4.33	
Nov.	1.21	1.53	1.86	2.24	2.51	2.94	3.41	3.88	4.23	4.38	
Dec.	1.23	1.56	1.89	2.27	2.54	2.99	3.46	3.92	4.23	4.44	

Each average is computed by first finding the 12-month moving totals and then dividing the sum of each consecutive pair of totals by 24. For example, the total for January, 1949, to December, 1949, is 14.18, and that for February, 1949, to January, 1950, is 14.25. The 12-month centered moving average for July, 1949, is thus $(14.18 + 14.25)/24 = 1.18$.

The ratios of the original observations to the corresponding centered 12-month moving averages are presented in Table 7.9. In this table the average of these ratios is computed for each month. The seasonal indices are proportional to these averages with a total of 1200.

Link Relatives. In this method the first step is to express each observation as a ratio of the preceding observation. The ratios l_{ij} so computed are called link relatives:

$$l_{i1} = y_{i1}/y_{i-1,12} \quad \text{and} \quad l_{ij} = y_{ij}/y_{i,j-1}, \qquad j = 2, 3, \ldots 12.$$

Since the trend and cyclical components for two consecutive observations are considered to be approximately the same, the link relatives measure, except for irregular fluctuations, the ratios of the corresponding seasonal components. For the jth month, a suitable measure of location of the link relatives, say l_j = arithmetic mean or median of $(l_{1j}, l_{2j}, \ldots,$ etc.), is taken. Then the seasonal component for month 1, say m_1, is arbitrarily taken to be 1 and the components for the other months are obtained by successive multiplication as $m_2 = 1 \times l_2$, $m_3 = m_2 \times l_3$, $m_4 = m_3 \times l_4$, $\ldots, m_{12} = m_{11} \times l_{12}$, and finally $m_1' = m_{12} \times l_1$. Any difference between m_1' and m_1 is due to the presence of a trend component. The correction for trend is made by computing $d = (m_1' - m_1)/12$ and then $q_1 = m_1$, $q_2 = m_2 - d$, $q_3 = m_3 - 2d, \ldots, q_{12} = m_{12} - 11d$. Finally, the indices of monthly variations are obtained by adjusting the q_j's to add to 1200.

Illustrative Example 7.6. The computation of seasonal indices by the method of link relatives, from the data on civil aviation traffic given in Table 7.7, is shown in Table 7.10.

The link relatives are computed first and shown as percentages against the month and the year to which they relate. Thus the first entry, against February, 1949, is the ratio of the February, 1949, figure to the January, 1949, figure: $0.91/0.92 = 98.9\%$. The average values of these link relatives are shown in the next column. Thus the average value for the ratio February to January is 93.16, that for March to February is 118.44, and so on. If then we take the January index as 100.00, that for February turns out to be $100.00 \times 93.16\% = 93.16$, and that for March is $93.16 \times 118.44\% = 110.34$. Proceeding this way, we obtain the index for December as 113.95, and completing the cycle, that for January again as $113.95 \times 102.97\% = 117.33$, the second factor being the average value of the

TABLE 7.9

RATIOS TO MOVING AVERAGES: COMPUTATION OF SEASONAL INDEX

Month						Year						Average	Seasonal index
	1949	1950	1951	1952	1953	1954	1955	1956	1957	1958	1959		
Jan.		79.8	91.8	90.6	90.9	90.7	96.7	94.3	95.2	97.4	93.1	92.05	92.2
Feb.		79.4	84.0	84.1	85.9	85.1	84.8	85.3	84.4	81.6	84.9	83.95	84.1
Mar.		93.0	103.6	96.0	98.7	95.4	96.8	98.0	99.0	95.8	100.6	97.69	97.8
Apr.		98.5	100.6	99.5	101.7	100.0	101.2	99.2	98.1	96.5	97.9	99.32	99.5
May		104.6	102.3	99.0	103.8	102.6	100.6	99.2	99.3	95.8	100.2	100.74	100.9
June		120.0	110.8	113.0	112.4	114.6	112.9	117.6	117.0	114.2	114.3	114.68	114.9
July	116.1	113.7	109.0	109.5	111.5	114.0	114.3	108.6	114.0	114.4		112.51	112.7
Aug.	112.6	114.1	111.7	113.6	113.4	105.7	111.8	113.6	118.0	120.7		113.52	113.7
Sept.	111.7	106.8	108.8	107.9	105.6	104.5	105.7	105.3	105.2	103.7		106.52	106.7
Oct.	105.0	101.3	102.7	103.2	100.0	98.6	100.0	99.5	97.9	99.3		100.75	100.9
Nov.	85.1	82.4	89.8	87.9	85.2	87.1	85.3	86.3	85.8	83.1		85.80	85.9
Dec.	82.1	91.0	91.5	91.6	92.1	95.0	91.9	91.6	96.2	82.9		90.59	90.7
											Total	1198.12	1200.0

TABLE 7.10

COMPUTATION OF SEASONAL INDEX BY THE METHOD OF LINK RELATIVES

Month	Year												Average	Chain relative	Adjusted chain relative	Seasonal index
	1949	1950	1951	1952	1953	1954	1955	1956	1957	1958	1959				
Jan.		98.0	102.8	100.6	101.0	100.0	103.2	103.8	105.3	101.2	113.8	102.97	100.00	100.00	91.2
Feb.	98.9	101.0	93.2	94.2	95.7	94.9	89.4	91.2	89.9	84.0	92.4	93.16	93.16	91.72	83.6
Mar.	123.1	119.0	126.5	115.8	116.4	113.1	116.0	116.6	118.8	117.3	120.2	118.44	110.34	107.46	98.0
Apr.	107.1	108.4	98.8	105.8	103.8	106.0	105.9	102.0	99.8	101.0	98.5	103.37	114.06	109.74	100.0
May	105.0	107.0	103.5	100.5	102.5	103.8	100.6	101.4	102.0	99.5	103.9	102.70	117.14	111.38	101.5
June	112.7	117.4	110.2	115.8	109.2	113.4	113.3	119.6	118.7	118.6	116.0	114.99	134.70	127.50	116.2
July	96.5	97.5	100.0	98.3	100.0	101.3	102.2	93.1	98.2	100.0	101.1	98.93	133.26	124.62	113.6
Aug.	97.8	102.5	103.6	105.2	102.6	94.0	98.7	105.7	104.0	106.0	104.6	102.24	136.25	126.17	115.0
Sept.	100.0	96.3	98.5	96.3	93.9	100.3	95.7	93.7	89.2	86.7	90.8	94.67	128.99	117.47	107.1
Oct.	94.0	97.4	95.4	97.4	95.0	95.6	95.5	95.5	93.2	96.6	92.8	95.31	122.94	109.98	100.3
Nov.	81.7	82.9	88.4	86.8	85.9	89.5	86.1	87.7	87.7	84.6	91.3	86.60	106.47	92.07	83.9
Dec.	98.0	112.7	103.6	105.6	109.3	110.9	109.3	107.2	112.1	101.1	107.5	107.03	113.95	98.11	89.4
													117.33	1316.22	1199.8

January to December ratio. The difference between the two January indices, $D = 117.33 - 100.00 = 17.33$, is due to trend and should be eliminated. Since D represents the annual growth, the monthly growth is $d = D/12 = 1.44$. From the unadjusted February index 93.16 we therefore subtract d to get 91.72; from the unadjusted March index we subtract $2d$ to get 107.46, and so on. These are shown in the column for adjusted chain relatives. The seasonal indices in the next column are proportional to these adjusted chain relatives and have a total of 1200.

7.4 CYCLICAL FLUCTUATIONS

To obtain the cyclical component of a time series data the first step is to compute the components of trend Y_t and seasonal variation S_t by the methods already discussed and then to eliminate these components from the observed data. Thus, under the assumption of the multiplicative model, the ratios $z_t = y_t/(Y_t S_t)$ measure the product of cyclical and irregular fluctuations. If the irregular fluctuations are of a minor nature, they may be removed by smoothing the z_t series with the method of moving averages.

Periodogram Analysis. In some simple cases, the cyclical component z_t may be represented by a trigonometric formula of the form

$$(7.4.1) \qquad z_t = \alpha + \beta \sin \frac{2\pi t}{T} + \gamma \cos \frac{2\pi t}{T} + \epsilon_t,$$

where T is the period of the cycle and ϵ_t is the irregular component. If T is known and the number of observations N is an integral multiple of T, say $N = mT$, where m is the number of complete cycles included in the analysis, the least-squares estimates of α, β, and γ are given by

$$\hat{\alpha} = \frac{1}{N} \sum_{t=1}^{N} z_t = \frac{1}{T} \sum_{u=1}^{T} \bar{Z}_u,$$

$$(7.4.2) \qquad \hat{\beta} = \frac{2}{T} \sum_{u=1}^{T} \bar{Z}_u \sin \frac{2\pi u}{T},$$

$$\hat{\gamma} = \frac{2}{T} \sum_{u=1}^{T} \bar{Z}_u \cos \frac{2\pi u}{T},$$

where

$$\bar{Z}_u = \frac{1}{m} \sum_{v=0}^{m-1} z_{u+vT}, \qquad u = 1, 2, \ldots, T.$$

If the period of the cycle T is not known, then a number of trial values, say $T_1, T_2, \ldots$, are taken and for each such trial value of T the estimates $\hat{\beta}_T$, $\hat{\gamma}_T$ are computed and the amplitude $S_T^2 = \hat{\beta}_T^2 + \hat{\gamma}_T^2$ is obtained. Then the desired period is the one which maximizes the amplitude. Since this method is laborious, an alternative method is, for each trial value of T, to arrange the successive values z_t in rows of T values each, omitting the incomplete rows. For each of T columns in this arrangement the mean value is computed, and the value of δ_T = largest mean minus smallest mean is obtained. Then the desired value of T is one which maximizes δ_T.

Illustrative Example 7.7. Table 7.11 gives the residuals (trend ratios) z_t of a certain time series.

TABLE 7.11

RESIDUALS (TREND RATIO) OF A TIME SERIES

t	z_t	t	z_t	t	z_t
1	103.6	13	95.5	25	104.8
2	98.3	14	97.6	26	106.0
3	94.4	15	104.1	27	100.1
4	96.8	16	104.0	28	93.8
				29	96.9
5	103.4	17	97.7	30	104.3
6	104.3	18	95.5	31	103.0
7	100.0	19	99.3	32	99.1
8	94.2	20	104.8	33	94.5
9	100.1	21	105.6	34	99.2
10	104.9	22	98.1	35	104.8
11	104.2	23	96.3		
12	97.2	24	99.8		

A harmonic curve of the form

$$Z_t = a + b \sin \frac{2\pi t}{T} + c \cos \frac{2\pi t}{T}$$

is chosen to fit the above data. Plotting z_t against t in Chart 7.2, we find that the graph is periodic with period $T = 5$, approximately. We then arrange the data in rows of five entries each as shown in Table 7.12. The average of the uth column is denoted by $\bar{Z}_u$, and we get $d_5 = \max (\bar{Z}_1, \bar{Z}_2, \ldots, \bar{Z}_5) - \min (\bar{Z}_1, \bar{Z}_2, \ldots, \bar{Z}_5) = 9.55$.

Similarly taking other trial values of $T = 3, 4, 6,$ and 7, we compute for each such T the value of d_T, omitting the last incomplete row, if any. These values are presented in Table 7.13. From this table we see that d_T reaches a maximum when $T = 5$. So we take $T = 5$ years as the period of the cycle and fit a harmonic curve of the form

$$Z_t = a + b \sin \frac{2\pi t}{5} + c \cos \frac{2\pi t}{5}.$$

TABLE 7.12

z_t ARRANGED IN ROWS OF 5

$u = 1$	1	2	3	4	5
	103.6	98.3	94.4	96.8	103.4
	104.3	100.0	94.2	100.1	104.9
	104.2	97.2	95.5	97.6	104.1
	104.0	97.7	95.5	99.3	104.8
	105.6	98.1	96.3	99.8	104.8
	106.0	100.1	93.8	96.9	104.3
	103.0	99.1	94.5	99.2	104.8
Total	730.7	690.5	664.2	689.7	731.1
Mean $\overline{Z}_u$	104.39	98.64	94.89	98.53	104.44

TABLE 7.13

PERIODOGRAM ANALYSIS: VALUES OF d_T

T	3	4	5	6	7
d_T	0.44	2.41	9.55	1.34	1.40

We now use formula 7.4.2 to evaluate the constants. The details of the computation are as follows:

TABLE 7.14

FITTING A HARMONIC CURVE

u	$\overline{Z}_u$	$\sin \dfrac{2\pi u}{5}$	$\cos \dfrac{2\pi u}{5}$	$a + b \sin \dfrac{2\pi u}{5} + c \cos \dfrac{2\pi u}{5}$
1	104.39	0.9511	0.3090	104.4462
2	98.64	0.5878	−0.8090	98.5861
3	94.89	−0.5878	−0.8090	94.9287
4	98.53	−0.9511	0.3090	98.5283
5	104.44	0.0000	1.0000	104.4106

Then, we obtain

$$a = \tfrac{1}{5} \Sigma \, \overline{Z}_u = 100.18,$$

$$b = \tfrac{2}{5} \, \Sigma \, \overline{Z}_u \sin \frac{2\pi u}{5} = 3.1111,$$

$$c = \tfrac{2}{5} \Sigma \, \overline{Z}_u \cos \frac{2\pi u}{5} = 4.2306.$$

The last column of Table 7.14 gives the fitted values. The trend ratios, together with the fitted harmonic curve, are shown on Chart 7.2.

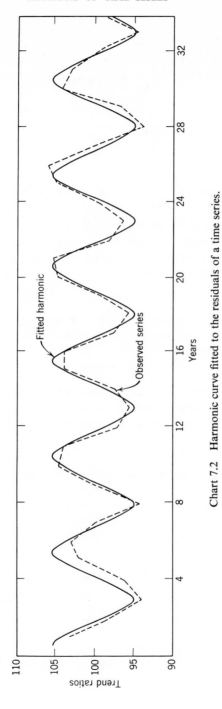

Chart 7.2   Harmonic curve fitted to the residuals of a time series.

7.5 CORRELOGRAM

Serial Correlation. The coefficient of correlation between the observations y_t and y_{t+k} (at an interval of k units apart) of a time series y_t, $t = 1$, $2, \ldots, N$ is called the serial or autocorrelation r_k of order k. Thus we have

$$r_k = \frac{\sum\limits_{t=1}^{N-k}(y_t - \bar{y}')(y_{t+k} - \bar{y}'')}{\left[\sum\limits_{t=1}^{N-k}(y_t - \bar{y}')^2 \sum\limits_{t=1}^{N-k}(y_{t+k} - \bar{y}'')^2\right]^{\frac{1}{2}}},$$

where

$$\bar{y}' = \frac{1}{N-k}\sum_{t=1}^{N-k}y_t \quad \text{and} \quad \bar{y}'' = \frac{1}{N-k}\sum_{t=1}^{N-k}y_{t+k}.$$

The graph obtained by plotting r_k against k is called the correlogram.

The correlogram may be used to distinguish between different types of time series. If the series is generated by a moving average of a finite number of random elements, say,

$$y_t = a_1\epsilon_t + a_2\epsilon_{t+1} + \cdots + a_m\epsilon_{t+m-1},$$

where ϵ_t's are uncorrelated random variables with a common variance and a_j's are constants, then the autocorrelations of order m vanish. If the series is harmonic of the form

$$y_t = \alpha \sin \theta_t + \epsilon_t,$$

then the correlogram is also harmonic with the same period as the original series. If y_t is the sum of several harmonic terms, the correlogram will be of a sinusoidal type. If the series is autoregressive of the from

$$y_t = \alpha y_{t-1} + \beta y_{t-2} + \epsilon_t, \qquad 4\beta > \alpha^2,$$

the correlogram is a damped harmonic, that is, periodic with diminishing amplitudes.

Lag Correlation. With two correlated time series x_t and y_t, $t = 1$, $2, \ldots, N$, the coefficient of correlation between the observations x_t and y_{t+k}, k units of time apart, is called the lag correlation R_k of lag k. Thus we have

$$R_k = \frac{\sum\limits_{t=1}^{N-k}(x_t - \bar{x}')(y_{t+k} - \bar{y}')}{\left[\sum\limits_{t=1}^{N-k}(x_t - \bar{x}')^2 \sum\limits_{t=1}^{N-k}(y_{t+k} - \bar{y}')^2\right]^{\frac{1}{2}}},$$

where

$$\bar{x}' = \frac{1}{N-k}\sum_{t=1}^{N-k}x_t \quad \text{and} \quad \bar{y}' = \frac{1}{N-k}\sum_{t=1}^{N-k}y_{t+k}.$$

7.6 EXERCISES

Trend

7.1–7.7. For each of the time series given below find the trend component by (a) *the method of moving averages and* (b) *fitting an appropriate polynomial or other mathematical function.*

Plot the original series and the trend component on a graph.

Compute the ratios of the original figures to the trend component and plot these trend ratios on a graph.

7.1. Table 7.15 gives the national income of the United States in billion dollars, 1919–57.

TABLE 7.15

NATIONAL INCOME IN THE UNITED STATES, 1919–57
(IN BILLION DOLLARS)

Year	National income	Year	National income	Year	National income
1919	70.2	1932	42.5	1945	181.2
20	79.1	33	40.2	46	180.9
21	64.0	34	49.0	47	198.2
22	63.1	35	57.1	48	223.5
23	74.3	36	64.9	49	217.7
24	75.2	37	73.6	50	241.9
25	78.2	38	67.6	51	279.3
26	83.7	39	72.8	52	292.2
27	81.7	40	81.6	53	305.6
28	82.8	41	104.7	54	301.8
29	87.8	42	137.7	55	330.2
30	75.7	43	170.3	56	349.4
31	59.7	44	182.6	57	364.0

Source: *Historical Statistics of the United States.*

7.2. Table 7.16 gives the production of bituminous coal in million short tons in the United States, 1850–1956.

7.3. Table 7.17 gives the index number of agricultural production in India, 1939–40 to 1958–59, with the crop year 1950–51 as base = 100.

7.4. Table 7.18 gives the mean annual temperature in degrees Fahrenheit and the annual total precipitation in inches in New York City, 1826–1957.

7.5. Table 7.19 gives the production, in million long tons, of iron ore and steel in the United States, 1880–1956.

TABLE 7.16

PRODUCTION OF BITUMINOUS COAL IN THE UNITED STATES,
1850–1956 (IN MILLION SHORT TONS)

Year	Production	Year	Production	Year	Production
1850	4	1886	75	1922	422
51	5	87	89	23	565
52	5	88	102	24	484
53	6	89	96	25	520
54	7	90	111	26	573
55	8	91	118	27	518
56	8	92	127	28	501
57	9	93	128	29	535
58	9	94	119	30	468
59	9	95	135	31	382
60	9	96	138	32	310
61	9	97	148	33	334
62	9	98	167	34	359
63	10	99	193	35	372
64	11	1900	212	36	439
65	12	01	226	37	446
66	13	02	260	38	349
67	14	03	283	39	395
68	16	04	279	40	461
69	20	05	315	41	514
70	20	06	343	42	583
71	23	07	395	43	590
72	27	08	332	44	620
73	32	09	380	45	578
74	31	10	417	46	534
75	33	11	406	47	631
76	32	12	450	48	600
77	34	13	478	49	438
78	36	14	423	50	516
79	40	15	443	51	534
80	51	16	502	52	467
81	52	17	552	53	457
82	59	18	579	54	392
83	65	19	466	55	465
84	72	20	569	56	501
85	72	21	416		

Source: *Historical Statistics of the United States.*

TABLE 7.17

INDEX NUMBER OF AGRICULTURAL PRODUCTION IN INDIA,
1939–40 TO 1958–59
Base: crop year 1950–51 = 100

Year	Index no.	Year	Index no.
1939–40	105.3	1949–50	106.4
40–41	104.3	50–51	100.0
41–42	101.1	51–52	101.1
42–43	108.5	52–53	111.7
43–44	112.8	53–54	127.7
44–45	107.4	54–55	129.8
45–46	100.0	55–56	130.9
46–47	102.0	56–57	139.4
47–48	106.4	57–58	127.7
48–49	101.1	58–59	148.9

Source: Records and statistics, *Eastern Economist*.

TABLE 7.18

Mean Temperature and Total Precipitation in New York City, 1826–1951

Year	Annual mean temperature (°F)	Annual total precipitation (in.)	Year	Annual mean temperature (°F)	Annual total precipitation (in.)
1826	52	55.7	1861	53	37.2
27	52	51.1	62	52	46.8
28	54	48.9	63	52	43.4
29	52	45.8	64	53	39.5
30	55	43.3	65	54	45.0
31	52	38.8	66	52	38.3
32	52	39.2	67	51	53.4
33	52	37.7	68	50	57.4
34	51	33.6	69	52	43.6
35	50	28.8	70	53	37.8
36	47	36.6	71	51	49.2
37	49	32.1	72	51	40.3
38	50	33.7	73	51	45.5
39	51	33.4	74	51	44.2
40	51	35.5	75	49	38.6
41	51	44.6	76	52	40.6
42	53	41.6	77	52	38.7
43	51	35.7	78	53	46.0
44	52	39.8	79	52	37.1
45	53	33.7	80	53	34.7
46	52	35.9	81	52	35.0
47	52	44.5	82	52	43.0
48	52	32.8	83	50	34.4
49	50	30.1	84	52	49.7
50	51	44.6	85	51	33.5
51	52	38.8	86	51	38.3
52	51	35.3	87	51	41.7
53	52	46.4	88	49	51.0
54	51	43.5	89	52	54.4
55	51	43.2	90	52	43.7
56	50	35.0	91	54	37.6
57	50	38.7	92	52	34.1
58	51	36.7	93	50	46.6
59	52	59.7	94	52	39.3
60	52	31.1	95	52	33.7

TABLE 7.18 (*continued*)

Year	Annual mean temperature (°F)	Annual total precipitation (in.)	Year	Annual mean temperature (°F)	Annual total precipitation (in.)
1896	53	40.1	1927	53	56.1
97	53	42.4	28	54	45.6
98	54	46.2	29	54	40.4
99	53	36.8	30	54	39.0
			31	56	36.1
1900	54	39.4	32	55	43.9
01	52	47.0	33	54	53.5
02	53	50.3	34	53	49.8
03	52	55.5	35	53	33.8
04	50	39.5	36	53	49.8
05	53	35.5	37	54	53.0
06	54	39.4	38	55	48.5
07	52	43.8			
08	55	39.4	39	55	38.6
09	53	39.9	40	52	45.1
10	53	32.7	41	55	39.0
11	53	46.5	42	54	48.5
12	52	44.2	43	54	36.7
13	55	56.1	44	55	45.0
14	52	38.5	45	54	45.0
15	53	43.1	46	55	38.4
16	52	36.7	47	54	40.8
17	50	39.6	48	54	46.9
18	53	36.9	49	57	36.2
19	54	50.8	50	54	36.9
20	52	53.2	51	55	44.4
21	55	37.8	52	55	41.5
22	54	44.7	53	57	45.2
23	53	40.6	54	55	35.6
24	52	41.7	55	55	39.9
25	53	41.4	56	54	36.2
26	51	47.8	57	56	36.5

Source: *Historical Statistics of the United States.*

TABLE 7.19

Production of Iron Ore and Steel in the United States, 1880–1956 (in million long tons)

Year	Iron ore	Steel	Year	Iron ore	Steel	Year	Iron ore	Steel
1880	7.1	1.2	1906	47.8	23.4	1932	9.8	13.7
81	7.1	1.6	07	51.7	23.4	33	17.6	23.2
82	9.0	1.7	08	36.0	14.0	34	24.6	26.1
83	8.4	1.7	09	51.3	24.0	35	30.5	34.1
84	8.2	1.6	10	57.0	26.1	36	48.8	47.8
85	7.6	1.7	11	43.9	23.7	37	72.1	50.6
86	10.0	2.6	12	55.2	31.3	38	28.4	28.3
87	11.3	3.3	13	62.0	31.3	39	51.7	47.1
88	12.1	2.9	14	41.4	23.5	40	73.7	59.8
89	14.5	3.4	15	55.5	32.2	41	92.4	74.0
90	16.0	4.3	16	75.2	42.8	42	105.5	76.8
91	14.6	3.9	17	75.3	45.1	43	101.2	79.3
92	16.3	4.9	18	69.7	44.5	44	94.1	80.0
93	11.6	4.0	19	61.0	34.7	45	88.4	71.2
94	11.9	4.4	20	67.6	42.1	46	70.8	59.5
95	16.0	6.1	21	29.5	19.8	47	93.1	75.8
96	16.0	5.3	22	47.1	35.6	48	101.0	79.1
97	17.5	7.2	23	69.4	44.9	49	84.9	69.6
98	19.4	8.9	24	54.3	37.9	50	98.0	86.5
99	24.6	10.6	25	61.9	45.4	51	116.5	93.9
1900	27.3	10.2	26	67.6	48.3	52	97.9	83.2
01	28.6	13.5	27	61.7	44.9	53	118.0	99.7
02	35.3	15.0	28	62.2	51.5	54	78.1	78.8
03	34.8	14.5	29	73.0	56.4	55	103.0	104.5
04	27.5	13.9	30	58.4	40.7	56	97.8	102.9
05	42.4	20.0	31	31.1	25.9			

Source: *Historical Statistics of the United States.*

TABLE 7.20

Consumer Price Index in the United States, 1931–57
Base 1947–49 = 100

Year	Index	Year	Index
1931	65.0	1945	76.9
32	58.4	46	83.4
33	55.3	47	95.5
34	57.2	48	102.8
35	58.7	49	101.8
		50	102.8
36	59.3	51	111.0
37	61.4	52	113.5
38	60.3	53	114.5
39	59.4	54	114.8
40	59.9	55	114.5
41	62.9	56	116.2
42	69.7	57	120.2
43	74.0		
44	75.2		

Source: *Historical Statistics of the United States.*

7.6. Table 7.20 gives the consumer price index in the United States, 1931–57, with the years 1947–49 as base = 100.

7.7. Table 7.21 gives the amount of checks in million rupees passing through the Calcutta clearing house annually during the period 1900–52.

TABLE 7.21

AMOUNT OF CHECKS PASSING ANNUALLY THROUGH
CALCUTTA CLEARING HOUSE, 1900–52 (IN MILLION RUPEES)
1 U.S. dollar = 7.50 Indian rupees approx.

Year	Amount	Year	Amount	Year	Amount
1900	1,390	1921	9,167	1941	12,021
01	1,330	22	9,443	42	10,577
02	1,460	23	8,915	43	15,446
03	1,420	24	9,225	44	22,228
04	1,410	25	10,183	45	26,497
05	1,750	26	9,494	46	29,740
06	2,060	27	10,239	47	25,396
07	2,244	28	10,882	48	27,079
08	2,128	29	9,977	49	24,591
09	1,978	30	8,931	50	22,724
10	2,224	31	7,563	51	31,188
11	2,576	32	7,555	52	27,040
12	2,883	33	8,237		
13	3,330	34	8,607		
14	2,803	35	9,331		
15	3,227	36	8,857		
16	4,802	37	10,054		
17	4,719	38	9,146		
18	7,442	39	10,753		
19	9,025	40	10,653		
20	15,339				

Source: *Banking and Monetary Statistics of India.*

Seasonal index

7.8–7.9. *For each of the time series given below calculate the indices of seasonal variations by the method of* (a) *the moving averages and* (b) *the link relatives.*

7.8. Table 7.22 gives the crude birth rates (number of live births per 1000) in the United States, 1949–59.

7.9. Table 7.23 gives the price of gold in the Bombay bullion market in rupees per tola, 1953–59.

TABLE 7.22

CRUDE BIRTH RATES (NUMBER OF LIVE BIRTHS PER 1000)
IN THE UNITED STATES, 1949–59

						Year					
Month	1949	1950	1951	1952	1953	1954	1955	1956	1957	1958	1959
Jan.	23.0	22.9	23.5	24.1	24.7	25.4	24.7	24.4	24.3	23.8	23.7
Feb.	23.8	23.4	23.7	24.1	24.7	24.7	24.5	24.5	24.5	23.9	24.4
Mar.	23.9	22.7	24.0	24.1	24.5	23.7	24.1	24.6	24.3	23.6	23.8
Apr.	22.5	20.8	23.2	23.0	22.0	23.1	22.8	23.2	23.6	23.1	23.3
May	22.1	21.1	23.7	22.5	22.9	23.2	23.4	22.3	23.8	23.3	22.6
June	23.5	23.1	24.1	24.1	24.4	24.5	23.7	24.4	24.8	24.3	24.0
July	25.1	24.7	25.1	25.8	26.3	26.1	25.4	26.1	26.6	24.8	25.3
Aug.	25.9	25.4	25.9	26.7	26.7	26.9	26.2	26.6	25.8	24.9	25.5
Sept.	25.9	25.3	25.9	26.9	26.5	26.6	26.8	27.5	26.7	26.3	25.6
Oct.	24.9	24.4	25.3	25.3	25.1	25.5	25.0	25.4	26.0	25.2	24.4
Nov.	24.2	23.5	24.3	24.4	24.0	25.1	24.8	25.2	24.5	23.8	23.5
Dec.	23.5	23.1	23.4	24.0	24.7	24.9	24.4	25.1	24.6	24.1	23.2

Source: *U.N. Monthly Bulletin of Statistics.*

TABLE 7.23

PRICE OF GOLD IN BOMBAY BULLION MARKET
(IN RUPEES PER TOLA)
1 U.S. dollar = 7.50 Indian rupees approx.
1 tola = 11.6 gm approx.

				Year			
Month	1953	1954	1955	1956	1957	1958	1959
Jan.	87	83	90	96	106	110	117
Feb.	90	87	93	98	108	113	118
Mar.	87	89	93	104	106	112	120
Apr.	87	93	96	104	106	113	122
May	87	91	94	104	108	112	122
June	91	85	94	103	106	109	121
July	88	85	94	101	107	106	120
Aug.	88	88	95	104	108	107	121
Sept.	87	87	95	103	108	108	122
Oct.	82	87	95	104	107	109	124
Nov.	83	88	96	105	109	113	125
Dec.	82	88	94	104	108	114	125

7.10. Table 7.24 gives the estimated personal expenditure on fuel and light in the United Kingdom. Assuming a linear trend, calculate the seasonal index. Forecast the expenditures for the first three quarters of 1948.

TABLE 7.24

EXPENDITURE ON FUEL AND LIGHT (IN MILLION POUNDS)
IN THE UNITED KINGDOM

Quarter	1945	1946	1947
First	78	84	92
Second	62	64	70
Third	56	61	63
Fourth	71	82	85

7.11. The numbers (in hundreds) of letters posted in a certain city on each day in a period of five consecutive weeks are given in Table 7.25. Calculate indices of fluctuations between the days in a week.

TABLE 7.25

NUMBER (IN HUNDREDS) OF LETTERS POSTED IN A CERTAIN CITY

Week	Sun-day	Mon-day	Tues-day	Wednes-day	Thurs-day	Friday	Satur-day
				Day			
First	18	161	170	154	143	161	76
Second	18	165	179	157	168	195	85
Third	21	162	169	153	139	185	82
Fourth	24	171	182	170	162	179	95
Fifth	27	172	196	180	170	202	120

Cyclical fluctuations

7.12–7.18. For each of the series of residuals (trend ratios) obtained in exercises 7.1–7.7, (a) determine the period of the cyclical fluctuations (if any) by the method of periodogram analysis, and (b) fit a suitable harmonic curve to the residual series.

PART III

Statistical Inference

CHAPTER 1

Probability

1.1 DEFINITION

The theory of probability is a branch of mathematics, evolved in connection with the study of the occurrence of chance phenomena. It had its origin in gambling and games of chance. But now, as a tool for drawing rigorous inductive inference, it has found applications in many branches of science.

Random Experiment. The concept of a random experiment is fundamental in the theory of probability. It is common knowledge that many experiments, when repeated even under identical conditions, do not always yield the same result, but the set of all possible outcomes of an experiment is fixed. For example, if the experiment consists in throwing a homogeneous die with faces marked one, two, . . . , six, and noting the side that turns up, there are only six possible outcomes: side one, two, . . . , six. But in repetitions of the experiment, we do not expect the same result throughout; sometimes side one will turn up, sometimes two and so on. Although the result of a single throw is unpredictable and varies in an apparently irregular manner from one throw to another, there is a striking regularity when a very large number of such throws is considered. When a homogeneous die is thrown independently and under identical conditions a very large number of times, the proportion of cases where a one (or a two · · · or a six) turns up is found to be nearly one sixth. This is a simple example of what is known as a random experiment. Some other examples are drawing a "hand" from a well-shuffled pack of cards, selecting a sample of articles from a lot for inspection, and repeated determinations of the velocity of light.

A random experiment thus has a well defined set of possible outcomes. It can be repeated an indefinitely large number of times, independently and under identical conditions. The outcome of any particular trial is unpredictable. However, if we denote by f_n the number of times a particular outcome E occurs in n repetitions of the experiment, as n increases indefinitely the relative frequency f_n/n tends to stabilize about a limiting value p, which we may intuitively call the *probability* of the outcome E.

For the random experiment of throwing a homogeneous die, we may then say that the probability is one sixth that the face marked one will turn up. Let us now consider the "event" A that in this random experiment a face marked with an odd digit will turn up. This can happen only if the face marked one, three, or five turns up.

Intuitively, we feel that in a large number of repetitions the event A will occur with a relative frequency of about $\frac{1}{6} + \frac{1}{6} + \frac{1}{6} = \frac{1}{2}$. This can also be experimentally verified. Intuition, however, may not be so readily useful in computing probabilities of more complicated events, like getting a total of 10 when three such dice are simultaneously thrown. A calculus of probability is required, and to develop this calculus certain abstractions are essential.

Sample Space. A random experiment has a well-defined set of possible outcomes which we may regard as points in a space, called the *sample space*. For the sake of simplicity we shall consider only discrete sample spaces consisting of a countable number of points. With each point in the sample space is associated a number p, $0 \leq p \leq 1$, called the *probability* of the point, such that the total of the probabilities for all the points in the sample space is unity. For purposes of mathematical treatment, the sample space and the probabilities attached to the points in the sample space are regarded as given entities. For practical applications of the mathematical theory, however, the enumeration of outcomes and the assignment of probabilities to them are done either from experience of past repetitions of the random experiment or from theoretical considerations of the subject-matter field.

Event. Consider an event A which consists in the occurrence of one out of a given subset of all the possible outcomes of the random experiment. Thus the event A may be looked upon as a given collection of points in the sample space. The probability of the event A is then defined as the sum of the probabilities of the points constituting the event A.

Illustrative Example 1.1. A lake contains an unknown number N of fish, from which M are caught, marked with red spots, and then released back into the lake. After a while, n fish are caught again. The probability that the second catch contains exactly m spotted fish can be computed in the following way.

The sample space in this case consists of $\binom{N}{n}$ points, each corresponding to a combination of n out of the total number of N fish in the lake. To each

of these we attach a probability $1/\binom{N}{n}$. The event of getting m spotted
fish in the second catch corresponds to those points in the sample space
that represent exactly $n - m$ unmarked and m marked fish. There are
obviously $\binom{N - M}{n - m}\binom{M}{m}$ such points. Hence, from definition, the
required probability is

$$P(m) = \binom{N - M}{n - m}\binom{M}{m}\Big/\binom{N}{n}.$$

In this expression, N is the only unknown number. If the number of
spotted fish in the second catch is actually m, intuition suggests that the
value $\hat{N}$ of N for which $P(N)$ is maximum may be taken as an estimate of
N. It is easily verified that $\hat{N} = [Mn/m]$, where $[x]$ denotes the largest
integer not exceeding x.

1.2 PROBABILITY CALCULUS

Combination of Events. Let A_1 and A_2 be two events. The notation
$A_1 + A_2$ is used for the event of the occurrence of at least one of the events
A_1 and A_2, and the notation A_1A_2 for the event of the simultaneous occurrence of both A_1 and A_2. Events are said to be *mutually exclusive* if the
occurrence of one precludes the occurrence of any of the others. They are
said to be *exhaustive* if at least one of them must occur. The notation $P(A)$
will be used for the probability that the event A will occur.

For the probability of occurrence of at least one of the two events A_1
and A_2, we then have the formula

(1.2.1) $\qquad P(A_1 + A_2) = P(A_1) + P(A_2) - P(A_1A_2).$

A generalization of this formula says that the probability of occurrence
of at least one of the m events $A_1, A_2, \ldots, A_m$ is given by

(1.2.2) $\quad P(A_1 + A_2 + \cdots + A_m) = S_1 - S_2 + S_3 - \cdots + (-1)^{m-1}S_m,$

where $S_1 = \sum\limits_{i=1}^{m} P(A_i)$, $S_2 = \sum\limits_{i<j=1}^{m} P(A_iA_j)$, $S_3 = \sum\limits_{i<j<k=1}^{m} P(A_iA_jA_k)$, and so
on, until finally $S_m = P(A_1A_2 \cdots A_m)$. If the events are mutually exclusive,
this reduces to

$$P(A_1 + A_2 + \cdots + A_m) = P(A_1) + P(A_2) + \cdots + P(A_m)$$

The probability $P_{(k)}$ that exactly k among the m events $A_1, A_2, \ldots, A_m$
will occur is likewise given by

(1.2.3) $\quad P_{(k)} = S_k - \binom{k + 1}{k}S_{k+1} + \binom{k + 2}{k}S_{k+2} - \cdots \pm S_m.$

Illustrative Example 1.2. To examine whether a person had extra-sensory perception (ESP) he was blindfolded and a set of m cards, numbered serially from 1 to m, was presented before him in a haphazard order. He was then asked to guess the numbers on these cards. What is the probability that, because of sheer chance, he would correctly read the numbers on exactly k of the cards?

We assume that the person has no ESP. There are $m!$ ways of reading out the numbers, which we take as the points in our sample space and attach to each point the probability $1/m!$. Let A_i denote the event that the number on the ith card will be read correctly. A little consideration then shows that $P(A_i) = 1/m$, $P(A_iA_j) = 1/m(m-1)$, etc., and finally $P(A_1A_2 \cdots A_m) = 1/m!$. To find the probability $P_{(k)}$ of the subject's reading exactly k cards correctly we use formula 1.2.3. Here S_t is the sum of $\binom{m}{t}$ terms, each equal to $1/[m(m-1) \cdots (m-t+1)] = (m-t)!/m!$, so that $S_t = 1/t!$. Hence, finally

$$P_{(k)} = \frac{1}{k!}\left(1 - \frac{1}{1!} + \frac{1}{2!} - \frac{1}{3!} + \cdots + (-1)^m \frac{1}{m!}\right).$$

Even for moderately large m, the approximation $P_{(k)} \simeq e^{-1}/k!$ gives quite good results.

Conditional Probability, Stochastic Independence. The conditional probability of an event A_2, given that A_1 has happened, is defined by

$$P(A_2 \mid A_1) = \frac{P(A_1A_2)}{P(A_1)},$$

provided that $P(A_1) \neq 0$. Thus we have

(1.2.4) $P(A_1A_2) = P(A_1)P(A_2 \mid A_1).$

The events A_1 and A_2 are said to be *stochastically independent* if

(1.2.5) $P(A_1A_2) = P(A_1)P(A_2)$

The concept of stochastic independence can be generalized for the case of an arbitrary number of events as follows. The events $A_1, A_2, \cdots, A_m$ are called mutually independent if the following relations hold:

$$P(A_iA_j) = P(A_i)P(A_j) \qquad \text{for all } i, j,$$

$$P(A_iA_jA_k) = P(A_i)P(A_j)P(A_k) \qquad \text{for all } i, j, k,$$

(1.2.6) $\cdots \qquad\qquad \cdots \qquad\qquad \cdots$

$$P(A_1A_2 \cdots A_m) = P(A_1)P(A_2) \cdots P(A_m).$$

Illustrative Example 1.3. The probability that a target will be hit in one shot is p. What is the probability that of n independent shots under identical conditions at least one will hit the target?

Let A_i denote the event that the ith shot fails to hit the target; then $P(A_i) = 1 - p$. The probability that the events $A_1, A_2, \ldots, A_n$ will occur simultaneously, that is, that all n shots will miss the target, is then given by $P(A_1 A_2 \cdots A_n) = (1 - p)^n$ because these events are independent. Hence the probability that at least one shot will hit the target is $P = 1 - (1 - p)^n$. It may be noted that from this formula we can determine the smallest number of shots at the target to ensure a high enough probability of at least one of them hitting it.

BAYES'S FORMULA. Suppose that an event B can happen only in combination with one of the m events $A_1, A_2, \ldots, A_m$, which are mutually exclusive. Let $P(A_j) = p_j$ and $P(B \mid A_j) = \pi_j, j = 1, 2, \ldots, m$. Then the conditional probability of A_j, given that B has occurred, is expressed by

$$(1.2.7) \qquad P(A_j \mid B) = \frac{p_j \pi_j}{\sum\limits_{j=1}^{m} p_j \pi_j}.$$

This is known as Bayes's formula.

1.3 RANDOM VARIABLES AND PROBABILITY DISTRIBUTIONS

Univariate Distribution. Sometimes the result of a random experiment is expressed as a numerical quantity, such as the number of heads obtained by tossing three coins. The variable quantity which represents the result of a random experiment is called a *random variable*, and we shall denote it by X. Formally, we can look upon a random variable X as a rule that associates with each point E in the sample space a number x. For a discrete sample space, we consider all the sample points with each of which a given number x is associated, and denote by $p(x)$ the sum of the probabilities of all these points. We can then say that the probability that the random variable X assumes the value x is $p(x)$. This statement is written as $P(X = x) = p(x)$. This, regarded as a function of x, is called the *probability distribution* of X.

The probability $F(x)$ that the random variable X assumes a value not exceeding x will be denoted by

$$(1.3.1) \qquad F(x) = P(X \leq x).$$

This, regarded as a function of x, is called the cumulative distribution function or simply the *distribution function* of the random variable X. When the sample space is discrete, we have $F(x) = \sum_{a \leq x} p(a)$. A rigorous treatment of random variables defined on general sample spaces, not necessarily discrete, requires the use of measure theory and will not be given here. However, in, most problems, once the distribution function of a random variable is available, further references to the original sample space become unnecessary. It is convenient therefore to study the properties of random variable through their distribution functions. We will now discuss two special types of distributions which are encountered very often in practical applications.

DISCRETE DISTRIBUTION. A random variable X is said to be of the *discrete type* if it takes only a finite or countably infinite number of values x_j ($j = 1, 2, \ldots$) with the probabilities p_j ($p_j \geq 0$), so that $P(X = x_j) = p_j$, where $\sum_j p_j = 1$. The distribution function $F(x)$ is then given by

$$(1.3.2) \qquad\qquad F(x) = \sum_{x_j \leq x} p_j.$$

The summation extends over all values of j for which $x_j \leq x$. The distribution function in this case is thus a step function.

ABSOLUTELY CONTINUOUS DISTRIBUTION. A random variable X is said to be of the *absolutely continuous type* if its distribution function $F(x)$ can be expressed as

$$(1.3.3) \qquad\qquad F(x) = \int_{-\infty}^{x} f(y)\, dy,$$

where $f(x) = F'(x)$ is called the *probability density function* of the random variable X. Obviously $f(x) \geq 0$ for every x, and $\int_{-\infty}^{\infty} f(x)\, dx = 1$.

A random variable X is said to be *bounded* if there exist two finite numbers a and b ($a < b$) such that $F(a) = 0$ and $F(b) = 1$, where $F(x)$ is the distribution function of X.

Bivariate Distributions. When the result of a random experiment is expressed by means of two numerical quantities, we get two random variables X and Y defined on the same sample space. For a given pair of real numbers x and y, we consider the probability of the simultaneous event that $X \leq x$ and $Y \leq y$. We denote it by

$$(1.3.4) \qquad\qquad F(x, y) = P(X \leq x, Y \leq y).$$

We call $F(x, y)$ the bivariate distribution function of the random variables X and Y.

MARGINAL AND CONDITIONAL DISTRIBUTIONS. In the discrete case each of the variables X and Y assumes only a set of countable values x_j and y_k, $j, k = 1, 2, \ldots$, with probabilities

$$p_{jk} = P(X = x_j, Y = y_k),$$

where $p_{jk} \geq 0$ and $\sum_{j,k} p_{jk} = 1$. We denote by p_{j0} the probability that X

assumes the value x_j without any regard to the values assumed by Y. Then

(1.3.5) $$p_{j0} = P(X = x_j) = \sum_k p_{jk},$$

so that $p_{j0} \geq 0$ and $\sum_j p_{j0} = 1$. This univariate discrete distribution is said to be the *marginal distribution* of X. In a similar manner we can define the marginal distribution of Y.

If p_{j0} as defined in 1.3.5 is positive, then the conditional probability of the event that Y assumes the value y_k, given that X has the value x_j, is defined as

(1.3.6) $$P(Y = y_k \mid X = x_j) = \frac{p_{jk}}{p_{j0}}.$$

This univariate discrete distribution is said to be the *conditional distribution* of Y, given that X assumes the value x_j. We can define the conditional distribution of X for a given value of Y in a similar manner.

For a bivariate distribution of the absolutely continuous type there exists a probability density function $f(x, y) = \partial^2 F(x, y)/(\partial x \, \partial y)$ for all x and y which satisfies the relations $f(x, y) \geq 0$ for every x and y, and $\int_{-\infty}^{\infty} \int_{-\infty}^{\infty} f(x, y) \, dx \, dy = 1$. In such a case the marginal distribution function of X is also absolutely continuous, and its probability density function is given by

(1.3.7) $$f_1(x) = \int_{-\infty}^{\infty} f(x, y) \, dy.$$

The probability density function of the marginal distribution of Y is similarly given by $f_2(y) = \int_{-\infty}^{\infty} f(x, y) \, dx$. For every fixed x for which $f_1(x) > 0$ the function

(1.3.8) $$f(y \mid x) = \frac{f(x, y)}{f_1(x)}$$

is defined as the conditional probability density function of Y, given that $X = x$. The other conditional probability density function of X, given that $Y = y$, is also similarly defined.

p-Variate Distributions $(p > 2)$. The preceding discussion can be readily generalized to the case of distributions of more than two random variables. Let $X_1, X_2, \ldots, X_p$ be p random variables, all of which are simultaneously observed in the same random experiment. Then we define

(1.3.9) $$F(x_1, x_2, \ldots, x_p) = P(X_1, \leq x_1, X_2 \leq x_2, \ldots, X_p \leq x_p)$$

as the p-variate distribution function of the random variables $X_1, X_2, \ldots, X_p$. We have p-variate distributions of the discrete type as well as of the absolutely continuous type. Marginal and conditional distributions are also defined as in the bivariate case.

INDEPENDENCE OF RANDOM VARIABLES. The p random variables $X_1, X_2, \ldots, X_p$ are said to be mutually independent if their joint distribution function is the product of the marginal distribution functions. In other words,

$$(1.3.10) \quad P(X_1 \leq x_1, X_2 \leq x_2, \ldots, X_p \leq x_p)$$
$$= P(X_1 \leq x_1)P(X_2 \leq x_2) \cdots P(X_p \leq x_p)$$

holds for all values of $x_1, x_2, \ldots, x_p$.

For p-variate discrete distributions, 1.3.10 is equivalent to the condition that

$$(1.3.11) \quad P(X_1 = x_1, X_2 = x_2, \ldots, X_p = x_p)$$
$$= P(X_1 = x_1)P(X_2 = x_2) \cdots P(X_p = x_p)$$

holds for all $x_1, x_2, \ldots, x_p$.

For p-variate absolutely continuous distributions condition 1.3.10 can be expressed in terms of probability density functions as

$$(1.3.12) \quad f(x_1, x_2, \ldots, x_p) = f_1(x_1)f_2(x_2) \cdots f_p(x_p) \quad \text{for all } x_1, x_2, \ldots, x_p,$$

where $f(x_1, x_2, \ldots, x_p)$ is the joint probability density function, and $f_j(x_j)$ is the marginal probability density function of the variable X_j $(j = 1, 2, \ldots p)$.

Functions of Random Variables. Consider a single-valued function $y = t(x)$ of the real variable x. Let X be a random variable. Then $Y = t(X)$ is defined as a random variable which takes the value $y = t(x)$ if the random experiment with which X is associated results in a value x of X. A function $Y = t(X_1, X_2, \ldots, X_n)$ of n random variables $X_1, X_2, \ldots, X_n$ can similarly be defined as a random variable which takes the value $y = t(x_1, x_2, \ldots, x_n)$ when the random experiment produces the values $x_1, x_2, \ldots, x_n$ of the random variables $X_1, X_2, \ldots, X_n$, respectively, t being a single-valued function of its arguments.

Given the probability distribution of the random variables $X_1, X_2, \ldots, X_n$, the probability distribution of $Y = t(X_1, X_2, \ldots, X_n)$ can be easily worked out. In the discrete case, let $P(X_1 = x_1, X_2 = x_2, \ldots, X_n = x_n) = p(x_1, x_2, \ldots, x_n)$. Then

$$(1.3.13) \quad P(Y = y) = \Sigma^* p(x_1, x_2, \ldots, x_n),$$

where Σ^* denotes summation over all values of $x_1, x_2, \ldots, x_n$ such that $t(x_1, x_2, \ldots, x_n) = y$. For absolutely continuous distributions, the probability density function $f(y)$ of Y can be obtained as

$$(1.3.14) \quad f(y) \, dy = \int_{dw} f(x_1, x_2, \ldots, x_n) \, dx_1 \, dx_2 \cdots dx_n$$

where $f(x_1, x_2, \ldots, x_n)$ is the joint probability density function of X_1, $X_2, \ldots, X_n$, and $\int_{dw}$ denotes multiple integration over the region dw: $y < t(x_1, x_2, \ldots, x_n) < y + dy$. In either case, the cumulative distribution function $F(y)$ of Y can be evaluated as a Stieltjes integral:

$$(1.3.15) \qquad F(y) = \int_{t(x_1, x_2, \ldots, x_n) \leq y} dF(x_1, x_2, \ldots, x_n),$$

where $F(x_1, x_2, \ldots, x_n)$ is the joint distribution function of $X_1, X_2, \ldots, X_n$.

1.4 MATHEMATICAL EXPECTATION

If X is a discrete random variable which assumes the values x_j with the probabilities p_j ($j = 1, 2, \ldots$), the *mathematical expectation* of X is then defined as

$$(1.4.1) \qquad \mu = E(X) = \sum_j x_j p_j,$$

provided that the series converges absolutely. On the other hand, if X follows an absolutely continuous distribution with probability density function $f(x)$, the expectation of X is defined by

$$(1.4.2) \qquad \mu = E(X) = \int_{-\infty}^{\infty} x f(x)\, dx,$$

provided that this integral is absolutely convergent.

According to the discussion in Section 1.3, a function $Y = g(X)$ is a random variable which has a certain distribution function. If the distribution of X is either discrete or absolutely continuous, then the expectation of the random variable Y can be expressed by means of the formulae:

$$E[g(X)] = \sum_j g(x_j) p_j, \qquad \text{(discrete)},$$

$$(1.4.3)$$

$$E[g(X)] = \int_{-\infty}^{\infty} g(x) f(x)\, dx \qquad \text{(absolutely continuous)},$$

provided that the defining sum or integral converges absolutely.

Expectation of Sum and Product of Random Variables. Let $X_1, X_2, \ldots, X_n$ be n random variables, each with a finite expectation. Then

$$(1.4.4) \quad E(X_1 + X_2 + \cdots + X_n) = E(X_1) + E(X_2) + \cdots + E(X_n).$$

If, furthermore, these random variables are independent, then

$$(1.4.5) \qquad E(X_1 X_2 \cdots X_n) = E(X_1) E(X_2) \cdots E(X_n).$$

Moments. The moments of a random variable X are defined in exactly the same way as in Section 2.2 of Part II. Thus $\mu_k' = E(X^k)$ is called the kth moment about origin, and $\mu_k = E(X - \mu_1')^k$ is called the kth moment about the mean, or simply the kth central moment. The second central moment $\mu_2 = E(X - \mu_1')^2$ is called the variance of X and denoted by $V(X)$. The positive square root of the variance is called the standard deviation. For bivariate distributions, moments about the origin are defined by $\mu_{r,s}' = E(X^r Y^s)$ and central moments by

$$\mu_{r,s} = E[(X - \mu_{1,0}')^r (Y - \mu_{0,1}')^s].$$

In particular, $\mu_{1,1} = E[(X - \mu_{1,0}')(Y - \mu_{0,1}')]$ is called the covariance of X and Y and denoted by Cov (X, Y).

For p-variate distributions, moments about the origin are defined as $\mu'(r_1, r_2, \ldots, r_p) = E(X_1^{r_1} X_2^{r_2} \ldots X_p^{r_p})$, and moments about the mean are also similarly defined. The notation $V(X_i) = \sigma_{ii}$ and Cov $(X_i, X_j) = \sigma_{ij}$ is very often used. The $p \times p$ matrix $\Sigma = ((\sigma_{ij}))$ is called the dispersion matrix (or variance-covariance matrix, of $X_1, X_2, \ldots, X_p$).

EXPECTATION AND VARIANCE OF A LINEAR FUNCTION. If $X_1, X_2, \ldots, X_n$ are n random variables, each with a finite variance, then the expectation and the variance of a linear function $X = l_1 X_1 + l_2 X_2 + \cdots + l_n X_n$ are given by

$$(1.4.6) \qquad \mu = E(X) = \sum_{i=1}^{n} l_i \mu_i; \qquad \sigma^2 = V(x) = \sum_{i,j=1}^{n} l_i l_j \sigma_{ij},$$

respectively, where $\mu_i = E(X_i)$, $\sigma_{ii} = V(X_i)$, and $\sigma_{ij} = $ Cov $(X_i X_j)$, $i \neq j$.

It should be remembered that, though the moments are very often useful in describing a distribution, they need not always exist, and that there are examples of different distributions having the same set of moments.

Chebycheff's Inequality. Let X be a random variable with $E(X) = \mu$ and $V(X) = \sigma^2$. Then for any given number $\lambda > 1$, we have the inequality

$$(1.4.7) \qquad \text{Prob} (|X - \mu| \geq \lambda \sigma) \leq \frac{1}{\lambda^2}$$

due to Chebycheff.

Illustrative Example 1.4. Consider a population of N individuals having values of a characteristic $x_1, x_2, \ldots, x_N$, one associated with each individual, and let $\mu = \sum_{i=1}^{N} x_i / N$. By a sampling unit is meant a collection of a number of these individuals, repetitions being allowed. Suppose that M such sampling units have been formed and that the ith individual occurs m_{ij} times in the jth sampling unit. Let $n_{ij} = 0$ if $m_{ij} = 0$ and $n_{ij} = 1$ if $m_{ij} \geq 1$. Consider the random experiment of choosing one of the M sampling units, the probability of selecting the jth unit being π_j.

Let Y_i be a random variable which takes the value 1 if the ith individual occurs in the selected sampling unit and 0 otherwise, $i = 1, 2, \ldots, N$. Write

$$P_{ii'} = P(Y_i = 1, Y_{i'} = 1) = \sum_{j=1}^{M} n_{ij} n_{i'j} \pi_j,$$

so that $P_{ii'}$ denotes the probability that both the ith and the i'th individuals occur simultaneously in the selected sampling unit. We shall assume that, for all i, $P_{ii} \neq 0$.

Consider now the random variable

$$T = \frac{1}{N} \sum_{i=1}^{N} \frac{x_i Y_i}{P_{ii}}.$$

Note that, for any selected sampling unit, the value of T can be determined as a linear combination of the characteristic values of the individuals occurring in the selected sampling unit. This is proposed as an estimate of μ based on the selected sampling unit. We easily see that $E(Y_i) = E(Y_i^2) = P_{ii}$ and $E(Y_i Y_{i'}) = P_{ii'}$. Hence, the expectation and the variance of T are obtained from formula 1.4.6 as

$$E(T) = \mu$$

and

$$V(T) = \frac{1}{N^2} \sum_{i,i'=1}^{N} \frac{P_{ii'}}{P_{ii} P_{i'i'}} x_i x_{i'} - \mu^2,$$

respectively.

If the sampling units are formed by taking all possible combinations without repetition of, say, n out of the N individuals, we have $M = \binom{N}{n}$.

If one out of these sampling units is chosen with equal probabilities, $\pi_j = 1/M$, we have what is known as a random sample of size n from a finite population of size N drawn without replacement. In this case $P_{ii} = n/N$ and $P_{ii'} = n(n-1)/N(N-1)$ for $i \neq i'$. Consequently T reduces to $T = \bar{X}$, where $\bar{X}$ is the arithmetic mean of the characteristic values of the individuals in the selected sampling unit. The variance of T simplifies to

$$V(T) = \frac{\sigma^2}{n} \cdot \frac{N - n}{N - 1},$$

where

$$\sigma^2 = \sum_{i=1}^{N} (x_i - \mu)^2 / N.$$

1.5 LIMIT DISTRIBUTIONS

Definitions. Consider a sequence of random variables $T_1, T_2, \ldots,$ and let $F_n(x)$ denote the distribution function of T_n, $n = 1, 2, \ldots$.

CONVERGENCE IN PROBABILITY TO A CONSTANT. The sequence of random variables $\{T_n\}$ is said to converge in probability to a constant c, in symbols plim $T_n = c$, if, for any given $\epsilon > 0$,

$$\text{plim } [\,|T_n - c| < \epsilon] = 1$$

as $n \to \infty$. The convergence is said to be almost everywhere if for every positive integer r the probability that the inequalities $|T_N - c| < \epsilon$ hold simultaneously for $N = n,\, n + 1,\, \ldots,\, n + r$ tends to 1 as $n \to \infty$ for any $\epsilon > 0$.

CONVERGENCE IN LAW TO A RANDOM VARIABLE. The sequence of random variables $\{T_n\}$ is said to converge (weakly) in law to a random variable T, in symbols $T_n \to T$, if as $n \to \infty$, lim $F_n(x) = F(x)$ at every continuity point of $F(x)$, where $F(x)$ is the distribution function of T. The convergence is said to be *uniform* if the convergence of the sequence of distribution functions is uniform in x.

In the following discussion we denote by ξ a random variable following the normal distribution with mean zero and variance unity.

ASYMPTOTIC NORMALITY. If there exist two sequences of real numbers $\{a_n\}$ and $\{b_n\}$, $b_n > 0$, such that $(T_n - a_n)/b_n \to \xi$, then T_n is said to have an *asymptotic normal distribution* with mean a_n and standard deviation b_n.

Let $X_1, X_2, \ldots$ be a sequence of independently and identically distributed random variables each with a finite expectation $\mu = E(X_i)$, and let $\bar{X}_n = (1/n) \sum_{i=1}^{n} X_i$. We then have the following results, which are widely applied in statistical theory.

Law of Large Numbers

$$(1.5.1) \qquad\qquad \text{plim } \bar{X}_n = \mu.$$

Central Limit Theorem. If $V(X_i) = \sigma^2$ exists,

$$(1.5.2) \qquad\qquad \frac{\sqrt{n}(\bar{X}_n - \mu)}{\sigma} \to \xi, \text{ uniformly}$$

where ξ is normally distributed with mean zero and variance unity.

The law of large numbers and the central limit theorem can be extended to the case where the X_i's are independently, but not necessarily identically, distributed. Writing $E(X_i) = \mu_i$, $V(X_i) = \sigma_i^2$, $\bar{\mu}_n = (1/n) \sum_{i=1}^{n} \mu_i$, and $B_n^2 = \sum_{i=1}^{n} \sigma_i^2$, these theorems can be expressed as

$$(1.5.3) \qquad\qquad \text{plim } (\bar{X}_n - \bar{\mu}_n) = 0,$$

$$(1.5.4) \qquad\qquad \frac{\sqrt{n}(\bar{X}_n - \bar{\mu}_n)}{B_n} \to \xi.$$

These are valid under certain additional conditions which we shall not describe here.

MULTIVARIATE EXTENSION OF THE CENTRAL LIMIT THEOREM. Let $\{\mathbf{X}_i\}$ be a sequence of p-dimensional random variables, each independently and identically distributed with mean vector $\boldsymbol{\mu}$ and dispersion matrix Σ. Let $\bar{\mathbf{X}}_n = (1/n)\sum_{i=1}^{n}\mathbf{X}_i$; then $\sqrt{n}(\bar{\mathbf{X}}_n - \boldsymbol{\mu}) \to \mathbf{X}$, where $\mathbf{X}$ is a p-dimensional random variable having the normal distribution with mean vector $\mathbf{0}$ and dispersion matrix Σ.

A Theorem on Asymptotic Normality. If $\{T_n\}$ is a sequence of random variables such that $\sqrt{n}(T_n - \theta)/\sigma(\theta) \to \xi$ and $g(x)$ is a well-behaved function of x, then $\sqrt{n}[g(T_n) - g(\theta)]/\lambda(\theta) \to \xi$, where

$$(1.5.5) \qquad \lambda(\theta) = |g'(\theta)|\,\sigma(\theta).$$

VARIANCE-STABILIZING TRANSFORMATION. If $g(\theta)$ is chosen as

$$(1.5.6) \qquad g(\theta) = \int \frac{c\,d\theta}{\sigma(\theta)},$$

where $c > 0$ is free of θ, then $\lambda(\theta) = c$, and $g(T_n)$ is asymptotically normally distributed with mean $g(\theta)$ and standard deviation $c/\sqrt{n}$, which is free of θ.

MULTIVARIATE EXTENSION. Let $\{T_{1n}, T_{2n}, \ldots, T_{pn}\}$ be a sequence of p-dimensional random variables such that

$$[\sqrt{n}(T_{1n} - \theta_1), \sqrt{n}(T_{2n} - \theta_2), \ldots, \sqrt{n}(T_{pn} - \theta_p)] \to \mathbf{X}$$

where the distribution of $\mathbf{X}$ is p-variate normal with mean vector $\mathbf{0}$ and dispersion matrix $((\sigma_{ij}))$. Let

$$g_r(x_1, x_2, \ldots, x_p), \qquad r = 1, 2, \ldots, k, \qquad k \le p,$$

be k functionally independent well-behaved functions of $(x_1, x_2, \ldots, x_p)$ and let

$$U_{rn} = \sqrt{n}[g_r(T_{1n}, \ldots, T_{pn}) - g_r(\theta_1, \ldots, \theta_p)].$$

Then $(U_{1n}, U_{2n}, \ldots, U_{kn}) \to \mathbf{Y}$, where $\mathbf{Y}$ has the k-variate normal distribution with mean vector $\mathbf{0}$ and dispersion matrix $((\lambda_{rs}))$, where

$$(1.5.7) \qquad \lambda_{rs} = \sum_{i,j=1}^{p} c_{ir}c_{js}\sigma_{ij}$$

and

$$c_{ir} = \frac{\partial g_r(\theta_1, \ldots, \theta_p)}{\partial \theta_i}.$$

Convergence in Law of a Function of Random Variables. If a sequence of p-dimensional random variables $\{X_{1n}, X_{2n}, \ldots, X_{pn}\}$ converges in law to a p-dimensional random variable $(X_1, X_2, \ldots, X_p)$, and $g(x_1, x_2, \ldots, x_p)$ is a continuous function of $(x_1, x_2, \ldots, x_p)$, then under certain conditions

(1.5.8) $g(X_{1n}, X_{2n}, \ldots, X_{pn}) \to g(X_1, X_2, \ldots, X_p).$

1.6 EXERCISES

1.1. Stating your assumptions carefully, compute the probability that a hand in bridge contains all four aces.

1.2. If the probability of hitting a target with a single shot is 0.80, find the probability that in 10 shots the target will be hit (a) at least once, (b) exactly once, (c) at least twice, (d) exactly twice.

1.3. One per cent of the people in a certain population is color blind. What is the smallest random sample you must draw from this population (with replacement) in order that the probability for the sample to contain a color-blind person will not be less than 0.95?

1.4. Ten tickets numbered serially from 1 to 10 are put in a box. A ticket is drawn from the box at random, the number on it is noted, and then it is put back in the box and another ticket is drawn at random.

If ten tickets are drawn this way, what are the chances that (a) all the tickets bearing numbers 1 to 10 will occur and (b) all the tickets with even numbers 2, 4, 6, 8, and 10 will occur?

1.5. The probability distribution of a discrete random variable X is as follows:

x	-5	-3	2	0	1	4	5
$p(x)$	0.10	0.15	0.10	0.20	0.05	0.30	0.10

where $p(x) = P(X = x)$. Find the probability distribution of the random variable $Y = X^2 + 2$.

1.6. Let X_1 and X_2 be two independent random variables each having the same probability distribution as the random variable X in exercise 1.5. Find the probability distributions of (a) $X_1 + X_2$, (b) $X_1^2 + X_2^2$, (c) $X_1 X_2$.

Find (i) the joint probability distribution of $X_1 + X_2$ and $X_1 - X_2$ and (ii) the conditional distributions of $X_1 + X_2$ for different given values of $X_1 X_2$.

1.7. Let X be a random variable having the probability density function:

$$f(x) = \begin{cases} 1 & \text{for } 0 \leq x \leq 1, \\ 0 & \text{otherwise.} \end{cases}$$

Find the probability density functions of the following random variables:
(a) $Y = \ln X$, (b) $Y = \arctan X$.

1.8. Let X_1, X_2 be two independent random variables, each having the same probability density function $f(x)$, defined in exercise 1.7. Find the probability density function of the following random variables: (a) $Y = \frac{1}{2}(X_1 + X_2)$, (b) $Z = X_1 X_2$.

Find also the joint probability density function of Y and Z and the conditional probability density function of Y, given that $Z = z$.

1.9. Let X_1, X_2, ..., X_n be independent random variables, with $E(X_i) = \mu$ and $V(X_i) = \sigma_i^2$. Determine constants $c_1, c_2, \ldots, c_n$ such that the random variable $Y = c_1 X_1 + c_2 X_2 + \cdots + c_n X_n$ has $E(Y) = \mu$ and minimum variance.

1.10. Show that the random variables X and Y can have equal variance if and only if the covariance between the random variables $X + Y$ and $X - Y$ is zero.

1.11. Let X be a random variable with $E(X) = \mu$. Write $Y = X - \mu$, so that $\mu_t = E(Y^t)$, $t = 2, 3, 4$, are the central moments of X. Let $\beta_1 = \mu_3^2 / \mu_2^3$ and $\beta_2 = \mu_4 / \mu_2^2$.

Determine the constant C for which the variance of $Z = Y^2 - CY$ is a minimum, and find the value of this minimum variance. Hence show that $\beta_2 \geq \beta_1 + 1$.

CHAPTER 2

Sampling and Statistical Inference

2.1 SAMPLING

Considerations of cost (in terms of money, effort, or time spent), accuracy, and administrative difficulties often make it impracticable to collect information from every individual in a population. On the other hand, it has been convincingly demonstrated that the required information can be obtained at less cost and with more accuracy from only a sample, that is, a part of the population selected by a suitable chance mechanism.

If n individuals are selected from a population of N individuals, sequentially one by one, such that at every stage the probability of selection of any individual is $1/N$ irrespective of whether this individual had been selected earlier or not, the procedure is known as *simple sampling* or random sampling *with replacement*. If at each stage of selection an individual is selected with equal probability only from among individuals not selected earlier, sampling is said to be random *without replacement*. These are the two types of sampling most often used; other schemes of sampling will be discussed elsewhere.

Inferences drawn from a sample about the population are inductive in nature and necessarily uncertain. However, it is possible to assess the magnitude of the uncertainty in terms of probability. Consequently such inferences, though uncertain, are rigorous.

2.2 USE OF RANDOM SAMPLING NUMBERS

A long sequence of the digits $0, 1, 2, \ldots, 9$ in which the positions are filled independently with one of the digits $0, 1, 2, \ldots, 9$, so that every digit has an equal chance of occupying a particular position, is known as a series of *random sampling numbers*. Many such series of random sampling numbers have been published; among them the following are well known:

Tippett, L. H. C.: *Tracts for Computers* No. 15, Cambridge University Press, 1927.
Kendall, M. G., and B. Smith: *Tracts for Computers* No. 24, Cambridge University Press, 1939.

Rand Corporation: *One Million Random Digits*, The Free Press, Glencoe, Ill., 1955.

Fisher, R. A., and F. Yates: Table XXXIII in *Statistical Tables for Biological, Agricultural and Medical Research*, Oliver & Boyd, Edinburgh (Hafner Publishing Co., New York), 1963

We will now discuss some uses of random sampling numbers.

Sampling with Equal Probabilities. To select a random number between 1 and N, if N is a k-digit number, the series of random sampling numbers is divided into consecutive sets of k digits. Starting from an arbitrary position in the series, the first such k-digit number between 1 and N is selected. Alternatively, the first such number between 1 and the maximum k-digit number divisible by N may be taken and divided by N. The remainder then provides the required random number; if the remainder is zero, the number N is taken.

Illustrative Example 2.1. Draw a random sample of size 5 with and without replacement from a serial list of 30.

Taking two-digit numbers in sequence, starting from the first row of Plate (1) of Fisher and Yates's Table XXXIII, we have

$$03, 47, 43, 73, 86, 36, 96, 47, 36, 61, \ldots .$$

Disregarding the numbers 00 and 91–99 and taking remainders after dividing by 30, we get

$$3, 17, 13, 13, 26, 6, \ldots .$$

The serial numbers of the five units to be included in the sample are 3, 17, 13, 13, 26 if sampling is with replacement and 3, 17, 13, 26, 6 if sampling is without replacement.

Sampling with Unequal Probabilities. To select an element from among k elements, with the probability of selecting the ith element proportional to the integer N_i, $i = 1, 2, \ldots, k$, cumulative totals $S_0 = 0$, $S_1 = N_1$, $S_2 = N_1 + N_2, S_3 = N_1 + N_2 + N_3, \ldots, S_k = N_1 + N_2 + \cdots + N_k$ are formed. A random number X is then taken between 1 and S_k, and the ith element is selected if

$$S_{i-1} + 1 \leq X \leq S_i.$$

An alternative procedure is to take two random numbers X and Y, X between 1 and k and Y between 1 and the maximum of $N_1, N_2, \ldots, N_k$. If $X = i$, the ith element is selected if simultaneously $Y \leq N_i$; otherwise these numbers are rejected and the whole process is repeated until an element is selected.

Illustrative Example 2.2. Draw one sample from the following list with probabilities of selection shown against each individual.

Serial no. of individual	1	2	3	4	5	6	7	8
Probability of selection	0.10	0.12	0.24	0.08	0.07	0.14	0.13	0.12

METHOD 1.   Cumulating the probabilities, we have

$$0.10, \quad 0.22, \quad 0.46, \quad 0.54, \quad 0.61, \quad 0.75, \quad 0.88, \quad 1.00$$

Two-digit numbers can then be associated with the individuals as follows:

Individual	1	2	3	4	5	6	7	8
Associated nos.	01–10	11–22	23–46	47–54	55–61	62–75	76–88	88–99, 00

The first two-digit number in Plate (II) of Fisher and Yates's Table XXXIII is 53, corresponding to the individual number 4, which is therefore taken in the sample.

METHOD 2.   Take one random number X between 1 and 8 and another two-digit random number Y between 01 and 96 (the largest two-digit multiple of 24, corresponding to the maximum probability). We take X from the first row of Plate (III) and Y from the first row of Plate (IV) in Fisher and Yates's Table XXXIII. Thus $X = 2$, and the second individual will be chosen if Y takes any of the following values:

$$01–12, \quad 25–37, \quad 49–60, \quad 73–84.$$

But $Y = 10$. Hence the second individual is selected.

Sampling from Theoretical Distributions. A k-digit random number with a decimal point at the extreme left may be regarded as a random sample from a uniform distribution in the interval $(0, 1)$ in which the observations are rounded off to the completed kth decimal place, neglecting fractions in excess. To draw a random sample from a population in which the variate X has the probability density function $f(x)$, the first step is to make a one-one transformation of the variate, the so-called probability integral transformation:

$$(2.2.1) \qquad\qquad Y = \int_{-\infty}^{X} f(t)\,dt = F(X), \quad \text{say}$$

such that the transformed variate Y is uniformly distributed in the interval $(0, 1)$. A random sample Y can then be drawn from the distribution of the transformed variate. Transforming back, a random sample X from the original population is obtained from the relation $X = F^{-1}(Y)$.

Illustrative Example 2.3.   Draw one sample from a normal population with mean zero and standard deviation unity.

The first four-digit number from Plate (V) of Fisher and Yates's Table XXXIII, 2889, is taken. Then x, defined by

$$\int_{-\infty}^{x} \frac{1}{\sqrt{2\pi}} e^{-\frac{1}{2}t^2} dt = 0.2889,$$

is a random sample from the normal population with mean zero and standard deviation unity. This gives $x = -0.557$, obtained by linear interpolation in Table 1 of *Biometrika Tables for Statisticians*.

Random samples from a standard normal population (with mean zero and variance unity) drawn this way are listed in several publications, of which the following are important:

Wold, H: Random Normal Deviates, *Tracts for Computers* No. 25, Cambridge University Press, 1948.
Rand Corporation: *One Million Random Digits with* 100,000 *Normal Deviates*, The Free Press, Glencoe, Ill., 1955.

2.3 SAMPLING DISTRIBUTION

Any quantity T computed from a sample by following a definite rule is called a *statistic*, which is thus a function of the sample observations. When the sample is selected by a chance mechanism, the statistic T is obviously a random variable. The probability distribution of a statistic T is called its *sampling distribution*, and this of course is determined by the functional form of T, the sampling scheme, and the form of the population. Sampling distributions of appropriate statistics play key roles in problems of statistical inference. We discuss now the sampling distributions of a number of statistics frequently used.

Mean and Dispersion of Samples from Normal Distribution. Let $X_1, X_2, \ldots, X_n$ be n independent normal variates, each with mean zero and variance unity. The following results are basic in deriving the sampling distributions of many useful statistics when the parent population is normal.

LINEAR FUNCTIONS. If $Y_r = \sum_{j=1}^{n} c_{rj} X_j, r = 1, 2, \ldots, m, m \leq n$, where the matrix of coefficients $((c_{rj}))$ is of rank m, then the joint distribution of $(Y_1, Y_2, \ldots, Y_m)$ is m-variate normal with mean vector $\mathbf{0}$ and dispersion matrix $((\lambda_{rs}))$, where $\lambda_{rs} = \sum_{j=1}^{n} c_{rj} c_{sj}$. In particular, if the coefficients c_{rj}'s satisfy the orthogonality conditions $\lambda_{rr} = 1$, $\lambda_{rs} = 0$ for $r \neq s = 1, 2, \ldots, m$, then $Y_1, Y_2, \ldots, Y_m$ are independent normal variates each with mean zero and variance unity.

SUM OF SQUARES. The statistic $T = \sum_{i=1}^{n} X_i^2$ follows the chi-square distribution with n degrees of freedom, defined by formula 4.4.2 in Part II. The statistic $U = \sum_{i=1}^{n} (X_i + \mu_i)^2$, where μ_i's are constants, follows the non-central chi-square distribution (see formula 4.5.3 in Part II) with n degrees of freedom and non-centrality parameter $\delta^2 = \sum_{i=1}^{n} \mu_i^2$.

STUDENT'S RATIO. If X and Y are independent random variables and X has the normal distribution with mean zero and variance unity, and Y has the chi-square distribution with n degrees of freedom, the random variable $T = X/\sqrt{Y/n}$ follows the t distribution with n degrees of freedom (see formula 4.4.1 in Part II).

SUM AND RATIO OF CHI SQUARES. If X and Y are independent random variables, having chi-square distributions with m and n degrees of freedom, respectively, then $Z = X + Y$ and $W = (X/m)/(Y/n)$ are stochastically independent. The sum $Z = X + Y$ has the chi-square distribution with $m + n$ degrees of freedom, and the ratio $W = (X/m)/(Y/n)$ follows the variance-ratio or F distribution with (m, n) degrees of freedom (see formula 4.4.3 in Part II).

UNIVARIATE CASE. We give now the principal results for the case of samples drawn from a univariate normal population. Let $x_1, x_2, \ldots, x_n$ be a random sample of size n from a normal population with mean μ and variance σ^2. Let

$$\bar{x} = \frac{1}{n} \sum_{i=1}^{n} x_i, \quad S^2 = \sum_{i=1}^{n} (x_i - \bar{x})^2, \quad s^2 = \frac{S^2}{n}, \quad \hat{\sigma}^2 = \frac{S^2}{n-1}.$$

We call $\bar{x}$ the sample mean, S^2 the corrected sum of squares, s^2 the sample variance, and $\hat{\sigma}^2$ the estimate of the population variance. Then
(a) $\bar{x}$ and S^2 are stochastically independent;
(b) $\bar{x}$ is distributed normally with mean μ and variance σ^2/n;
(c) $S^2/\sigma^2 = ns^2/\sigma^2 = (n-1)\hat{\sigma}^2/\sigma^2$ has a chi-square distribution with $n - 1$ degrees of freedom.

MULTIVARIATE CASE. Let $(x_{1\lambda}, x_{2\lambda}, \ldots, x_{p\lambda})$, $\lambda = 1, 2, \ldots, n$, be a sample of size n from a p-variate normal population with mean vector $(\mu_1, \mu_2, \ldots, \mu_p)$ and dispersion matrix $((\sigma_{ij}))$. Let

$$\bar{x}_i = \frac{1}{n} \sum_{\lambda=1}^{n} x_{i\lambda}, \quad S_{ij} = \sum_{\lambda=1}^{n} (x_{i\lambda} - \bar{x}_i)(x_{j\lambda} - \bar{x}_j), \quad s_{ij} = \frac{S_{ij}}{n}, \quad \hat{\sigma}_{ij} = \frac{S_{ij}}{n-1}.$$

We call $\bar{\mathbf{x}} = (\bar{x}_1, \bar{x}_2, \ldots, \bar{x}_p)$ the sample mean vector, $S = ((S_{ij}))$ the matrix of corrected sums of squares and products (SP matrix), $((s_{ij}))$ the sample dispersion matrix, and $((\hat{\sigma}_{ij}))$ the estimate of the population dispersion matrix. Then
(a) the random vector $\bar{\mathbf{x}}$ and the random matrix S are stochastically independent;
(b) $\bar{\mathbf{x}}$ has the p-variate normal distribution with mean vector $(\mu_1, \mu_2, \ldots, \mu_p)$ and dispersion matrix $((\sigma_{ij}/n))$;

(c) the joint probability density function of the elements of the random matrix $S = ((S_{ij}))$ is

$$(2.3.1) \qquad C_{p,v} |\sigma_{ij}|^{-\frac{1}{2}v} |S|^{\frac{1}{2}(v-p-1)} \exp\left(-\frac{1}{2}\sum_{i,j=1}^{p}\sigma^{ij}S_{ij}\right),$$

where $v = n - 1$, $((\sigma^{ij})) = ((\sigma_{ij}))^{-1}$, $|\sigma_{ij}| = $ determinant of $((\sigma_{ij}))$, and

$$\frac{1}{C_{p,v}} = 2^{\frac{1}{2}pv}\pi^{\frac{1}{4}p(p-1)}\prod_{j=0}^{p-1}\Gamma\left(\frac{v-j}{2}\right).$$

This distribution is called *Wishart's distribution* with v degrees of freedom and parameter matrix $((\sigma_{ij}))$.

Order Statistics. Any function of sample observations arranged in ascending order of magnitude is known as an *order statistic*. Let $x_{(1)} < x_{(2)} \leq \cdots \leq x_{(n)}$ be a sample of size n, arranged in ascending order, from a population with distribution function $F(x)$. To avoid complications, we consider the case where the population has a continuous frequency density function $f(x) = F'(x)$. The probability density function of $X = x_{(r)}(1 \leq r \leq n)$ in such a case is

$$(2.3.2) \qquad \frac{n!}{(r-1)!(n-r)!}[F(x)]^{r-1}[1-F(x)]^{n-r}f(x).$$

Let $1 \leq r_1 < r_2 < \cdots < r_k \leq n$ be k given integers, and let $Y_1 = F[x_{(r_1)}]$, $Y_i = F[x_{(r_i)}] - F[x_{(r_{i-1})}]$, $i = 2, 3, \ldots, k$. Then the joint probability density function of the random variables $Y_1, Y_2, \ldots, Y_k$ is

$$(2.3.3) \qquad \frac{n!}{s_1!s_2!\cdots s_{k+1}!}y_1^{s_1}y_2^{s_2}\cdots y_k^{s_k}(1 - y_1 - \cdots - y_k)^{s_{k+1}},$$

where $s_1 = r_1 - 1$, $s_i = r_i - r_{i-1} - 1$ $(i = 2, 3, \ldots, k)$, and

$$s_{k-1} = n - r_k - 1.$$

Asymptotic Sampling Distributions. The exact sampling distribution of a statistic is often very difficult to obtain, but its limiting form as the sample size increases indefinitely is usually simple and easy to determine. When the sample size is fairly large, this limiting form of the sampling distribution of the statistic is used as an approximation. We give below some important results.

MOMENTS. Since sample moments are of the form of arithmetic means, the central limit theorem can be applied to well behaved functions of moments.

We denote the rth sample moment about a fixed point c by m_r', the rth sample moment about the sample mean by m_r, and the analogous quantities in the population by μ_r' and μ_r, respectively. The size of the sample is denoted by n, and sampling is assumed to be simple (with replacement and equal probabilities). Under mild restrictions on the parent population, the sample moments are asymptotically (for large n) jointly normally distributed. The expectation and the variances and covariances of the sample moments are given below. Here the sign $=$ indicates that the result is exact, and $\doteq$ that the results hold only asymptotically for large n:

$$E(m_r') = \mu_r',$$

$$(2.3.4) \qquad V(m_r') = \frac{1}{n}[\mu_{2r}' - (\mu_r')^2],$$

$$\text{Cov}(m_r', m_s') = \frac{1}{n}[\mu_{r+s}' - \mu_r'\mu_s'];$$

$$E(m_r) \doteq \mu_r,$$

$$(2.3.5) \quad V(m_r) \doteq \frac{1}{n}[\mu_{2r} - \mu_r^2 + r^2\mu_{r-1}^2\mu_2 - 2r\mu_{r-1}\mu_{r+1}],$$

$$\text{Cov}(m_r, m_s) \doteq \frac{1}{n}[\mu_{r+s} - \mu_r\mu_s + rs\mu_{r-1}\mu_{s-1}\mu_2 - r\mu_{r-1}\mu_{s+1} - s\mu_{s-1}\mu_{r+1}].$$

Denoting bivariate moments in the sample and the population by $m_{r,s}$ and $\mu_{r,s}$, we have similarly, for moments about a fixed point c,

$$E(m_{r,s}') = \mu_{rs}',$$

$$(2.3.6) \qquad V(m_{r,s}') = \frac{1}{n}[\mu_{2r,2s}' - (\mu_{r,s}')^2],$$

$$\text{Cov}(m_{r,s}', m_{u,v}') = \frac{1}{n}[\mu_{r+u,s+v}' - \mu_{r,s}'\mu_{u,v}'],$$

and for moments about the mean

$$E(m_{r,s}) \doteq \mu_{r,s},$$

$$V(m_{r,s}) \doteq \frac{1}{n}[\mu_{2r,2s} - \mu_{r,s}^2 + r^2\mu_{2,0}\mu_{r-1,s}^2$$
$$+ s^2\mu_{0,2}\mu_{r,s-1}^2 + 2rs\mu_{1,1}\mu_{r-1,s}\mu_{r,s-1}$$
$$- 2r\mu_{r+1,s}\mu_{r-1,s} - 2s\mu_{r,s+1}\mu_{r,s-1}],$$

$$(2.3.7) \quad \text{Cov}(m_{r,s}, m_{u,v}) \doteq \frac{1}{n}[\mu_{r+u,s+v} - \mu_{r,s}\mu_{u,v}$$
$$+ ru\mu_{2,0}\mu_{r-1,s}\mu_{u-1,v} + sv\mu_{0,2}\mu_{r,s-1}\mu_{u,v-1}$$
$$+ rv\mu_{1,1}\mu_{r-1,s}\mu_{u,v-1} + su\mu_{1,1}\mu_{r,s-1}\mu_{u-1,v}$$
$$- r\mu_{r-1,s}\mu_{u+1,v} - s\mu_{r,s-1}\mu_{u,v+1}$$
$$- u\mu_{r+1,s}\mu_{u-1,v} - v\mu_{r,s+1}\mu_{u,v-1}].$$

FUNCTIONS OF MOMENTS.   Well-behaved functions of sample moments
are asymptotically normally distributed with means and dispersion which
can be computed from 2.3.4, 1.5.5, and 1.5.7. Table 2.1 gives the asymptotic variance of a few such functions of sample moments which are
commonly used, under the assumption that the parent population is
normal.

TABLE 2.1

ASYMPTOTIC VARIANCE OF SOME FUNCTIONS OF SAMPLE MOMENTS

Function of sample moments	Asymptotic variance
$s = \sqrt{m_2}$	$\mu_2/2n$
$v = \sqrt{m_2}/m_1'$	$V^2(1 + 2V^2)/2n$ where $V = \sqrt{\mu_2}/\mu_1'$
$g_1 = m_3/m_2^{3/2}$	$6/n$
$g_2 = (m_4/m_2^2) - 3$	$24/n$
$r = \dfrac{m_{1,1}}{\sqrt{m_{2,0}m_{0,2}}}$	$\dfrac{(1 - \rho^2)^2}{n}$ when $\rho = \dfrac{\mu_{1,1}}{\sqrt{\mu_{2,0}\mu_{0,2}}}$

FRACTILE.   For a given p, $0 < p < 1$, let θ_p be the fractile in a population with frequency density function $f(x)$, and T_p the corresponding
fractile for a sample of size n drawn from this population. If $f'(x)$ is
continuous in a neighborhood of θ_p, then T_p is asymptotically (for large
n) normally distributed with mean θ_p and variance $p(1 - p)/n[f(\theta_p)]^2$.

Transformation of Statistics.   The following variance-stabilizing transformations are all asymptotically normally distributed with mean zero and
variance unity.

ARC SINE.   If x successes are observed in n independent trials, in each of
which the probability of success is p, then the variance-stabilizing transformation is

$$(2.3.8) \qquad T = 2\sqrt{n}\left(\arcsin\sqrt{\frac{x}{n}} - \arcsin\sqrt{p}\right).$$

SQUARE ROOT.   For a Poisson variable x with mean μ, the transformation is

$$(2.3.9) \qquad T = 2(\sqrt{x} - \sqrt{\mu}).$$

This is valid for large μ.

LOGARITHM.   For the standard deviation s in a sample of size n from a
normal population with standard deviation σ, the transformation is

$$(2.3.10) \qquad T = \sqrt{2n}\,(\ln s - \ln \sigma).$$

INVERSE HYPERBOLIC TANGENT. For the correlation coefficient r computed from a sample of size n from a bivariate normal population in which this coefficient is ρ, the transformation is

$$(2.3.11) \qquad\qquad T = \sqrt{n-3}\,(z - \zeta),$$

where

$$z = \tanh^{-1} r = \tfrac{1}{2} \log_e \frac{1+r}{1-r} ; \quad \zeta = \tanh^{-1} \rho.$$

2.4 ESTIMATION

Criteria for a Good Estimate. To assess the value of a numerical characteristic, or *parameter*, as it is called, for a population on the basis of a sample drawn from the population is known as the problem of *estimation*. If a statistic T is taken as an estimate of the parameter θ, the first point to recognize is that in any particular sample the observed value of T may differ from θ. Consequently, the performance of T as an estimate of θ is to be judged in relation to the sampling distribution of T. We may require, for instance, that the probability for T to deviate from θ by more than a preassigned quantity ϵ be as small as possible. Various requirements of this type may be put forth, but in practice the following have been found useful.

CONSISTENCY. A sequence of statistics $\{T_n\}$, where T_n is an estimator of θ based on a sample of size n, is said to be consistent if, as $n \to \infty$, plim $T_n = \theta$.

ASYMPTOTIC EFFICIENCY. If the limiting distribution of $\sqrt{n}(T_n - \theta)/c$ is normal with mean zero and variance unity, the asymptotic efficiency of T_n is defined as

$$(2.4.1) \qquad\qquad e = \frac{1}{c^2 i(\theta)} , \quad \text{where } i(\theta) = -E\left(\frac{d^2 \ln f}{d\theta^2}\right).$$

$f(x, \theta)$ is the density function (or relative frequency in the discrete case) of the parent population. If $e = 1$, the sequence of estimators is said to be asymptotically efficient or best asymptotically normal (BAN).

UNBIASEDNESS. A statistic T is said to be an *unbiased* estimate for θ if

$$E(T) = \theta$$

for all values of θ. A parameter θ is said to be estimable if an unbiased estimate for it exists.

MINIMUM VARIANCE. Among unbiased estimates of θ, the one that has smallest variance is preferred. Under mild regularity conditions, for the variance of any unbiased estimator T of θ, we have the lower limit

$$(2.4.2) \qquad\qquad V(T) \geq \frac{1}{ni(\theta)} ,$$

where $i(\theta)$, defined by 2.4.1, is called *the amount of information per observation*.

The standard deviation of the sampling distribution of a statistic T, or its asymptotic standard deviation in a large sample, or a consistent estimate of this is called the *standard error* of the statistic T.

SUFFICIENCY. A statistic T is said to be *sufficient* for θ if the conditional probability distribution of the sample observations for any fixed value of T does not involve the parameter θ.

If U is an unbiased estimate of θ and T is a sufficient statistic, then the statistic U^*, obtained by taking the conditional expectation of U for a fixed value of T, $U^* = E(U \mid T)$, which is obviously only a function of the sufficient statistic T, is also an unbiased estimate with variance not greater than that of U: $V(U^*) \leq V(U)$. For unbiased minimum variance estimation we need therefore be restricted only to functions of a sufficient statistic, if one such exists. A sufficient statistic T is said to be *complete* if there exists no non-trivial function of T whose expectation is zero for all values of θ. If for a parameter θ a complete sufficient statistic T exists and also an unbiased estimator, then there is an (essentially) unique function of T which is an unbiased estimate of θ, and this has minimum variance among all unbiased estimates.

Various procedures that generally lead to estimates with desirable properties are described in Chapter 3.

2.5 TESTING OF HYPOTHESES

The Nature of Statistical Hypotheses. A statistical hypothesis is one that specifies the probability distribution underlying the observations. The hypothesis is said to be *simple* when the functional form of the probability law, together with the values of all the parameters in it, is completely specified; otherwise it is said to be *composite*. A composite hypothesis is said to have c degrees of freedom if the values of c parameters in the probability law are not specified by the hypothesis. For instance, for data on the number of male children in families of five children, the hypothesis that the distribution is binomial with probability $1/2$ for a child to be a male, is a simple hypothesis. On the other hand, the hypothesis that the distribution is binomial with the probability for a male child unspecified is a composite hypothesis with one degree of freedom.

Procedure for Testing a Hypothesis. On the basis of a sample S from a population, to test a hypothesis H_0 the general procedure is as follows. All samples that could possibly arise are divided beforehand into two types: (1) those that are more or less in conformity with the hypothesis and (2) those that are regarded as discordant. The second type of samples is said to form the *critical region*, and if the observed sample S is of this type (S falls in the critical region) the hypothesis H_0 is rejected. A test procedure is thus determined by the choice of the critical region.

Criteria for a Good Test. Let $P(f)$ be the probability that the test procedure will lead to the rejection of the hypothesis H_0, computed on the assumption that the probability law underlying the observations is f. The performance of the test procedure is usually judged on the basis of this probability. For any probability law f which is implied by the hypothesis H_0, rejection of the hypothesis is an error—*error of the first kind*, as it is called—and therefore, for all such f, the probability $P(f)$ of rejection of H_0 should be as small as possible. Ordinarily only those test procedures are considered for which the probability of an error of the first kind is at most α, where α is a small preassigned quantity called the *level of significance*. The usual practice is to take $\alpha = 0.05$ or $\alpha = 0.01$, the 5% or the 1% level of significance. On the other hand, for any probability law f which is contradicted by the hypothesis H_0, acceptance of the hypothesis is an *error of the second kind*, and consequently, for all such f, the probability $P(f)$ of rejection, known as the *power* of the test at f, should be as high as possible. There are elaborate theories for the construction of test procedures with such optimum properties. We shall describe in Chapter 4 a number of methods of test construction which usually lead to good procedures.

2.6 INTERVAL ESTIMATION

If T_1 and T_2 ($T_2 > T_1$) are two statistics and θ is a parameter occurring in their joint distribution such that $\mathrm{Prob}\,(T_1 \leq \theta \leq T_2 \,|\, \theta) = \gamma$ for all values of θ, where γ is a preassigned constant, then the interval (T_1, T_2) is said to provide an *interval estimate* or a *confidence interval* for the parameter θ with confidence coefficient γ. Many alternative confidence intervals with the same confidence coefficient may be proposed for a given parameter. From these, a suitable one can be selected by using some criterion of optimality, but we shall not enter into a discussion of such criteria.

A confidence interval for a parameter θ is usually derived from the statistic T, which is used in testing a specified value for the parameter. The acceptance region is frequently of the form $h_1(\theta) \leq T \leq h_2(\theta)$, where $h_1(\theta)$ and $h_2(\theta)$ are monotonic functions of θ, $h_2(\theta) \geq h_1(\theta)$, and $\mathrm{Prob}\,[h_1(\theta) \leq T \leq h_2(\theta)] = \gamma$, the level of significance of the test procedure being $1 - \gamma$. Let T_1 and T_2 be, respectively, the solutions of the following two equations in θ: $h_1(\theta) = T$, $h_2(\theta) = T$. Then the interval (T_1, T_2) provides a confidence interval for θ with a confidence coefficient γ. Test procedures described in later chapters can all be inverted in this way to give confidence intervals for the corresponding parameters.

In like manner, if for m unknown parameters $\theta_1, \theta_2, \ldots, \theta_m$ we can find statistics $T_1^{(i)}, T_2^{(i)}, T_2^{(i)} > T_1^{(i)}, i = 1, 2, \ldots, m$, such that

$$\text{Prob}\{T_1^{(i)} < \theta_i < T_2^{(i)}, \qquad i = 1, 2, \ldots, m\} = \gamma,$$

then the intervals $(T_1^{(i)}, T_2^{(i)})$, $i = 1, 2, \ldots, m$, are called a set of simultaneous confidence intervals for the parameter $\theta_1, \ldots, \theta_m$ with confidence coefficient γ.

2.7 TOLERANCE LIMITS

Let $x_1, x_2, \ldots, x_n$ be a sample of size n drawn from a population, and let $L_1(x_1, x_2, \ldots, x_n)$ and $L_2(x_1, x_2, \ldots, x_n)$ be two functions of sample observations (statistics) such that the probability that the interval (L_1, L_2) will include at least $100\gamma\%$ of the population is equal to β. Then the limits L_1 and L_2 are called the $100\gamma\%$ *tolerance limits* for the population with confidence coefficient $100\beta\%$. We will now give some methods of construction of tolerance limits.

If the population has a continuous frequency density function, tolerance limits can be constructed from order statistics without any assumption about the form of the frequency function. In such a case, let P denote the proportion of the population that lies between the maximum and minimum values of a random sample of size n. Then the sampling distribution of P has the density function

$$f(P) = n(n - 1)P^{n-2}(1 - P), \qquad 0 \leq P \leq 1.$$

The probability that the proportion covered will not be less than γ is then given by

$$(2.7.1) \quad \text{Prob}\,(P \geq \gamma) = \int_\gamma^1 f(P)\,dP = 1 - n\gamma^{n-1}(1 - \gamma) - \gamma^n.$$

To determine the sample size n in such a manner that this probability is equal to a preassigned quality β leads to a complicated equation for n, and a simple approximate solution is given by the formula

$$(2.7.2) \qquad n \doteq \frac{1}{4} \cdot \frac{1 + \gamma}{1 - \gamma} \chi_4^2(1 - \beta) + \frac{1}{2},$$

where $\chi_4^2(1 - \beta)$ is the upper $100(1 - \beta)\%$ point of the chi-square distribution with 4 degrees of freedom. This value of n thus ensures that the range of a sample of size n will cover at least a proportion γ of the population with probability equal to β.

If the population is normal with unknown mean and variance, then the sample mean $\bar{x}$ and standard deviation s may be calculated from a sample of size n, and a quantity k may be so set that the interval $(\bar{x} - ks, \bar{x} + ks)$ will cover at least a fraction γ of the population with probability β. For large n the formula for determining k is

$$(2.7.3) \qquad\qquad k = u\sqrt{\frac{n-1}{\chi^2_{n-1}(\beta)}},$$

where $\chi^2_{n-1}(\beta)$ is the upper $100\beta\%$ point of the chi-square distribution with $n - 1$ degrees of freedom, and u is given by the relation

$$\frac{1}{\sqrt{2\pi}} \int_{(1/\sqrt{n})-u}^{(1/\sqrt{n})+u} e^{-\frac{1}{2}t^2}\, dt = \gamma.$$

Table 2.2 gives the values of k for $\beta = 0.90$ and 0.99 and $\gamma = 0.90$, 0.95, and 0.999 and for various values of n.

TABLE 2.2

TOLERANCE FACTORS FOR A NORMAL POPULATION

n \ β	$\gamma = 0.90$		$\gamma = 0.95$		$\gamma = 0.999$	
	0.90	0.99	0.90	0.99	0.90	0.99
25	2.077	2.494	2.474	2.972	4.151	4.985
50	1.916	2.162	2.284	2.576	3.833	4.323
75	1.856	2.042	2.211	2.433	3.712	4.084
100	1.822	1.977	2.172	2.355	3.646	3.954
150	1.785	1.905	2.127	2.270	3.571	3.811
200	1.764	1.865	2.102	2.222	3.529	3.731
500	1.717	1.777	2.046	2.117	3.434	3.555
1000	1.695	1.736	2.019	2.068	3.390	3.472
∞	1.645	1.645	1.960	1.960	3.291	3.291

2.8   EXERCISES

Sampling

2.1. Draw a random sample of size 5 (a) with and (b) without replacement from a population in which the individuals are serially numbered from 1 to 137.

2.2. Obtain a random permutation of the letters A B C D E F G H I J K.

2.3. Draw a simple sample of size 20 from the frequency distribution shown in Table 2.3 of scores of candidates in a certain public examination.

TABLE 2.3

FREQUENCY DISTRIBUTION OF SCORES

Range of score	Frequency	Range of score	Frequency
0–10	31	50–60	328
10–20	104	60–70	183
20–30	326	70–80	98
30–40	561	80–90	66
40–50	505	90–100	51

2.4. Draw a simple random sample of size 20 from the persons classified in Table 2.4 according to profession and age.

TABLE 2.4

DISTRIBUTION OF PERSONS BY PROFESSION AND AGE

Profession	Age (years)			
	21–30	31–40	41–50	51–60
Law	53	12	19	15
Medicine	28	52	23	19
Engineering	64	23	72	21
Teaching	14	25	33	38

2.5. An elliptical region is determined in terms of rectangular Cartesian coordinates by the relation

$$x^2 + 4y^2 \leq 144 \text{ square miles.}$$

Select 10 points randomly inside this region, indicating the position of the selected points in terms of the coordinates correct to a hundredth of a mile.

2.6. Suppose that there is a pond exactly in the shape of a hemisphere of radius 50 ft. (Obviously the upper surface of the pond forms the plane boundary, and the bottom forms the curved-surface boundary.)

Locate six points at random inside the pond in order to sample the water for bacteriological examination. A depth of 2 ft from the upper surface is to be excluded from sampling.

2.7. Table 2.5 gives the agricultural population (number of persons dependent on agriculture for a living) of 50 villages. Draw a sample of five villages with replacement and probability of selection proportional to the agricultural population.

TABLE 2.5

AGRICULTURAL POPULATION OF 50 VILLAGES

Serial no. of village	Agricultural population	Serial no. of village	Agricultural population
1	520	26	933
2	772	27	591
3	878	28	750
4	665	29	1088
5	803	30	736
6	859	31	1164
7	1134	32	792
8	880	33	860
9	641	34	555
10	1296	35	771
11	687	36	212
12	937	37	363
13	765	38	277
14	680	39	754
15	822	40	589
16	574	41	600
17	581	42	542
18	183	43	745
19	1015	44	1223
20	532	45	1251
21	747	46	978
22	656	47	883
23	1270	48	415
24	1055	49	910
25	671	50	942

2.8–2.12. Draw a simple random sample of size 5 from each of the following discrete distributions:

(a) Binomial: $\binom{10}{x}(.6)^x(.4)^{10-x}$, $\quad x = 0, 1, 2, \ldots, 10$,

(b) Poisson: $e^{-2.5}(2.5)^x/x$, $\quad x = 0, 1, 2, \ldots, \infty$;

and also from each of the following continuous distributions with densities:

(c) Uniform: 1, $0 \leq x \leq 1,$

(d) Cauchy: $\dfrac{1}{\pi(1 + x^2)},$ $-\infty < x < \infty,$

(e) Normal: $\dfrac{1}{\sqrt{2\pi}} e^{-\frac{1}{2}x^2},$ $-\infty < x < \infty.$

2.13. Draw a random sample of size 5 from a trivariate normal population with the following means, variances, and covariances:

$$\mu_x = 1, \quad \mu_y = 2, \quad \mu_z = 3,$$
$$\sigma_{xx} = 4, \quad \sigma_{xy} = 1, \quad \sigma_{xz} = 2,$$
$$\sigma_{yy} = 1, \quad \sigma_{yz} = 2,$$
$$\sigma_{zz} = 9.$$

2.14. Draw 200 independent samples, each of size 5, from a normal population with mean zero and standard deviation unity. For each of these samples, obtain:

Mean: $\bar{x} = \frac{1}{5}(x_1 + x_2 + \cdots + x_5).$

Standard deviation: $s = \sqrt{\dfrac{1}{4}\sum_{i=1}^{5}(x_i - \bar{x})^2}.$

Maximum: $x_{max} = \max(x_1, x_2, \ldots, x_5).$

Minimum: $x_{min} = \min(x_1, x_2, \ldots, x_5).$

Range: $R = x_{max} - x_{min}.$

Student's ratio: $t = \sqrt{5}\bar{x}/s.$

Student's non-central ratio: $t' = \sqrt{5}(\bar{x} + \delta)/s,$ separately for $\delta = 0.1,$ 0.25, 0.5, 0.75, and 1.0.

From these results, examine the sampling distribution of each of these statistics. Obtain empirically (a) the mean, (b) the standard deviation, and (c) the upper 5% point of the sampling distribution of each of these statistics.

Estimation

2.15. It has been suggested that the standard deviation σ of a normal population can be estimated from a sample of size 5 by computing $T_1 = cs$ or $T_2 = dR,$ where s is the standard deviation and R the range of the sample, and c and d are constants to be chosen so as to make these estimates unbiased.

Using the results of the model sampling experiments in exercise 2.14, determine c and d. Also examine empirically which is the better estimate in the sense of having a smaller variance.

2.16. Two normal populations have the same mean μ but possibly different variances σ_1^2 and σ_2^2. Samples of sizes n_1 and n_2 are drawn from the two populations, and the sample means and standard deviations are $\bar{x}_i$ and s_i^2, respectively ($i = 1, 2$).

If σ^2 and σ_2^2 are known, the best linear combination of $\bar{x}_1$ and $\bar{x}_2$ in the sense of providing an unbiased linear estimator of μ with minimum variance is $T = (w_1\bar{x}_1 + w_2\bar{x}_2)/(w_1 + w_2)$, where $w_i = n_i/\sigma_i^2$ ($i = 1, 2$) and the variance of T is $V_0 = 1/(w_1 + w_2)$.

When σ_i^2 ($i = 1, 2$) are not known, the estimates s_i^2 may be substituted to get $\hat{T} = ((\hat{w}_1\bar{x}_1 + \hat{w}_2\bar{x}_2)/(\hat{w}_1 + \hat{w}_2)$ as an unbiased estimator of μ, where $\hat{w}_i = n_i/s_i^2$ ($i = 1, 2$). The variance of $\hat{T}$ is approximately

$$V(\hat{T}) \sim V_0 + \frac{2w_1w_2}{(w_1 + w_2)^3}\left(\frac{1}{n_1} + \frac{1}{n_2}\right).$$

A third simple unbiased estimator of μ is $T^* = (n_1\bar{x}_1 + n_2\bar{x}_2)/(n_1 + n_2)$, whose variance is

$$V(T^*) = \frac{n_1\sigma_1^2 + n_2\sigma_2^2}{(n_1 + n_2)^2}.$$

Compute the ratios $V(\hat{T})/V_0$ and $V(\hat{T}^*)/V_0$ for $n_1 = 20, 50, 100, 200$; $n_2/n_1 = 1, 2, 5, 10$; $\sigma_2^2/\sigma_1^2 = 0.1, 0.2, 0.5, 0.75, 1, 2, 5, 10$. On the basis of these computations give your recommendations on how to combine $\bar{x}_1$ and $\bar{x}_2$.

Testing hypotheses

2.17. The following procedure has been suggested for examining on the basis of a sample of size 5 the hypothesis that the mean of a normal population is zero: "Reject the hypothesis if $\sqrt{5}\bar{x}/s > 2.132$, where $\bar{x}$ is the mean and s the standard deviation in the sample, otherwise accept the hypothesis."

Using the results of the model sampling experiments in exercise 2.10, estimate the probability that this procedure will lead to rejection of the hypothesis when $\mu/\sigma = 0.0, 0.1, 0.25, 0.5, 0.75$, and 1.0, where μ is the mean and σ the standard deviation of the population.

2.18–2.20. *For each of the following test procedures, compute the powers and draw the power curves.*

2.18. Reject the hypothesis that a coin is unbiased if in 100 tosses of the coin the number of heads obtained does not lie between 40 and 60.

2.19. Reject the hypothesis that the mean of a normal population with unit variance is zero if the mean of a sample of 25 does not lie between ±0.3.

2.20. Reject the hypothesis that the variance of a normal population is unity if the variance in a sample of 4 exceeds 7.

Confidence and tolerance limits

2.21. If the probability of success in a single trial is p and if in n such independent trials x successes are obtained, how would you set up 95% (equal-tail) confidence limits for p on the basis of (x, n)? Prepare a chart from which such confidence limits can be obtained for all possible values of x and for $n = 10, 15, 20$.

2.22. If $\bar{x}$ and s are, respectively, the mean and the standard deviation in a sample of size n from a normal population with mean μ and standard deviation σ, how would you set up 90% (equal-tail) confidence limits separately for μ and σ on the basis of $(\bar{x}, s)$? Illustrate numerically, using $n = 25$, $\bar{x} = 5.3$, $s = 1.27$.

2.23. If $(\bar{x}_1, s_1)$ and $(\bar{x}_2, s_2)$ are the mean and the standard deviation in samples of sizes n_1 and n_2 from two normal populations with mean and standard deviation (μ_1, σ_1) and (μ_2, σ_2), respectively, how would you set up confidence limits for (a) $\mu_1 - \mu_2$, (b) σ_1/σ_2, (c) μ_1/μ_2 (when $\mu_2 \neq 0$)? Illustrate numerically when $n_1 = 15$, $\bar{x}_1 = 6.42$, $s_1 = 3.51$, $n_2 = 20$, $\bar{x}_2 = 5.68$, $s_2 = 2.97$.

2.24. The mean and the standard deviation in a sample of size $n = 250$ from a normal population are $\bar{x} = 28.36$ and $s = 7.24$, respectively. Set up 95% tolerance limits for the population.

CHAPTER 3

Estimation

We have discussed in Chapter 2 the properties desirable in an estimator of a parameter. In this chapter we describe a number of methods of estimation which generally lead to estimators having desirable properties.

3.1 METHOD OF MOMENTS

Functions of Moments. From intuitive considerations it is reasonable to take, as an estimator of a given function of population moments, the same function of the corresponding sample moments. Such estimators are generally consistent and asymptotically normally distributed. The asymptotic variance can be computed by using formula 1.5.7 and the expressions for the asymptotic variances and covariances of sample moments given by equations 2.3.4–2.3.6.

Parameters in a Distribution of Specified Form. When the distribution has a specified form, involving, say, k unknown parameters $\theta_1, \theta_2, \ldots, \theta_k$, to estimate them by the method of moments the first k sample moments m_r' $(r = 1, 2, \ldots, k)$ are computed and equated to the corresponding moments $\mu_r' \equiv \mu_r'(\theta_1, \theta_2, \ldots, \theta_k)$ $(r = 1, 2, \ldots, k)$ in the population, which are, of course, functions of the parameters. Estimates are thus obtained by solving the equations

$$(3.1.1) \qquad \mu_r'(\theta_1, \theta_2, \ldots, \theta_k) = m_r', \qquad r = 1, 2, \ldots, k$$

if these are functionally independent. The estimates so obtained are thus functions of the first k sample moments $m_1', m_2', \ldots, m_k'$; $\theta_r = f_r(m_1', m_2', \ldots, m_k')$, say. Under certain mild regularity conditions, such estimates are consistent and asymptotically jointly normally distributed. The asymptotic variances and covariances of the estimates can be computed from formulae 2.3.4–2.3.6.

Illustrative Example 3.1. It is believed that the proportion of household spending \$$x$ per month or less on food in a certain city is given by

$\phi[(\ln x - \mu)/\sigma]$, where $\phi(x) = \int_{-\infty}^{x} (1/\sqrt{2\pi})e^{-\frac{1}{2}t^2}\,dt$. That is, if X is the monthly expenditure on food, the distribution of $\ln X$ is normal with mean μ and standard deviation σ. The mean m and the coefficient of variation v of the distribution of monthly expenditure on food per household were found from a survey to be $m = \$25$ and $v = 80\%$. Estimate μ and σ.

We know from formula 4.2.14 of Part II that the moments about origin of the distribution of X are $m = m_1' = e^{\mu+\frac{1}{2}\sigma^2}$ and $m_2' = e^{2\mu+2\sigma^2}$. From this we obtain the coefficient of variation theoretically as $v = 100\sqrt{e^{\sigma^2} - 1}\%$. Solving, we get

$$\hat{\sigma}^2 = \ln(1 + v)^2 = \log_{10}(1 + 0.64) \times \ln 10 = 0.494696$$

so that $\hat{\sigma} = 0.70335$ and $\hat{\mu} = \ln M - \frac{1}{2}\hat{\sigma}^2 = 8.9156$.

Illustrative Example 3.2. Assume that the estimates $\hat{\mu}$ and $\hat{\sigma}$ in illustrative example 3.1 are based on a simple sample of size $n = 100$ households. Find the asymptotic variances and covariance of these estimates.

We write $g_1 = \ln m_1'$ and $g_2 = \ln m_2'$, where m_1' and m_2' are the first two sample moments about zero. The estimates can be expressed as $\mu = 2g_1 - \frac{1}{2}g_2$ and $\sigma^2 = -2g_1 + g_2$. The moments of the log normal distribution obtained from 4.2.14 of Part II are $\mu_t' = e^{t\mu+\frac{1}{2}t^2\sigma^2}$. We therefore have, from 2.3.4,

$$V(m_1') \doteq \frac{1}{n}\mu_1'^2(A - 1), \quad V(m_2') \doteq \frac{1}{n}\mu_2'^2(A^4 - 1),$$

and

$$\text{Cov}(m_1'm_2') \doteq \frac{1}{n}\mu_1'\mu_2'(A^2 - 1),$$

where $A = e^{\sigma^2}$. Consequently from 1.5.5 and 1.5.7 we get

$$V(g_1) \doteq \frac{1}{n}(A - 1), \quad V(g_2) \doteq \frac{1}{n}(A^4 - 1),$$

and

$$\text{Cov}(g_1g_2) \doteq \frac{1}{n}(A^2 - 1).$$

Therefore

$$V(\hat{\mu}) = 4V(g_1) - 2\,\text{Cov}(g_1g_2) + \frac{1}{4}V(g_2)$$

$$= \frac{1}{n}(\frac{1}{4}A^4 - 2A^2 + 4A - \frac{9}{4}).$$

Similarly

$$V(\hat{\sigma}^2) = 4V(g_1) - 4 \operatorname{Cov}(g_1 g_2) + V(g_2)$$

$$= \frac{1}{n}(A^4 - 4A^2 + 4A - 1),$$

and

$$\operatorname{Cov}(\hat{\mu}, \hat{\sigma}^2) = -4V(g_1) + 3 \operatorname{Cov}(g_1 g_2) - \tfrac{1}{2}V(g_2)$$

$$\doteq \frac{1}{n}(-\tfrac{1}{2}A^4 + 3A^2 - 4A + \tfrac{3}{2}).$$

To obtain $V(\hat{\sigma})$ and $\operatorname{Cov}(\hat{\mu}, \hat{\sigma})$ we make use of the asymptotic formula

$$V(\hat{\sigma}) = V(\hat{\sigma}^2)/4\sigma^2 \quad \text{and} \quad \operatorname{Cov}(\hat{\mu}, \hat{\sigma}) \doteq \operatorname{Cov}(\hat{\mu}, \hat{\sigma}^2)/2\sigma.$$

Substituting $A = e^{\sigma^2} = 1 + v^2 = 1.64$, and $\sigma^2 = 0.494696$, we get

$$V(\hat{\mu}) = 0.007393, \quad V(\hat{\sigma}) = 0.010287,$$

and

$$\operatorname{Cov}(\hat{\mu}, \hat{\sigma}) = -0.004324.$$

3.2 LEAST SQUARES

The method of least squares for estimation of parameters occurring linearly in the expectations of uncorrelated random variables with equal variance consists in taking as estimates those values that minimize the sum of squares of deviations of the random variables from their respective expected values. Let $y_1, y_2, \ldots, y_n$ be n uncorrelated random variables, each with the same unknown variance σ^2 and expectations given by

$$(3.2.1) \quad E(y_i) = a_{i1}\theta_1 + a_{i2}\theta_2 + \cdots + a_{im}\theta_m, \qquad i = 1, 2, \ldots, n,$$

where a_{ij}'s are known constants and θ_j's unknown parameters.

To estimate the parameters, we use the method of least squares and minimize the sum of squares of deviations:

$$S = \sum_{i=1}^{n}(y_i - a_{i1}\theta_1 - a_{i2}\theta_2 - \cdots - a_{im}\theta_m)^2$$

with respect to $\theta_1, \theta_2, \ldots, \theta_m$. Equating the partial derivatives $\partial S/\partial \theta_j$ to zero leads to the following system of *normal equations* in $\theta_1, \theta_2, \ldots, \theta_m$:

$$(3.2.2) \quad c_{j1}\theta_1 + c_{j2}\theta_2 + \cdots + c_{jm}\theta_m = Q_j, \qquad j = 1, 2, \ldots, m,$$

where

$$c_{jk} = a_{1j}a_{1k} + a_{2j}a_{2k} + \cdots + a_{nj}a_{nk},$$

$$Q_j = a_{1j}y_1 + a_{2j}y_2 + \cdots + a_{nj}y_n.$$

There always exists at least one solution of equations 3.2.2. Let θ_1, $\theta_2, \ldots, \theta_m$ be one such solution.

Consider a linear parametric function, say $\theta = l_1\theta_1 + l_2\theta_2 + \cdots + l_m\theta_m$, with known coefficients $l_1, l_2, \ldots, l_m$. Such a linear parametric function θ is said to be *estimable* if there exists an unbiased estimate of θ, linear in $y_1, y_2, \ldots, y_n$. If θ is estimable, its minimum variance unbiased estimate is given by $\hat{\theta} = l_1\hat{\theta}_1 + l_2\hat{\theta}_2 + \cdots + l_m\hat{\theta}_m$. Since each $\hat{\theta}_j$ is a linear function of $Q_1, Q_2, \ldots, Q_m$, $\hat{\theta}$ itself can be expressed as a linear function of $Q_1, Q_2, \ldots, Q_m$, say $\hat{\theta} = \lambda_1 Q_1 + \lambda_2 Q_2 + \cdots + \lambda_m Q_m$. Then the variance of $\hat{\theta}$ can be computed as

$$(3.2.3) \qquad V(\hat{\theta}) = (l_1\lambda_1 + l_2\lambda_2 + \cdots + l_m\lambda_m)\sigma^2.$$

Again, if $\hat{\phi} = \gamma_1 Q_1 + \gamma_2 Q_2 + \cdots + \gamma_m Q_m$ is the minimum variance unbiased estimate of another linear parametric function $\phi = c_1\theta_1 + \cdots + c_m\theta_m$, then

$$(3.2.4) \qquad \mathrm{Cov}\,(\hat{\theta}, \hat{\phi}) = (c_1\lambda_1 + c_2\lambda_2 + \cdots + c_m\lambda_m)\sigma^2$$
$$= (l_1\gamma_1 + l_2\gamma_2 + \cdots + l_m\gamma_m)\sigma^2.$$

The minimum value of S is given by

$$(3.2.5) \qquad S_0 = \sum_{i=1}^{n} y_i^2 - (Q_1\theta_1 + Q_2\theta_2 + \cdots + Q_m\theta_m),$$

and this is known as the *error sum of squares* (ss). If only r of the m equations in the system of normal equations are linearly independent, then the error ss is said to have $n - r$ *degrees of freedom* (df). Thus r is the rank of the matrix $A = ((a_{ij}))$. An unbiased estimate of σ^2 is provided by

$$(3.2.6) \qquad s^2 = \frac{S_0}{n - r},$$

which is called the *error mean square* (ms).

Illustrative Example 3.3.

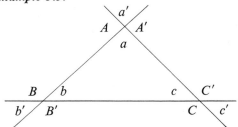

Independent measurements on the angles of the triangle above are given below in degrees:

$$a = 59.1, \quad b = 60.4, \quad c = 60.1,$$
$$a' = 58.6, \quad b' = 61.3, \quad c' = 59.2,$$
$$A = 120.5, \quad B = 119.8, \quad C = 120.7,$$
$$A' = 122.1, \quad B' = 118.7, \quad C' = 121.5.$$

Making use of geometrical properties known, estimate the internal angles of the triangle and also the precision of measurements. Let

$$y_1 = a \qquad = 59.1, \quad y_5 = b \qquad = 60.4, \quad y_9 = 180 - c = 119.9,$$
$$y_2 = a' \qquad = 58.6, \quad y_6 = b' \qquad = 61.3, \quad y_{10} = 180 - c' = 120.8,$$
$$y_3 = 180 - A = 59.5, \quad y_7 = 180 - B = 60.2, \quad y_{11} = C \qquad = 120.7,$$
$$y_4 = 180 - A' = 57.9, \quad y_8 = 180 - B' = 61.3, \quad y_{12} = C' \qquad = 121.5,$$

We assume that the observations $y_1, \ldots, y_{12}$ are independent and subject to a common variance σ^2. Denoting the true values of the angles a, b, and c by α, β, and $\gamma = 180 - \alpha - \beta$, respectively, we can write the expected values of the y_i's as

$$E(y_i) = \begin{cases} \alpha & \text{for } i = 1, 2, 3, 4, \\ \beta & \text{for } i = 5, 6, 7, 8, \\ \alpha + \beta & \text{for } i = 9, 10, 11, 12. \end{cases}$$

The quadratic form to be minimized according to the principle of least squares is

$$S = \sum_{i=1}^{4} (y_i - \alpha)^2 + \sum_{i=5}^{8} (y_i - \beta)^2 + \sum_{i=9}^{12} (y_i - \alpha - \beta)^2.$$

Equating the partial derivatives of L with respect to α and β to zero, we get the normal equations

$$Q_1 = 8\alpha + 4\beta \quad \text{and} \quad Q_2 = 4\alpha + 8\beta,$$

where

$$Q_1 = \sum_{i=1}^{4} y_i + \sum_{i=9}^{12} y_i = 718.0 \quad \text{and} \quad Q_2 = \sum_{i=5}^{12} y_i = 726.1.$$

Solving, we find

$$\hat{\alpha} = \tfrac{1}{6} Q_1 - \tfrac{1}{12} Q_2 = 59.158, \quad \hat{\beta} = \tfrac{1}{6} Q_2 - \tfrac{1}{12} Q_1 = 61.183 \quad \text{and}$$
$$\hat{\gamma} = 180 - \hat{\alpha} - \hat{\beta} = 59.659.$$

The variances and covariance of these estimates are as follows: $V(\hat{\alpha}) = V(\hat{\beta}) = \frac{1}{6}\sigma^2$, $\text{Cov}(\hat{\alpha}, \hat{\beta}) = -\frac{1}{12}\sigma^2$, where σ^2 is estimated by

$$s^2 = \frac{\sum\limits_{i=1}^{12} y_i^2 - \hat{\alpha}Q_1 - \hat{\beta}Q_2}{12 - 2} = 0.59797.$$

3.3 MAXIMUM LIKELIHOOD

Suppose that x_i $(i = 1, 2, \ldots, n)$ constitutes a simple sample of size n from a population with relative frequency (in the discrete case) or frequency density (in the continuous case) $f(x, \theta_1, \theta_2, \ldots, \theta_k)$, where $\theta_1, \theta_2, \ldots, \theta_k$ are k parameters to be estimated. The product

$$L(\theta_1, \theta_2, \ldots, \theta_k) = \prod_{i=1}^{n} f(x_i, \theta_1, \theta_2, \ldots, \theta_k),$$

considered as a function of the parameters, is called the *likelihood function*. The method of maximum likelihood consists in taking, as estimates of the parameters, the values of θ_i's that maximize the likelihood function. The partial derivatives of the logarithm of the likelihood function with respect to the parameters

$$(3.3.1) \quad \phi_j = \frac{\partial \ln L}{\partial \theta_j} = \sum_{i=1}^{n} \frac{\partial \ln f(x_i, \theta_1, \theta_2, \ldots, \theta_k)}{\partial \theta_j}, \qquad j = 1, 2, \ldots, k$$

are called the *efficient scores*. Maximum-likelihood estimates are usually obtained by equating these efficient scores to zero:

$$(3.3.2) \quad \phi_j(\theta_1, \theta_2, \ldots, \theta_k) = 0, \qquad j = 1, 2, \ldots k.$$

These equations are called *likelihood equations*.

Single Parameter. When there is a single parameter θ to be estimated, the likelihood equation reduces to

$$(3.3.3) \quad \phi(\theta) = \sum_{i=1}^{m} \frac{d \ln f(x_i, \theta)}{d\theta} = 0.$$

Under mild regularity conditions there exists a solution $\hat{\theta}$ of this equation which is asymptotically (for large n) normally distributed with mean θ and variance $1/\mathscr{I}(\theta)$. Here $\mathscr{I}(\theta)$ is called the *information*, and

$$(3.3.4) \quad \mathscr{I}(\theta) = ni(\theta) = -E\left(\frac{\partial^2 \ln L}{\partial \theta^2}\right) = -nE\left(\frac{\partial^2 \ln f}{\partial \theta^2}\right);$$

$i(\theta)$ is called the *information per unit observation*.

When it is not possible to get a solution of the likelihood equation 3.3.3 in an explicit form, iterative methods are used. Starting with an approximate solution $\theta^{(0)}$, the efficient score $\phi^{(0)} = \phi(\theta^{(0)})$ and the information $\mathscr{I}^{(0)} = \mathscr{I}(\theta^{(0)})$ are evaluated. A second approximation is then obtained as

$$(3.3.5) \qquad \theta^{(1)} = \theta^{(0)} + \frac{\phi^{(0)}}{\mathscr{I}^{(0)}}.$$

This process may be continued until the likelihood equation is satisfied.

Illustrative Example 3.4. Table 3.1 gives the probabilities and the observed frequencies in four phenotypic classes, AB, Ab, aB, and ab, in a genetical experiment. Estimate the parameter θ by the maximum-likelihood method and find its standard error.

TABLE 3.1

FREQUENCIES IN PHENOTYPIC CLASSES IN A
GENETICAL EXPERIMENT

Phenotypic class	Probability	Observed frequency
AB	$\frac{1}{4}(2 + \theta)$	$n_1 = 102$
Ab	$\frac{1}{4}(1 - \theta)$	$n_2 = 25$
aB	$\frac{1}{4}(1 - \theta)$	$n_3 = 28$
ab	$\frac{1}{4}\theta$	$n_4 = 5$

We assume that n_1, n_2, n_3, n_4 follow a multinomial distribution, so that the logarithm of the likelihood function is

$$\ln L = \text{constant} + n_1 \ln [\tfrac{1}{4}(2 + \theta)] + n_2 \ln [\tfrac{1}{4}(1 - \theta)]$$
$$+ n_3 \ln [\tfrac{1}{4}(1 - \theta)] + n_4 \ln (\tfrac{1}{4}\theta).$$

The efficient score is

$$\frac{d \ln L}{d\theta} = \frac{n_1}{2 + \theta} - \frac{n_2 + n_3}{1 - \theta} + \frac{n_4}{\theta}.$$

Equating this to zero and substituting the observed values of n_1, n_2, n_3, and n_4, the maximum-likelihood equation turns out to be $160\theta^2 + 9\theta - 10 = 0$, a consistent solution of which is $\hat{\theta} = 0.22345$.

The information is given by

$$\mathscr{I}(\theta) = E\left(-\frac{d^2 \ln L}{d\theta^2}\right) = \frac{n}{4}\left(\frac{1}{2 + \theta} + \frac{2}{1 - \theta} + \frac{1}{\theta}\right).$$

This, evaluated at $\hat{\theta}$, gives $\mathscr{I}(\hat{\theta}) = 300.0208$, so that the standard error of the estimate is $\sqrt{1/\mathscr{I}(\hat{\theta})} = 0.05773$.

Illustrative Example 3.5. Table 3.2 gives the number of flowerheads f_x each having exactly x gall cells. The frequency distribution of gall cells may be assumed to be of the truncated Poisson type, the theoretical relative frequencies being given by

$$p_x = (e^\theta - 1)^{-1}\theta^x/x!, \qquad x = 1, 2, \ldots .$$

TABLE 3.2

DISTRIBUTION OF GALL CELLS

No. of gall cells x in a flower head	1	2	3	4	5	6	7	8	9	10
No. of flower heads f_x	287	272	196	79	29	20	2	0	1	0

Source: D. J. Finney, and G. C. Varley, An example of the truncated Poisson distribution, *Biometrics*, Vol. 11, pp. 387–394.

To estimate the parameter θ by the method of maximum likelihood we note that, if the observed values of the number of gall cells in a flower head are denoted by $x_1, x_2, \ldots, x_n$, the likelihood function is

$$L = (e^\theta - 1)^{-n}\theta^{\Sigma x_i}/\prod x_i!,$$

where n is the number of flower heads. Thus

$$\ln L = \text{constant} - n \ln (e^\theta - 1) + T \ln \theta,$$

where $T = \sum_{i=1}^{n} x_i$. The efficient score is therefore

$$\phi = \frac{d \ln L}{d\theta} = -\frac{ne^\theta}{e^\theta - 1} + \frac{T}{\theta},$$

and the information is

$$\mathscr{I} = -E\left(\frac{d^2 \ln L}{d\theta^2}\right) = \frac{ne^\theta}{e^\theta - 1}\left(\frac{1}{\theta} - \frac{1}{e^\theta - 1}\right).$$

Here, we have $T = \Sigma x f_x = 2023$, and $n = \Sigma f_x = 886$. The likelihood equation $\phi = 0$ thus reduces to

$$\frac{\theta e^\theta}{e^\theta - 1} = \frac{T}{n} = 2.283296,$$

which can be solved by iterative methods. As a starting point, we may take the unbiased estimate suggested by Plackett (*Biometrics*, Vol. 9, 1953):

$$\theta_0 = \sum_{x=2}^{\infty} x f_x/n = 1.9594.$$

The efficient score and the information at this point are $\phi^{(0)} = 1.09554$, $\mathscr{I}^{(0)} = 357.154$, so that the next approximation is $\theta^{(1)} = \theta^{(0)} + \phi^{(0)}/\mathscr{I}^{(0)} = 1.9625$. The efficient score and the information at $\theta = 1.9625$ are then computed; these come out as $\phi^{(1)} = -0.01185$ and $\mathscr{I}^{(1)} = 356.751$, respectively. The next approximation, $\theta^{(2)} = \theta^{(1)} + \phi^{(1)}/\mathscr{I}^{(1)}$, does not differ from $\theta^{(1)}$ to four places of decimals. The maximum-likelihood estimate is thus $\hat{\theta} = 1.9625$, and its asymptotic variance is $\hat{V}(\hat{\theta}) = 1/\mathscr{I}(\hat{\theta}) = 0.002803$.

Several Parameters. In the case of k parameters under mild regularity conditions, the likelihood equations 3.3.2 have a solution $\hat{\theta}_j (j = 1, 2, \ldots, k)$ such that the joint distribution of $(\hat{\theta}_1, \hat{\theta}_2, \ldots, \hat{\theta}_k)$ is asymptotically (for large n) normal with means $(\theta_1, \theta_2, \ldots, \theta_k)$ and dispersion matrix $((\mathscr{I}^{rs}))$, where $((\mathscr{I}^{rs})) = ((\mathscr{I}_{rs}))^{-1}$ and

$$\mathscr{I}_{rs} = ni_{rs} = E(\phi_r \phi_s)$$

(3.3.6)
$$= -E\left(\frac{\partial^2 \ln L}{\partial \theta_r \, \partial \theta_s}\right)$$

$$= -nE\left(\frac{\partial^2 \ln f}{\partial \theta_r \, \partial \theta_s}\right).$$

Here the matrix $((\mathscr{I}_{rs}))$ is called the *information matrix*, and the matrix $((i_{rs}))$ is called the *information matrix per unit observation*.

When the likelihood equations 3.3.6 do not admit explicit solution, iterative methods are used. Starting with an approximate solution $\theta_j^{(0)} (j = 1, 2, \ldots, k)$, we evaluate the efficiency scores $\phi_j^{(0)}$ and the information matrix $((\mathscr{I}_{rs}^{(0)}))$ at the point $\theta_1^{(0)}, \theta_2^{(0)}, \ldots, \theta_k^{(0)}$. A second approximation is then obtained as

(3.3.7) $\qquad \theta_j^{(1)} = \theta_j^{(0)} + \sum_{r=1}^{k} \phi_r^{(0)} \mathscr{I}_{(0)}^{jr}, \qquad j = 1, 2, \ldots, k,$

where $((\mathscr{I}_{(0)}^{rs})) = ((\mathscr{I}_{(0)}^{rs}))^{-1}$. Repetitions of this process will finally give the solutions.

Illustrative Example 3.6. In a population under panmixia, the relative frequencies of the blood groups O, A, B, and AB are, respectively, r^2, $p^2 + 2pr$, $q^2 + 2qr$, and $2pq$, where p, q, r ($p + q + r = 1$) are the relative frequencies of the genes G^A, G^B, and g, respectively.

Table 3.3 gives the distribution of blood groups in a sample of 615 Hindus from the Punjab in the Indian Army. There are two independent

TABLE 3.3

BLOOD GROUP DISTRIBUTION OF PUNJAB HINDUS IN THE INDIAN ARMY

Blood group	O	A	B	AB	Total
Frequency	199	137	213	66	615

parameters p and q, r being given by $r = 1 - p - q$. We obtain maximum-likelihood estimates of these two parameters.

We denote the observed frequencies and the theoretical relative frequencies for the blood groups O, A, B, AB by n_1, n_2, n_3, n_4 and π_1, π_2, π_3, π_4, respectively. Here $\pi_1 = r^2$, $\pi_2 = p^2 + 2pr$, $\pi_3 = q^2 + 2qr$, and $\pi_4 = 2pq$. On the assumption that the distribution is multinomial, the logarithm of the likelihood function is $\ln L = \text{constant} + \sum_{i=1}^{4} n_i \ln \pi_i$.

The efficient scores are given by

$$\phi_p = \sum_{i=1}^{4} \frac{n_i}{\pi_i} \cdot \frac{\partial \pi_i}{\partial p} \quad \text{and} \quad \phi_q = \sum_{i=1}^{4} \frac{n_i}{\pi_i} \cdot \frac{\partial \pi_i}{\partial q},$$

and the elements of the information matrix are

$$\mathscr{I}_{pp} = n i_{pp} = n \sum_{i=1}^{n} \frac{1}{\pi_i} \left(\frac{\partial \pi_i}{\partial p} \right)^2,$$

$$\mathscr{I}_{pq} = n i_{pq} = n \sum_{i=1}^{4} \frac{1}{\pi_i} \frac{\partial \pi_i}{\partial p} \frac{\partial \pi_i}{\partial q},$$

$$\mathscr{I}_{qq} = n i_{qq} = n \sum_{i=1}^{4} \frac{1}{\pi_i} \left(\frac{\partial \pi_i}{\partial q} \right)^2,$$

where $n = n_1 + n_2 + n_3 + n_4$. The partial derivatives are as follows:

i	1	2	3	4
$\dfrac{\partial \pi_i}{\partial p}$	$-2r$	$2r$	$-2q$	$2q$
$\dfrac{\partial \pi_i}{\partial q}$	$-2r$	$-2p$	$2r$	$2p$

We have to use iterative methods to solve the likelihood equations. As first approximations we take

$$p^{(0)} = 1 - \sqrt{(n_1 + n_3)/n} = 0.1815,$$
$$q^{(0)} = 1 - \sqrt{(n_1 + n_2)/n} = 0.2608,$$
$$r^{(0)} = 1 - p^{(0)} - q^{(0)} \quad = 0.5577.$$

The efficient scores and the elements of the information matrix per unit observation, for these values of p, q, and r, are

$$\phi_p = -1.9797, \quad i_{pp} = 12.8967, \quad i_{pq} = 2.7029,$$
$$\phi_q = -27.8500, \qquad\qquad\quad i_{qq} = 9.3241.$$

These are computed by first preparing Table 3.4.

STATISTICAL INFERENCE

TABLE 3.4

EVALUATION OF EFFICIENT SCORES AND INFORMATION MATRIX

Blood group	Frequency n	π	$\dfrac{1}{\pi}$	$\dfrac{\partial \pi}{\partial p}$	$\dfrac{1}{\pi} \cdot \dfrac{\partial \pi}{\partial q}$	$\dfrac{\partial \pi}{\partial q}$	$\dfrac{1}{\pi} \cdot \dfrac{\partial \pi}{\partial q}$
O	199	0.311029	3.215134	−1.1154	−3.586160	−1.1154	−3.586160
A	137	0.235387	4.248323	1.1154	4.738579	−0.3630	−1.542141
B	213	0.358913	2.710666	−0.5216	−1.413883	1.1154	3.023477
AB	66	0.094670	10.563008	0.5216	5.509665	0.3630	3.834372
Total	615	0.999999					

The elements of the inverse of the information matrix are given by

$$\begin{pmatrix} \mathscr{I}^{pp} & \mathscr{I}^{pq} \\ \mathscr{I}^{qp} & \mathscr{I}^{qq} \end{pmatrix} = \frac{1}{n} \begin{pmatrix} i_{pp} & i_{pq} \\ i_{pq} & i_{qq} \end{pmatrix}^{-1},$$

and these become

$$\mathscr{I}^{pp} = 1.3424 \times 10^{-4}, \qquad \mathscr{I}^{pq} = -0.3891 \times 10^{-4},$$
$$\mathscr{I}^{qq} = 1.8567 \times 10^{-4}.$$

The next approximation is thus

$$p^{(1)} = p^{(0)} + \phi_p \mathscr{I}^{pp} + \phi_q \mathscr{I}^{pq} = 0.1823,$$
$$q^{(1)} = q^{(0)} + \phi_p \mathscr{I}_{pq} + \phi_q \mathscr{I}^{qq} = 0.2557,$$

and consequently $r^{(1)} = 1 - p^{(1)} - q^{(1)} = 0.5620$. This process is repeated a number of times, and the successive results are shown in Table 3.5.

TABLE 3.5

ITERATIVE SOLUTION OF LIKELIHOOD EQUATION FOR GENE FREQUENCIES

Cycle	p	q	ϕ_p	ϕ_q
0	0.1815	0.2608	−1.9797	−27.8500
1	0.1823	0.2557	−8.2730	18.8038
3	0.1805	0.2594	−0.0443	−0.0757

Cycle	$\mathscr{I}^{pp}$	$\mathscr{I}^{pq}$	$\mathscr{I}^{qq}$
0	1.3424×10^{-4}	-0.3891×10^{-4}	1.8567×10^{-4}
1	1.3418×10^{-4}	-0.3717×10^{-4}	1.8029×10^{-4}
3	1.3299×10^{-4}	-0.3733×10^{-4}	1.8249×10^{-4}

We have, then, the following maximum-likelihood estimates of the gene frequencies: $\hat{p} = 0.1805, \hat{q} = 0.2594, \hat{r} = 1 - \hat{p} - \hat{q} = 0.5601$, and the asymptotic dispersion matrix of $\hat{p}, \hat{q}$ is

$$V(\hat{p}) = 1.3299 \times 10^{-4}, \quad \text{Cov}(\hat{p}, \hat{q}) = -0.3733 \times 10^{-4},$$
$$V(\hat{q}) = 1.8249 \times 10^{-4}.$$

3.4 MINIMUM CHI SQUARE

Consider a distribution in c mutually exclusive and exhaustive categories in which the probability for the ith category $p_i(\boldsymbol{\theta})$ is a given function involving the parameters $\boldsymbol{\theta} = (\theta_1, \theta_2, \ldots, \theta_k)$. If n_i is the observed frequency in the ith category in a random sample of size n, then the minimum chi-square method for estimation of parameters consists in taking as estimates the value of $\boldsymbol{\theta}$ that minimizes

$$\chi^2 = \sum_{i=1}^{c} [n_i - np_i(\boldsymbol{\theta})]^2 / np_i(\boldsymbol{\theta}).$$

Under mild regularity conditions this is asymptotically equivalent to the maximum likelihood method of estimation from the likelihood equations

$$\sum_{i=1}^{c} \frac{n_i}{p_i} \frac{\partial p_i}{\partial \theta_j} = 0, \quad j = 1, 2, \ldots, k.$$

A *modified* method is to minimize $\chi^2 = \sum_{i=1}^{c} [n_i - np_i(\boldsymbol{\theta})]^2 / n_i$ with respect to $\boldsymbol{\theta}$, which leads to the equations:

(5.4.1)
$$\sum_{i=1}^{c} \frac{p_i}{n_i} \frac{\partial p_i}{\partial \theta_j} = 0, \quad j = 1, 2, \ldots, k.$$

These equations are sometimes modified to

(5.4.2)
$$\sum_{i=1}^{c} \frac{p_i}{n_i + 1} \frac{\partial p_i}{\partial \theta_j} = 0, \quad j = 1, 2, \ldots, k$$

to avoid the possibility of a zero in the denominator.

Illustrative Example 3.7. From the data in illustrative example 3.4 estimate θ by the method of modified minimum chi square.

Equation 3.4.1 in this case reduces to

$$\frac{2 + \theta}{n_1} - \frac{1 - \theta}{n_2} - \frac{1 - \theta}{n_3} + \frac{\theta}{n_4} = 0,$$

from which the estimate is obtained as

$$\theta^* = \left(-\frac{2}{n_1} + \frac{1}{n_2} + \frac{1}{n_3} \right) \Big/ \left(\frac{1}{n_1} + \frac{1}{n_2} + \frac{1}{n_3} + \frac{1}{n_4} \right) = 0.22602.$$

3.5 EXERCISES

Least squares

3.1. Table 3.6 gives the parallax of a star together with the standard error of estimate as determined by several observers. Find the minimum variance unbiased linear estimate of the parallax and its standard error.

TABLE 3.6

PARALLAX OF A STAR AND ITS STANDARD ERROR
(IN SECONDS OF ARC)

Observer	Parallax	Standard error
1	0.316	0.016
2	0.216	0.029
3	0.333	0.035
4	0.290	0.009
5	0.300	0.007
6	0.387	0.015
7	0.328	0.029
8	0.298	0.005

3.2. *A, C, D, B* are four points in order on a straight line. Table 3.7 gives the averages of a number of measurements of the length of the segments.

Find least-squares estimates of the lengths and obtain their standard errors.

TABLE 3.7

LENGTHS OF SEGMENTS

Segment	No. of measurements	Average length (cm)
AC	2	45.10
AD	3	77.95
CD	3	32.95
CB	4	98.36
DB	2	65.55
AB	3	143.54

3.3. Three objects *A*, *B*, and *C* were weighed ten times in a chemical balance, by putting some objects on the left pan and some on the right

TABLE 3.8
RESULTS OF WEIGHING THREE OBJECTS

Objects on		Standard weight in	
Right pan	Left pan	Right pan	Left pan
A, C	...	...	14.15
A	C	4.65	...
A, B	C	...	3.15
A, C	B	...	8.47
B, C	A	...	11.87
...	A, B, C	15.41	...
B, C	A	...	12.10
...	A, B	8.31	...
B	C	.91	...
C	B	...	3.95

pan and balancing against standard weights put on the pans. The results of the weighing are given in Table 3.8.

(a) Estimate separately the weights of the three objects A, B, and C.

(b) Find the standard errors of these estimates.

(c) Estimate the total weight of all three objects and find the error of the estimate.

(d) The three objects are alleged to be all the pieces into which an object weighing 20 gm was broken accidentally. Assuming that this statement is true, how would you modify the estimates of the weights of the individual pieces?

3.4. To estimate the average life of a batch of electric lamps, a random sample of 10 was taken. These 10 lamps were switched on, but the experiment had to be discontinued as soon as the third lamp went out. The

TABLE 3.9
MEANS, VARIANCES, AND COVARIANCES OF THE FIRST THREE ORDER STATISTICS IN A SAMPLE OF 10 FROM A NORMAL DISTRIBUTION WITH MEAN ZERO AND STANDARD DEVIATION UNITY

Variate	Mean	Dispersion matrix		
		x_1	x_2	x_3
x_1	−1.53875	0.34435	0.17126	0.11626
x_2	−1.00136		0.21452	0.14662
x_3	−0.65606			0.17500

lengths of the lives of first three lamps to go out were 1500, 1600, and 1650 hours, respectively. On the assumption that the length of life of lamps is normally distributed, estimate the average life and obtain the standard error of estimate.

You may make use of Table 3.9 (p. 291), which gives the means, variances, and covariances of the three smallest members, x_1, x_2, x_3 ($x_1 \leq x_2 \leq x_3$), in a random sample of 10 from a normal population with mean zero and standard deviation unity.

Maximum likelihood

3.5. Table 3.10 gives the observed frequency of different combinations of color and pollen shape in sweet pea in a certain genetical experiment

TABLE 3.10

FREQUENCY DISTRIBUTION OF SWEET
PEA PLANTS

Pollen shape	Color	
	Purple	Red
Long	296	27
Round	19	85

(Bateson's data). The theoretical frequencies in the presence of linkage are as follows:

Pollen shape	Color	
	Purple	Red
Long	$\frac{1}{4}(2 + \theta)$	$\frac{1}{4}(1 - \theta)$
Round	$\frac{1}{4}(1 - \theta)$	$\frac{1}{4}\theta$

where $\theta = (1 - p)^2$, p being called the recombination fraction.

Estimate p by the method of (a) maximum likelihood and (b) modified minimum chi square. Compute the standard error of the estimate in each case.

3.6. For the data on the life (in hours) of 337 electronic tubes given in exercise 4.32 in Part II estimate the parameter θ by the method of maximum likelihood and also calculate the standard error of the estimate.

3.7. Estimate by the method of maximum likelihood the proportion of albino children in families capable of producing them on the basis of the data in exercise 2.28 in Part II, and find the standard error of the estimate.

3.8. Table 3.11 gives the frequencies of eggs laid by gallflies in flower heads. The count of flower heads with no eggs is not available.

Assuming that the number of eggs laid follows Poisson's law, estimate by the method of maximum likelihood the average number of eggs laid and calculate the standard error of the estimate.

TABLE 3.11

FREQUENCY DISTRIBUTION OF EGGS LAID

No. of eggs	1	2	3	4	5	6	7	8	9
No. of flower heads	22	18	18	11	9	6	3	0	1

3.9. On the assumption that, excluding zero counts, the frequency distribution of the number of dust nuclei follows a truncated Poisson distribution, obtain the maximum-likelihood estimate of the average number of dust nuclei in the volume of air on the basis of the data in exercise 2.29 in Part II.

3.10. The data in Table 3.12 from K. Pearson (1913) give the distributions of families having at least one albino child and the number of albino children by family size.

Estimate by the method of maximum likelihood the probability p of a child being albino in families capable of producing albino children. Compute also the standard error of the estimate.

3.11. On the assumption that the frequency distribution of scores in English given in exercise 2.32 in Part II is truncated normal, estimate the mean and the standard deviation of the complete distribution by the method of maximum likelihood. Find the asymptotic dispersion matrix of the estimates.

How will you modify your estimates of the mean and the standard deviation when you are given the supplementary information that the number of students failing in English (that is, scoring below 36) is 835?

3.12. On the assumption that a dosage x of an insecticide kills, on an average, a proportion $\phi\left(\dfrac{x-\mu}{\sigma}\right)$ of insects treated, where μ and σ are unknown constants and $\phi(x) = \displaystyle\int_{-\infty}^{\infty} \dfrac{1}{\sqrt{2\pi}}\, e^{-\frac{1}{2}t^2}\, dt$, estimate the dosage required for an average kill of 50% (as well as the standard error of estimate) from the results of an experiment tabulated in Table 3.13. Different dosages of the insecticide were tried on different batches of insects, and the table shows the number of insects killed in the various trials.

TABLE 3.12

DISTRIBUTION OF FAMILIES HAVING AT LEAST ONE ALBINO CHILD
AND NUMBER OF ALBINO CHILDREN BY FAMILY SIZE

No. of children in family n_j	No. of families N_j	Total no. of albino children in the families T_j
2	40	49
3	55	76
4	50	85
5	60	110
6	53	116
7	46	103
8	27	77
9	29	73
10	20	52
11	14	50
12	3	28
13	4	19
14	4	16
15	1	10
Total	411	864

TABLE 3.13

RESULTS OF INSECTICIDE TRIALS

Dosage	No. of insects	
	Used in experiment	Killed
10.2	50	44
7.7	49	42
5.1	46	24
3.8	48	16
2.6	50	6

3.13. Table 3.14 gives the blood group distribution of Hindus from Uttar Pradesh in the Indian Army. Estimate the gene frequencies p, q, and $r = 1 - p - q$ by the method of maximum likelihood.

TABLE 3.14

BLOOD GROUP DISTRIBUTION OF HINDUS

Blood group	Frequency	Relative frequency under panmixia
O	261	r^2
A	226	$p^2 + 2pr$
B	289	$q^2 + 2qr$
AB	62	$2pq$

3.14. In a survey for estimating the yield of jute fiber, the weight of green plant x and the weight of dry fiber y derived from the plant were both recorded for 100 sampling units. For a different set of 1000 sampling units, only the weight of green plants was recorded. Some statistics computed from these samples are given in Table 3.15.

TABLE 3.15

SOME STATISTICS OF WEIGHT IN TOLAS OF GREEN JUTE PLANTS x AND OF DRY FIBER y

Sample size	Mean		Standard deviation		Correlation
	x	y	x	y	
100	5305	412.2	315.6	23.47	0.8356
1000	3278	...	327.0	...	...

Assuming the distribution of x and y to be bivariate normal, estimate the means, standard deviations, and the coefficient of correlation by the method of maximum likelihood.

CHAPTER 4

General Methods for Testing Parameters

4.1 INTRODUCTION

In this chapter we present a number of general procedures for testing hypotheses concerning parameters of populations, when the samples available are fairly large in size. We first describe certain notations which will be used repeatedly in this and following chapters.

The upper $100\alpha\%$ points of certain distributions will be denoted as follows:

Normal with zero mean and unit variance: $\xi(\alpha)$.
Chi square with n degrees of freedom (df): $\chi_n^2(\alpha)$.
Student's ratio t with n df: $t_n(\alpha)$.
Variance ratio F with m df for the numerator and n df for the denominator: $F_{m,n}(\alpha)$.

One asterisk (*) or two asterisks (**) will be used to indicate that a statistic is significant at the 5% or 1% level, respectively.

4.2 USE OF ASYMPTOTICALLY NORMAL ESTIMATES

Single Parameter. To test a hypothesis H_0 that a parameter θ has a specified value θ^0

$$H_0 : \quad \theta = \theta^0$$

we can start with a "good" estimate $\hat{\theta}$ of θ which is asymptotically (in large samples) distributed normally with mean θ and variance v. Then, against both-sided alternatives, $H : \quad \theta \neq \theta^0$, the hypothesis H_0 is to be rejected at (approximate) level of significance α if

$$(4.2.1) \qquad\qquad T = \frac{|\hat{\theta} - \theta^0|}{\sqrt{v}} > \xi(\tfrac{1}{2}\alpha).$$

If v is not known, a consistent estimate for it may be substituted.

Illustrative Example 4.1. In illustrative example 3.4 we obtained for the parameter θ the maximum-likelihood estimate $\hat{\theta} = 0.22345$ and found its standard error to be 0.05773. A hypothesis of genetical interest is $\theta = 0.25$. To test this we compute $T = |0.22345 - 0.25|/0.05773 = 0.46$, which is not significant at the 5% level. We cannot therefore reject the hypothesis that $\theta = 0.25$.

Illustrative Example 4.2. Two independent estimates of the area under cultivation (in million acres) in rural India are 348.151 and 330.402. The standard errors of these estimates are 7.553 and 4.934, respectively. Is it possible to explain the difference between the two estimates as due to fluctuations of sampling?

Denoting the real difference by θ, we have to test the hypothesis $H_0 : \theta = 0$. For an estimate of θ, we have $\hat{\theta} = 348.151 - 330.402 = 17.749$, and its standard error is $\sqrt{v}$, where $v = (7.553)^2 + (4.934)^2 = 81.3922$. Hence $T = |\hat{\theta}|/\sqrt{v} = 1.967*$. At the 5% level, we therefore reject the hypothesis that the difference is due to fluctuations of sampling.

Several Parameters. To test a hypothesis H_0 that k parameters θ_1, $\theta_2, \ldots, \theta_k$ have specified values $\theta_i = \theta_i^0$ $(i = 1, 2, \ldots, k)$,

$$H_0 : \quad \theta_1 = \theta_1^0, \theta_2 = \theta_2^0, \ldots, \theta_k = \theta_k^0$$

we can start with "good" estimates $\hat{\theta}_1, \hat{\theta}_2, \ldots, \hat{\theta}_k$ for the parameters $\theta_1, \theta_2, \ldots, \theta_k$, respectively, such that $\hat{\theta}_1, \hat{\theta}_2, \ldots, \hat{\theta}_k$ asymptotically (for large samples) follow a k-variate normal distribution with means θ_1, $\theta_2, \ldots, \theta_k$ and dispersion matrix $((v_{ij}))$ which is non-singular. The hypothesis H_0 is to be rejected at (approximate) level of significance α if

$$(4.2.2) \qquad T = \sum_{i,j=1}^{k} v^{ij}(\hat{\theta}_i - \theta_i^0)(\hat{\theta}_j - \theta_j^0) > \chi_k^2(\alpha),$$

where $((v^{ij})) = ((v_{ij}))^{-1}$. If v_{ij}'s are not known, consistent estimates for them may be substituted.

An important case is the hypothesis of equality of k parameters:

$$H_0 : \quad \theta_1 = \theta_2 = \cdots \theta_k,$$

the common value being unspecified. This hypothesis is to be rejected at (approximate) level of significance α if

$$(4.2.3) \qquad T \equiv \sum_{i,j=1}^{k} v^{ij}(\hat{\theta}_i - \bar{\theta})(\hat{\theta}_j - \bar{\theta}) > \chi_{k-1}^2(\alpha),$$

where

$$\bar{\theta} = \sum_{i=1}^{k} w_i \hat{\theta}_i, \quad \text{and} \quad w_i = \sum_{j=1}^{k} v^{ij} \Big/ \sum_{i,j=1}^{k} v^{ij}.$$

Illustrative Example 4.3. In illustrative example 3.6 we obtained the maximum-likelihood estimates of the frequencies p, q of the blood group genes G^A and G^B for a sample of Hindus from the Punjab in the Indian Army as $\hat{p} = 0.1805$, $\hat{q} = 0.2594$ with asymptotic variances and covariances given by $\mathscr{I}^{pp} = V(\hat{p}) = 1.3299 \times 10^{-4}$, $\mathscr{I}^{pq} = \text{Cov}(\hat{p}, \hat{q}) = -0.3733 \times 10^{-4}$, and $\mathscr{I}^{qq} = V(\hat{q}) = 1.8249 \times 10^{-4}$. The values of p, q for all Hindus in the Indian Army are $p = 0.1871$ and $q = 0.2242$. Are the differences between the Hindus from the Punjab and all the other Hindus, in respect to blood group gene frequencies, statistically significant?

The inverse of the asymptotic dispersion matrix is

$$\begin{bmatrix} \mathscr{I}_{pp} & \mathscr{I}_{pq} \\ \mathscr{I}_{pq} & \mathscr{I}_{qq} \end{bmatrix} = \begin{bmatrix} \mathscr{I}^{pp} & \mathscr{I}^{pq} \\ \mathscr{I}^{pq} & \mathscr{I}^{qq} \end{bmatrix}^{-1} = \begin{bmatrix} 0.79774 & 0.16319 \\ 0.16319 & 0.58136 \end{bmatrix} \times 10^4.$$

We then compute T from formula 4.2.2 as

$$T = \mathscr{I}_{pp}(\hat{p} - p)^2 + 2\mathscr{I}_{pq}(\hat{p} - p)(\hat{q} - q) + \mathscr{I}_{qq}(\hat{q} - q)^2$$
$$= 6.793^* > \chi_2^2(0.05) = 5.99.$$

The differences are thus significant at the 5% level.

Illustrative Example 4.4. Table 4.1 gives estimates together with their standard errors of the expenditure in rupees per person per month on food grains in rural India in four independent large-scale surveys. (One U.S. dollar = 7.50 Indian rupees approx.) Are the estimates in statistical agreement?

Let us denote the estimate from the ith survey by $\hat{\theta}_i$ and its asymptotic variance (which is the square of the standard error) by v_i, $i = 1, 2, 3, 4$. Since the estimates are independent, formula 4.2.3 for the statistic T reduces to

$$(4.2.4) \qquad T = \Sigma \frac{(\hat{\theta}_i - \bar{\theta})^2}{v_i} = \Sigma \frac{\hat{\theta}_i^2}{v_i} - \left(\Sigma \frac{\hat{\theta}_i}{v_i}\right)^2 \bigg/ \Sigma\left(\frac{1}{v_i}\right),$$

TABLE 4.1

ESTIMATES OF EXPENDITURE ON FOOD GRAINS
AND THEIR STANDARD ERRORS

Survey	Expenditure on food grains (rupees per person per month), estimate ± standard error
1	8.15 ± 0.832
2	7.60 ± 0.357
3	7.25 ± 0.721
4	7.46 ± 0.618

where $\bar{\theta} = \Sigma(\theta_i/v_i)/\Sigma(1/v_i)$ is the pooled estimate for the parameter. The hypothesis of statistical agreement of the estimates would have to be rejected at (approximate) level of significance α if $T > \chi_3^2(\alpha)$.

By direct computation, we get $A = \Sigma(1/v_i) = 13.83287$, $B = \Sigma\theta_i/v_i = 104.88451$, $C = \Sigma\theta_i^2/v_i = 795.98278$, so that

$$T = C - B^2/A = 0.720 < \chi_3^2(0.05),$$

which is not significant at the 5% level. The estimates may therefore be taken to be in statistical agreement. They may be combined to give $\bar{\theta} = B/A = 7.582$. The asymptotic variance of $\bar{\theta}$ is $v = 1/A = 0.07229$ so that the standard error of $\bar{\theta}$ is $\sqrt{v} = 0.269$.

Illustrative Example 4.5. Table 4.2 gives the distributions of the blood groups O, A, B, and AB in two samples of the Punjab Hindus in the

TABLE 4.2

BLOOD GROUP DISTRIBUTION IN TWO SAMPLES
OF PUNJAB HINDUS IN THE INDIAN ARMY

Blood group	Frequency		
	Sample 1	Sample 2	Total
O	48	151	199
A	32	105	137
B	45	168	213
AB	11	55	66
Total	136	479	615

Indian Army. Do you think that the two samples are in agreement with respect to the frequencies p, q of the blood group genes G^A and G^B? (For definitions of p and q see illustrative example 3.6.)

The maximum-likelihood estimates of p, q from the two samples are $\hat{p}_1 = 0.1730$, $\hat{q}_1 = 0.2330$, and $\hat{p}_2 = 0.1826$, $\hat{q}_2 = 0.2670$, respectively. The asymptotic variances and covariances of these estimates are $V(\hat{p}_1) = 5.7926 \times 10^{-4}$, $\text{Cov}(\hat{p}_1, \hat{q}_1) = -1.4584 \times 10^{-4}$, $V(\hat{q}_1) = 7.5365 \times 10^{-4}$; and $V(\hat{p}_2) = 1.7251 \times 10^{-4}$, $\text{Cov}(\hat{p}_2, \hat{q}_2) = -0.4986 \times 10^{-4}$, $V(\hat{q}_2) = 2.4000 \times 10^{-4}$. These are obtained by methods shown in illustrative example 3.6, and the details are omitted here.

To examine whether the differences $d_1 = \hat{p}_1 - \hat{p}_2 = -0.0096$ and $d_2 = \hat{q}_1 - \hat{q}_2 = -0.0340$ are statistically significant, we first compute the asymptotic variances and covariance of d_1 and d_2. Since $(\hat{p}_1, \hat{q}_1)$ and

$(\hat{p}_2, \hat{q}_2)$ are independent, we get $v_{11} = V(d_1) = V(\hat{p}_1) + V(\hat{p}_2) = 7.5177 \times 10^{-4}$, $v_{12} = \text{Cov}(d_1, d_2) = \text{Cov}(\hat{p}_1, \hat{q}_1) + \text{Cov}(\hat{p}_2, \hat{q}_2) = -1.9570 \times 10^{-4}$, and $v_{22} = V(d_2) = V(\hat{q}_1) + V(\hat{q}_2) = 9.9365 \times 10^{-4}$. The elements of the inverse of this dispersion matrix are given by $v^{11} = 1.4021 \times 10^3$, $v^{12} = 0.2761 \times 10^3$, and $v^{22} = 1.0608 \times 10^3$. Therefore from 4.2.2 we obtain

$$T = v^{11}d_1^2 + 2v^{12}d_1d_2 + v^{22}d_2^2 = 1.536 < \chi_2^2(0.05).$$

The differences in the gene frequencies are thus not significant.

4.3 LIKELIHOOD-RATIO METHOD

Let $L(\theta)$ be the likelihood function of the one or more parameters θ. Let $\hat{\theta}$ be the maximum-likelihood estimate of θ. Suppose that H_0 is the hypothesis on θ to be tested, and let $\hat{\theta}^*$ be the maximum-likelihood estimate of θ when H_0 is true. The likelihood-ratio method is to reject H_0 if

(4.3.1)
$$R \equiv \frac{L(\hat{\theta}^*)}{L(\hat{\theta})} < K,$$

where K is a constant ensuring the preassigned level of significance. If H_0 is a hypothesis which specifies the values of r functionally independent parametric functions and the probability law satisfies certain regularity conditions, the test procedure in large samples is to reject H_0 at (approximate) level of significance α if

(4.3.2)
$$T \equiv -2 \ln R > \chi_r^2(\alpha).$$

Illustrative Example 4.6. We illustrate the use of the likelihood-ratio method by considering again the problem discussed in illustrative example 4.5. We denote the observed frequencies of the blood groups (O, A, B, AB) in the first and second samples by n_1', n_2', n_3', n_4' and $n_1'', n_2'', n_3'', n_4''$, respectively. The corresponding theoretical relative frequencies in the two cases are denoted by $\pi_1', \pi_2', \pi_3', \pi_4'$ and $\pi_1'', \pi_2'', \pi_3'', \pi_4''$, respectively. Then $\pi_1' = p_1^2$, $\pi_2' = p_1^2 + 2p_1r_1$, $\pi_3' = q_1^2 + 2q_1r_1$, $\pi_4' = 2p_1q_1$, where (p_1, q_1) are the frequencies of the genes G^A, G^B in the first case, and $r_1 = 1 - p_1 - q_1$. In the second case, the π_i'''s are defined in the same way in terms of (p_2, q_2), which are the corresponding gene frequencies in the second case. The likelihood function L is then given by

$$\log L(p_1, q_1, p_2, q_2) = C + \Sigma n_i' \log \pi_i' + \Sigma n_i'' \log \pi_i'',$$

where C is some constant. Under this model, the maximum-likelihood estimates of the parameters are $\hat{p}_1 = 0.1730$, $\hat{q}_1 = 0.2330$, $\hat{p}_2 = 0.1826$, $\hat{q}_2 = 0.2670$. Consequently, we get the maximum value of the likelihood as

$$A = \log L(\hat{p}_1, \hat{q}_1, \hat{p}_2, \hat{q}_2) = C + \overline{350.9753673}.$$

The hypothesis to be tested is $H_0 :$ $p_1 = p_2, q_1 = q_2$, so that the values of the two functionally independent parametric functions $p_1 - p_2$ and $q_1 - q_2$ are specified by the hypothesis. Thus $r = 2$. Under H_0, the maximum-likelihood estimates of the parameters are $\hat{p}_1{}^* = \hat{p}_2{}^* = 0.1805$, $\hat{q}_1{}^* = \hat{q}_2{}^* = 0.2594$, as obtained in illustrative example 3.6 from the two samples pooled together. Therefore the maximum value of the likelihood under the hypothesis is

$$B = \log L(\hat{p}_1{}^*, \hat{q}_1{}^*, \hat{p}_2{}^*, \hat{q}_2{}^*) = C + \overline{350.6499175}.$$

From 4.3.2 we thus obtain

$$T = 2 \ln 10 \times (A - B) = 1.499 < \chi_2{}^2(0.05),$$

which is not significant at the 5% level.

4.4 LAGRANGIAN MULTIPLIER TEST

When the hypothesis can be expressed in the form:

$$H_0 : \quad \psi_t(\theta_1, \theta_2, \ldots, \theta_k) = 0, \qquad t = 1, 2, \ldots, r,$$

where ψ_t's are given functions of the unknown parameters, C. R. Rao (*Journal of the Royal Statistical Society*, 1948) suggested the following procedure. Let $\hat{\boldsymbol{\theta}}^* = (\hat{\theta}_1{}^*, \hat{\theta}_2{}^*, \ldots, \hat{\theta}_k{}^*)$ be a solution of the equations

(4.4.1)
$$\frac{\partial \log L}{\partial \theta_i} + \sum_{t=1}^{r} \lambda_t \frac{\partial \psi_t}{\partial \theta_i} = 0, \qquad t = 1, 2, \ldots, k,$$

$$\psi_t = 0, \qquad t = 1, 2, \ldots, r,$$

where λ_t's are Lagrangian multipliers and L is the likelihood function. Thus $\hat{\boldsymbol{\theta}}^*$ is the maximum-likelihood estimate of $\boldsymbol{\theta}$ when H_0 is true. Evaluate the efficient scores $\phi_i(\boldsymbol{\theta}) = (\partial \log L)/\partial \theta_i$ and the elements of the information matrix $\mathscr{I}_{ij}(\boldsymbol{\theta}) = -E(\partial^2 \log L/\partial \theta_i\, \partial \theta_j)$ at $\boldsymbol{\theta} = \hat{\boldsymbol{\theta}}^*$. Then, in large samples, the hypothesis H_0 is to be rejected at (approximate) level of significance α if

(4.4.2)
$$T = \sum_{i,j=1}^{k} \mathscr{I}^{ij}(\hat{\boldsymbol{\theta}}^*)\phi_i(\hat{\boldsymbol{\theta}}^*)\phi_j(\hat{\boldsymbol{\theta}}^*) > \chi_r{}^2(\alpha),$$

where $((\mathscr{I}^{ij})) = ((\mathscr{I}_{ij}))^{-1}$.

Illustrative Example 4.7. We illustrate the application of this method by considering again the problem discussed in illustrative examples 4.5 and 4.6. From the likelihood function given in illustrative example 4.6, we find that the efficient scores are

$$\phi_{p_1} = \frac{\partial \log L}{\partial p_1} = \sum \frac{n_i{}'}{\pi_i{}'} \cdot \frac{\partial \pi_i{}'}{\partial p_1}, \text{ etc.}$$

The elements of the information matrix are

$$\mathscr{I}_{p_1 p_1} = -E\left(\frac{\partial^2 \log L}{\partial p_1{}^2}\right) = n' \Sigma \frac{1}{\pi_i'} \cdot \left(\frac{\partial \pi_i'}{\partial p_1}\right)^2,$$

$$\mathscr{I}_{p_1 q_1} = -E\left(\frac{\partial^2 \log L}{\partial p_1 \partial q_1}\right) = n' \Sigma \frac{1}{\pi_i'} \cdot \left(\frac{\partial \pi_i'}{\partial p_1}\right)\left(\frac{\partial \pi_i'}{\partial q_1}\right) \text{ etc.}$$

These quantities are evaluated by substituting for the parameters p_1, q_1, p_2, q_2 their maximum-likelihood estimates under the hypothesis, namely, $\hat{p}_1{}^* = \hat{p}_2{}^* = 0.1805$ and $\hat{q}_1{}^* = \hat{q}_2{}^* = 0.2594$. We thus obtain

$$\phi_{p_1} = -23.00 \quad \begin{bmatrix} \mathscr{I}_{p_1 p_1} & \mathscr{I}_{p_1 q_1} \\ \mathscr{I}_{q_1 p_1} & \mathscr{I}_{q_1 q_1} \end{bmatrix} = 136J,$$

$$\phi_{q_1} = -37.32$$

$$\phi_{p_2} = +23.00 \quad \begin{bmatrix} \mathscr{I}_{p_2 p_1} & \mathscr{I}_{p_2 q_1} \\ \mathscr{I}_{q_2 p_1} & \mathscr{I}_{q_2 q_1} \end{bmatrix} = O, \quad \begin{bmatrix} \mathscr{I}_{p_2 p_2} & \mathscr{I}_{q_2 p_2} \\ \mathscr{I}_{p_2 q_2} & \mathscr{I}_{q_2 q_2} \end{bmatrix} = 479J,$$

$$\phi_{q_2} = +37.32$$

where $J = \begin{bmatrix} 12.9712 & 2.6536 \\ 2.6536 & 9.4536 \end{bmatrix}$, and O is a 2×2 null matrix.

Formula 4.4.2 then gives

$$T = \sum_{i=1}^{2}(\phi_{p_i}{}^2 \mathscr{I}^{p_i p_i} + 2\phi_{p_i}\phi_{q_i} \mathscr{I}^{p_i q_i} + \phi_{q_i}{}^2 \mathscr{I}^{p_i q_i}$$

$$= (\tfrac{1}{631} + \tfrac{1}{479})(\phi_{p_1}{}^2 J^{11} + 2\phi_{p_1}\phi_{q_1} J^{12} + \phi_{q_1}{}^2 J^{22}),$$

where $((J^{ij})) = J^{-1} = \begin{bmatrix} 0.081791 & -0.022958 \\ -0.022958 & 0.112224 \end{bmatrix}$.

Therefore

$$T = 1.512 < \chi_2{}^2(0.05),$$

which is not significant at the 5% level.

4.5 CHI-SQUARE TEST IN MULTINOMIAL DISTRIBUTIONS

Consider r multinomial distributions, each with k cells. Let $\pi_i^{(j)}$ be the theoretical probability and $n_i^{(j)}$ the observed frequency in the ith cell of the jth multinomial distribution, $i = 1, 2, \ldots, k$, $j = 1, 2, \ldots, r$, so that $n^{(j)} = \sum_{i=1}^{k} n_i^{(j)}$ is the (fixed) size of the sample drawn from the jth population. Suppose that the cell probabilities are all functions of given forms $\pi_i^{(j)} = \pi_i^{(j)}(\boldsymbol{\theta})$, say, where $\boldsymbol{\theta} = (\theta_1, \ldots, \theta_m)$ are m unknown parameters. Then $m_i^{(j)}(\boldsymbol{\theta}) = n^{(j)}\pi_i^{(j)}(\boldsymbol{\theta})$ is the expected frequency in the ith cell of the jth distribution. Let

$$T(\boldsymbol{\theta}) = \sum_{j=1}^{r} \sum_{i=1}^{k} [n_i^{(j)} - m_i^{(j)}(\boldsymbol{\theta})]^2/m_i^{(j)}(\boldsymbol{\theta}).$$

Let $\hat{\theta}$ be a best asymptotically normal estimate of θ, say the minimum chi-square estimate obtained by minimizing $T(\theta)$ or the maximum-likelihood estimate.

Consider now the hypothesis H_0 that a given function of the parameters have specified values, say:

$$H_0 : \quad f_t(\theta) = 0, \quad t = 1, 2, \ldots, s.$$

Let $\hat{\theta}^*$ be a best asymptotically normal estimate of θ when the hypothesis H_0 is true. Let $T_1 = T(\hat{\theta})$, $T_2 = T(\hat{\theta}^*)$, and $T_0 = T_2 - T_1$. Then, under certain mild restrictions on the functional forms of $\pi_i^{(j)}$'s and f_t's and the range θ, it can be shown that asymptotically for large $n^{(j)}$'s the statistics T_0 and T_1 are independently distributed as chi squares with s and $r(k-1) - m$ degrees of freedom, respectively. The hypothesis H_0 is rejected at (approximate) level of significance α if

$$T_0 = T(\hat{\theta}^*) - T(\hat{\theta}) > \chi_s^2(\alpha).$$

See also Section 5.3.

4.6 EXERCISES

4.1. Examine whether the combined estimate of the parallax of the star obtained in exercise 3.1 is significantly different from 0.3.

4.2. Examine whether the data in exercise 3.5 are consistent with the hypothesis that $p = \frac{1}{2}$.

4.3. Using computations made in exercise 3.6, set up 95% confidence limits on the average life of the electric bulbs.

4.4. Examine whether the estimate obtained in exercise 3.7 of the proportion of albino children in families capable of producing them differs significantly from 0.25.

TABLE 4.3

BLOOD GROUP FREQUENCIES OF TWO GROUPS

Blood group	Army cadets	Others
O	56	120
A	60	122
B	18	42
AB	6	11

Source: C. R. Rao, *Advanced Statistical Methods in Biometric Research*, John Wiley & Sons, New York, 1952.

4.5. Using the data given in exercise 3.8, set 95% confidence limits on the average number of eggs laid by gallflies on flower heads.

4.6. On the basis of the data given in exercise 3.1, would you say that the different estimates of the parallax are in statistical agreement?

4.7. On the basis of the data given in exercise 3.10, examine whether the proportion of albino children in families capable of producing them depends on the size of the family.

4.8. On the basis of the estimate of the mean and the standard deviation of the scores obtained in exercise 3.11, examine whether the coefficient of variation differs significantly from 80%.

4.9. Table 4.3 (p. 303) gives the blood group frequencies for two groups: Army cadets and others. Examine whether the two groups are homogeneous in respect to the blood group gene frequencies.

CHAPTER 5

Tests of Parameters
of Discrete Distributions

5.1 BINOMIAL DISTRIBUTION

Test for a Specified Value of a Proportion. If x successes are obtained in n independent trials, in each of which the probability of success is p, then to test the hypothesis that p has a specified value p_0,

$$H_0 : \quad p = p_0,$$

against one-sided alternatives $H : \quad p > p_0$, we compute

(5.1.1)
$$P = \sum_{r=x}^{n} \binom{n}{r} p_0^r (1 - p_0)^{n-r}$$

and reject H_0 at (approximate) level of significance α if $P < \alpha$. For large n, H_0 is rejected against alternatives $p > p_0$ if

(5.1.2)
$$T \equiv \frac{x - np_0}{\sqrt{np_0(1 - p_0)}} = \frac{\hat{p} - p_0}{\sqrt{p_0(1 - p_0)/n}} > \xi(\alpha),$$

where $\hat{p} = x/n$ is an estimate of p. Against both-sided alternatives $H : \quad p \neq p_0$, the procedure, in large samples, is to reject H_0 at (approximate) level of significance α if $|T| > \xi(\tfrac{1}{2}\alpha)$.

Illustrative Example 5.1. Out of eight fossils discovered, two and six were identified as being male and female, respectively. Is this compatible with the sex ratio 1 : 1, or are female fossils more numerous?

Here we have to test the hypothesis $H_0 : \quad p = \tfrac{1}{2}$ against one-sided alternatives $H : \quad p > \tfrac{1}{2}$, where p is the proportion of females. We compute

$$P = 2^{-8} \sum_{r=6}^{8} \binom{8}{r} = \frac{37}{256} = 0.1445,$$

305

which is larger than 5%. Thus the hypothesis that the sex ratio is 1 : 1 cannot be rejected at the 5% level of significance.

Illustrative Example 5.2.   The proportion of defective articles manufactured by a certain process is 20%. After the introduction of some modifications in the process, a random sample of 100 articles on inspection revealed 16 defectives. Has the new method reduced the proportion of defectives significantly?

We have to test the hypothesis $p = 0.2$ against the one-sided alternatives $H : p < 0.2$, where p is the proportion of defectives. Here $n = 100$ and $\hat{p} = 0.16$, so that

$$T = \frac{\hat{p} - p_0}{\sqrt{p_0(1 - p_0)/n}} = -1.0.$$

But the lower 5% value of the standardized normal deviate is -1.64. Therefore the reduction is not significant at the 5% level.

Illustrative Example 5.3.   Weldon threw twelve dice 26,306 times and, counting the occurrence of a 5 or 6 as a success, obtained in all 106,602 successes. Is this consistent with the hypothesis that the dice are unbiased, that is, that the probability of success with a single die is one third?

Here we have to test the hypothesis $p = p_0 = \frac{1}{3}$ against both-sided alternatives $p \neq \frac{1}{3}$. Here $n = 26{,}306 \times 12$ and $\hat{p} = 106{,}602/(26{,}306 \times 12) = 0.337609$ so that

$$T = \frac{|\hat{p} - p_0|}{\sqrt{p_0(1 - p_0)/n}} = 5.203**,$$

which is larger than $\xi(0.01) \doteq 2.58$. Therefore at the 1% level the data are not consistent with the hypothesis $p = \frac{1}{3}$.

Test for Equality of Two Proportions.   If x_i successes are observed in n_i independent trials, in each of which the probability of success is p_i, $i = 1, 2$, then to test the hypothesis

$$H_0 : \quad p_1 = p_2$$

against both-sided alternatives $H : p_1 \neq p_2$ the procedure, in large samples, is to reject H_0 at (approximate) level of significance α if

$$(5.1.3) \qquad T = \frac{|\hat{p}_1 - \hat{p}_2|}{\sqrt{\left[\hat{p}(1 - \hat{p})\left(\dfrac{1}{n_1} + \dfrac{1}{n_2}\right)\right]}} > \xi(\tfrac{1}{2}\alpha),$$

where $\hat{p}_i = x_i/n_i (i = 1, 2)$, $\hat{p} = (x_1 + x_2)/(n_1 + n_2)$.

Sample	No. of Successes	No. of Failures	Total
1	x_1	$n_1 - x_1$	n_1
2	x_2	$n_2 - x_2$	n_2
Total	$x_1 + x_2$	$n_1 + n_2 - x_1 - x_2$	$n_1 + n_2$

If samples are small in size, a 2×2 contingency table can be prepared, and the exact procedure for testing independence in such tables (described in Section 5.3) can be used.

Illustrative Example 5.4. Estimates of the percentage of employed persons in a certain city obtained from two independent random sample surveys are given in the table. Is this difference in the two estimates due to fluctuations of sampling?

Survey	Sample size	Percentage employed
A	2350	39.66
B	1675	38.60

Here $n_1 = 2350$, $n_2 = 1675$, and estimates of the proportions employed are $\hat{p}_1 = 0.3966$, $\hat{p}_2 = 0.3860$. Under the hypothesis $H_0 : p_1 = p_2$, the common value of the proportion is estimated by

$$\hat{p} = (n_1\hat{p}_1 + n_2\hat{p}_2)/(n_1 + n_2) = 0.39169.$$

Hence, the statistic to use against both-sided alternatives is

$$T = \frac{|\hat{p}_1 - \hat{p}_2|}{\sqrt{\left[\hat{p}(1 - \hat{p})\left(\dfrac{1}{n_1} + \dfrac{1}{n_2}\right)\right]}} = 0.6791.$$

As a standard normal deviate, this is not significant at the 5% level, so that the difference between the two estimates can be explained by the fluctuations of sampling.

Test for Equality of k Proportions ($k \geq 2$). If x_i successes are observed in n_i independent trials, in each of which the probability of success is p_i, $i = 1, 2, \ldots, k$, to test the hypothesis of equality of the p_i's:

$$H_0 : p_1 = p_2 = \cdots = p_k,$$

the procedure, in large samples, is to reject H_0 at (approximate) level of significance α if

$$(5.1.4) \quad T = \frac{n^2}{x(n-x)}\left(\sum_{i=1}^{k}\frac{x_i^2}{n_i} - \frac{x^2}{n}\right) = \frac{\sum_{i=1}^{k}n_i\hat{p}_i^2 - n\hat{p}^2}{\hat{p}(1-\hat{p})} > \chi_{k-1}^2(\alpha),$$

where $x = \sum_{i=1}^{k}x_i$, $n = \sum_{i=1}^{k}n_i$, $\hat{p}_i = x_i/n_i$, $i = 1, 2, \ldots, k$, and $\hat{p} = x/n$.

Illustrative Example 5.5. Samples of different sizes were selected from lots supplied by four different manufacturers 1, 2, 3, 4; the numbers of defective articles detected are given below. Is there any significant difference between the quality of the lots produced by the different manufacturers?

		Manufacturer, i				
		1	2	3	4	Total
Sample size	n_i	100	200	150	250	$n = 700$
No. of defectives	x_i	20	35	37	43	$x = 135$

Here the observed proportions of defectives are $\hat{p}_1 = 0.2000$, $\hat{p}_2 = 0.1750$, $\hat{p}_3 = 0.2467$, and $\hat{p}_4 = 0.1720$, respectively, where $\hat{p}_i = x_i/n_i$. Under the hypothesis $H_0: p_1 = p_2 = p_3 = p_4$ the common value of the proportion is estimated by

$$\hat{p} = x/n = 0.1929.$$

Therefore

$$T = \frac{\sum_{i=1}^{4}n_i\hat{p}_i^2 - n\hat{p}^2}{\hat{p}(1-\hat{p})} = 3.934 < \chi_3^2(0.05).$$

Hence at the 5% level the lots are not significantly different in quality.

5.2 POISSON DISTRIBUTION

Test for a Specified Value of the Mean. On the basis of a sample $x_1, x_2, \ldots, x_n$ of size n from a Poisson distribution with mean μ, to test the hypothesis that μ has a specified value μ_0,

$$H_0: \quad \mu = \mu_0,$$

against alternatives $\mu > \mu_0$, the procedure is to reject H_0 at (approximate) level of significance α if

$$(5.2.1) \qquad\qquad P = \sum_{r=s}^{\infty}e^{-n\mu_0}(n\mu_0)^r/r! < \alpha,$$

where $s = \sum_{i=1}^{n} x_i$. Against alternatives $\mu < \mu_0$, the same procedure is used, except that now $P = \sum_{r=0}^{s} e^{-n\mu_0}(n\mu_0)^r/r!$. For large n, H_0 is rejected against the alternatives $\mu > \mu_0$ if

$$T = \frac{s - n\mu_0}{\sqrt{n\mu_0}} = \frac{\bar{x} - \mu_0}{\sqrt{\mu_0/n}} > \xi(\alpha),$$

where $\bar{x} = (1/n)\sum_{i=1}^{n} x_i$. Against both-sided alternatives $H : \mu \neq \mu_0$ the procedure, in large samples, is to reject H_0 at (approximate) level of significance α if $|T| > \xi(\frac{1}{2}\alpha)$.

Illustrative Example 5.6. The average number of accidents per month in a factory was 4.5. In the first month after the introduction of some safety measures, the number of accidents came down to 3. Have the new measures significantly decreased the number of accidents?

The number of accidents per month, after introduction of the safety measures, may be taken to be distributed in the Poisson form with mean μ, say. Then we have to test the hypothesis $H_0 : \mu = 4.5$ against alternatives $\mu < 4.5$. Since $n = 1$, we compute

$$P = \sum_{r=0}^{3} e^{-4.5} \cdot \frac{(4.5)^r}{r!} = 0.34320.$$

Hence H_0 cannot be rejected at the 5% level, and thus the reduction is not significant. That is to say, we do not have enough evidence to state with assurance that there has been a reduction.

Illustrative Example 5.7. Are the data given in illustrative example 3.4 of Part II consistent with the hyopthesis that the mean number of red blood corpuscles (rbc) per cell is 1?

The distribution of the number of rbc is of the Poisson form. Denote the mean number by μ. The hypothesis to be tested is $H_0 : \mu = 1$, and the mean based on a sample of size $n = 400$ is given by $\bar{x} = s/n = 0.995$, so that

$$T = \frac{|\bar{x} - \mu_0|}{\sqrt{\mu_0/n}} = 0.1,$$

which as a standard normal deviate is not significant at the 5% level. Therefore the data are consistent with the hypothesis $H_0 : \mu = 1$.

Test for Equality of Two Means. Under the hypothesis that two independent Poisson variables x_1, x_2 have the same mean, the conditional probability distribution of x_1, x_2 for a given value of $x_1 + x_2$ is given by

(5.2.2)
$$\frac{(x_1 + x_2)!}{x_1! \, x_2!} \cdot \left(\frac{1}{2}\right)^{x_1+x_2}.$$

Then to test the hypothesis that the two Poisson distributions have the same mean, $H_0: \mu_1 = \mu_2$, against one-sided alternatives $\mu_1 > \mu_2$, we compute

(5.2.3)
$$P = \sum_{r=x_1}^{x_1+x_2} \binom{x_1 + x_2}{r} \left(\frac{1}{2}\right)^{x_1+x_2}$$

and reject H_0 at (approximate) level of significance α if $P < \alpha$.

Illustrative Example 5.8.   The numbers of deaths from road accidents in a city in two consecutive months were 7 and 3, respectively. Can the reduction from the first to the second month be due to chance fluctuations?

We assume that the number of deaths from road accidents follows a Poisson distribution, and we have to test the hypothesis that the mean number of deaths from road accidents for the two months are the same. The conditional probability for x deaths in the second month, given that the total for the two months is $7 + 3 = 10$, is $\binom{10}{x}\left(\frac{1}{2}\right)^{10}$. Therefore the conditional probability of 7 or more deaths in the first month, given that the total for the two months is 10, is

$$P = \sum_{r=0}^{3} \binom{10}{r}\left(\frac{1}{2}\right)^{10} = 0.172,$$

which is not significant at the 5% level. Therefore the reduction in the number of accidents in the second month can be regarded as due to chance fluctuations.

Test for Equality of k ($k > 2$) Means.   To test the hypothesis that k independent Poisson variables x_i ($i = 1, 2, \ldots k$) have the same mean, the procedure is to reject this hypothesis at (approximate) level of significance α if

(5.2.4)
$$T = \sum_{i=1}^{k} \frac{(x_i - \bar{x})^2}{\bar{x}} = \frac{\sum_{i=1}^{k} x_i^2 - k\bar{x}^2}{\bar{x}} > \chi_{k-1}^2(\alpha),$$

where $\bar{x} = 1/k \sum_{i=1}^{k} x_i$.

Illustrative Example 5.9.   The numbers of deaths from drowning in a certain river in three successive years are 12, 10, and 8. Can the differences be considered as due to chance fluctuations?

Under the assumption that the number of deaths follows a Poisson distribution we have to test the hypothesis that the means are the same. Here $\bar{x} = 10$, so that

$$T = \sum_{i=1}^{3} \frac{(x_i - \bar{x})^2}{\bar{x}} = 0.8.$$

Since this value is less than the 5% value of χ^2 with 2 degrees of freedom, the reduction may be due to chance fluctuations.

5.3 MULTINOMIAL DISTRIBUTION

Test for Specified Values of the Means of Linear Functions of Frequencies.
In a random sample of size n, classified into k mutually exclusive and exhaustive categories, let n_j be the observed frequency in the jth category and let p_j be the probability for a single individual to belong to the jth category, so that $\sum_{j=1}^{k} n_j = n$, $\sum_{j=1}^{k} p_j = 1$. Then the random variables $n_1, n_2, \ldots, n_k$ follow the multinomial distribution

$$(5.3.1) \quad \text{Prob}\,(n_1 = x_1, n_2 = x_2, \ldots, n_k = x_k)$$

$$= \frac{n!}{x_1!\,x_2!\cdots x_k!}\, p_1^{x_1} p_2^{x_2}, \ldots, p_k^{x_k},$$

where $x_1, x_2, \ldots, x_k$ are non-negative integers such that $\sum_{i=1}^{k} x_j = n$.
Now consider r $(r < k)$ linear functions $L_i = \sum_{j=1}^{k} l_{ij} n_j$ $(i = 1, 2, \ldots, r)$ of the frequencies n_j's, where l_{ij}'s are given constants. The expectations, variances, and covariances of these linear functions are given by

$$\mu_i = E(L_i) = n \sum_{j=1}^{k} l_{ij} p_j,$$

$$(5.3.2) \quad \lambda_{ii} = V(L_i) = n\left[\sum_{j=1}^{k} l_{ij}^{2} p_j - \left(\sum_{j=1}^{k} l_{ij} p_j\right)^2\right],$$

$$\lambda_{ii'} = \text{Cov}\,(L_i, L_{i'}) = n\left[\sum_{j=1}^{k} l_{ij} l_{i'j} p_j - \left(\sum_{j=1}^{k} l_{ij} p_j\right)\left(\sum_{j=1}^{k} l_{i'j} p_j\right)\right],$$

$$i = 1, 2, \ldots, r; i \neq i' = 1, 2, \ldots, r.$$

For large n, the linear functions $L_1, L_2, \ldots, L_r$ follow (approximately) the r-variate normal distribution with means $\mu_1, \mu_2, \ldots, \mu_r$ and dispersion matrix $((\lambda_{ii'}))$. Thus, normal deviate or chi-square tests described in Section 4.2 can be used for examining whether means of given linear functions of frequencies have specified values.

Tests of Specified Values of Cell Probabilities. We consider a random sample of size n classified according to k mutually exclusive and exhaustive categories. Let n_i be the observed frequency in the ith category and p_i the corresponding probability for an individual to belong to this category. Then $\sum_{i=1}^{k} n_i = n$ and $\sum_{i=1}^{k} p_i = 1$. In order to test the hypothesis H_0 that the probabilities p_i have the specified values p_i^0,

$$H_0: \quad p_i = p_i^0, \quad i = 1, 2, \ldots k,$$

the procedure, in large samples, is to reject H_0 at (approximate) level of significance α if

(5.3.3) $$T = \sum_{i=1}^{k} \frac{(n_i - np_i^0)^2}{np_i^0} = \sum_{i=1}^{k} \frac{n_i^2}{np_i^0} - n > \chi_{k-1}^2(\alpha).$$

Suppose that the hypothesis H_0 merely specifies that the probabilities p_i's are functions of known form of s ($s < k - 1$) unknown parameters $\theta_1, \theta_2, \ldots, \theta_s$:

$$H_0: \quad p_i = p_i(\theta_1, \theta_2, \ldots, \theta_s), \qquad i = 1, 2, \ldots, k.$$

Then the procedure is to obtain best asymptotically normal estimates $\hat{\theta}_1, \hat{\theta}_2, \ldots, \hat{\theta}_s$ by the method of, say, maximum likelihood or minimum chi square from the sample and to substitute these estimates in the functional forms so as to obtain the estimates $\hat{p}_i = p_i(\hat{\theta}_1, \hat{\theta}_2, \ldots, \hat{\theta}_s)$, $i = 1$, $2, \ldots, k$, for the probabilities. Then H_0 is to be rejected at (approximate) level of significance α if

(5.3.4) $$T = \sum_{i=1}^{k} \frac{(n_i - n\hat{p}_i)^2}{n\hat{p}_i} = \sum_{i=1}^{k} \frac{n_i^2}{n\hat{p}_i} - n > \chi_{k-1-s}^2(\alpha).$$

Illustrative Example 5.10. For the frequency distribution of offsprings given in illustrative example 3.4, examine whether the observed frequencies 102, 25, 28, and 5 in the four phenotypic classes AB, Ab, aB, and ab are in agreement with the expected ratios: 9:3:3:1.

Under the hypothesis the expected frequencies in these four classes are $160 \times \frac{9}{16} = 90$, $160 \times \frac{3}{16} = 30$, $160 \times \frac{3}{16} = 30$, and $160 \times \frac{1}{16} = 10$, respectively. Therefore

$$T = \frac{(102 - 90)^2}{90} + \frac{(25 - 30)^2}{30} + \frac{(28 - 30)^2}{30} + \frac{(5 - 10)^2}{10}$$

$$= 5.066 < \chi_3^2(0.05) = 7.814,$$

which is thus not significant. The observed frequencies may therefore be taken to be in agreement with the ratios 9:3:3:1.

Tests of Specified Values of Cell Probabilities and Marginal Probabilities in Contingency Tables. We consider a random sample of size n, classified according to two attributes for which each individual can be described as belonging to one of r categories $A_1, A_2, \ldots, A_r$ with respect to attribute A and simultaneously to one of s categories $B_1, B_2, \ldots, B_s$ with respect to a different attribute B. Then we have a frequency distribution of the individuals into $r \times s$ categories, a typical category being A_iB_j ($i = 1$, $2, \ldots, r$; $j = 1, 2, \ldots, s$). Such a frequency table is said to be a *contingency table*. Let n_{ij} be the observed frequency in the category A_iB_j, and let p_{ij} be the corresponding probability for an individual to belong to this category. Let

$$\sum_{j=1}^{s} n_{ij} = n_{i0}; \quad \sum_{j=1}^{s} p_{ij} = p_{i0}, \quad (i = 1, 2, \ldots, r);$$

$$\sum_{i=1}^{r} n_{ij} = n_{0j}; \quad \sum_{i=1}^{r} p_{ij} = p_{0j}, \quad (j = 1, 2, \ldots, s).$$

Then

$$\sum_{i=1}^{r} \sum_{j=1}^{s} n_{ij} = n \quad \text{and} \quad \sum_{i=1}^{r} \sum_{j=1}^{s} p_{ij} = 1.$$

To test the hypothesis H_0 that the cell probabilities have the specified values $p_{ij}{}^0$,

$$H_0: \quad p_{ij} = p_{ij}{}^0, \quad i = 1, 2, \ldots, r; \quad j = 1, 2, \ldots, s,$$

the procedure, in large samples, is to reject H_0 at (approximate) level of significance α if

$$(5.3.5) \qquad T_1 \equiv \sum_{i=1}^{r} \sum_{j=1}^{s} \frac{(n_{ij} - np_{ij}{}^0)^2}{np_{ij}{}^0} > \chi^2_{rs-1}(\alpha).$$

Similarly, to test the hypothesis H_0 that the marginal probabilities p_{i0} for the A categories have the specified values $p_i{}^0$,

$$H_0: \quad p_{i0} = p_{i0}{}^0, \quad i = 1, 2, \ldots, r,$$

the procedure, in large samples, is to reject the hypothesis H_0 at (approximate) level of significance α if

$$(5.3.6) \qquad T_2 \equiv \sum_{i=1}^{r} \frac{(n_{i0} - np_{i0}{}^0)^2}{np_{i0}{}^0} > \chi^2_{r-1}(\alpha).$$

In the same manner, the hypothesis that the marginal probabilities p_{0j} have specified values $p_{0j}{}^0$ ($j = 1, 2, \ldots, s$) is to be rejected at (approximate) level of significance α in large samples if

$$(5.3.7) \qquad T_3 \equiv \sum_{j=1}^{s} \frac{(n_{0j} - np_{0j}{}^0)^2}{np_{0j}{}^0} > \chi^2_{s-1}(\alpha).$$

Tests of Independence in a Contingency Table. Attributes A and B are said to be independent if

$$p_{ij} = p_{i0}p_{0j} \quad \text{for } i = 1, 2, \ldots, r; \quad j = 1, 2, \ldots, s.$$

If the marginal probabilities have the specified values $p_{i0}{}^0$ and $p_{0j}{}^0$ ($i = 1, 2, \ldots r$; $j = 1, 2, \ldots, s$), then, to test the hypothesis that attributes A and B are independent, the procedure, in large samples, is to reject this hypothesis at (approximate) level of significance α if

$$(5.3.8) \qquad T \equiv T_1 - T_2 - T_3 > \chi^2_{(r-1)(s-1)}(\alpha),$$

where T_1, T_2, and T_3 are given by 5.3.5, 5.3.6, and 5.3.7, respectively.

When marginal probabilities are not specified, to test the hypothesis of independence the procedure, in large samples, is to reject the hypothesis at (approximate) level of significance α if

$$(5.3.9) \qquad T \equiv \sum_{i=1}^{r} \sum_{j=1}^{s} \frac{\left(n_{ij} - \dfrac{n_{i0} \cdot n_{0j}}{n}\right)^2}{\dfrac{n_{i0} n_{0j}}{n}} > \chi^2_{(r-1)(s-1)}(\alpha).$$

Illustrative Example 5.11. The results of a survey regarding radio listeners' preferences for different types of music are given in Table 5.1, with listeners classified by age group. Is preference for types of music influenced by age?

Under the hypothesis that the two attributes are independent, the expected frequency for the first cell is given by $(306 \times 149)/921 = 49.505$. The expected frequencies for the other cells are computed in a similar manner and are given in Table 5.1 in parentheses. Therefore

$$T = \sum_{i,j} \frac{\left(n_{ij} - \dfrac{n_{i0} n_{0j}}{n}\right)^2}{\dfrac{n_{i0} n_{0j}}{n}} = 375.266^{**} > \chi_4^2(0.01).$$

Hence we reject the hypothesis that age and preference for type of music are independent.

TABLE 5.1

PREFERENCE OF LISTENERS, CLASSIFIED BY AGE, FOR
VARIOUS TYPES OF MUSIC

Type of music preferred	Age group			Total
	19–25	26–35	Above 36	
National music	80	60	9	149
	(49.505)	(69.566)	(29.929)	
Foreign music	210	325	44	579
	(192.371)	(270.326)	(116.303)	
Indifferent	16	45	132	193
	(64.124)	(90.109)	(38.768)	
Total	306	430	185	921

Exact Test of Independence in a 2 × 2 *Contingency Table.* If the two attributes A and B are independent, the conditional probability distribution of n_{ij} ($i, j = 1, 2$) for fixed values of the marginal frequencies $n_{10}, n_{20}, n_{01}, n_{02}$ is given by

(5.3.10)
$$\frac{n_{10}! \, n_{01}! \, n_{20}! \, n_{02}!}{n! \, n_{11}! \, n_{12}! \, n_{21}! \, n_{22}!}.$$

To test the hypothesis of independence, we add the probabilities of all configurations (that is, the values of n_{ij}'s with the marginal frequencies fixed) which are not more likely than the observed configuration. Then the hypothesis of independence is to be rejected at level of significance α if the sum of the probabilities of all these configurations is less than α.

Illustrative Example 5.12. Twelve workers, of whom 6 had records of previous accidents, were watched for 1 year. During the year 5 were involved in accidents; among them 4 had suffered accidents before. Do the data justify the contention that workers with records of previous accidents are more likely to be involved in accidents in the future?

TABLE 5.2

RECORD OF ACCIDENTS DURING THE YEAR AND ALSO OF
PREVIOUS ACCIDENTS

Record of accidents during the year	Record of previous accidents		
	Involved	Not involved	Total
Involved	4	1	5
Not involved	2	5	7
Total	6	6	12

The problem is one of testing independence in the 2 × 2 contingency table (Table 5.2). Under the hypothesis of independence the conditional probability, given the marginals, that x workers with previous accidents will be involved in accidents during the year, that is, probability of the configuration

x	$5 - x$	5
$6 - x$	$1 + x$	7
6	6	12

is

$$p(x) = \frac{6! \, 6! \, 5! \, 7!}{12! \, x! \, (6 - x)! \, (5 - x)! \, (1 + x)!}.$$

The configurations which are at least as discordant with the hypothesis of independence as the observed one are given by $x = 4$ and 5 only. Then we have

$$P = p(4) + p(5) = 0.1212 > 0.05.$$

Hence at the 5% level there is no significant evidence of dependence between previous record and involvement in future accidents.

5.4 EXERCISES

Binomial

5.1–5.3. Examine whether the estimates of the binomial parameter p obtained in exercises 3.1–3.3 are in agreement with their respective theoretical values.

5.4. In an excavation 10 fossils were discovered, of which 6 could be definitely classified as male, and 3 as female. The sex of the last fossil could not be precisely determined. Are these findings compatible with a 1:1 sex ratio?

5.5. The proportion of defective articles manufactured by a certain process was 10%. After the introduction of some modifications in the process, a random sample of 250 on inspection revealed 16 defectives. Has the new method reduced the proportion of defectives significantly?

5.6. Table 5.3 shows the results of a study of anticoagulant therapy for myocardial infraction reported by Loudon (1953). Examine the data and give your comments on the efficacy of anticoagulant therapy.

TABLE 5.3

MORTALITY FROM MYOCARDIAL INFRACTION

Treatment	Survived	Died	Total
Control	74	51	125
Anticoagulant	56	19	75
Total	130	70	200

Source: D. J. Finney, *Experimental Design and Its Statistical Basis*, University of Chicago Press, Chicago, 1955.

5.7. Table 5.4 gives the result of an experiment to compare the effect of a newly discovered medicine on a certain disease with that of the prevailing treatment (control). Do the data confirm the superiority of the new medicine?

TABLE 5.4

COMPARISON OF THE EFFECTS OF A NEW MEDICINE
WITH THOSE OF THE STANDARD PREVAILING TREATMENT
(CONTROL)

Treatment	Cured	Not cured	Total
Control	3	5	8
New medicine	5	3	8
Total	8	8	16

5.8. A woman claimed that she was able to judge by tasting a cup of tea whether tea infusion or milk had been added first. An experiment was arranged to test her claim. She was told that 20 cups of tea would be presented to her in a random order, in 10 of which tea would be added first and in the other 10 milk and that she would have to give her opinion about these 20 cups. The results of the experiment are given in Table 5.5.

Is the woman's claim substantiated by the experiment?

TABLE 5.5

RESULTS OF A TEA-TASTING EXPERIMENT

According to the woman	Actually		Total
	Tea added first	Milk added first	
Tea added first	7	3	10
Milk added first	3	7	10
Total	10	10	20

5.9. Five F_2 families of a cotton cross (Baroda lintless × Dharwar glabrous lintless) segregating for the character lintlessness had the numbers of plants in the linted and lintless classes shown in Table 5.6.

Are the families in agreement regarding the ratio linted:lintless that they indicate?

5.10. Table 5.7 gives the number of germinations out of 100 spores for four different strains (S_1, S_2, S_3, S_4) under four different concentrations of copper sulphate (D_1, D_2, D_3, D_4). Analyse the data and give your comments.

TABLE 5.6

DISTRIBUTION OF LINTLESS AND LINTED COTTON
PLANTS IN F_2 FAMILIES

Family	Lintless	Linted
1	72	53
2	37	24
3	58	27
4	36	30
5	40	22

Source: V. G. Panse and P. V. Sukhatme,
Statistical Methods for Agricultural Workers,
Indian Council of Agricultural Research, New
Delhi, 1957.

TABLE 5.7

NUMBER OF GERMINATIONS OUT OF 100 SPORES

Concentration	Strain			
	S_1	S_2	S_3	S_4
D_1	70	64	65	56
D_2	56	57	46	48
D_3	31	20	45	38
D_4	16	8	15	8

5.11. To study the effect of a newly discovered polio vaccine, doctors
tried it on a large number of school children in two different regions of
North America. The numbers of polio cases among the vaccinated as well
as among the non-vaccinated children are recorded in Table 5.8.

Using large sample approximations, make appropriate statistical

TABLE 5.8

EFFECT OF POLIO VACCINE

Region		No. of children	No. of polio cases
A	Vaccinated	200,745	57
	Not vaccinated	540,007	299
B	Vaccinated	211,998	56
	Not vaccinated	848,778	445

analysis of the data to determine whether the new vaccine was effective in reducing the number of polio cases in both regions.

Poisson

5.12. The average number of deaths from road accidents in a certain city was 6.2 per week. The first week after an intensive safety campaign, the death toll came down to 4. Is this a significant improvement?

5.13. The numbers of deaths from drowning in a certain river in three consecutive months were 8, 4, and 5, respectively. Are these fluctuations due to chance?

5.14. Four printers asked by a publisher to supply samples of their work sent four booklets of pages 20, 12, 14, and 15, each page containing approximately the same number of words. It was found that the booklets contained 51, 32, 28, and 34 printing mistakes, respectively. Are the printers equally bad so far as errors are concerned?

5.15. When women were first employed in airplane factories in the United States, one official predicted that the number of accidents involving

TABLE 5.9

NUMBER OF PERSONS INVOLVED IN ACCIDENTS

| Factory | No. of persons involved in accidents | |
	Male	Female
A	15	22
B	12	19
C	18	28
D	20	32
E	18	26

women would be twice the number involving men. Use the data in Table 5.9 from five factories to test the hypothesis that the number of women involved in accidents is (a) as large as the number of men involved in accidents, (b) twice as large. Assume that the factories were of the same size and employed the same number of men and women.

What other hypothesis would it be advisable to test by using the same data? State the hypothesis carefully and draw a conclusion.

Multinomial

5.16. Table 5.10 gives the frequency distributions of the duration of fever under two different treatments. Examine whether the two distributions differ significantly.

TABLE 5.10

FREQUENCY DISTRIBUTION OF DURATION OF FEVER UNDER TWO DIFFERENT TREATMENTS

Treatment	Duration of fever (days)				Total
	1–4	5–6	7–8	9–12	
Quinine	6	9	11	7	33
Eubasin	44	26	19	13	102

Source: G. H. Herdan, *Statistics of Therapeutic Trials*, Elsevier Publishing Co., Amsterdam, 1955.

5.17. The data in Table 5.11 relate to the degree of speech defects and physical defects of a number of handicapped school children. Examine whether there is any association between the degree of the two types of defects.

TABLE 5.11

DISTRIBUTION OF HANDICAPPED CHILDREN BY DEGREE OF DEFECT

Physical defect	Speech defect		
	Serious	Intermediate	Mild
Serious	45	26	12
Intermediate	32	50	21
Mild	4	10	17

5.18. Table 5.12 shows the distribution by color of hair and color of eyes of a random sample of 6800 persons drawn from a certain population. Test whether there is any association between the two attributes hair color and eye color.

TABLE 5.12

DISTRIBUTION OF 6800 PERSONS BY HAIR COLOR AND EYE COLOR

Eye color	Hair color			
	Fair	Brown	Black	Red
Blue	1768	807	189	47
Gray	946	1387	746	53
Brown	115	438	288	16

5.19. The results of a public opinion survey in a certain city revealed for adult males, classified into four age groups, the frequencies shown in

TABLE 5.13

OPINION OF ADULT MALES ON CENSORSHIP OF FILMS

Opinion	No. of males expressing the opinion in age group			
	19–25	26–35	36–55	Above 55
Against all kinds of censorship	49	79	69	9
In favor of censorship by motion picture association	149	296	297	43
In favor of governmental censorship	18	59	95	23

Table 51.3 for three different opinions on the question of censorship of films. Examine whether age influences the type of opinion expressed.

CHAPTER 6

Tests of Parameters
of Normal Populations

6.1 NOTATIONS

Samples from Univariate Populations.   Let $x_1, x_2, \ldots, x_n$ be a sample of
size n from a univariate population. The following notations will be used
for various statistics computed from the sample:

Total:
$$T = \sum_{i=1}^{n} x_i.$$

Crude sum of squares (ss): $T_2 = \sum_{i=1}^{n} x_i^2.$

Mean:
$$\bar{x} = T/n.$$

Correction factor:
$$CF = T^2/n.$$

Corrected ss:
$$S^2 = \sum_{i=1}^{n} (x_i - \bar{x})^2 = T_2 - CF.$$

Estimate of variance:
$$\hat{\sigma}^2 = S^2/(n-1).$$

The mean and the standard deviation in the population will be denoted by
μ and σ, respectively. If several populations are involved, subscripts will
be used to distinguish them. For example, $\bar{x}_i$ will denote the mean of a
sample of size n_i from the ith population.

Samples from Multivariate Populations.   When a sample of size n is
available from a p-variate distribution, the value of the ith characteristic of
the λth individual will be denoted by $x_{i\lambda}, i = 1, 2, \ldots, p; \lambda = 1, 2, \ldots, n.$
The ith characteristic as such will be denoted by $X_i, i = 1, 2, \ldots, p.$
The following notations will be used for various statistics computed from
the sample:

322

Totals:
$$T_i = \sum_{\lambda=1}^{n} x_{i\lambda}.$$

Crude sums of squares and products (sp): $T_{ij} = \sum_{\lambda=1}^{n} x_{i\lambda} x_{j\lambda}.$

Means: $\qquad \bar{x}_i = T_i/n$

Sample mean vector: $\qquad \bar{\mathbf{x}} = (\bar{x}_1, \bar{x}_2, \ldots, \bar{x}_p)$

Corrected sp: $\qquad S_{ij} = T_{ij} - T_i T_j / n$

Corrected sp matrix: $\qquad S = ((S_{ij}))$

Estimates of variances and covariances : $\hat{\sigma}_{ij} = S_{ij}/(n-1)$.

The mean vector and the dispersion matrix in the population will be denoted by $\boldsymbol{\mu} = (\mu_1, \mu_2, \ldots, \mu_p)$ and $\boldsymbol{\Sigma} = ((\sigma_{ij}))$, respectively.

The product moment coefficient of correlation between X_i and X_j in the population will be denoted by ρ_{ij}, and its value in a sample of size n by r_{ij}. Whenever it is not necessary, the subscripts ij will be dropped and the correlation coefficients in the population and the sample will be denoted by ρ and r, respectively.

The multiple correlation coefficient of X_1 on $X_2, X_3, \ldots, X_p$ in the population will be denoted by $\rho_{1*23\ldots p}$, and the value in a sample of n will be denoted by $R_{1*23\ldots p}$.

The partial correlation coefficient between X_1 and X_2 eliminating the effects of $X_3, \ldots, X_p$ will be denoted by $\rho_{12*3\ldots p}$ in the population and by $r_{12*3\ldots p}$ in a sample of size n drawn from the population.

6.2 TESTS OF MEANS

Test for a Specified Value of a Mean. To test the hypothesis that in a normal population with unspecified variance the mean μ has a specified value μ_0,

$$H_0 : \quad \mu = \mu_0,$$

the procedure is to reject H_0 against alternatives $H : \quad \mu > \mu_0$ at level of significance α if

$$(6.2.1) \qquad T = \frac{\sqrt{n}\,(\bar{x} - \mu_0)}{\hat{\sigma}} > t_{n-1}(\alpha).$$

Against two-sided alternatives $H : \quad \mu \neq \mu_0$, the hypothesis H_0 is rejected at level of significance α if $|T| > t_{n-1}(\frac{1}{2}\alpha)$. For large n, say $n > 30$, we may use the fact that $t_n(\alpha) \doteq \xi(\alpha)$.

Illustrative Example 6.1. In illustrative example 2.10 of Part II, we found from a sample of $n = 250$ the mean and the standard deviation of scores in English to be $\bar{x} = 39.72$ and $s = 9.8894$, respectively. To test the hypothesis that the mean score in the population is $\mu_0 = 38$, we compute T from formula 6.2.1, using s for $\hat{\sigma}$ since n is large. We obtain

$$T = \sqrt{250}\,(39.72 - 38)/9.8894 = 2.750^{**}.$$

Since n is large, we may use the percentage points of the standard normal distribution instead of the t distribution. The upper 0.5% point of the standard normal distribution is $\xi(0.005) = 2.5758$. The computed value of $|T|$ exceeds this. The hypothesis is therefore rejected at the 1% level of significance.

Test for the Difference of Two Populations Means. On the basis of independent samples from two normal populations having a common but unspecified variance, to test the hypothesis that the difference between the means $\delta = \mu_1 - \mu_2$ has a specified value δ_0,

$$H_0: \quad \delta = \delta_0,$$

the procedure is to reject H_0 against alternatives $H: \quad \delta > \delta_0$ at level of significance α if

$$(6.2.2) \qquad T \equiv \frac{(\bar{x}_1 - \bar{x}_2) - \delta_0}{\sqrt{\left[\dfrac{S_1{}^2 + S_2{}^2}{n_1 + n_2 - 2}\left(\dfrac{1}{n_1} + \dfrac{1}{n_2}\right)\right]}} > t_\nu(\alpha),$$

where $\nu = n_1 + n_2 - 2$. Against both-sided alternatives $H: \quad \delta \neq \delta_0$, the hypothesis H_0 is rejected at level of significance α if $|T| > t_\nu(\tfrac{1}{2}\alpha)$.

Illustrative Example 6.2. The heart weights in grams of 12 female and 15 male cats are given below. Does the heart of a male cat on an average weigh more than that of a female cat?

Males	12.7, 15.6, 9.1, 12.8, 8.3, 11.2, 9.4, 8.0, 14.9, 10.7, 13.6, 9.6, 11.7, 9.3, 7.6.
Females	7.4, 7.3, 7.1, 9.0, 7.6, 9.5, 10.1, 10.2, 10.1, 9.5, 8.7, 7.2.

Let μ_1 and μ_2 denote the mean weights in grams of the hearts of male and female cats, respectively. To test $H_0: \quad \mu_1 = \mu_2$ against alternatives $\mu_1 > \mu_2$ we compute the statistic T defined by 6.2.2. Here $n_1 = 15$, $n_2 = 12$, and on computation we find the sample means $\bar{x}_1 = 10.9667$, $\bar{x}_2 = 8.6417$, and the corrected sums of squares $S_1{}^2 = 88.7333$, $S_2{}^2 = 17.1692$. Thus

$$T = \frac{10.9667 - 8.6417}{\sqrt{\left[\dfrac{88.7333 + 17.1692}{15 + 12 - 2}\left(\dfrac{1}{15} + \dfrac{1}{12}\right)\right]}} = 2.917^{**}.$$

The number of degrees of freedom is $v = 15 + 12 - 2 = 25$ and $t_{25}(0.01) = 2.485$. Hence we reject, at the 1% level of significance, the hypothesis of equality of average heart weights of male and female cats.

For methods of testing equality of two or more means and other related problems, the reader is referred to Chapter 7 on the analysis of variance.

Test for a Single Outlier. In a given sample any observation which deviates too much from the others is called an *outlier*. If the parent population is normal, the following procedure is used to decide whether an outlier is too rare to be accepted.

One of the following three statistics: $(x_{max} - \bar{x})/\hat{\sigma}$, $(\bar{x} - x_{min})/\hat{\sigma}$, $(\max |x_i - \bar{x}|)/\hat{\sigma}$, is selected, depending on the direction of the deviation. The outlier is to be rejected at level of significance α if the statistic exceeds the upper $100\alpha\%$ point given in Table 26 of *Biometrika Tables for Statisticians*.

Test for Equality of Means of Two Correlated Variates. On the basis of a sample of size n from a bivariate normal population, to test the hypothesis that the means of the two variates are equal,

$$H_0 : \quad \mu_1 = \mu_2,$$

the procedure is to reject H_0, against alternatives $H : \quad \mu_1 > \mu_2$, at level of significance α, if

$$(6.2.3) \qquad T \equiv \frac{\sqrt{n}(\bar{x}_1 - \bar{x}_2)}{\sqrt{(\hat{\sigma}_{11} + \hat{\sigma}_{22} - 2\hat{\sigma}_{12})}} > t_{n-1}(\alpha).$$

Against both-sided alternatives $H : \quad \mu_1 \neq \mu_2$, the hypothesis H_0 is to be rejected at level of significance α if $|T| > t_{n-1}(\frac{1}{2}\alpha)$. Writing $d_\lambda = x_{1\lambda} - x_{2\lambda}$, and $\bar{d} = (1/n) \sum_{\lambda=1}^{n} d_\lambda$, $\hat{\sigma}^2 = \sum_{\lambda=1}^{n} (d_\lambda - \bar{d})^2/(n-1)$, where $x_{1\lambda}, x_{2\lambda}$ are the first- and the second-variate values for the λth individual in the sample $\lambda = 1, 2, \ldots, n$, we obtain an alternative expression for T, that is, $T = \sqrt{n}\bar{d}/\hat{\sigma}$.

Illustrative Example 6.3. Given in Table 6.1 are the weights in grams of the anterior muscles of both hind legs of 16 normal rabbits. Is there any difference between the left and right legs in respect to the average weight of the anterior muscle?

The weights of the anterior muscles of the two legs are of course highly correlated. To examine whether the mean weights for the two legs are equal, we write d_λ for the excess in weight of the muscle of the left leg over that of the right leg for the λth rabbit. We then obtain the following values of d_λ:

λ	1	2	3	4	5	6	7	8	9	10	11	12	13	14	15	16
d_λ	0.1	−0.2	0	−0.2	0	0	0.2	−0.4	0.1	−0.2	−0.2	0	−0.3	0	0	−1.0

TABLE 6.1

WEIGHT OF ANTERIOR MUSCLES OF HIND LEGS OF 16 RABBITS

Sample no. of rabbit	Weight (gm) of anterior muscle of		Sample no. of rabbit	Weight (gm) of anterior muscle of	
	Left leg	Right leg		Left leg	Right leg
1	5.0	4.9	9	5.3	5.2
2	4.8	5.0	10	5.3	5.5
3	4.3	4.3	11	5.3	5.5
4	5.1	5.3	12	5.9	5.9
5	4.1	4.1	13	6.5	6.8
6	4.0	4.0	14	6.3	6.3
7	7.1	6.9	15	6.6	6.6
8	5.9	6.3	16	5.2	6.3

so that $\Sigma d_\lambda = -1.2$, $\Sigma d_\lambda^2 = 0.48$, based on $n = 16$ observations. Thus the mean is $\bar{d} = \Sigma d_\lambda/n = -0.075$, and the corrected ss is $S^2 = \Sigma d_\lambda^2 - (\Sigma d_\lambda)^2/n = 0.39$. Hence $\hat{\sigma} = \sqrt{[S^2/(n-1)]} = 0.16125$. To examine whether the mean difference is zero, we compute

$$T = \sqrt{n}\bar{d}/\hat{\sigma} = -1.860.$$

Since $t_{15}(0.025) = 2.131$ and $|T|$ is less than this value, against both-sided alternatives, the difference is not significant at the 5% level.

6.3 TESTS OF VARIANCES

Test for a Specified Value of a Variance.   To test the hypothesis that the variance of a normal population with unspecified mean has a specified value σ_0,

$$H_0: \quad \sigma = \sigma_0,$$

the procedure is to reject H_0 against alternatives $H: \quad \sigma > \sigma_0$ at level of significance α if

(6.3.1) $$T \equiv \frac{S^2}{\sigma_0^2} > \chi_{n-1}^2(\alpha).$$

Against both-sided alternatives $H: \quad \sigma \neq \sigma_0$, we reject H_0 if $T > \chi_1^2$ or if $T < \chi_2^2$, where χ_1^2 and χ_2^2 are constants called *unbiased tails of chi square* for $n - 1$ df, given by C. R. Rao in Table 6a 1 α of *Advanced Statistical Methods in Biometric Research* for the 5% and the 1% levels of significance.

Illustrative Example 6.4.   The standard deviation of $n = 20$ measure-ments made by a technician is $s = 6.23$. Is this significantly larger than the hypothetical value $\sigma_0 = 5$?

Here we have $S^2 = ns^2 = 776.26$ and $T = S^2/\sigma_0^2 = 31.05 < \chi_{19}^2(0.05)$ which is not significant at the 5% level.

Test for Equality of Variances in Two Populations. To test the hypoth-esis that variances in two normal populations are equal,

$$H_0 : \quad \sigma_1^2 = \sigma_2^2,$$

on the basis of independent samples from the two populations, the pro-cedure is to reject H_0 against alternatives $H : \quad \sigma_1^2 > \sigma_2^2$ at level of significance α if

(6.3.2) $$T \equiv \frac{\hat{\sigma}_1^2}{\hat{\sigma}_2^2} > F_{n_1-1, n_2-1}(\alpha).$$

Against both-sided alternatives $H : \quad \sigma_1 \neq \sigma_2$, the appropriate procedure is to reject H_0 if $T > F'$ or if $T < F''$, where F', F'' are the unbiased tails of F with $n_1 - 1, n_2 - 1$ df. Since tables of F', F'' are not readily available, an equal-tail procedure is generally used and H_0 is rejected if $T > F_{n_1-1 \ n_2-1}(\frac{1}{2}\alpha)$ or if $T < F_{n_2-1, \ n_1-1}(\frac{1}{2}\alpha)$. Or, in, large samples, the method given below may be used for testing equality of variances of k populations.

Illustrative Example 6.5.   An investigator was asked to take 10 inde-pendent measurements on the maximum internal diameter of a pot. The standard deviation of these measurements was 0.0345 mm. The experi-ment was repeated after a few days when the investigator had had sufficient practice, and the standard deviation of the 10 measurements was 0.0126 mm. Does this mean that with practice the investigator has become more consistent?

Let us denote by σ_1 and σ_2, respectively, the standard deviations of the measurements before and after the investigator had had sufficient practice. We then have the estimates $\hat{\sigma}_1 = 0.0345$, $\hat{\sigma}_2 = 0.0126$, based on samples of sizes $n_1 = n_2 = 10$. To examine the hypothesis $H_0 : \quad \sigma_1^2 = \sigma_2^2$ against alternatives $H : \quad \sigma_1^2 > \sigma_2^2$, we compute T using formula 6.3.2 and find

$$T = (0.0345)^2/(0.0126)^2 = 7.497**.$$

Since $F_{9,9}(0.01) = 5.35$, we reject at the 1% level of significance the hypothesis of equality of variances. There is thus some evidence that the investigator is more consistent after practice.

Test for Equality of Variances of k Populations ($k \geq 2$). On the basis of samples drawn independently from k different normal populations with unspecified means, to test the hypothesis that the variances are equal,

$$H_0: \quad \sigma_1^2 = \sigma_2^2 = \cdots = \sigma_k^2,$$

the procedure, in large samples, is to reject H_0 at (approximate) level of significance α if $T > \chi_{k-1}^2(\alpha)$, where

(6.3.3) $$T \equiv \nu \ln\left(\frac{1}{\nu}\sum_{i=1}^{k} \nu_i \hat{\sigma}_i^2\right) - \sum_{i=1}^{k} \nu_i \ln \hat{\sigma}_i^2$$

and $\nu_i = n_i - 1$, $\nu = \sum_{i=1}^{k} \nu_i$. When samples are only moderately large, a better procedure is to compute

(6.3.4) $$P \equiv \frac{\sum \beta_i Q_{k-1+2i}(T)}{\sum \beta_i},$$

where $Q_m(T)$ stands for the probability that a chi-square variate with m df exceeds T, and the first few values of β_i's are

(6.3.5) $$\beta_0 = 1, \quad \beta_1 = \frac{1}{6}\left(\sum_{i=1}^{k}\frac{1}{\nu_i} - \frac{1}{\nu}\right), \quad \beta_2 = \frac{1}{2}\beta_1^2.$$

Illustrative Example 6.6. Estimates of variance obtained from three independent samples of sizes 7, 9, and 12 were 3223, 8370, and 2606, respectively. Can these be regarded as equal except for fluctuations of sampling?

Denoting the degrees of freedom and the estimate of variance of the ith sample by ν_i and $\hat{\sigma}_i^2$, respectively, we have Table 6.2.

We thus obtain $\nu = \Sigma\nu_i = 25$, $A = \Sigma\nu_i\hat{\sigma}_i^2/\nu = 4598.56$, and $B = \log_{10}\hat{\sigma}_i^2 = 90.0070850$, so that from 6.3.3

$$T = \ln 10[\nu \log_{10} A - B] = 3.590.$$

TABLE 6.2

COMPUTATIONS FOR TESTING EQUALITY OF VARIANCES

i	ν_i	$\hat{\sigma}_i^2$	$1/\nu_i$
1	6	3223	0.1666667
2	8	8370	0.1250000
3	11	2606	0.0909091

Since samples are not large in size, we then take $\beta_0 = 1$, $\beta_1 = \frac{1}{6}[\Sigma 1/\nu_i - 1/\nu] = 0.057096$, $\beta_2 = \frac{1}{2}\beta_1^2 = 0.001630$. Here $k = 3$, and 6.3.4 reduces to

$$P = \frac{Q_2(T) + \beta_1 Q_4(T) + \beta_2 Q_6(T)}{1 + \beta_1 + \beta_2},$$

where $Q_n(T)$ denotes the probability that a chi-square statistic with n degrees of freedom exceeds T, By linear interpolation in Table 7 of *Biometrika Tables for Statisticians*, we get $Q_2(T) = 0.16617$, $Q_4(T) = 0.46436$, and $Q_6(T) = 0.73195$. Hence $P = 0.18312$, which is larger than 5%. The hypothesis of equality of the variance cannot therefore be rejected at the 5% level of significance.

A quick procedure for testing equality of variances, when each one of the estimates of the variances is based on the same number of degrees of freedom, is to compute the ratio of the maximum of the estimates of variance to the minimum, and to reject H_0 at 5% or 1% level of significance if this exceeds the 5% or 1% point of the statistic given in Table 31 of *Biometrika Tables for Statisticians*.

Test for Equality of Variances of Two Correlated Variates. On the basis of a sample of size n from a bivariate normal population, to test the hypothesis that the two variates have equal variances,

$$H_0 : \quad \sigma_{11} = \sigma_{22},$$

against alternatives $H : \quad \sigma_{11} \neq \sigma_{22}$, the procedure is to reject H_0 at level of significance α if

(6.3.6) $$|T| > t_{n-1}(\tfrac{1}{2}\alpha),$$

where

$$T \equiv \frac{r}{\sqrt{1 - r^2}}\sqrt{n - 2},$$

r being the coefficient of correlation between $s_\lambda = x_{1\lambda} + x_{2\lambda}$ and $d_\lambda = x_{1\lambda} - x_{2\lambda}$, $\lambda = 1, 2, \ldots, n$. An alternative expression for T is

$$T \equiv \frac{S_{11} - S_{22}}{2\sqrt{S_{11}S_{22} - S_{12}^2}}\sqrt{n - 2},$$

where $((S_{ij}))$ is the corrected sp matrix for $(x_{1\lambda}, x_{2\lambda})$, $\lambda = 1, 2, \ldots, n$.

Illustrative Example 6.7. Examine on the basis of the data given in illustrative example 6.3 whether the variances of muscle weights of right and left legs of rabbits are equal.

We first compute for the λth rabbit the sum $s_\lambda = L_\lambda + R_\lambda$ and the

TABLE 6.3

SUM AND DIFFERENCE OF MUSCLE WEIGHTS OF
RIGHT AND LEFT LEGS OF RABBITS

λ	1	2	3	4	5	6	7	8
s_λ	9.9	9.8	8.6	10.4	8.2	8.0	14.0	12.2
d_λ	0.1	−0.2	0	−0.2	0	0	0.2	−0.4

λ	9	10	11	12	13	14	15	16
s_λ	10.5	10.8	10.8	11.8	13.3	12.6	13.2	12.5
d_λ	0.1	−0.2	−0.2	0	−0.3	0	0	−0.1

difference $d_\lambda = L_\lambda - R_\lambda$ of the weights of the left leg muscle L_λ and the right leg muscle R_λ, which are given in Table 6.3. Here $n = 16$, $\Sigma s_\lambda = 176.6$, $\Sigma s_\lambda^2 = 2001.16$, $\Sigma d_\lambda = -1.2$, $\Sigma d_\lambda^2 = 0.48$, $\Sigma s_\lambda d_\lambda = -13.64$, so that the coefficient of correlation between s and d is

$$r = \frac{n \Sigma s_i d_i - \Sigma s_i \Sigma d_i}{\sqrt{[\{n \Sigma s_i^2 - (\Sigma s_i)^2\}\{n \Sigma d_i^2 - (\Sigma d_i)^2\}]}} = -0.0878,$$

We thus get from 6.3.6

$$T = \frac{r}{\sqrt{1 - r^2}} \sqrt{n - 2} = -0.330.$$

Since $t_{14}(0.025) = 2.145$ and $|T|$ does not exceed this, the hypothesis of equality of variances cannot be rejected at the 5% level.

6.4 TESTS OF CORRELATIONS

Tests for a Specified Value of a Correlation Coefficient. To test, on the basis of a large sample of size n from a bivariate normal population, the hypothesis that the correlation coefficient has a specified non-zero value,

$$H_0: \quad \rho = \rho_0, \qquad \rho_0 \neq 0,$$

the procedure is to reject H_0 against alternatives $H: \quad \rho > \rho_0$ at (approximate) level of significance α if

(6.4.1) $$T = \sqrt{n - 3}\,(z - \zeta_0) > \xi(\alpha),$$

where

$$z = \tanh^{-1} r = \frac{1}{2} \ln \frac{1 + r}{1 - r} \quad \text{and} \quad \zeta_0 = \tanh^{-1} \rho_0.$$

Against both-sided alternatives H : $\rho \neq \rho_0$, H_0 is rejected at (approximate) level of significance α if $|T| > \xi(\frac{1}{2}\alpha)$.

To test the hypothesis that the correlation is zero,

$$H_0 : \quad \rho = 0,$$

against alternatives H : $\rho > 0$, the procedure is to reject H_0 if

(6.4.2)
$$T \equiv \frac{r}{\sqrt{1 - r^2}} \sqrt{n - 2} > t_{n-2}(\alpha).$$

Against both-sided alternatives H : $\rho \neq \rho_0$, the hypothesis H_0 is to be rejected at level of significance α if $|T| > t_{n-2}(\frac{1}{2}\alpha)$.

Illustrative Example 6.8.   On the basis of the data in illustrative example 5.1 of Part II examine whether the coefficient of correlation between the weight of a jute plant and the weight of dry fiber is (a) significantly different from zero, (b) significantly different from 0.8.

(a) Here $n = 40$, $r = 0.8895$, and to test whether the correlation coefficient $\rho = 0$, we compute

$$T = \frac{r\sqrt{n - 2}}{\sqrt{1 - r^2}} = 12.000**.$$

Since $t_{38}(0.005) < 2.75$ and $|T|$ exceeds this, against alternative $\rho \neq 0$ the hypothesis $\rho = 0$ is rejected at the 1 % level of significance.

(b) To test whether $\rho = 0.8$, we have to use the $\tanh^{-1}$ transformation given in Table 14 of *Biometrika Tables for Statisticians*. We have

$$z = \frac{1}{2} \ln \frac{1 + r}{1 - r} = 1.4195, \quad \text{and} \quad \zeta = \frac{1}{2} \ln \frac{1 + \rho}{1 - \rho} = 1.0990.$$

Thus

$$T = \sqrt{n - 3}(z - \zeta) = 1.9495.$$

But $\xi(0.025) = 1.96$ and $|T|$ falls short of this. Hence at the 5 % level of significance, the hypothesis $\sigma = 0.8$ cannot be rejected.

Test for Equality of k Correlation Coefficients $(k \geq 2)$.   To test, on the basis of independent large samples, whether the correlation coefficients ρ_i, $i = 1, 2, \ldots, k$, in k $(k \geq 2)$ different bivariate normal populations are equal,

$$H_0 : \quad \rho_1 = \rho_2 = \cdots \rho_k,$$

the procedure is to reject H_0 at (approximate) level of significance α if

$$(6.4.3) \quad T \equiv \sum_{i=1}^{k} (n_i - 3)z_i^2 - \frac{\left[\sum_{i=1}^{k}(n_i - 3)z_i\right]^2}{\sum_{i=1}^{k}(n_i - 3)} > \chi_{k-1}^2(\alpha),$$

where $z_i = \tanh^{-1} r_i$. For $k = 2$, T reduces to

$$(6.4.4) \quad T \equiv \frac{(n_1 - 3)(n_2 - 3)}{(n_1 - 3) + (n_2 - 3)}(z_1 - z_2)^2.$$

Illustrative Example 6.9.   The correlation coefficients between the scores in two halves of a psychological test applied on three groups of 30, 20, and

TABLE 6.4

TRANSFORMATIONS OF THE CORRELATION COEFFICIENTS

i	n_i	r_i	z_i	z_i^2
1	30	0.63	0.7414	0.549674
2	20	0·48	0·5230	0·273529
3	25	0.71	0.8872	0.787124

25 students were 0.63, 0.48, and 0.71, respectively. Examine whether the groups are different with respect to the correlation coefficient.

Denoting the sample size, correlation coefficient, and the $\tanh^{-1}$ transforms for the ith sample by n_i, r_i, and z_i, respectively, we have Table 6.4; $A = \Sigma(n_i - 3) = 66$, $B = \Sigma(n_i - 3)z_i = 48.4272$, and $C = \Sigma(n_i - 2)z_i^2 = 36.807919$. From 6.4.3 we obtain

$$T = C - B^2/A = 1.275 < \chi_2^2(0.05) = 5.99.$$

The hypothesis of equality of correlation coefficients cannot be rejected at the 5% level of significance.

Tests of Partial Correlation Coefficients.   Tests of hypotheses concerning a partial correlation coefficient $\rho_{12*3\ldots p}$ can be made by using the sample partial correlation coefficient $r_{12*3\ldots p}$ in the same way. The only difference is that, in the expression for T, n should be replaced by $n' = n - p + 2$.

Illustrative Example 6.10.   Examine on the basis of the computations in illustrative example 6.1 of Part II whether the partial correlation coefficient $r_{04.123}$ between gasoline yield percentage x_0 and gasoline end point x_4, eliminating the effects of crude oil gravity x_1, vapor pressure x_2, and 10% point ASTM x_3, is significantly different from zero.

Here $n = 32$, $p = 5$, and the computed value of the partial correlation coefficient is $r_{04*123} = 0.3091$. To examine whether the population value $\rho_{04*123} = 0$, we note that $n' = n - 3$, so that

$$T = \frac{r_{04*123}\sqrt{n-5}}{\sqrt{1 - r^2_{04*123}}} = 1.689.$$

The number of degrees of freedom in this case is $n' - 2 = 27$. Since $t_{27}(0.025) = 2.052$ and $|T|$ does not exceed this, the hypothesis of zero partial correlation cannot be rejected at the 5% level of significance, against both-sided alternatives.

Test of the Hypothesis That a Multiple Correlation Coefficient Is Zero. The hypothesis of no multiple correlation between the variates X_1 and $X_2, \ldots, X_p$

$$H_0: \quad \rho_{1*2\ldots p} = 0,$$

against alternatives $H: \quad \rho_{1*2\ldots p} \neq 0$, is to be rejected at level of significance α if

$$(6.4.5) \qquad T \equiv \frac{n - p}{p - 1} \cdot \frac{R^2_{1*2\ldots p}}{1 - R^2_{1*2\ldots p}} > F_{p-1, n-p}(\alpha).$$

Illustrative Example 6.11. In illustrative example 6.1 of Part II, the multiple correlation coefficient of X_0 on X_1, X_2, X_3, X_4 was obtained as $R_{0*1234} = 0.9809$ on the basis of a sample of size $n = 32$. Does this differ significantly from zero?

Here $p = 5$, and from 6.4.5 we get

$$T = \frac{32 - 5}{5 - 1} \times \frac{(0.9809)^2}{1 - (0.9809)^2} = 171.73.$$

Since $F_{4,27}(0.01) = 4.11$ and T very greatly exceeds this, the hypothesis of zero multiple correlation is rejected at the 1% level of significance.

For tests of regression coefficients see Chapter 7 on analysis of variance. For tests of other hypotheses regarding parameters of multivariate normal populations see Chapter 9 on multivariate analysis.

6.5 EXERCISES

Mean

6.1. The average income and the standard deviation computed from a sample of 1500 persons were $276.50 and $30.72, respectively. Test whether this average income differs significantly from $300.

6.2. Fisher gives the following values of the mean and the variance of the excess in the stature of a brother over his sister in 1401 pairs: mean $= 4.895$ in., variance $= 6.5480$ sq in. Examine whether on an average the stature of a brother exceeds that of his sister by 4 in.

Source: R. A. Fisher, *Statistical Methods for Research Workers,* Oliver & Boyd, Edinburgh.

6.3. From the first 500 values of Wold's *Random Normal Deviates* (x), the following statistics were computed: $\sum x = -23.72$, $\sum x^2 = 435.6340$. Do you regard the departure of the mean value from zero as statistically significant?

6.4. Measurements on the length of hind femur of males of two species of desert locusts were taken, and the statistics given in Table 6.5 were computed. Do you think the two species differ significantly in respect to the mean length of the hind femur?

TABLE 6.5

MEAN AND STANDARD DEVIATION OF THE LENGTHS OF HIND
FEMUR OF TWO SPECIES OF DESERT LOCUSTS

Species	Sample size	Length of hind femur (mm)	
		Mean	Standard deviation
Gregaria	567	24.21	1.15
Kakko swarm	852	24.92	1.64

6.5. The mean and the standard deviation of the monthly income of workers employed in industries in a certain city in the two years 1945 and 1946 as estimated from sample surveys are given in Table 6.6. Do you think that there was an improvement in the average income of the workers in the year 1946 as compared with 1945?

TABLE 6.6

MEAN AND STANDARD DEVIATION OF THE MONTHLY
INCOME OF WORKERS

Year	Sample size	Monthly income (rupees)	
		Mean	Standard deviation
1945	230	82.4	18.6
46	346	85.1	17.2

6.6. A chemical compound containing 12.5% iron was given to two technicians A and B for chemical analysis. Their results are given in Table 2.29 on p. 128. Do you think that their analyses are free of bias? In any case, are the amounts of bias the same for the two technicians?

6.7. Table 6.7 gives the additional hours of sleep gained by 10 patients in an experiment to test the efficiency of a certain soporofic drug. Do the data give evidence that the drug produces additional sleep?

TABLE 6.7

ADDITIONAL HOURS OF SLEEP GAINED

Patient	1	2	3	4	5	6	7	8	9	10
Hours gained	0.7	−1.1	−0.2	1.2	0.1	3.4	3.7	0.8	1.8	2.0

6.8. A measure of quality of reeled silk is its "denier"—a number expressing the weight of a fixed length. Among many factors that affect denier, a temperature of the bath in which the cocoons are cooked is likely to be important. An experiment was conducted with two different temperatures, 105°F and 110°F, of the bath. The figures in Table 6.8 represent the deniers in milligrams of 20 samples of silk at 105°F and 18 samples at 110°F.

Examine whether the average deniers at the two temperatures are different.

TABLE 6.8

VALUES OF DENIER AT TWO TEMPERATURES OF BATH

Temperature of bath (°F)	Sample size	Individual denier values									
105	20	250	229	206	220	226	255	258	243	222	221
		225	205	228	249	237	206	214	236	225	243
110	18	235	258	225	207	260	268	256	220	224	258
		230	245	315	250	247	254	251	225		

6.9. To determine the yield rate in pounds per acre of paddy by the method of random sampling, ten plots were chosen in a certain locality. Within each plot, a point was located at random, and with this as the center, two concentric circles of radii 2 ft and 4 ft were marked out. The crop inside the circles was harvested, and then the yield rate was calculated.

Is there any evidence from the data in Table 6.9 that there is considerable bias in the estimation of the crop yield from circles of different radius?

6.10. On the basis of the data in exercise 6.2 of Part II examine separately whether (a) the average height of a twin brother is equal to that of a twin sister, (b) the average weight of a twin brother is equal to that of a twin sister.

TABLE 6.9

YIELD OF PADDY (IN POUNDS PER ACRE) FROM
TEN PAIRS OF CONCENTRIC CIRCLES

Serial no.	Circle of 2′ radius	Circle of 4′ radius
1	618	552
2	543	604
3	562	475
4	630	593
5	515	560
6	638	612
7	597	574
8	566	549
9	447	521
10	613	587

6.11. Table 6.10 gives the milk yields (in pounds) of cows calving in two different seasons, winter and summer, at eight different dairy farms. Under suitable assumptions make appropriate statistical tests to determine whether the cows calving in winter are, on the average, yielding more milk than those calving in summer.

TABLE 6.10

MILK YIELD OF COWS

	Winter		Summer	
Dairy farm	No. of cows	Average yield (lb)	No. of cows	Average yield (lb)
1		484	2	316
2	7	350	1	262
3	2	414	2	270
4	2	286	4	223
5	5	176	3	180
6	7	386	4	320
7	3	385	3	398
8	4	438	5	340

6.12. On the basis of the data in exercise 6.3 examine whether the standard deviation of the first 500 entries in H. Wold's *Random Normal Deviates* differs significantly from unity.

6.13. From the data given in exercise 6.4 would you regard the standard deviations of the length of the hind femur for the two species of desert locusts to be different?

6.14. Do the data given in exercise 6.5 justify the conclusion that the dispersion of the monthly incomes of workers came down in 1946?

6.15. Kemsley obtained the values of the standard deviations of statures of 27,515 males and 33,562 females as 2.85 and 2.58, respectively. Is there any reason to believe that the females are less variable in stature than the males?

Source: C. R. Rao, *Advanced Statistical Methods in Biometric Research*, John Wiley and Sons, New York, 1952.

6.16. Using the data in exercise 6.6, compare the accuracies of the chemical assays made by *A* and *B*.

6.17. From the data given in exercise 6.8 would you conclude that temperature affects the uniformity of the quality of reeled silk?

6.18. The standard deviations of stature (in inches) of two groups of boys, one of ages 11–13 and the other of ages 14–16, estimated from two samples of sizes 10 and 15, respectively, are 1.15 and 2.36. Does this prove that in respect to stature adolescent boys (ages 14–16) are more heterogeneous than younger boys?

6.19. Table 6.11 gives the variance of stature in centimeters for Muslims in eight different districts of Bengal (now East and West Bengal) as

TABLE 6.11

VARIANCES OF STATURE OF MUSLIMS IN EIGHT
DISTRICTS OF BENGAL

District	Sample size	Variance of stature (sq cm)
Barisal	131	39.5068
Burdwan	59	24.4685
Dacca	337	39.2262
Faridpur	77	24.8924
Murshidabad	124	24.3490
Mymensingh	299	38.3306
Nadia	170	32.4325
Rangpur	139	33.4436

obtained in the Bengal Anthropometric Survey, 1945. Examine whether the variance differs from district to district. If not, obtain a pooled estimate for the common variance.

6.20. On the basis of data in exercise 6.2 of Part II, examine separately whether the variances in (a) heights and (b) weight of twin brothers and sisters are equal.

Correlation

6.21. Examine the significance of the correlation coefficient between the length measurements taken by the two persons X and Y given in exercise 5.1 of Part II.

6.22–6.23. Test whether the correlation coefficients obtained in exercises 5.7 and 5.8 of Part II are significantly different from zero.

6.24–6.28. Set up 95% confidence limits on the correlation coefficients in exercises 5.13–5.17.

6.29. The coefficients of correlation between two characteristics estimated by two investigators from samples of sizes 20 and 25 were 0.318 and 0.253, respectively. Would you regard the difference as due to fluctuations of sampling? If so, obtain a pooled estimate of the correlation coefficient.

6.30. Table 6.12 gives the values of the correlation coefficient between stature and sitting height of Muslims in eight districts of Bengal as obtained in the Bengal Anthropometric Survey, 1945.

Examine whether the correlation coefficients can be regarded as equal except for fluctuations of sampling.

TABLE 6.12

CORRELATION BETWEEN STATURE AND SITTING HEIGHT
OF MUSLIMS IN EIGHT DISTRICTS OF BENGAL

District	Sample size	Correlation coefficient
Barisal	131	0.719
Burdwan	59	0.696
Dacca	337	0.824
Faridpur	77	0.685
Murshidabad	124	0.701
Mymensingh	299	0.547
Nadia	170	0.793
Rangpur	139	0.687

6.31. Given in Table 6.13 are the means, the standard deviations, and the correlation coefficient of scores x, y on two halves of a psychological test on 20 boys.

(a) Examine whether the scores on the two halves are uncorrelated. If not, obtain a 95% confidence interval for the coefficient of correlation.

(b) Examine whether the scores on the two halves are equally variable.

(c) Examine whether the average scores on the two halves differ significantly.

TABLE 6.13

MEAN STANDARD DEVIATION AND CORRELATION OF SCORES

Score	Mean	Standard deviation	Correlation
x	45.5	9.51	
y	50.2	5.25	0.76

6.32. Test the significance of the multiple correlation coefficient of the efficiency index y on the scores X_1, X_2, X_3 on the three psychological tests, using the data given in exercise 6.3 of Part II. Also test the significance of the partial correlation coefficient of Y and X_3, eliminating the effects of X_1 and X_2.

Write a report in non-technical language explaining your findings.

6.33. On the basis of the data given in exercise 6.4 of Part II examine whether cranial capacity C can be predicted at all from the three measurements L, B, and H' by means of a formula linear in the logarithms (that is, whether the multiple correlation of $\log C$ on $\log L$, $\log B$, and $\log H'$ is zero).

6.34. Using the data in exercise 6.5, test the significance of the multiple correlation between the criterion C and the "best" set of four tests. Also test whether significant loss in the accuracy of prediction is incurred through the omission of the fifth test.

Give your comments on whether the statistical procedure used is strictly valid or not.

CHAPTER 7

Analysis of Variance

7.1 LINEAR MODELS

Let $y_1, y_2, \ldots, y_n$ be n observed quantities which can be regarded, except for errors of observation, as linear functions of a number of unknown effects with given compounding coefficients. Thus, we have the additive model:

$$(7.1.1) \quad y_i = a_{i1}\theta_1 + a_{i2}\theta_2 + \cdots + a_{im}\theta_m + \epsilon_i, \qquad i = 1, 2, \ldots, n,$$

where a_{ij}'s are known constants, θ_j's are the unknown "effects" to be estimated, and ϵ_i's are the "errors" of observation. Given the effects, the errors ϵ_i's are assumed to be distributed independently and normally, each with mean zero and equal but unknown variance σ^2. The effects θ_j's may be regarded as constant unknown parameters or as unobservable random variables. The model is said to be "fixed," "mixed," or "random" according as none, some, or all the effects are regarded as random variables. Generally the random effects are also assumed to be normally distributed.

7.2 TESTING LINEAR HYPOTHESES IN FIXED-EFFECT MODELS

In a fixed-effect model, the observations $y_1, y_2, \ldots, y_n$ are assumed to be distributed independently and normally, with the same unknown variance σ^2 and expectations given by

$$E(y_i) = a_{i1}\theta_1 + a_{i2}\theta_2 + \cdots + a_{im}\theta_m, \qquad i = 1, 2, \ldots, n,$$

where a_{ij}'s are known constants and θ_j's unknown parameters. We shall denote the rank of the matrix $((a_{ij}))$ by r. For estimating θ_j's and σ^2 the method of least squares given in Section 3.2 is used.

Test for a Specified Value of an Estimable Linear Parametric Function. We consider an estimable linear parametric function $\theta = l_1\theta_1 + l_2\theta_2 + \cdots + l_m\theta_m$ with known coefficients $l_1, l_2, \ldots, l_m$. Then to test the hypothesis that θ has a specified value θ_0,

$$H_0 : \quad \theta = \theta_0,$$

we reject H_0 at level of significance α, against both-sided alternatives $\theta \neq \theta_0$, if

(7.2.1)
$$|T| = \frac{|\hat{\theta} - \theta_0|}{\left(s^2 \sum_{i=1}^{m} l_j \lambda_j\right)^{1/2}} > t_{n-r}(\tfrac{1}{2}\alpha),$$

where $\hat{\theta}$ is the least squares estimate of θ, and λ_j's and s^2 have already been defined in Section 3.2.

Test for Specified Values of a Set of Linear Parametric Functions. Let $\phi_j = b_{j1}\theta_1 + b_{j2}\theta_2 + \cdots + b_{jm}\theta_m$ $(j = 1, 2, \ldots, q)$ be a set of q given linear parametric functions with known coefficient $((b_{jt}))$. Consider the problem of testing the hypothesis that they have specified values

$$H_0 : \quad \phi_j = \phi_j^0, \quad j = 1, 2, \ldots, q.$$

We assume that the ϕ_j's are all linearly independent and estimable. Let $\hat{\phi}_j$ be the least-squares estimate of ϕ_j, and let the dispersion matrix of $\hat{\phi}_1, \hat{\phi}_2, \ldots, \hat{\phi}_q$ be $((d_{jj'}))\sigma^2$. The elements $d_{jj'}$ can be computed by using formulae 3.2.3 and 3.2.4. The quadratic form,

(7.2.2)
$$S_h = \sum_{j,j'=1}^{q} d^{jj'}(\hat{\phi}_j - \phi_j^0)(\hat{\phi}_{j'} - \phi_{j'}^0),$$

is called the sum of squares due to the hypothesis H_0. Then the hypothesis H_0 is rejected at level of significance α if

(7.2.3)
$$T \equiv \frac{S_h/q}{S_e/(n-r)} > F_{q,n-r}(\alpha),$$

where S_e is the error sum of squares defined by 3.2.5.

An alternative formula for computing the sum of squares due to the hypothesis is

(7.2.4)
$$S_h = S_e^* - S_e,$$

where S_e^* is the error sum of squares, when H_0 is true. Thus S_e^* is the minimum value of $S = \sum_{i=1}^{n}(y_i - \sum_{j=1}^{m} a_{ij}\theta_j)^2$ with respect to the parameters θ_j's subject to the restrictions imposed by H_0.

Illustrative Example 7.1. On the basis of the measurements given in illustrative example 3.3, we want to examine (a) whether the angles α and γ of the triangle are equal, (b) whether the triangle is equiangular, that is, whether $\alpha = \beta = \gamma = 60°$.

(a) We have already obtained in illustrative example 3.3 the estimates (in degrees) $\hat{\alpha} = 59.158$, $\hat{\gamma} = 59.659$. The variances and the covariance of these estimates are $V(\hat{\alpha}) = V(\hat{\gamma}) = \frac{1}{6}\sigma^2$ and $\mathrm{Cov}\,(\hat{\alpha}, \hat{\gamma}) = -\frac{1}{12}\sigma^2$, where σ^2 is the error variance. The estimate for σ^2 is the error mean square $s^2 = 0.59797$ with 10 df. For the difference $\delta = \alpha - \gamma$, we have the estimate $\hat{\delta} = \hat{\alpha} - \hat{\gamma} = -0.501$. The variance of $\hat{\delta}$ is

$$V(\hat{\delta}) = V(\hat{\alpha}) + V(\hat{\gamma}) - 2\,\mathrm{Cov}\,(\hat{\alpha}, \hat{\gamma})$$

$$= \left(\frac{1}{6} + \frac{1}{6} + 2 \times \frac{1}{12}\right)\sigma^2 = \frac{\sigma^2}{2},$$

which is estimated as $\hat{V}(\hat{\delta}) = \frac{1}{2}s^2 = 0.29898$. The standard error of $\hat{\delta}$ is thus

$$\mathrm{se}\,(\hat{\delta}) = \sqrt{0.29898} = 0.5468.$$

The statistic to use for examining whether $\delta = 0$ is

$$T = \frac{\hat{\delta}}{\mathrm{se}\,(\hat{\delta})} = \frac{-0.501}{0.5468} = -0.916,$$

which is a Student's t statistic with 10 df and is not significant at the 5% level. We have not enough evidence to dispute that $\alpha = \gamma$.

(b) To examine whether the triangle is equiangular, we note that, if this hypothesis is true, the observations y_1 through y_8 would each have expectation 60 and the observations y_9 through y_{12} would each have expectation 120. Consequently, the error sum of squares under the hypothesis would be $S_e{}^* = \sum_{i=1}^{8} (y_i - 60)^2 + \sum_{i=9}^{12} (y_i - 120)^2 = 14.40$, and this would have 12 df. Remembering that the error sum of squares is actually $S_e = \sum_{i=1}^{12} y_i{}^2 - \hat{\alpha}Q_1 - \hat{\beta}Q_2 = 5.9797$ with 10 df, we find that the sum of squares due to the hypothesis is $S_h = S_e{}^* - S_e = 8.4203$ with 2 df. Since

$$T = \frac{S_h/2}{S_e/10} = 7.041^* > F_{2,10}(0.05)$$

at the 5% level, we reject the hypothesis that the triangle is equiangular.

7.3 TESTS OF MEANS: ONE-WAY CLASSIFICATION

In whatever follows, we use the notations employed in Section 6.1. On the basis of samples of sizes n_i from k normal populations with possibly different means μ_i, $i = 1, 2, \ldots, k$, but a common unspecified variance σ^2, to test the hypothesis that the means are equal,

$$H_0: \quad \mu_1 = \mu_2 = \cdots = \mu_k,$$

the procedure is to reject H_0 at level of significance α if

$$(7.3.1) \qquad T \equiv \frac{B/(k-1)}{W/(N-k)} > F_{k-1,N-k}(\alpha),$$

where $N = \sum n_i$, $T = \sum T_i$, $B = \sum_{i=1}^{k}(T_i^2/n_i) - (T^2/N)$, $W = \sum_{i=1}^{k} S_i^2$. The computations are better shown in the form of Table 7.1.

TABLE 7.1

ANALYSIS OF VARIANCE: ONE-WAY CLASSIFICATION

Source	df	ss	ms	F
Between samples	$k-1$	B	$b = B/(k-1)$	b/s_e
Error (within samples)	$N-k$	W	$s_e = W/(N-k)$	
Total	$N-1$	$B+W$		

Illustrative Example 7.2. On a dairy farm an experiment was conducted to compare the effects of three types of feed 1, 2, and 3 and a control (4) on yield of milk. The average yield of milk in liters, the corrected sum of squares of yields, and the number of cows in each group are given in Table 7.2. Is there any significant difference between the four types of feed with regard to the effect on milk yield?

The sums of squares in the analysis of variance can be computed as:

Error: $\qquad W = \Sigma S_i^2 = 1{,}279{,}311.$

Between feeds: $\quad B = \Sigma n_i \bar{x}_i^2 - \dfrac{(\Sigma n_i \bar{x}_i)^2}{\Sigma n_i} = 16{,}542{,}414.$

Here the total number of observations is $N = 12 + 14 + 15 + 13 = 54$, and the number of feeds is $k = 4$. The error sum of squares W thus has

TABLE 7.2

STATISTICS OF YIELD OF MILK FROM COWS GIVEN DIFFERENT FEEDS

Type of feed	i	1	2	3	4 (control)
No. of cows	n_i	12	14	15	13
Average yield of milk (liters)	$\bar{x}_i$	2,180	1,978	3,246	1,936
Corrected sum of squares of milk yield	S_i^2	259,308	349,496	408,375	262,132

TABLE 7.3

ANALYSIS OF VARIANCE

Source	df	SS	ms	F
Between feeds	3	16,542,414	5,514,138	215.5**
Error	50	1,279,311	25,586	

$N - k = 50$ df, and the ss between feeds B has $k - 1 = 3$ df. Table 7.3 is the analysis of variance table. The differences between feeds are thus highly significant.

7.4 FIXED MODEL: TWC-WAY CLASSIFICATION

Main Effect and Interaction. Suppose there are $r \times s$ normal populations, classified in two ways: in r classes with respect to a characteristic A and in s classes with respect to a second characteristic B. The mean of the (i, j)th population is μ_{ij}, and the variance σ^2 is the same for all the populations, $i = 1, 2, \ldots, r; \ j = 1, 2, \ldots, s$. The means can obviously be written as

$$\mu_{ij} = \mu + \alpha_i + \beta_j + \gamma_{ij},$$

where

$$\mu = \frac{1}{rs} \sum_{i=1}^{r} \sum_{j=1}^{s} \mu_{ij}, \qquad \alpha_i = \frac{1}{s} \sum_{j=1}^{s} \mu_{ij} - \mu,$$

$$\beta_j = \frac{1}{r} \sum_{i=1}^{r} \mu_{ij} - \mu, \quad \text{and} \quad \gamma_{ij} = \mu_{ij} - \mu - \alpha_i - \beta_j.$$

The α_i's are called the main effects of A, β_j's the main effects of B, and γ_{ij}'s the interaction effects of A and B. It is often of practical importance to examine the following hypotheses on the basis of samples drawn from these populations:

(a) That there is no main effect of A, that is,

$$H_A: \quad \alpha_1 = \alpha_2 = \cdots = \alpha_r = 0.$$

(b) That there is no main effect of B, that is,

$$H_B: \quad \beta_1 = \beta_2 = \cdots = \beta_s = 0.$$

(c) That there is no interaction between A and B, that is,

$$H_{AB}: \quad \gamma_{ij} = 0 \quad \text{for} \quad i = 1, 2, \ldots, r; \ j = 1, 2, \ldots, s.$$

The procedure for testing any of these hypotheses is described below. First a table of analysis of variance is prepared which gives the mean squares due to the different hypotheses, the error mean squares and their corresponding degrees of freedom. Let s_h be the mean square due to a hypothesis H and s_e be the error mean square, and suppose that their degrees of freedom are h and e, respectively. The hypothesis H is then rejected at level of significance α if

$$T = \frac{s_h}{s_e} > F_{h,e}(\alpha).$$

One Observation per Cell. When just one observation x_{ij} is available from the normal population with mean μ_{ij} and variance σ^2, $i = 1, 2, \ldots, r$; $= 1, 2, \ldots, s$, it is customary to start with the fundamental assumption

TABLE 7.4

ANALYSIS OF VARIANCE: TWO-WAY CLASSIFICATION
(ONE OBSERVATION PER CELL)

Source	df	ss	ms	F
Main effect of A	$r - 1$	S_A	$s_A = S_A/(r - 1)$	s_A/s_e
Main effect of B	$s - 1$	S_B	$s_B = S_B/(s - 1)$	s_B/s_e
Error	$(r - 1)(s - 1)$	S_e	$s_e = S_e/(r - 1)(s - 1)$	...
Total	$rs - 1$	S_T		

that interaction is absent, that is,

$$\mu_{ij} = \mu + \alpha_i + \beta_j,$$

and proceed to test the hypotheses about the main effects. The analysis of variance table is prepared as shown in Table 7.4.

Here

$$T = \sum\sum x_{ij}, \quad T_2 = \sum\sum x_{ij}^{2}, \quad R_i = \sum_{j=1}^{s} x_{ij}, \quad C_j = \sum_{i=1}^{r} x_{ij},$$

$$\text{CF (correction factor)} = \frac{T^2}{rs}, \quad S_T = T_2 - \text{CF},$$

$$S_A = \frac{1}{s}\sum_{i=1}^{r} R_i^{2} - \text{CF}, \quad S_B = \frac{1}{r}\sum_{j=1}^{s} C_j^{2} - \text{CF},$$

and

$$S_e = S_T - S_A - S_B.$$

Illustrative Example 7.3. In order to compare four different methods M_1, M_2, M_3, M_4 of learning, 20 students of a class were divided into five homogeneous groups G_1, G_2, G_3, G_4, G_5 of four students each, according to their background knowledge. The four methods of learning were

TABLE 7.5

Scores of Twenty Students in a Learning Experiment

Group of students	Method of learning				Total
	M_1	M_2	M_3	M_4	
G_1	8	4	7	5	24
G_2	3	3	5	10	21
G_3	9	6	5	10	30
G_4	5	7	8	12	32
G_5	7	7	12	8	34
Total	32	27	37	45	141

followed, one each by the four students in a group. The scores of these students on a later test are given in Table 7.5. Analyze the data to examine whether there is any real difference between the methods.

Here the total number of observations is $N = 4 \times 5 = 20$, the total of all observations is $T = 141$, and the total of squares of all observations is $T_2 = 1127$. Thus

$$CF = \frac{T^2}{N} = 994.05.$$

ss between methods $= \frac{1}{5}[(32)^2 + (27)^2 + (37)^2 + (45)^2] - CF = 35.35.$

ss between groups $= \frac{1}{4}[(24)^2 + \cdots + (34)^2] - CF = 30.20.$

Total ss $= T_2 - CF = 132.95.$

Error ss $= 132.95 - 3020 - 35.35 = 67.40.$

Table 7.6 is the analysis of variance table. As none of the variance ratios exceeds the corresponding upper 5% values of F distribution, differences between methods and differences between groups cannot be regarded as significant.

When more than one observation is available from each cell, it is not

TABLE 7.6

Analysis of Variance

Source	df	ss	ms	F
Between methods	3	35.35	11.7833	2.098
Between groups	4	30.20	7.5500	1.344
Error	12	67.40	5.6167	
Total	19	132.95		

necessary to assume absence of interaction; it is possible to test separately
the main effects of A and B as well as the interaction between A and B.
Let x_{ijk}, $k = 1, 2, \ldots, n_{ij}$, be the n_{ij} observations from the normal
population with mean μ_{ij} and variance σ^2. We first consider the case when
the numbers of observations per cell are equal.

Equal Number of Observations (*Two or More*) *per Cell.* The computations are much easier when $n_{ij} = n$, $n \geq 2$, that is, when the number of
observations in each cell is the same. The analysis of variance in this case

TABLE 7.7

ANALYSIS OF VARIANCE: TWO-WAY CLASSIFICATION
(n OBSERVATIONS PER CELL)

Variation due to	df	SS	ms	F
Main effect of A	$r - 1$	S_A	s_A	s_A/s_e
Main effect of B	$s - 1$	S_B	s_B	s_B/s_e
Interaction $A \times B$	$(r - 1)(s - 1)$	S_{AB}	s_{AB}	s_{AB}/s_e
Between cells	$rs - 1$	B	...	...
Error (within cells)	$rs(n - 1)$	W	s_e	...
Total	$rsn - 1$	S_T	...	...

is done as shown in Table 7.7. Here

$$T_{ij} = \sum_{k=1}^{n} x_{ijk}, \quad T_{i0} = \sum_{j=1}^{s} T_{ij}, \quad T_{0j} = \sum_{i=1}^{r} T_{ij},$$

$$T = \sum_{i=1}^{r} \sum_{j=1}^{s} T_{ij}, \quad T_2 = \sum_{i=1}^{r} \sum_{j=1}^{s} \sum_{k=1}^{n_{ij}} x_{ijk}^2, \quad CF = \frac{T^2}{rsn},$$

$$S_T = T_2 - CF, \quad S_A = \frac{1}{s} \sum_{i=1}^{r} T_{i0}^2 - CF, \quad S_B = \frac{1}{r} \sum_{j=1}^{s} T_{0j}^2 - CF.$$

$$B = \frac{1}{n} \sum_{i=1}^{r} \sum_{j=1}^{s} T_{ij}^2 - CF, \quad S_{AB} = B - S_A - S_B, \quad \text{and} \quad W = S_T - B.$$

However, if it is known a priori that there is no interaction, the error
mean square has to be computed as

(7.4.1)
$$s_e = \frac{W + S_{AB}}{rsn - r - s + 1}$$

with $rsn - r - s + 1$ degrees of freedom.

Illustrative Example 7.4. The volumes of 10 pots were measured in
cubic centimeters by four investigators, each investigator measuring every

TABLE 7.8

VOLUME (IN CUBIC CENTIMETERS) OF TEN POTS AS
MEASURED BY FOUR INVESTIGATORS

Pot	Investigator			
	A	B	C	D
1	38, 40	27, 34	39, 30	44, 46
2	42, 40	42, 40	35, 40	38, 47
3	38, 40	23, 43	34, 42	46, 50
4	12, 12	20, 16	15, 26	17, 22
5	26, 18	28, 22	19, 30	11, 26
6	6, 8	15, 20	8, 14	10, 16
7	50, 52	52, 50	44, 52	51, 50
8	34, 26	40, 41	30, 42	34, 24
9	22, 24	31, 28	26, 30	30, 17
10	48, 42	56, 53	52, 42	50, 47

pot twice. The results are given in Table 7.8. Examine whether the variation in measurements by different investigators on a pot differs significantly from one pot to another and also find whether there are significant differences between pots.

To carry out the analysis of variance of these $N = 10 \times 4 \times 2 = 80$ observations, we proceed as follows. First the total of all the observations is found to be $T = 2625$, and the total of the squares of all the observations is $T_2 = 100,269$. This gives

$$CF = \frac{T^2}{N} = 86,132.8125,$$

Total ss $= T_2 - CF = 14,136.1875.$

Next Table 7.9 is prepared, showing the totals for each pot $\times$ investigator combination. From this table, we compute:

ss between pots $= \frac{1}{8}[(298)^2 + (324)^2 + \cdots + (390)^2] - CF$
$\qquad = 11,948.5625,$

ss between investigators $= \frac{1}{20}[(618)^2 + \cdots + (676)^2] - CF$
$\qquad = 147.6875.$

There are 40 cells in this table, and next we compute

ss between cells $= \frac{1}{2}[(78)^2 + (61)^2 + \cdots + (94)^2 + (97)^2] - CF$
$\qquad = 13,046.6875.$

TABLE 7.9

TOTALS OF THE DUPLICATE MEASUREMENTS

Pot	Investigator				Total
	A	B	C	D	
1	78	61	69	90	298
2	82	82	75	85	324
3	78	66	76	96	316
4	24	36	41	39	140
5	44	50	49	37	180
6	14	35	22	26	97
7	102	102	96	101	401
8	60	81	72	58	271
9	36	59	56	47	208
10	90	109	94	97	390
Total	618	681	650	676	2625

By subtraction we obtain

ss due to interaction = (ss between cells) − (ss between pots)

− (ss between investigators)

= 950.4375.

Also, by subtraction

ss within cells (error) = (total ss) − (ss between cells)

= 1089.5000.

The analysis of variance can then be presented as shown in Table 7.10.

TABLE 7.10

ANALYSIS OF VARIANCE

Source	df	ss	ms	F
Pots	9	11,948.5625	1327.6181	48.742**
Investigators	9	147.6875	49.2292	1.807
Interaction: pots × investigators	27	950.4375	35.2014	1.292
Between cells	39	13,046.6875	334.5304	
Error	40	1,089.5000	27.2375	
Total	79	14,136.1875		

350 STATISTICAL INFERENCE

Thus only the variation between the pots is found to be significant, not the variation between investigators or the interaction between pots and investigators.

Unequal Number of Observations per Cell. When unequal numbers n_{ij} of independent observations x_{ijk}, $k = 1, 2, \ldots, n_{ij}$, are available from the (i,j)th normal population with mean μ_{ij}, $i = 1, 2, \ldots, r$; $j = 1, 2, \ldots, s$, and a common unknown variance σ^2, the analysis of variance procedure is as follows.

$$T_{ij} = \sum_{k=1}^{n_{ij}} x_{ijk}, \quad \bar{x}_{ij} = \frac{T_{ij}}{n_{ij}}, \quad T_{i0} = \sum_{j=1}^{s} T_{ij},$$

$$T_{0j} = \sum_{i=1}^{r} T_{ij}, \quad n_{i0} = \sum_{j=1}^{s} n_{ij}, \quad n_{0j} = \sum_{i=1}^{r} n_{ij},$$

$$T = \sum_{i=1}^{r} \sum_{j=1}^{s} T_{ij}, \quad N = \sum_{i=1}^{r} \sum_{j=1}^{s} n_{ij}.$$

Then the following sums of squares are to be computed:

Total: $\quad S_T = \sum_{i=1}^{r} \sum_{j=1}^{s} \sum_{k=1}^{n_{ij}} x_{ijk}^2 - \text{CF},$

Between cells: $\quad B = \sum_{i=1}^{r} \sum_{j=1}^{s} \frac{T_{ij}^2}{n_{ij}} - \text{CF},$

Between A classes (unadjusted): $\quad S_A^* = \sum_{i=1}^{r} \frac{T_{i0}^2}{n_{i0}} - \text{CF},$

Between B classes (unadjusted): $\quad S_B^* = \sum_{j=1}^{s} \frac{T_{0j}^2}{n_{0j}} - \text{CF},$

Within cells: $\quad W = S_T - B.$

where $\text{CF} = T^2/N$.

To compute the sum of squares due to interaction, the procedure is as follows. First we have to solve for $\alpha_1, \alpha_2, \ldots, \alpha_r$ the set of linear equations:

$$(7.4.2) \quad c_{i1}\alpha_1 + c_{i2}\alpha_2 + \cdots + c_{ir}\alpha_r = Q_i; \quad i = 1, 2, \ldots, r,$$

where

$$Q_i = T_{i0} - \sum_{j=1}^{s} \frac{n_{ij}T_{0j}}{n_{0j}}$$

and

$$c_{it} = \begin{cases} n_{i0} - \sum_{j=1}^{s} \frac{n_{ij}^2}{n_{0j}} & \text{if } i = t, \\ -\sum_{j=1}^{s} \frac{n_{ij}n_{tj}}{n_{0j}} & \text{if } i \neq t. \end{cases}$$

Let $\hat{\alpha}_1, \hat{\alpha}_2, \ldots, \hat{\alpha}_r$ denote a solution of these equations. Then compute the following sums of squares:

Between A classes (adjusted): $\quad S_A = \sum_{i=1}^{r} \hat{\alpha}_i Q_i,$

Between B classes (adjusted): $\quad S_B = S_A + S_B{}^* - S_A{}^*,$

Interaction: $\qquad\qquad\qquad S_{AB} = S_T - W - S_A{}^* - S_B.$

An alternative way is to compute the interaction sum of squares directly as follows. First we compute $(r-1)(s-1)$ "tetrad differences" of the sample means:

$$d_{ij} = \bar{x}_{11} + \bar{x}_{ij} - \bar{x}_{1j} - \bar{x}_{i1},$$

$i = 2, 3, \ldots, r; \; j = 2, 3, \ldots, s.$ Let these tetrad differences be denoted by $d_1, d_2, \ldots$, etc., in some order. The dispersion matrix of these tetrad differences can be easily computed. For instance, if we write $d_1 = d_{22}$ and $d_2 = d_{23}$, we have

$$V(d_1) = \left(\frac{1}{n_{11}} + \frac{1}{n_{22}} + \frac{1}{n_{12}} + \frac{1}{n_{21}} \right) \sigma^2,$$

$$\text{Cov}\,(d_1, d_2) = \left(\frac{1}{n_{11}} + \frac{1}{n_{21}} \right) \sigma^2, \qquad \text{etc.}$$

Let the dispersion matrix of the $(r-1)(s-1)$ tetrad differences be denoted by $((a_{ij}))\sigma^2$. Then the interaction sum of squares is given by

(7.4.3) $\qquad\qquad\qquad S_{AB} = \Sigma\Sigma a^{ij} d_i d_j,$

where $((a^{ij})) = ((a_{ij}))^{-1}$. Any set of $(r-1)(s-1)$ independent tetrad differences can be used in this way, and we should choose them so that most of the covariances vanish. The computations are usually presented in the form of a table, such as Table 7.11. Tests of significance are carried out as in the case of equal number of observations per cell.

TABLE 7.11

ANALYSIS OF VARIANCE: TWO-WAY CLASSIFICATION
(UNEQUAL NUMBERS IN CELLS)

Source	ss	df	ss	Source
Between A classes (unadjusted)	$S_A{}^*$	$r-1$	S_A	Between A classes (adjusted)
Between B classes (adjusted)	S_B	$s-1$	$S_B{}^*$	Between B classes (unadjusted)
Interaction	S_{AB}	$(r-1)(s-1)$	S_{AB}	Interaction
Between cells	B	$rs-1$	B	Between cells
Within cells	W	$N-rs$	W	Within cells
Total	S_T	$N-1$	S_T	Total

Illustrative Example 7.5. Table 7.12 is a record of replicated measurements of profile distances of three subjects S_1, S_2, S_3, taken by three observers O_1, O_2, O_3. Examine whether there are significant differences between observers and between subjects and also whether there is any observer × subject interaction.

TABLE 7.12

MEASUREMENTS OF PROFILE DISTANCE (IN CENTIMETERS)

Observer	Subject		
	S_1	S_2	S_3
O_1	9.88	9.22	9.60
	9.84	9.26	9.66
		9.23	
O_2	10.08	9.10	9.82
	9.98	9.24	9.54
	10.02		9.60
O_3	10.08	9.20	9.50
	9.80		
	9.88	9.16	9.32

To carry out the analysis of variance for these two-way classified data with unequal number of observations per cell, we proceed as follows. To simplify computations, we subtract 9 from each observation and multiply the remainder by 100; that is, we work with $y = 100(x - 9)$, where x stands for the original measurement. Table 7.13 is now obtained. The

TABLE 7.13

PROFILE MEASUREMENTS (CODED)

Observer	Subject		
	S_1	S_2	S_3
O_1	88	22	60
	84	26	66
		23	
O_2	108	10	82
	98	24	54
	102		60
O_3	108	20	50
	80	16	32
	88		

total of all these values is $T = 1301$, and the total of squares is $T_2 = 100{,}021$. There are in all $N = 22$ observations. Thus

$$CF = \frac{T^2}{N} = 76{,}936.41,$$

$$\text{Total ss} = T_2 - \frac{T^2}{N} = 23{,}084.59.$$

Next we prepare a table in which for each observer × subject combination are shown (a) the total of the observations, (b) the number of observations, and (c) the ratio of (b) to the column total for (b).

Observer		S_1	S_2	S_3	Total
O_1	(a)	172	71	126	369
	(b)	(2)	(3)	(2)	(7)
	(c)	0.250000	0.428571	0.285714	
O_2	(a)	308	34	196	538
	(b)	(3)	(2)	(3)	(8)
	(c)	0.375000	0.285714	0.428571	
O_3	(a)	276	36	82	394
	(b)	(3)	(2)	(2)	(7)
	(c)	0.375000	0.285714	0.28714	
Total	(a)	756	141	404	1301
	(b)	(8)	(7)	(7)	(22)

Then we compute

$$\text{ss between cells} = \tfrac{1}{2}(172)^2 + \tfrac{1}{3}(71)^2 + \cdots + \tfrac{1}{2}(82)^2 - CF$$
$$= 21{,}880.59,$$

so that, by subtraction, we get

$$\text{ss within cells (error)} = (\text{total ss}) - (\text{ss between cells})$$
$$= 1204.00.$$

Also:

$$\text{ss between subjects (unadjusted)} = \tfrac{1}{8}(756)^2 + \tfrac{1}{7}(141)^2 + \tfrac{1}{7}(404)^2 - CF$$
$$= 20{,}662.30,$$

$$\text{ss between observers (unadjusted)} = \tfrac{1}{7}(369)^2 + \tfrac{1}{8}(538)^2 + \tfrac{1}{7}(394)^2 - CF$$
$$= 872.23.$$

To obtain the adjusted ss between observers, we have to solve equations 7.3.3 of the form $\Sigma c_{it}\alpha_t = Q_i$, whose coefficients are as follows:

α_1	α_2	α_3	Q
4.642859	−2.464284	−2.178570	4.143
	5.017859	−2.553570	41.071
		4.732144	−45.214

For instance,

$$c_{11} = 7 - 2(0.25000) - 3(0.428571) - 2(0.285714) = 4.642859,$$

$$c_{12} = -2(0.375000) - 3(0.285714) - 2(0.428571) = -2.464284,$$

$$Q_1 = 369 - 756(0.250000) - 141(0.428571) - 404(0.285714) = 4.143, \text{ etc.}$$

These equations are of rank 2. A solution of these equations under the restriction $\alpha_1 + \alpha_2 + \alpha_3 = 0$ is

$$\hat{\alpha}_1 = 0.8341, \qquad \hat{\alpha}_2 = 5.4146, \qquad \hat{\alpha}_3 = -6.2487.$$

Thus:

ss between observers (adjusted) $= Q_1\hat{\alpha}_1 + Q_2\hat{\alpha}_2 + Q_3\hat{\alpha}_3 = 508.37,$

ss between subjects (adjusted) $=$ (ss observers adjusted)

$+$ (ss subjects unadjusted)

$-$ (ss observers unadjusted)

$= 20{,}298.44,$

TABLE 7.14

ANALYSIS OF VARIANCE

Source	ss	df		Source
Subjects (unadjusted)	20,662.30	2	20,298.44	Subjects (adjusted)
Observers (adjusted)	508.37	2	872.23	Observers (unadjusted)
Interaction: subject × observers	709.92	4	709.92	Interaction
Between cells	21,880.59	8	21,880.59	Between cells
Within cells (error)	1,204.00	13	1,204.00	Within cells
Total	23,084.59	21	23,084.59	Total

ss due to interaction = (ss between cells) − (ss observers adjusted)

$$- \text{(ss subjects unadjusted)}$$

$$= 709.92.$$

The results are presented in Table 7.14.

To carry out tests of significance, each component has to be tested against the error mean square. The computations can be arranged as shown in Table 7.15. Differences between subjects and between observers are significant. Interaction is not significant.

TABLE 7.15

VARIANCE-RATIO TESTS

Source	df	ms	F
Subjects (adjusted)	2	10,149.22	109.58**
Observers (adjusted)	2	254.18	27.44**
Interaction	4	177.48	1.92
Error	13	92.62	

7.5 FIXED MODEL: THREE-WAY CLASSIFICATION

Suppose there are r normal populations classified in three ways: A, B, and C (called factors). The normal population belonging to the cell determined by the combination $A_i B_j C_k$ of the three classifications has mean μ_{ijk}, $i = 1, 2, \ldots, r$; $j = 1, 2, \ldots, s$; $k = 1, 2, \ldots, t$, and the variance is the same σ^2 for all the populations.

We can write μ_{ijk} as

$$\mu_{ijk} = \mu + \alpha_i + \beta_j + \gamma_k + \delta_{ij} + \epsilon_{jk} + \theta_{ik} + \eta_{ijk}.$$

Here μ is the general effect; α_i, β_j, γ_k are the main effects of the three factors A, B, C, respectively; δ_{ij}, ϵ_{jk}, θ_{ik} are the two-factor interaction effects of $A \times B$, $B \times C$, and $C \times A$, respectively; and η_{ijk} is the three-factor $A \times B \times C$ interaction effect. Numerically, $\mu = \mu_{000}$, $\alpha_i = \mu_{i00} - \mu_{000}$, $\delta_{ij} = \mu_{ij0} - \mu_{i00} - \mu_{0j0} + \mu_{000}$, $\eta_{ijk} = \mu_{ijk} - \mu - \alpha_i - \beta_j - \gamma_k - \delta_{ij} - \epsilon_{jk} - \theta_{ik}$, etc. Here replacement of subscripts by zero indicates averaging over these subscripts, for instance,

$$\mu_{000} = \frac{1}{rst} \sum_i \sum_j \sum_k \mu_{ijk}, \quad \mu_{ij0} = \frac{1}{t} \sum_k \mu_{ijk}, \quad \mu_{i00} = \frac{1}{st} \sum_j \sum_k \mu_{ijk}, \text{ etc.}$$

Hypotheses of interest in this connection are as follows:

H_A: That there is no main effect of A, that is,

$$\alpha_1 = \alpha_2 = \cdots = \alpha_r = 0.$$

H_{AB}: That there is no interaction between A and B, that is,

$$\delta_{ij} = 0 \quad \text{for } i = 1, 2, \ldots, r,$$
$$j = 1, 2, \ldots, s.$$

H_{ABC}: That there is no interaction between the three factors A, B, and C, that is,

$$\eta_{ijk} = 0 \quad \text{for } i = 1, 2, \ldots, r,$$
$$j = 1, 2, \ldots, s,$$
$$k = 1, 2, \ldots, t.$$

Other hypotheses like H_B (absence of main effect of B) and H_{BC} (absence of interaction between B and C) are similarly defined.

We shall consider only the case where an equal number, say n, of observations is available from each of the $r \times s \times t$ populations. Let $x_{ijku}, u = 1, 2, \ldots, n$, be the n observations from the (i, j, k)th population. Then, to examine the above hypotheses, we first compute the following totals:

$$T_{ijk} = \sum_{u=1}^{n} x_{ijku}, \quad T_{ij0} = \sum_{k=1}^{t} T_{ijk}, \quad T_{i0k} = \sum_{j=1}^{s} T_{ijk},$$

$$T_{0jk} = \sum_{i=1}^{r} T_{ijk}, \quad T_{i00} = \sum_{j=1}^{s} T_{ij0}, \quad T_{0j0} = \sum_{i=1}^{r} T_{ij0},$$

$$T_{00k} = \sum_{i=1}^{r} T_{i0k}, \quad T = \sum_{i=1}^{r} T_{i00}.$$

Then the sums of squares due to the various hypotheses are computed as follows:

Total ss: $S_T = \sum_{i=1}^{r} \sum_{j=1}^{s} \sum_{k=1}^{t} \sum_{u=1}^{n} x_{ijku}^2 - \text{CF}$, where $\text{CF} = \dfrac{T^2}{rstn}$,

ss due to the main effect of A: $S_A = \dfrac{1}{stn} \sum_{i=1}^{r} T_{i00}^2 - \text{CF}.$

S_B and S_C, the ss due to the main effects of the other two factors, can be computed similarly:

ss due to $A \times B$ interaction:

$$S_{AB} = \frac{1}{tn} \sum_{i=1}^{r} \sum_{j=1}^{s} T_{ij0}^2 - \text{CF} - S_A - S_B.$$

The ss due to other two-factor interactions, namely, S_{BC} and S_{AC}, can be computed in the same way. The ss due to the three-factor interaction $A \times B \times C$ is given by

$$S_{ABC} = \frac{1}{n} \sum_{i=1}^{r} \sum_{j=1}^{s} \sum_{k=1}^{t} T_{ijk}^2 - CF - (S_A + S_B + S_C + S_{AB} + S_{AC} + S_{BC}),$$

and the error sum of squares is:

$$S_e = S_T - (S_A + S_B + S_C + S_{AB} + S_{AC} + S_{BC} + S_{ABC}).$$

The computations are shown in Table 7.16 in the form of an analysis of variance table.

TABLE 7.16

ANALYSIS OF VARIANCE: THREE-WAY CLASSIFICATION
(EQUAL NUMBERS IN CELLS)

Source	df	ss	ms	F
Main effects				
A	$(r-1)$	S_A	s_A	s_A/s_e
B	$(s-1)$	S_B	s_B	s_B/s_e
C	$(t-1)$	S_C	s_C	s_C/s_e
Two-factor interactions				
$A \times B$	$(r-1)(s-1)$	S_{AB}	s_{AB}	s_{AB}/s_e
$B \times C$	$(s-1)(t-1)$	S_{BC}	s_{BC}	s_{BC}/s_e
$C \times A$	$(r-1)(t-1)$	S_{AC}	s_{AC}	s_{AC}/s_e
Three-factor interaction				
$A \times B \times C$	$(r-1)(s-1)(t-1)$	S_{ABC}	s_{ABC}	s_{ABC}/s_e
Error				
(within cells)	$rst(n-1)$	S_e	s_e	
Total	$rstn-1$	S_T		

7.6 HIERARCHAL CLASSIFICATION

Suppose that a number of populations are first classified into r classes, say, $A_1, A_2, \ldots, A_r$ with respect to a way of classification A. The populations in the class A_i are then further subdivided into s_i classes with respect to a second way of classification B; these classes may be denoted by $A_i B_j$, $j = 1, 2, \ldots, s_i$. There is, however, no correspondence between the classes $A_1 B_1$ and, say, $A_2 B_1$. For instance, households in a state may first be classified by districts and then by villages within a district, and there is no correspondence between the first village of the first district and the first village of the second district. The populations in the class

$A_i B_j$ may again be further subdivided with respect to a third way of classification C into t_{ij} classes, which may be denoted by $A_i B_j C_k$, $k = 1, 2, \ldots, t_{ij}$, and so on. This type of classification is known as *hierarchal classification.*

The analysis of data for two hierarchal classifications A and B is given below. With more than two ways of classifications the analysis can be carried out similarly.

Suppose that there is one normal population belonging to the class $A_i B_j$, with mean μ_{ij} and variance σ^2 common for all the classes, $j = 1, 2, \ldots, s_i$; $i = 1, 2, \ldots, r$. Let $\mu_{i0} = (1/s_i) \sum_{j=1}^{s_i} \mu_{ij}$ be the mean of the ith A class. The hypotheses of interest are as follows:

H_A: That there are no differences between the A classes in respect to the average value of the mean:

$$H_A : \quad \mu_{10} = \mu_{20} = \cdots = \mu_{r0}$$

$H_{B|A}$: That within each class of A the means are all equal for the different subclasses in respect to B:

$$H_{B|A} : \quad \mu_{i1} = \mu_{i2} = \cdots = \mu_{is_i} \quad \text{for for } i = 1, 2, \ldots, r.$$

Table 7.17 is the analysis of variance table. Here

$$n_{i0} = \sum_{j=1}^{s_i} n_{ij}, \quad N = \sum_{i=1}^{r} n_{i0}, \quad T_{ij} = \sum_{k=1}^{n_{ij}} x_{ijk},$$

$$T_{i0} = \sum_{j=1}^{s_i} T_{ij}, \quad T = \sum_{i=1}^{r} T_{i0}, \quad T_2 = \sum_i \sum_j \sum_k x_{ijk}^2, \quad CF = \frac{T^2}{N},$$

$$S_T = T_2 - CF, \quad S_A = \sum_{i=1}^{r} \frac{T_{i0}^2}{n_{i0}} - CF,$$

$$S_{B|A} = \sum_i \sum_j \frac{T_{ij}^2}{n_{ij}} - \sum_{i=1}^{r} \frac{T_{i0}^2}{n_{i0}}, \quad W = S_T - S_A - S_{B|A}.$$

TABLE 7.17

ANALYSIS OF VARIANCE: HIERARCHAL CLASSIFICATION

Source	df	ss	ms	F
Between A classes	$r - 1$	S_A	s_A	s_A/s_e
Between B classes within A	$\Sigma s_i - r$	$S_{B|A}$	$s_{B|A}$	$s_{B|A}/s_e$
Error (within cells)	$N - \Sigma s_i$	W	s_e	
Total	$N - 1$	S_T		

7.7 MIXED MODEL: TWO-WAY CLASSIFICATION

Suppose that a large number of normal populations are classified according to two ways of classification, namely, A with r classes A_1, $A_2, \ldots, A_r$ and B with a large number of classes from which only s classes, call them $B_1, B_2, \ldots, B_s$, are chosen at random. From each of these $r \times s$ normal populations a random sample of size n is taken. Let μ_{ij} be the mean of the normal population in the class $A_i B_j$, and σ^2 the variance common for all the populations, and let the samples from these populations be denoted by x_{ijk}, $k = 1, 2, \ldots, n$; $j = 1, 2, \ldots, s$; $i = 1, 2, \ldots, r$.

Because of sampling from the classes of B, μ_{ij}'s are random variables which will be assumed to be distributed normally with means $E(\mu_{ij}) = \mu_i$, a common variance V for all, and equal positive correlation ρ for any two μ's belonging to the same class of B and zero correlation for any two μ's in two different classes of B. The total of the μ's for any class of B has the same variance $\sigma_B^2 = rV[1 + (r - 1)\rho]$, which will be called the variance due to the main effect of B. Any standardized contrast of the μ's belonging to a particular class of B has the same variance $\sigma_{AB}^2 = V(1 - \rho)$, which is the variance due to the interaction between A and B. Let

$$\sigma_A^2 = \frac{1}{r-1} \sum_{i=1}^{r} (\mu_i - \mu)^2, \quad \text{where } \mu = \frac{\sum_{i=1}^{r} \mu_i}{r}.$$

Then σ_A^2 is the variance due to the main effect of A. The hypotheses of interest are (a) that there is no main effect of A, that is, H_A : $\sigma_A^2 = 0$; (b) that there is no main effect of B, that is, H_B : $\sigma_B^2 = 0$; (c) that there is no interaction between A and B, that is, H_{AB} : $\sigma_{AB}^2 = 0$.

To test these hypotheses, the first step is to form the analysis of variance table in the same manner as for two-way classified data with equal number of observations per cell, described earlier. The expectations of the various mean squares are shown in Table 7.18. The expectations of the mean

TABLE 7.18

EXPECTATIONS OF MEAN SQUARES

Source	df	ms	Expectation of ms
Main effect of A	$r - 1$	s_A	$\sigma^2 + n\sigma_{AB}^2 + ns\sigma_A^2$
Main effect of B	$s - 1$	s_B	$\sigma^2 + nr\sigma_B^2$
Interaction $A \times B$	$(r - 1)(s - 1)$	s_{AB}	$\sigma^2 + n\sigma_{AB}^2$
Error	$rs(n - 1)$	s_e	σ^2

squares s_A and s_{AB} are equal if and only if $\sigma_A{}^2 = 0$. The hypothesis H_A is rejected at level of significance α if $T \equiv s_A/s_{AB} > F_{r-1,(r-1)(s-1)}(\alpha)$.

Similarly the expectations of the mean squares s_B and s_e are equal if and only if $\sigma_B{}^2 = 0$, and the hypothesis H_B is rejected at level of significance α if $T = s_B/s_e > F_{s-1,rs(n-1)}(\alpha)$.

Again, the hypothesis H_{AB} is rejected at level of significance α if $T \equiv s_{AB}/s_e > F_{(r-1)(s-1),rs(n-1)}(\alpha)$. Statistical analysis under general mixed-effects models is usually carried out in the following way. First an ordinary analysis of variance table is prepared, and the expectations of the various component mean squares are worked out. To examine a certain hypothesis H, the variance ratio is formed by taking those two mean squares whose expectations are equal under the H.

Illustrative Example 7.6. To compare the average yields of three different varieties V_1, V_2, V_3 of wheat an experiment was conducted in which each variety was tried in three plots in each of four villages selected at random. The yields are given in Table 7.19 in convenient units. Analyze the data.

TABLE 7.19

YIELDS IN A VARIETAL TRIAL

	Variety		
Village	V_1	V_2	V_3
1	8	7	8
	2	3	6
	5	5	10
2	4	5	11
	9	3	9
	5	2	8
3	6	8	12
	8	7	10
	5	10	15
4	7	10	8
	5	3	9
	9	8	11

The analysis of variance for these two-way classified data with three observations per cell can be carried out as in illustrative example 7.4. The results are given in Table 7.20. If the four villages are regarded as a sample from a population of villages, the appropriate error for testing

TABLE 7.20

ANALYSIS OF VARIANCE

Source	df	ss	ms
Villages	3	53.6389	17.880
Varieties	2	112.6667	56.333
Interaction:			
variety × village	6	26.4444	4.407
Error	24	118.0000	4.917
Total	35		

the differences between varieties is the interaction mean square. Thus we get the variance ratio $T \equiv 56.333/4.407 = 12.783**$, which with 2 and 6 df is significant at the 1% level. Obviously, the interaction which is to be tested against the error mean square is not significant. The mean square due to villages has to be tested against the mean square due to error. This gives a variance ratio $T = 17.880/4.917 = 3.636*$, which with 3 and 24 df is significant at the 5% level (but not at the 1% level).

7.8 MULTIPLE COMPARISONS

Various procedures are available for simultaneous comparison of the means of $k \geq 2$ populations or of any subset of such means on the basis of samples drawn from such populations. Suppose that the populations are all normal, with a common variance, and that independent samples of the same size, say n, are available from each. Let $\bar{x}_i$ denote the mean of the sample from the ith population, $i = 1, 2, \ldots, k$. Suppose further that an independent estimate e^2 of the common sampling variance of these means is available, and that this is based on f degrees of freedom: thus $V(\bar{x}_i) = E(e^2)$, for $i = 1, 2, \ldots, k$.

When the sample means are arranged in descending order of magnitude, we shall denote them by

$$\bar{x}_{(1)} \geq \bar{x}_{(2)} \geq \cdots \geq \bar{x}_{(k)}.$$

Fisher's Procedure. First carry out a variance-ratio test for equality of the k means, using the statistic

$$T = \frac{\left[\sum \bar{x}_i^2 - \frac{(\sum \bar{x}_i)^2}{k} \right] \bigg/ (k-1)}{e^2}.$$

At a chosen level of significance α, if $T < F_{k-1,f}(\alpha)$ the means can all be regarded as equal. Otherwise we have to compute the critical difference, or the least significant difference as it is also called, defined by $l = \sqrt{2} e t_f(\tfrac{1}{2}\alpha)$. The difference between two sample means is to be regarded as significant if it exceeds l.

The Student–Newman–Keuls Test. Let $q_\alpha(k, f)$ denote the upper $100\alpha\%$ point of the distribution of the *studentized range statistic* $(\bar{x}_{(1)} - \bar{x}_{(k)})/s$, tabulated in Table 29 of *Biometrika Tables for Statisticians* for $k = 2\,(1)\,20$, $f = 10\,(1)\,20, 24, 30, 60, 120, \infty$, and $\alpha = 0.05, 0.01$.

Let $w_k = eq_\alpha(k, f)$, $w_{k-1} = eq_\alpha(k-1, f)$, ..., etc. The next step is to compute $d_k = \bar{x}_{(1)} - \bar{x}_{(k)}$, and if $d_k \leq w_k$ all the means are to be regarded as equal. If $d_k > w_k$, regard $\bar{x}_{(1)}$ and $\bar{x}_{(k)}$ as significantly different and compute $d'_{k-1} = \bar{x}_{(1)} - \bar{x}_{(k-1)}$ and $d''_{k-1} = \bar{x}_{(2)} - \bar{x}_{(k)}$. If $d'_{k-1} \leq w_{k-1}$, regard all the means in the set $\bar{x}_{(1)}, \bar{x}_{(2)}, \ldots, \bar{x}_{(k-1)}$ as homogeneous; if $d'_{k-1} > w_{k-1}$, regard $\bar{x}_{(1)}$ as significantly different from $\bar{x}_{(k-1)}$. Similar tests are to be carried out with d''_{k-1}. The procedure is to be continued until all the means in a group are found to be homogeneous.

Duncan's Test. This test procedure is the same as that for the Student–Newman–Keuls test except that values $D_\alpha(k, f)$ tabulated by D. B. Duncan in *Biometrics*, Vol. 11, have to be used instead of $q_\alpha(k, f)$.

Scheffé's Test. To judge simultaneously the significance of all contrasts of the form $x = c_1\bar{x}_1 + c_2\bar{x}_2 + \cdots + c_k\bar{x}_k$, where $c_1 + c_2 + \cdots + c_k = 0$ and $c_1^2 + c_2^2 + \cdots + c_k^2 = 1$ at level of significance α, compute $S = e\sqrt{[(k-1)F_{k-1, f}(\alpha)]}$. If $|x| > S$, x is to be judged significant.

7.9 TESTS OF REGRESSION

Notations. The dependent variate will be denoted by X_0, and the independent or auxiliary variates by $X_1, X_2, \ldots, X_p$. For samples from multivariate populations and statistics computed from them, we shall use the notations given in Section 6.1. If a number of different populations are involved, superscripts will be used to distinguish them.

Test for Linearity of Regression on One Independent Variate. With two variates X_0 and X_1, the basic assumption is that the conditional distribution of X_0, given that $X_1 = x_1$, is normal for all values of x_1, with variance σ^2, which is the same for all values of x_1, and mean to be denoted by $E(X_0 \mid X_1 = x_1) = \mu(x_1)$. The hypothesis to be tested is that the regression function $\mu(x_1)$ is linear in x_1, that is,

$$H: \quad \mu(x_1) = \alpha + \beta x_1.$$

Suppose that in the available observations on the two variates there are only k different values of X_1, namely, x_{1i}, $i = 1, 2, \ldots, k$, and that corresponding to the value x_{1i} of X_1 there are n_i values of X_0, namely, x_{0ij}, $j = 1, 2, \ldots, n_i$. The available pairs of observations can thus be denoted by (x_{0ij}, x_{1i}), $j = 1, 2, \ldots, n_i$, which form the *i*th *array*, and there are k such arrays, $i = 1, 2, \ldots, k$. The total number of pairs of observations is thus $n = \sum_{i=1}^{k} n_i$. Let the total of X_0 for the ith array be denoted by $X_{0i} = \sum_{j=1}^{n_i} x_{0ij}$. The totals and the crude sums of squares and products will be denoted by $T_0 = \sum_{i=1}^{k} X_{0i}$, $T_1 = \sum_{i=1}^{k} n_i x_{1i}$, $T_{00} = \sum_{i=1}^{k} \sum_{j=1}^{n_i} x_{0ij}^2$, $T_{11} = \sum_{i=1}^{k} n_i x_{1i}^2$, $T_{01} = \sum_{i=1}^{k} X_{0i} x_{1i}$. The corrected sums of squares and products are then given by $S_{00} = T_{00} - T_0^2/n$, $S_{11} = T_{11} - T_1^2/n$, $S_{01} = T_{01} - T_0 T_1/n$. Then, we compute the following sums of squares:

Between-arrays ss: $\quad B = \sum_{i=1}^{k} \dfrac{X_{0i}^2}{n_i} - \dfrac{T_0^2}{n}$,

Within-arrays ss: $\quad W = S_{00} - B$,

ss due to linear regression: $\quad L = \dfrac{S_{01}^2}{S_{11}}$,

and complete Table 7.21.

TABLE 7.21

ANALYSIS OF VARIANCE: LINEARITY OF REGRESSION

Source	df	ss	ms	F
Linear regression	1	$L = S_{01}^2/S_{11}$		
Deviation from linear regression	$k - 2$	$D = B - L$	$d = D/(k-2)$	d/w
Between arrays	$k - 1$	B		
Within arrays	$n - k$	W	$w = W/(n-k)$	
Total	$n - 1$	S_{00}		

The hypothesis of linearity of regression is rejected at level of significance ϵ if $T > F_{k-2,n-k}(\epsilon)$, where

$$(7.9.1) \qquad T = \frac{D/(k-2)}{W/(n-k)} = \frac{\eta^2 - r^2}{1 - \eta^2} \cdot \frac{n-k}{k-2},$$

r being the correlation coefficient and η the correlation ratio in the sample, as defined in Section 5.2 of Part II.

Illustrative Example 7.7. Examine whether the regression of the yield of dry bark y on the age x of *Cinchona* plants given in illustrative example 5.3 of Part II is linear. Here $n = 157$, $k =$ number of arrays of y's $= 6$, $r = 0.6636$, and $\eta = 0.6687$. Therefore, to test the linearity of regression, we compute

$$T = \frac{\eta^2 - r^2}{1 - \eta^2} \cdot \frac{n-k}{k-2} = 0.464 < F_{4,151}(0.05)$$

so that the deviation of the regression from linearity is not significant at the 5% level.

Test for Assigned Linear Regression on One Variate. When the regression of X_0 on X_1 is linear, $E(X_0 \mid X_1 = x_1) = \alpha + \beta x_1$, it may be of interest to examine whether either or both of the parameters α, β have specified values α_0, β_0. The hypotheses may be put into the following forms:

H_1 : $\alpha = \alpha_0$, $\beta = \beta_0$ (values of both α and β are specified),

H_2 : $\alpha = \alpha_0$ (only α is specified, but not β),

H_3 : $\beta = \beta_0$ (only β is specified, but not α).

Let $\bar{x}_i$ be the means and S_{ij} the corrected ss and sp computed from a sample of size n from the bivariate distribution of X_0 and X_1. Estimates a, b of α, β are given by $a = \bar{x}_0 - b\bar{x}_1$ and $b = S_{01}/S_{11}$. We shall write $R_{00} = S_{00} - S_{01}{}^2/S_{11}$ for the residual sum of squares of X_0 from its linear regression on X_1.

The hypothesis H_1 : $\alpha = \alpha_0$, $\beta = \beta_0$ is rejected at level of significance ϵ if

$$(7.9.2) \qquad T \equiv \frac{\left[\sum_{\lambda=1}^{n} (x_{0\lambda} - \alpha_0 - \beta_0 x_{1\lambda})^2 - R_{00} \right] \Big/ 2}{R_{00}/(n-2)} > F_{2,\,n-2}(\epsilon).$$

Against alternatives $\alpha > \alpha_0$, the hypothesis H_2 : $\alpha = \alpha_0$ is rejected at level of significance ϵ if

$$(7.9.3) \qquad\qquad T \equiv \frac{a - \alpha_0}{s_a} > t_{n-2}(\epsilon),$$

where s_a is the estimated standard error of a, given by

$$s_a{}^2 = \left(\frac{1}{n} + \frac{\bar{x}_1{}^2}{S_{11}} \right) \frac{R_{00}}{n-2} .$$

Similarly, against alternatives $\beta > \beta_0$, the hypothesis H_3 : $\beta = \beta_0$ is rejected at level of significance ϵ if

$$(7.9.4) \qquad\qquad T \equiv \frac{b - \beta_0}{s_b} > t_{n-2}(\epsilon),$$

where s_b is the estimated standard error of b, given by

$$s_b{}^2 = \frac{R_{00}/(n-2)}{S_{11}}.$$

Illustrative Example 7.8. Examine on the basis of the computations done in illustrative example 5.1 of part II whether the regression of the weight of dry jute fiber X_0 on the weight of green plant X_1 can be taken as (a) $x_0 = 0.25 + 0.1x_1$, (b) $x_0 = cx_1$, where c is some suitable constant. Here

$$n = 40, \quad \Sigma x_0 = 159.7, \quad \Sigma x_1 = 2111, \quad \Sigma x_0^2 = 846.75,$$
$$\Sigma x_0 x_1 = 10,766.95, \quad \Sigma x_1^2 = 144,461, \quad S_{00} = 209.148,$$
$$S_{01} = 2338.733, \quad S_{11} = 33,052.975, \quad a = 0.25830,$$
$$b = 0.070757.$$

Therefore $R_{00} = S_{00} - bS_{01} = 43.6663$, $\Sigma(x_0 - 0.25 - 0.1x_1)^2 = 166.17$, and to test whether $x_0 = 0.25 + 0.1x_1$ can be taken as the regression we compute

$$T = \frac{(166.1700 - 43.6663)/2}{43.6663/38} = 53.304^{**},$$

which as a variance ratio with 2 and 38 df is highly significant. So $x_0 = 0.25 + 0.1x_1$ cannot be taken as the equation of the regression line.

To test (b), that is, $\alpha = 0$ in the regression equation $x_0 = \alpha + \beta x_1$, we compute s_a, the standard error of a,

$$s_a = \sqrt{\left[\left(\frac{1}{n} + \frac{\bar{x}_1^2}{S_{11}} \right) \frac{R_{00}}{n-2} \right]} = 0.3543,$$

and then the statistic T is obtained as

$$T = \frac{a - 0}{s_a} = \frac{0.25830}{0.3542} = 0.729 < t_{38}(0.05),$$

which is not significant. So the regression equation may be taken as $x_0 = cx_1$.

Comparison of k Linear Regression Functions. Suppose that k independent samples of sizes $n^{(r)}$, $r = 1, 2, \ldots, k$, are available from k bivariate populations, in each of which the regression of X_0 on X_1 is linear. Let the regression equation of X_0 on X_1 in the rth population be denoted by $\alpha^{(r)} + \beta^{(r)}x_1$. The hypotheses of interest in this connection are as follows.

H_1 : That the regression lines are identical, namely,

$$\alpha^{(1)} = \alpha^{(2)} = \cdots = \alpha^{(k)},$$
$$\beta^{(1)} = \beta^{(2)} = \cdots = \beta^{(k)}.$$

H_2 : That the regression lines have the same intercept on the X_0 axis, that is,

$$\alpha^{(1)} = \alpha^{(2)} = \cdots = \alpha^{(k)}.$$

H_3 : That the regression lines are all parallel, that is,

$$\beta^{(1)} = \beta^{(2)} = \cdots = \beta^{(k)}.$$

The sums, crude ss and sp and corrected ss and sp, computed from the rth sample, will be denoted by $T_i^{(r)}$, $T_{ij}^{(r)}$, $S_{ij}^{(r)}$, respectively, $i, j = 0, 1$; $r = 1, 2, \ldots, k$. Let $n = \sum_{r=1}^{k} n^{(r)}$ denote the total number of observations. We shall also write $T_i = \sum_{r=1}^{k} T_i^{(r)}$, $T_{ij} = \sum_{r=1}^{k} T_{ij}^{(r)}$, $S_{ij} = \sum_{r=1}^{k} S_{ij}^{(r)}$, $i, j = 0, 1$. The residual ss of X_0 in the rth sample will be denoted by $R_{00}^{(r)} = S_{00}^{(r)} - [S_{01}^{(r)}]^2/S_{11}^{(r)}$, and we shall write $R_{00} = \sum_{r=1}^{k} R_{00}^{(r)}$.

The hypothesis H_1 that the regression lines are identical is rejected at level of significance α if

$$(7.9.5) \qquad T \equiv \frac{(R_{00}^* - R_{00})/(2k - 2)}{R_{00}/(n - 2k)} > F_{2k-2, n-2k}(\alpha),$$

where $R_{00}^* = S_{00}^* - (S_{01}^*)^2/S_{11}^*$ and $S_{ij}^* = T_{ij} - T_i T_j/n$.

To test the hypothesis H_2 that the regression lines have a common intercept on the X_0 axis, the procedure is to compute

$$(7.9.6) \qquad T \equiv \frac{\left[T_{00} - aT_0 - \sum_{r=1}^{k} b^{(r)} T_{01}^{(r)} - R_{00} \right] \Big/ (k - 1)}{R_{00}/(n - 2k)},$$

where a and $b^{(r)}$ are the estimates of the common intercept and the slope of the rth regression line, given by

$$(7.9.7) \qquad a = \frac{T_0 - \sum_{r=1}^{k} T_{01}^{(r)} T_1^{(r)}/T_{11}^{(r)}}{n - \sum_{r=1}^{k} [T_1^{(r)}]^2/T_{11}^{(r)}} \quad \text{and} \quad b^{(r)} = \frac{T_{01}^{(r)} - aT_1^{(r)}}{T_{11}^{(r)}},$$

respectively. The hypothesis H_2 is rejected at level of significance α if $T > F_{k-1, n-2k}(\alpha)$.

The hypothesis H_3 that the regression lines are parallel is rejected at level of significance α if

$$(7.9.8) \qquad T \equiv \frac{\left\{ \dfrac{S_{01}^2}{S_{11}} - \sum_{r=1}^{k} \dfrac{[S_{01}^{(r)}]^2}{S_{11}^{(r)}} \right\} \Big/ (k - 1)}{R_{00}/(n - 2k)} > F_{k-1, n-2k}(\alpha).$$

Illustrative Example 7.9. Table 7.22 gives the means and the corrected sums of squares and products of the systolic blood pressure in millimeters of mercury y and the age in years x of three groups of persons. Examine whether the linear regression equations of y on x for the three groups are identical.

We write the regression equation for the ith group in the form $y = a^{(i)} + b^{(i)}x$, where $a^{(i)} = \bar{y}^{(i)} - b^{(i)}\bar{x}^{(i)}$ and $b^{(i)} = S_{xy}^{(i)}/S_{xx}^{(i)}$, and denote the residual ss by $R_{yy}^{(i)} = S_{yy}^{(i)} - b^{(i)}S_{xy}^{(i)}$. Then we have Table 7.23. To

TABLE 7.22

MEANS AND CORRECTED SUMS OF SQUARES AND PRODUCTS FOR THREE GROUPS

Group i	Sample size $n^{(i)}$	Mean $\bar{x}^{(i)}$	Mean $\bar{y}^{(i)}$	Corrected sums of squares and products $S_{xx}^{(i)}$	Corrected sums of squares and products $S_{xy}^{(i)}$	Corrected sums of squares and products $S_{yy}^{(i)}$
1	80	26.625	90.375	137.875	74.125	127.875
2	120	28.000	92.167	390.000	124.000	515.667
3	70	28.857	90.857	94.857	54.287	390.857
			Total	622.732	252.412	1034.339

TABLE 7.23

REGRESSION CONSTANTS AND RESIDUAL SS FOR THREE GROUPS

Group i	Regression $a^{(i)}$	Constants $b^{(i)}$	Residual ss $R_{yy}^{(i)}$	df
1	76.0614	0.5376	88.025	78
2	83.2658	0.3179	476.247	118
3	74.3421	0.5723	359.789	68
		Total $R_{yy} = 924.061$		$= 264$

examine whether the regression lines are identical, we have to compute the means, the corrected sums of squares, and the products for all the $n = \Sigma n^{(i)} = 270$ observations combined. Thus, we have for the means:

$$\bar{x}^* = \frac{\Sigma n^{(i)}\bar{x}^{(i)}}{n} = 27.8148, \quad \bar{y}^* = \frac{\Sigma n^{(i)}\bar{y}^{(i)}}{n} = 91.2964;$$

and for the corrected sums of squares and products:

$$S_{xx}^* = \Sigma S_{xx}^{(i)} + \Sigma n^{(i)}[\bar{x}^{(i)}]^2 - n\bar{x}^2 = 815.797,$$

$$S_{xy}^* = \Sigma S_{xy}^{(i)} + \Sigma n^{(i)}\bar{x}^{(i)}\bar{y}^{(i)} - n\bar{x}\,\bar{y} = 326.915,$$

$$S_{yy}^* = \Sigma S_{yy}^{(i)} + \Sigma n^{(i)}[\bar{y}^{(i)}]^2 - n\bar{y}^2 = 1206.151.$$

Thus, for the regression constants, we obtain $a^* = \bar{y}^* - b^*\bar{x}^* = 80.1502$, and $b^* = S_{xy}^*/S_{xx}^* = 0.40073$; the residual sum of squares is $R_{yy}^* = S_{yy}^* - b^*S_{xy}^* = 1075.707$ with $\nu^* = 270 - 2 = 268$ df.

We then have the variance ratio

$$T = \frac{(R_{yy}^* - R_{yy})/(\nu^* - \nu)}{R_{yy}/\nu} = \frac{151.646/4}{924.061/264} = \frac{37.9115}{3.500} = 10.832^{**},$$

which with 4 and 264 df is highly significant. The regression lines cannot therefore be taken as identical.

To examine whether they are parallel, we estimate the common regression coefficient from

$$b** = \frac{\Sigma S_{xy}^{(i)}}{\Sigma S_{xx}^{(i)}} = \frac{252.412}{622.732} = 0.40533,$$

and the residual sum of squares in this case is given by

$$R_{yy}** = \Sigma S_{yy}^{(i)} - b**\Sigma S_{xy}^{(i)} = 932.089,$$

which has $\nu** = 270 - 4 = 266$ df. The variance ratio is

$$T = \frac{(R_{yy}** - R_{yy})/(\nu** - \nu)}{R_{yy}/\nu} = \frac{8.028/2}{924.061/264} = \frac{4.014}{3.500} = 1.147$$

$$< F_{2264}(0.05),$$

which is not significant. The rates of increase in systolic blood pressure with age for the three groups are not thus significantly different.

Tests of Multiple Regression Function. Let $(x_{0\lambda}, x_{1\lambda}, \ldots, x_{p\lambda})$, $\lambda = 1, 2, \ldots, n$, be n independent observations on the $p + 1$ variates X_0, $X_1, \ldots, X_p$. The conditional expectation of X_0, given that $X_1 = x_1, \ldots,$ $X_p = x_p$, is assumed to be linear of the form

$$\alpha + \beta_1 x_1 + \cdots + \beta_p x_p.$$

Let the means and the corrected ss and sp be denoted by $\bar{x}_i$ and S_{ij}, $i, j = 0, 1, 2, \ldots, p$, respectively. Then estimates $a, b_1, \ldots, b_p$ of $\alpha, \beta_1, \ldots, \beta_p$ are given by

$$a = \bar{x}_0 - b_1\bar{x}_1 - \cdots - b_p\bar{x}_p,$$

and $b_1, \ldots, b_p$ are the solutions of the equations

$$b_1 S_{i1} + b_2 S_{i2} + \cdots + b_p S_{ip} = S_{i0}, \quad i = 1, 2, \ldots, p.$$

The residual sum of squares of X_0 after elimination of the effects of $X_1, X_2, \ldots, X_p$ is given by

$$R_{00}^{(p)} = S_{00} - b_1 S_{01} - \cdots - b_p S_{0p}.$$

Let us denote by S the matrix $((S_{ij}))$, $i, j = 1, 2, \ldots, p$, and let the elements of the inverse matrix be denoted by $S^{-1} = ((S^{ij}))$. The dispersion matrix of $b_1, b_2, \ldots, b_p$ is $((S^{ij}))\sigma^2$, and $\bar{x}_0$ is uncorrelated with the b_i's.

The hypothesis that a particular regression coefficient, say β_i, has a specified value β_i^0 against alternatives $\beta_i > \beta_i^0$ is rejected at level of significance ϵ if

(7.9.9) $$T = \frac{b_i - \beta_i^0}{\sqrt{[S^{ii}R_{00}^{(p)}/(n - p - 1)]}} > t_{n-p-1}(\epsilon).$$

The hypothesis that all the regression coefficients have specified values $\beta_1 = \beta_1{}^0, \beta_2 = \beta_2{}^0, \ldots, \beta_p = \beta_p{}^0$ is rejected at level of significance ϵ if

$$(7.9.10) \qquad T = \frac{\displaystyle\sum_{i=1}^{p}\sum_{j=1}^{p}(b_i - \beta_i{}^0)(b_j - \beta_j{}^0)S_{ij}/p}{R_{00}^{(p)}/(n - p - 1)} > F_{p,n-p-1}(\epsilon).$$

7.10 ANALYSIS OF COVARIANCE

Suppose that we have under study m factors, the effects of which are denoted by the parameters $\theta_1, \theta_2, \ldots, \theta_m$, and n observations $y_1, y_2, \ldots, y_n$ from which to estimate these parameters. When all other factors likely to affect the observations are held constant, the assumption is that $y_i = a_{i1}\theta_1 + a_{i2}\theta_2 + \cdots + a_{im}\theta_m + \epsilon_i$, where a_{ij}'s are given constants and ϵ_i's errors of observation. If ϵ_i's are regarded as independent normal variates, each with mean zero and a common unknown variance, we obtain the fixed-effects model for analysis of variance.

In many situations, however, it may be impracticable or uneconomic to keep all other factors constant; then variation in the levels of these factors will tend to inflate the error. If measurements are available on these extraneous variables, or concomitant variates as they are called, it is possible to correct for variations in them by a technique called *analysis of covariance*.

Suppose that there are p concomitant variates, $X_1, X_2, \ldots, X_p$ and that their values are $x_{1i}, x_{2i}, \ldots, x_{pi}$, respectively, for the ith observation. It is assumed that these contribute linearly to the error, so that $\epsilon_i = \beta_1 x_{1i} + \beta_2 x_{2i} + \cdots + \beta_p x_{pi} + e_i$, where e_i is the residual error, after eliminating the contribution of the concomitant variates. The assumption is that $\beta_1, \beta_2, \ldots, \beta_p$ are unknown parameters and $e_1, e_2, \ldots, e_n$ are independently distributed normal variates, each with mean zero and common unknown variance σ^2. The model thus becomes

$$(7.10.1) \qquad E(y_i) = \sum_{j=1}^{m} a_{ij}\theta_j + \sum_{t=1}^{p} \beta_t x_{ti}.$$

Starting from 7.9.1, which is a fixed-effects normal model, we can use the methods given in Section 7.1 for estimating or testing hypotheses about the parameters $\theta_1, \theta_2, \ldots, \theta_m$. The computations, however, can be greatly simplified by using the following technique.

Let $A = ((a_{ij}))$, $X = ((x_{ti}))$. We assume that rank $(A) = r$ and rank of the augmented matrix $(A:X') = r + p$, so that $n \geq r + p$.

Let

$$Q_{j0} = \sum_{i=1}^{n} a_{ij}y_i, \quad Q_{jt} = \sum_{i=1}^{n} a_{ij}x_{ti}, \quad c_{jk} = \sum_{i=1}^{n} a_{ij}a_{ik}$$
$$(t = 1, 2, \ldots, p; \quad j, k = 1, 2, \ldots, m).$$

Let $\theta_{1t}, \theta_{2t}, \ldots, \theta_{mt}$ be a solution of the normal equations

$$(7.10.2) \quad c_{j1}\theta_1 + c_{j2}\theta_2 + \cdots + c_{jm}\theta_m = Q_{jt}, \quad j = 1, 2, \ldots, m,$$

for $t = 0, 1, 2, \ldots, p$.

We note that, if concomitant variates were absent, $\theta_{10}, \theta_{20}, \ldots, \theta_{m0}$ would be the least-squares solution for $\theta_1, \theta_2, \ldots, \theta_m$. Similarly, $\theta_{1t}, \theta_{2t}, \ldots, \theta_{mt}$ may be interpreted as the least-squares solution for $\theta_1, \theta_2, \ldots, \theta_m$ if, instead of y, the observations on X_t are substituted.

Then we compute the sum of products (sp) matrix due to error whose elements are

$$(7.10.3) \quad E_{tu} = P_{tu} - \sum_{j=1}^{m} Q_{jt}\theta_{ju}, \quad t, u = 0, 1, 2, \ldots, p,$$

where

$$P_{00} = \sum_{i=1}^{n} y_i^2, \quad P_{0t} = \sum_{i=1}^{n} y_i x_{ti}, \quad \text{and} \quad P_{tu} = \sum_{i=1}^{n} x_{ti} x_{ui}, \quad t, u = 1, 2, \ldots, p.$$

Estimates $b_1, b_2, \ldots, b_p$ of $\beta_1, \beta_2, \ldots, \beta_p$ are obtained by solving the equations

$$(7.10.4) \quad E_{0t} = E_{t1}\beta_1 + E_{t2}\beta_2 + \cdots + E_{tp}\beta_p, \quad t = 1, 2, \ldots, p.$$

The least-squares estimates of θ_j are finally obtained as

$$(7.10.5) \quad \hat{\theta}_j = \hat{\theta}_{j0} - \sum_{t=1}^{p} b_t \hat{\theta}_{jt}, \quad j = 1, 2, \ldots, m.$$

Then any estimable linear parametric function, say $\Theta = \sum_{j=1}^{m} l_j \theta_j$, would be estimated by $\hat{\Theta} = \sum_{j=1}^{m} l_j \hat{\theta}_j$. The variance of $\hat{\Theta}$ can be computed by first expressing it in the form $\hat{\Theta} = \sum_{j=1}^{m} \lambda_j Q_{j0} + \sum_{t=1}^{p} d_t E_{0t}$ as a linear function of $Q_{10}, Q_{20}, \ldots, Q_{m0}$ and $E_{01}, E_{02}, \ldots, E_{0p}$. Then

$$(7.10.6) \quad V[\hat{\Theta}] = \left(\sum_{j=1}^{m} l_j \lambda_j + \sum_{t=1}^{p} \sum_{u=1}^{p} d_t d_u E_{tu} \right) \sigma^2.$$

An estimate of σ^2 is then given by

$$(7.10.7) \quad \frac{E_{00}{}^*}{n - r - p},$$

where $E_{00}{}^*$ is the residual error sum of squares given by $E_{00}{}^* = E_{00} - \sum_{t=1}^{p} b_t E_{0t}$, which has $n - r - p$ degrees of freedom.

To test simultaneously the hypothesis H that the given linearly independent estimable parametric functions Θ_k have specified values $\Theta_k{}^0$, $k = 1, 2, \ldots, h$, the procedure is to assume the hypothesis to be true and to compute the sp matrix due to error under H; call that $((S_{tu}))$, $t, u = 0, 1, 2, \ldots, p$. One way of computing this is to get the sp matrix $((H_{tu}))$

due to the hypothesis, and then $S_{tu} = T_{tu} + H_{tu}$ by addition. The residual error sum of squares under the hypothesis S_{00}^* is then computed as

(7.10.8)
$$S_{00}^* = S_{00} - \sum_{t=1}^{p} \beta_t^* S_{0t},$$

where $\beta_1^*, \beta_2^*, \ldots, \beta_p^*$ are obtained by solving the equations

(7.10.9) $\quad S_{0t} = \beta_1 S_{1t} + \beta_2 S_{2t} + \cdots + \beta_p S_{pt}, \qquad t = 1, 2, \ldots, p.$

The hypothesis H is rejected at level of significance α if

(7.10.10)
$$T \equiv \frac{(S_{00}^* - E_{00}^*)/h}{E_{00}^*/(n - r - p)} > F_{h, n-r-p}(\alpha).$$

The concomitant variates are useful only if the regression coefficients are non-zero. To examine the hypothesis $H: \quad \beta_1 = \beta_2 = \cdots = \beta_p = 0$, we compute

(7.10.11)
$$T \equiv \frac{(E_{00} - E_{00}^*)/p}{E_{00}^*/(n - r - p)}.$$

The hypothesis is rejected at level of significance α if T, defined by 7.9.11, exceeds $F_{p, n-r-p}(\alpha)$.

The computations are usually presented in the form of a table such as Table 7.24.

TABLE 7.24

ANALYSIS OF VARIANCE AND COVARIANCE

Source	df	sp matrix	Regression coefficients	Residual ss	Residual df
Hypothesis	h	H_{tu}			
Error	$n - r$	E_{tu}	$\hat{\beta}_t$	E_{00}^*	$n - r - p$
Error under hypothesis	$n - r + h$	$S_{tu} = H_{tu} + E_{tu}$	$\hat{\beta}_t^*$	S_{00}^*	$n - r + h - p$

Illustrative Example 7.10. The data in Table 7.25 relate to the initial weights (in pounds) and growth rates (in pounds per week) of 15 pigs classified according to pen and type of feed given. Examine the differences between the three types of feed A, B, C in their effect on the growth of pigs, correcting for the differences in the initial weights of the animals.

The initial weight is the concomitant variable here, and we denote it by x. The growth rate is the variable under study, and we denote it by y. For these two-way classified data with one observation in each cell, the sources of variation are due to (a) pens, with $5 - 1 = 4$ df, (b) feeds, with

STATISTICAL INFERENCE

TABLE 7.25
Initial Weight and Growth Rate of Pigs

Pen	Type of feed	Initial weight (lb)	Growth rate (lb/week)
I	A	48	9.94
	B	48	10.00
	C	48	9.75
II	B	32	9.24
	C	28	8.66
	A	32	9.48
III	C	33	7.63
	A	35	9.32
	B	41	9.34
IV	C	50	10.37
	A	48	10.56
	B	46	9.68
V	B	37	9.67
	A	32	8.82
	C	30	8.57

$3 - 1 = 2$ df, and (c) error, with $(5 - 1) \times (3 - 1) = 8$ df. We then get Table 7.26 of analysis of variance and covariance.

This is computed in the following way. If we ignore the concomitant variable x, the analysis of variance of y for two-way classified data with one observation per cell can be carried out as described in Section 7.4. This is presented in the third column of Table 7.26 under yy. The fifth column is obtained in an identical manner, using x's instead of y's. To

TABLE 7.26
Analysis of Variance and Covariance

Source	df		Sum of squares and products	
		yy	yx	xx
Pens	4	4.5494	53.8607	823.0667
Feeds	2	1.2399	4.0920	22.8000
Error	8	2.1704	9.0313	56.5333
Total	14	7.9597	66.9840	902.4000

compute the components of the sum of products (sp) yx all that we have to do is to replace in the corresponding formula for the ss of y one of the y's by x. For example, the formula for the total ss of y is $\Sigma y^2 - (\Sigma y)^2/n$, where n is the total number of observations, 15 in this case. The formula for the total sp of yx is thus $\Sigma yx - (\Sigma y)(\Sigma x)/n$, which in this case gives 66.9840. Similarly, the sp due to feeds is given by $\sum_{i=1}^{3} T_i(y)T_i(x) - (\Sigma y)(\Sigma x)/n$, where $T_i(x)$ stands for the total of x for the ith feed. This comes out as 4.0920. The component due to pens is similarly computed. Finally the sp due to error is obtained by subtraction.

In the present problem, we have only one concomitant variable, and therefore only one regression coefficient is to be estimated. This is obtained by taking the ratio of the sp of yx to the ss of x. If we are interested in examining the hypothesis that the feeds are not significantly different in their effects, the further computations required can be arranged as shown in Table 7.27.

TABLE 7.27

COMPUTATION OF RESIDUAL SS

Source	df	xy	yx	xx	b	Residual ss	Residual df	Mean square
Feeds	2	1.2399	4.0920	22.8000	...	...	...	...
Error	8	$E_{00} = 2.1704$	9.0313	56.5333	0.1598	$E_{00}^* = 0.7276$	7	0.1039
Feeds + error	10	3.4103	13.1233	79.3333	0.1654	$E_{00}^* = 1.2394$	9	
Feeds (adjusted)	...	...	...	...	...	0.5118	2	0.2559

To test whether the concomitant variable is useful, that is, whether the regression coefficient is zero, we compute T from formula 7.10.11 and get

$$T = \frac{2.1704 - 0.7276}{0.7276/7} = 13.89 * > F_{1,7}(0.01),$$

which is highly significant. To test the significance of the feed differences we find from formula 7.10.10

$$T = \frac{(1.2394 - 0.7276)/2}{0.7276/7} = 2.46 < F_{2,7}(0.05),$$

which is not significant.

7.11 EXERCISES

Linear hypotheses

7.1. Consider the results of the weighing experiment given in exercise 3.3.

(a) A question was raised whether or not the chemical balance was adjusted for the zero point before the weights were taken. Examine whether the given data reveal that the observer failed to adjust the balance.

(b) The three objects *A*, *B*, and *C* are alleged to be all the pieces into which an object weighing 20 gm accidentally broke. Do you think that the statement is true, or are any pieces missing?

7.2. On the basis of the data given in exercise 3.2 examine whether the points *C* and *D* divide the straight line *AB* in the ratios $AC:CD:DB = 3:2:4$.

One-way classification

7.3. In one evening, three persons suspected to be driving under the influence of liquor were stopped and blood samples taken from each were sent to the laboratory. Five determinations on percentage of alcohol in the blood were made on each sample. According to law, drivers who have more than 0.05% alcohol in their blood should be sent to jail.

Do the data in Table 7.28 suggest that all three drivers were equally intoxicated as determined by percentage of alcohol in their blood? Should any or all of them be sent to jail?

TABLE 7.28

DETERMINATION OF PERCENTAGE OF ALCOHOL IN
BLOOD SAMPLES OF THREE DRIVERS

Person	Alcohol (%) in blood sample				
	1	2	3	4	5
1	0.08	0.06	0.06	0.07	0.09
2	0.14	0.18	0.16	0.15	0.12
3	0.00	0.02	0.01	0.02	0.03

7.4. Twenty samples were taken from a container of a particular brand of hydrogenated vegetable oil. Each of four analysts was given five different samples and asked to determine the melting point. The results are given in Table 7.29.

TABLE 7.29

MELTING POINT OF HYDROGENATED VEGETABLE OIL

Analyst	Individual determinations of melting points (°F)				
1	93.60,	94.64,	96.30,	93.62,	93.51
2	96.44,	96.53,	98.38,	97.00,	97.63
3	92.57,	94.01,	92.49,	93.29,	90.87
4	95.55,	95.90,	94.25,	95.80,	96.21

Examine whether the analysts are consistent in their determinations of the melting point.

7.5. The data in Table 7.30 relate to lives in hours of sample lamps taken from four batches of electric lamps. Test whether the batches differ among themselves in average length of life.

TABLE 7.30

LIFE OF ELECTRIC LAMPS

Batch	Sample size	Life (hr) of individual lamp						
A	7	1600,	1610,	1650,	1680,	1700,	1720,	1800
B	5	1580,	1640,	1640,	1700,	1750		
C	8	1500,	1550,	1600,	1620,	1640,	1660,	1740, 1820
D	6	1510,	1520,	1530,	1570,	1600,	1680	

Two-way classification

7.6. In an electroplating experiment five nickel rods put into a metallic clamp at five different positions were jointly immersed in the electrolyte, and the thickness of coating in microns was observed at three different heights H_1, H_2, H_3 on each of these five rods R_1, R_2, R_3, R_4, R_5. The results are given in Table 7.31 (Hamaker's data).

Examine how the thickness of coating deposited varies with position and height.

TABLE 7.31

THICKNESS OF ALUMINUM OXIDE COATING

Height	Thickness (μ) of coatings on rods				
	R_1	R_2	R_3	R_4	R_5
H_1	125	130	128	134	143
H_2	126	150	127	124	118
H_3	130	155	168	159	138

7.7. Biggs and Macmillan (1948) compared five doctors A, B, C, D, E in the counting of red blood cells. Ten different pipettes and counting chambers were used, each doctor making one count with each. Table 7.32 records the fifty counts, all on the same sample of blood.

Analyze the data and write a report on your findings.

TABLE 7.32

NUMBERS OF RED BLOOD CELLS COUNTED BY FIVE
DOCTORS USING TEN DIFFERENT PIPETTES AND
COUNTING CHAMBERS

Doctor	I	II	III	IV	V	VI	VII	VIII	IX	X
					Pipette and counting chamber					
A	427	372	418	440	349	484	430	416	449	464
B	434	420	385	472	415	420	415	396	439	424
C	480	421	473	496	474	411	472	423	502	488
D	451	369	500	464	444	410	422	396	459	471
E	462	453	450	520	489	409	508	347	440	391

Source: D. J. Finney, *Experimental Design and Its Statistical Basis*, University of Chicago Press, Chicago, 1955.

7.8. C. R. Hicks, *Industrial Quality Control*, Vol. 13, p. 5 (1956), reports the results of an experiment conducted to study the effect of glass type and phosphor type on the brightness of a television-tube. The measured variable is the current in microamperes necessary to produce a certain brightness, the larger this current, the poorer the tube-screen characteristics. The results of the experiment are given in Table 7.33.

Analyze the data and give your recommendations.

TABLE 7.33

CURRENT (IN MICROAMPERES) NECESSARY TO
PRODUCE A CERTAIN BRIGHTNESS ON THE TELEVISION SCREEN

| Glass type | Phosphor type | | |
	A	B	C
1	280	300	270
	290	310	285
	285	295	290
2	230	260	220
	235	240	225
	240	235	230

7.9. Mahalanobis conducted an experiment involving three rice varieties in combination with no inorganic fertilizer (control) and two inorganic fertilizers, ammonium sulphate at 30.4 lb per plot and ammonium phosphate at 40.5 lb per plot. There were six replicates, a replicate being a block of nine plots (12′ × 39′ plots were used) to which the nine treatments were allocated at random. The yields of the plots are recorded in Table 7.34 in chattaks per plot.

Make an analysis of variance of the data and perform tests of significance to detect differences between fertilizers, differences between varieties, and interaction between varieties and fertilizers.

TABLE 7.34

Yield of Grain from Paddy Grown in 39′ × 12′
Plots (in chattaks per plot)
1 chattak = 58 gm approx.

Treatment		Block					
Variety	Fertilizer	1	2	3	4	5	6
Red Aus	Ammophos	112	128	118	128	92	152
	Ammonium sulphate	168	116	144	100	100	80
	Control	106	84	68	156	156	128
Kashiful	Ammophos	112	81	108	96	53	48
	Ammonium sulphate	61	98	58	86	65	98
	Control	97	86	92	80	99	66
Dudkalama	Ammophos	134	112	116	114	101	128
	Ammonium sulphate	125	106	110	102	56	110
	Control	62	60	99	90	58	87

Source: P. C. Mahalanobis, Statistical notes for agricultural workers. No. 4—Rice and potato experiments at Sriniketan, 1931, *Indian Journal of Agricultural Science*, Vol. 2.

7.10. Table 7.35 gives certain statistics relating to the lactation yields x of 168 dairy cows classified according to how they were milked and to whether or not they have calved before. In each cell, the first figure given is the number n of cows, the second the sum Σx of the yields of these cows during the lactation period, and the third the sum of squares Σx^2 of the yields (uncorrected).

Is there evidence that yield is lowered by machine milking for (a) first calvers and (b) others? In case there is evidence of decrease in yield for both the first calvers and others, examine whether the amount of decrease

TABLE 7.35
STATISTICS OF LACTATION YIELD

Method of milking	First calvers	Others
Hand milked	$n = 34$ $\Sigma x = 4771$ $\Sigma x^2 = 747{,}243$	$n = 50$ $\Sigma x = 8357$ $\Sigma x^2 = 1{,}475{,}865$
Machine milked	$n = 34$ $\Sigma x = 4197$ $\Sigma x^2 = 591{,}795$	$n = 50$ $\Sigma x = 6783$ $\Sigma x^2 = 1{,}000{,}048$

is the same in both cases. Do first calvers yield less milk than the other cows?

7.11. Table 7.36 gives the mean values of nasal height and in parentheses the numbers of skulls excavated from three different strata by three different observers, as well as the total corrected sum of squares.

Analyze the data and give your comments on the differences between the strata and between the observers in respect of the mean nasal height.

TABLE 7.36
MEAN VALUES OF NASAL HEIGHT (AND THE NUMBER OF SKULLS)

Observer	Stratum		
	S_1	S_2	S_3
O_1	51.00 (21)	49.14 (32)	50.75 (18)
O_2	46.83 (42)	45.40 (51)	47.82 (36)
O_3	48.76 (25)	46.48 (45)	46.23 (40)

Total corrected sum of squares with 309 df = 5398.4206.

Source: C. R. Rao, *Advanced Statistical Methods in Biometric Research*, John Wiley & Sons, New York, 1952.

7.12. Each of five different samples of earthworm casting was divided into a number of portions. Each portion was given to one of two analysts for determination of percentage ash content. The results are given in Table 7.37.

TABLE 7.37

RESULTS OF DETERMINATION OF PERCENTAGE ASH CONTENT
IN FIVE SAMPLES OF EARTHWORM CASTINGS BY TWO ANALYSIS

Analyst	Sample				
	1	2	3	4	5
1	57.30	58.19	56.21	57.01	57.31
	57.65	56.59	46.15	55.35	57.90
	57.70	57.57	56.03	56.83	
		57.28		57.37	
2	56.81	58.78	57.52	58.08	58.41
	58.44	56.65	56.40	55.35	57.90
	58.00	57.88	57.45		57.32
	58.31		57.16		
			56.52		

Analyze the data to detect differences, if any, between samples and between analysts.

7.13. To investigate whether use of different methods of instruction affects the performance of the examinees in a general intelligence test, an experiment was carried out as follows. Three higher secondary schools— A (private), B (government), and C (private missionary)—were selected, and from each school a number of boys of about the same level of general intelligence were selected and divided into four groups. During the administration of the test, four different methods of instruction— M_1 (written in English), M_2 (written in Hindi), M_3 (read out in English), M_4 (read out in Hindi)—were tried, one on each group. The scores of the examinees are given in Table 7.38.

Analyze the data to find out whether results for the different methods of instruction are different. If so, find out the method which leads to best performance. Does the best method differ for the different schools

7.14. The acetylcholine content of strips of a guinea pig's small intestine is increased if the strips are subjected to incubation in Tyrode's solution. It is possible that, if the incubation is accompanied by the addition of potassium chloride solution, the acetylcholine yield is further increased. A series of five experiments, each involving a different guinea pig, was performed to investigate the effect of this addition of potassium chloride. In each experiment three strips of intestine were used as controls. One of these control strips was extracted without incubation to give the acetylcholine content before incubation, and the other two control strips were

TABLE 7.38

SCORES OF CANDIDATES FROM THREE DIFFERENT SCHOOLS
USING DIFFERENT METHODS OF INSTRUCTION

| School | Method of instruction | | | |
	M_1	M_2	M_3	M_4
A	47.3	53.0	42.2	53.7
	60.0	41.0	54.1	55.8
	66.4	42.2	52.5	56.1
	68.1	57.3	57.8	67.3
	64.8	54.0	54.5	72.6
B	58.4	47.1	57.5	52.9
	63.1	43.2	40.2	53.3
	54.0	53.0	32.0	51.6
C	73.1	46.1	55.7	66.4
	61.5	55.2	48.2	40.2
	61.9	49.5	58.6	58.1
	66.5	49.0	55.2	64.6

incubated without the addition of potassium chloride. The remaining strips used in the experiment were incubated and also had potassium chloride solution added. It may be assumed that intestinal strips from the same animal have the same acetylcholine content before incubation. The experimental results are given in Table 7.39.

Analyze the data with the object of deciding whether the presence of potassium chloride affects the increase of yield of acetylcholine from strips of guinea pig intestine when they are incubated.

TABLE 7.39

YIELD OF ACETYLCHOLINE (IN MICROGRAMS ACETYLCHOLINE
PER GRAM OF TISSUE)

| Experiment | Control strips | | Incubated strips with potassium chloride (3 mg/cc) added |
	Not incubated	Incubated	
1	6.0	8.5, 9.0	10.3
2	6.0	8.1, 8.7	8.8
3	7.0	8.8, 8.7	12.0
4	7.4	8.8, 12.6	9.9, 11.0
5	9.0	9.9, 11.1	12.5, 12.0

Three-way classification

7.15. The data in Table 7.40 on the lengths of steel bars were obtained from an experiment designed to study the effect of two heat treatments W and L, three times: (1) 8 A.M., (2) 11 A.M., and (3) 3 P.M., and four machines A, B, C, and D. For each combination of these three factors, the lengths of four bars were measured to the nearest thousandth of an inch. These measurements are expressed in the table as deviation from 4.380 in. multiplied by 1000.

Analyze the data and write your comments.

TABLE 7.40

LENGTHS OF STEEL BARS (IN TRANSFORMED UNITS)

	Heat treatment W				Heat treatment L			
	Machine				Machine			
Time	A	B	C	D	A	B	C	D
1	6	7	1	6	4	6	−1	4
	9	9	2	6	6	5	0	5
	1	5	0	7	0	3	0	5
	3	5	4	3	1	4	1	4
2	6	8	3	7	3	6	2	9
	3	7	2	9	1	4	0	4
	1	4	1	11	1	1	1	6
	−1	8	0	6	−2	3	−1	3
3	5	10	−1	10	6	8	0	4
	4	11	2	5	0	7	−2	3
	9	6	6	4	3	10	4	7
	6	4	1	8	7	0	−4	0

Source: W. D. Baten, *Industrial Quality Control*, Vol. 12, p. 8 (1956).

Hierarchal classification

7.16. Two methods, an old and a new, of loading a gun are to be compared in respect to the number of rounds loaded per minute. The men used for loading the gun are classified into three groups: (I) the slight men, (II) the average, and (III) the heavy and more rugged type, with three teams in each group, each team loading the gun twice. The results are given in Table 7.41.

Analyze the data and give your comments.

TABLE 7.41

GUN-LOADING EXPERIMENTS: ROUNDS LOADED PER MINUTE

| | Group I | | | Group II | | | Group III | | |
| | Team | | | Team | | | Team | | |
Method	1	2	3	4	5	6	7	8	9
New	20.2	26.2	23.8	22.0	22.6	22.9	23.1	22.9	21.8
	24.1	26.9	24.9	23.5	24.6	25.0	22.9	23.7	23.5
Old	14.2	18.0	12.5	14.1	14.0	13.7	14.1	12.2	12.7
	16.2	19.1	15.4	16.1	18.1	16.0	16.1	13.8	15.1

Source: C. R. Hicks, *Industrial Quality Control*, Vol. 13, p. 13 (1956).

Mixed model

7.17. An experiment was conducted in three villages selected at random to compare three varieties of rice *A*, *B*, and *C*. In each village three plots were sown with the same variety. Table 7.42 gives the yield rate in maunds per acre.

Examine whether the yield rates of the different varieties differ from village to village. Prescribe the best variety, if any.

TABLE 7.42

YIELD OF PADDY (IN MAUNDS PER ACRE)
1 maund = 82 lb approx.

| | Village | | |
Variety	1	2	3
A	19.1	36.5	14.0
	15.1	41.2	14.8
	16.7	38.5	23.6
B	34.5	45.4	17.4
	38.1	43.2	15.6
	35.4	45.7	18.7
C	31.2	53.8	31.0
	22.8	52.6	29.4
	34.5	51.7	35.4

TABLE 7.43

RECORD OF MEASUREMENTS ON STATURE (IN MILLIMETERS)

Serial no.	Investigator B				Investigator M			
	Evening		Morning		Evening		Morning	
1	1717	1723	1727	1728	1724	1717	1730	1730
2	1528	1531	1535	1538	1526	1529	1540	1540
3	1454	1451	1462	1462	1454	1451	1463	1462
4	1778	1775	1783	1780	1775	1778	1783	1784
5	1664	1663	1671	1669	1668	1673	1672	1672
6	1573	1569	1580	1581	1572	1570	1583	1583
7	1662	1664	1673	1672	1667	1665	1676	1674
8	1709	1705	1722	1718	1709	1711	1723	1724
9	1633	1633	1648	1647	1639	1639	1646	1645
10	1782	1780	1796	1793	1782	1783	1793	1793
11	1815	1816	1823	1825	1814	1811	1826	1827
12	1788	1783	1804	1801	1788	1789	1700	1801
13	1729	1727	1739	1741	1732	1731	1746	1744
14	1711	1712	1722	1720	1713	1710	1721	1720
15	1714	1713	1725	1729	1723	1719	1728	1731
16	1743	1740	1752	1754	1744	1744	1753	1756
17	1715	1714	1722	1725	1718	1720	1728	1727
18	1593	1589	1589	1596	1595	1592	1596	1602
19	1747	1744	1755	1753	1748	1749	1758	1759
20	1663	1660	1669	1670	1662	1665	1679	1678
21	1676	1675	1688	1687	1678	1679	1689	1691
22	1678	1678	1687	1685	1686	1682	1691	1692
23	1610	1610	1620	1617	1617	1617	1620	1626
24	1665	1668	1679	1678	1669	1671	1679	1680
25	1552	1549	1554	1555	1551	1549	1560	1560
26	1694	1692	1702	1702	1699	1701	1706	1708
27	1619	1615	1631	1632	1621	1621	1634	1634
28	1583	1581	1586	1587	1579	1583	1588	1587
29	1587	1591	1598	1596	1593	1591	1600	1601
30	1583	1582	1591	1589	1585	1584	1596	1593
31	1709	1708	1717	1716	1710	1710	1722	1723
32	1792	1794	1803	1804	1797	1797	1812	1811
33	1619	1618	1622	1624	1621	1620	1624	1626
34	1692	1694	1701	1705	1695	1697	1708	1707
35	1687	1688	1694	1691	1683	1686	1693	1693
36	1779	1783	1790	1794	1785	1781	1798	1799
37	1628	1626	1642	1640	1629	1632	1646	1646
38	1672	1669	1674	1673	1665	1667	1679	1683
39	1637	1638	1649	1645	1645	1646	1649	1648
40	1609	1607	1618	1619	1609	1608	1623	1620
41	1721	1720	1728	1726	1722	1722	1738	1728

Source: D. N. Majumdar and C. R. Rao, Bengal anthropometric survey, 1945: a statistical study, *Sankhya*, Vol. 19.

7.18. In order to examine whether any difference exists between statures in the morning and in the evening and to estimate the actual magnitude if it exists, Rao (1958) conducted the following experiment.

Measurements on 41 students of a class, belonging to the age group 20–25, were taken by two investigators B and M. The evening measurements were taken between 6:30 and 8:30 P.M., and the morning measurements on the following day between 6.30 and 8.30 A.M. Each investigator measured the stature of each student twice in the evening and twice in the morning. One of the investigators, B, was a trained anthropologist, while M, a student of statistics, learned the technique from B only two weeks before the experiment. Both investigators used the same measuring rod. Standing height up to the vertex was determined correct to the nearest millimeter. The data collected for this experiment are given in Table 7.43.

Make an analysis of variance of the data and test for the significance of differences between times, investigators, and interaction between time and investigators, using appropriate error mean squares. Give your comments on the need for standardization of anthropometric measurements.

Regression

7.19–7.20. On the basis of the data given in exercises 5.7 and 5.8 of Part II, obtain the standard error of the estimated average value of Y when X has a given value, say x. Use these results to set up 95% confidence limits on (a) average abrasion loss for specimens of synthetic rubber of hardness 80, and (b) average achievement score of students getting 50 on the psychological test.

7.21–7.25. Examine whether the linear regression functions fitted in exercises 5.13–5.17 are adequate. In each case where linear regression is inadequate, fit a polynomial regression equation of the appropriate degree.

7.26. The statistics required for computing the regression equation of chest expansion in inches y on age x for two different groups of school children are given in Table 7.44. Examine whether the two regression lines are (a) identical, (b) parallel.

TABLE 7.44

MEANS AND SUMS OF SQUARES AND PRODUCTS

Group	No. of observations	Mean		Sum of squares and products		
		x	y	S_{xx}	S_{xy}	S_{yy}
1	12	13.481	1.560	3.416	0.234	8.623
2	16	13.573	3.002	3.759	0.263	13.632

7.27. The statistics in Table 7.45 were computed to study the length-weight relationship in three common species of fish in an experimental tank in a fishery. It has been suggested that weight varies as $(length)^n$.

Examine whether the length-weight relationship is identical for the three species. Comment on the suggestion that n does not depend on the species and is nearly 3.

TABLE 7.45

MEAN AND CORRECTED SUMS OF SQUARES AND PRODUCTS

		Mean		Corrected sum of squares and products		
Species	No. of fish	Log length x	Log weight y	x^2	y^2	xy
Catla catla	394	1.5723	0.7805	108.443	1340.003	371.861
Labeo rohita	121	1.4571	0.4846	37.000	431.748	124.122
Cirrhina mrigala	124	1.7493	1.3468	40.923	467.813	135.927

7.28. Medical practitioners believe that the proper dose of digitalis is proportional to heart weight. In an experiment on cats a preliminary investigation was carried out by R. A. Fisher to develop a formula for estimating the heart weight of a cat from its body weight. The measurements of body weights (in kilograms) and heart weights (in grams) of 47 female and 97 male cats were taken, and the sums of squares and products are given in Table 7.46.

TABLE 7.46

SUMS OF SQUARES AND PRODUCTS

	df	$(Body)^2$	Body × heart	$(Heart)^2$
Females				
Total	47	265.13	1,029.13	4,064.71
Correction factor	1	261.677	1,020.516	3,979.92
Males				
Total	97	836.75	3,275.55	13,056.17
Correction factor	1	815.77	3,185.07	12,435.70

386 STATISTICAL INFERENCE

Analyze the data and construct a linear prediction equation for each sex. Make suitable statistical tests to ascertain whether it is worthwhile to use these linear equations for prediction purposes.

Also test whether the same prediction equation can be used for both sexes.

7.29. Lettuce plants require iron as one of the nutrients for proper growth. This nutrient may be applied either in form A (Fe^{++}) or form B (Fe^{+++}). To investigate whether A and B have similar effects on yield of these plants, an experiment was conducted. As previous experience suggested that relationship between yield and log dose might be linear, three equispaced levels on the log scale were chosen for both forms. Each dose was tried on four different plants, and the data are given in Table 7.47.

TABLE 7.47

FIELD OF LETTUCE PLANTS (IN OUNCES)

Dose of A			Dose of B		
0.0025	0.0050	0.01	0.0125	0.0250	0.05
11	9	7	13	8	3
15	13	11	13	11	10
6	6	3	12	8	8
11	11	4	14	10	11

(a) Examine whether the effects of A and B on yield are similar (i.e., whether the regression lines are parallel).

(b) If (a) is true, estimate the (common) regression coefficient and test for its significance.

(c) Test for the adequacy of fit of linear regression.

7.30. The following experiment was conducted to test whether subjecting the seed to temperature treatment before planting has any effect on yield. Five pots were taken, and in each ten seeds were planted at random, five pairs of the seeds being subjected to five different levels of temperature. The yields in grams from individual plants are given in Table 7.48.

Analyze the data to find the optimum temperature for treatment of seeds, if any.

7.31. To determine the effect of the dilution of the electrolyte and the strength of the current on the thickness of the coating of aluminum foil in an electroplating experiment, four different dilutions and three different current strengths were used. In each experimental setup the thicknesses of coating on two aluminum foils were recorded.

Analyze the data in Table 7.49 and give your comments.

TABLE 7.48

YIELDS FROM PLANTS

Plot no.	60°F		75°F		90°F		105°F		120°F	
1	28.2	29.8	38.2	36.5	43.2	40.9	43.2	42.5	37.7	39.2
2	33.6	32.2	41.1	43.6	47.2	46.1	46.8	47.2	41.3	41.8
3	25.4	26.1	35.3	37.4	40.0	39.3	40.2	40.4	36.6	36.9
4	31.1	29.2	39.1	38.0	42.9	42.2	43.7	45.8	40.9	41.5
5	34.1	34.0	46.4	44.2	48.4	49.3	48.1	49.5	44.5	42.6

TABLE 7.49

THICKNESS OF COATING IN AN ELECTROPLATING EXPERIMENT

Dilution	Current strength					
	1.0		1.5		2.0	
5.0	10.5	11.3	12.9	11.2	5.9	7.6
6.0	10.6	11.6	12.5	13.4	10.3	7.6
7.0	7.5	9.4	10.6	12.0	5.0	5.6
8.0	6.8	7.2	8.8	8.0	3.2	2.7

7.32. On the basis of the data given in exercise 6.4 of Part II, examine whether, for predicting cranial capacity C, a simple product formula of the type (1) $C = K(LBH')$ or (2) $C = K(LBH')^\beta$ can be used. In any case, examine whether the dimension of the cranial capacity is the cube of the dimension of length measurement, that is, with a formula of the type $C = KL^{\beta_1}B^{\beta_2}H'^{\beta_3}$, whether $\beta_1 + \beta_2 + \beta_3 = 3$ holds.

Covariance

7.33. The data (Wishart's) in Table 7.25 on p. 372 relate to the initial weights in pounds and growth rates in pounds per week of 15 pigs classified according to pen and type of feed given.

Examine the differences between the three types of feed A, B, C in their effect on the growth of pigs, correcting for the differences in the initial weights of the animals.

7.34. In estimating the yield of jute fiber in a survey, one great difficulty is that the cultivator's process for extraction of fiber from the green jute plant by steeping in water takes several days. An experiment was conducted by J. M. Sengupta to investigate whether the use of quick chemical processes of extraction affects the weight of the fiber. The green bark was

TABLE 7.50

WEIGHT OF GREEN BARK AND OF DRY FIBER OF JUTE PLANTS EXTRACTED BY FOUR DIFFERENT PROCESSES

Plant	Weight (tolas)		Plant	Weight (tolas)	
	Green bark	Dry fiber		Green bark	Dry fiber
Process 1: Steeping in water (cultivator's process)					
1	3.0	0.30	16	3.8	0.44
2	2.5	0.24	17	2.5	0.29
3	3.4	0.35	18	2.2	0.20
4	9.0	1.20	19	1.4	0.13
5	1.0	0.12	20	0.5	0.05
6	4.6	0.50	21	2.0	0.29
7	2.9	0.44	22	1.4	0.11
8	1.5	0.10	23	4.4	0.56
9	3.6	0.40	24	3.0	0.41
10	2.8	0.35	25	3.6	0.41
11	1.7	0.15	26	1.5	0.15
12	3.7	0.25	27	5.2	0.61
13	2.0	0.22	28	0.7	0.05
14	2.8	0.24	29	2.4	0.14
15	3.5	0.25	30	0.4	0.05
Process 2: Boiling with ammonium oxalate					
1	1.5	0.22	16	2.4	0.39
2	2.5	0.41	17	2.1	0.42
3	2.0	0.34	18	1.3	0.30
4	0.6	0.09	19	2.4	0.37
5	4.3	0.71	20	2.1	0.28
6	3.8	0.74	21	4.1	0.74
7	0.8	0.07	22	0.8	0.11
8	0.9	0.22	23	3.5	0.69
9	6.4	1.07	24	2.5	0.49
10	2.6	0.47	25	0.4	0.60
11	6.1	1.10	26	5.8	1.10
12	1.7	0.34	27	2.2	0.45
13	3.5	0.62	28	0.4	0.04
14	2.0	0.40	29	2.7	0.45
15	4.2	0.70	30	5.9	0.65

TABLE 7.50 (*continued*)

Plant	Weight (tolas)		Plant	Weight (tolas)	
	Green bark	Dry fiber		Green bark	Dry fiber
Process 3: Boiling with sodium silicate					
1	1.1	0.14	16	2.8	0.40
2	6.1	0.95	17	1.1	0.12
3	1.4	0.20	18	1.7	0.23
4	5.5	0.95	19	6.5	0.95
5	2.3	0.31	20	0.9	0.10
6	3.2	0.45	21	0.5	0.06
7	0.8	0.08	22	0.8	0.09
8	0.5	0.06	23	2.3	0.31
9	1.8	0.25	24	0.3	0.04
10	0.5	0.07	25	1.8	0.27
11	4.6	0.55	26	3.5	0.50
12	1.8	0.28	27	1.7	0.26
13	6.8	0.80	28	0.6	0.07
14	2.1	0.28	29	3.7	0.55
15	0.9	0.13	30	3.8	0.57

taken from 120 jute plants and weighed. These plants were divided into four groups, and three chemical processes, as well as the cultivator's process of extraction, were tried, one process on each group of 30. Table 7.50 gives the weight of green bark and the weight of the dry fiber for each of these 120 jute plants.

Analyze the data and give your comments on the following points: (a) whether the regression of weight of dry fiber on weight of green bark can be taken to be the same for all four processes of extraction; (b) if not, whether the regression lines are parallel; (c) in any case, whether the average weight of dry fiber obtained is different for the different processes if correction is made for differences in the weight of green bark.

CHAPTER 8

Tests of Models

The validity of refined statistical analysis of a set of available observations is often dependent on various basic assumptions like normality, independence, randomness or homogeneity of the observations. It is therefore of primary importance to make sure that these basic assumptions hold true, before a refined statistical analysis is attempted. A number of procedures for examining the validity of such basic assumptions or statistical models are described in this chapter.

8.1 GOODNESS OF FIT

Sometimes the form of the probability distribution characterizing a population is suggested either from past experience or from theoretical considerations relating to the field of the subject matter. We will describe a number of methods which are used to examine whether the sample observations are in statistical agreement with the form so suggested. These procedures are generally called tests of goodness of fit.

Chi-Square Test of Goodness of Fit. In order to examine whether a sample is drawn from a specified probability distribution, we prepare a frequency distribution of the sample observations in a suitable number of classes. If the probability distribution is completely specified, the problem reduces to testing the hypotheses H_0 that the probability p_i for an observation to belong to the ith class has a specified value p_i^0. Let n_i be the number of sample observations in the ith class ($i = 1, 2, \ldots k$; $\Sigma n_i = n$; $\Sigma p_i = 1$) Then the chi-square test of goodness of fit is given by formula 5.3.3 in Section 5.3. But if only the mathematical form of the population is specified and the parameters involved are not known, we prepare, as usual, a frequency distribution of the sample observations in a suitable number of classes and then obtain the best asymptotically normal estimates of these parameters from the frequency distribution. Then the chi-square test of goodness of fit is carried out in the same way as in Section 5.3 and is given by formula 5.3.4.

In order to ensure the validity of the chi-square test, the grouping of the sample observations into classes should be done in such a manner that the expected frequency in each class is not too small, usually not less than five for all practical purposes.

Illustrative Example 8.1.   Table 8.1 gives the first 100 entries, corrected to two decimal places, in Sengupta and Bhattacharya's tables of random normal deviates. Examine whether this can be regarded as a sample from a normal population with mean zero and variance unity.

TABLE 8.1
RANDOM NORMAL DEVIATES

−0.54	0.42	0.26	2.04	0.83	0.23	−0.48	0.16	−0.21	1.67
−1.02	−1.08	0.58	0.09	−1.13	−0.62	−0.60	0.67	−0.41	−0.59
−0.37	−1.23	0.50	0.74	−1.59	0.06	−1.22	0.28	0.26	0.89
−0.19	1.16	−0.60	1.37	−1.08	1.30	0.52	0.28	1.18	0.37
0.22	−0.56	−0.00	−0.97	−0.55	0.30	0.27	−0.59	1.45	−0.68
−0.41	0.11	1.14	0.26	0.01	−0.62	−0.84	0.79	−0.96	0.68
−1.72	1.01	1.12	0.56	1.72	−0.57	1.58	−0.34	−0.64	1.18
−0.86	0.39	0.93	−1.00	−0.87	0.01	−0.40	0.55	−0.26	0.57
0.17	−0.38	1.45	0.33	0.36	0.62	0.81	0.79	−1.27	0.49
−1.17	0.40	−0.77	0.00	−1.45	−0.70	0.48	0.03	0.17	−0.31

Source: J. M. Sengupta and N. Bhattacharya, Tables of random normal deviates, *Sankhya*, Vol. 20, pp. 249–286 (1958).

To apply the chi-square test of goodness of fit, we prepare a frequency distribution in six classes. The theoretical frequencies in these classes are obtained from normal probability tables. The details are shown in Table 8.2.

TABLE 8.2
CHI-SQUARE TEST OF GOODNESS OF FIT

	Frequency		
Class interval	Observed f_o	Theoretical f_e	$\dfrac{(f_o - f_e)^2}{f_e}$
−∞ to −1.0	12	15.87	0.94
−1.0 to −0.5	19	14.98	1.08
−0.5 to 0.0	13	19.15	1.98
0.0 to 0.5	27	19.15	3.22
0.5 to 1.0	15	14.98	0.00
1.0 to ∞	14	15.87	0.22
Total	100	100.00	7.44

Thus $T = \Sigma (f_o - f_e)^2/f_e = 7.44$. Since there are six classes and no parameters are estimated, the number of degrees of freedom is $6 - 1 = 5$. The upper 5% value of chi square with 5 df is $\chi_5^2 (0.05) = 11.07$. Since the value of T is less than this, the standard normal fit is acceptable.

Illustrative Example 8.2. By applying the chi-square test, examine the goodness of fit of the normal distribution fitted to the frequency distribution of scores in English given in illustrative example 4.4 of Part II.

TABLE 8.3

CHI-SQUARE TEST OF GOODNESS OF FIT

	Frequency		
	Observed	Expected	$\dfrac{(f_o - f_e)^2}{f_e}$
Class limits	f_o	f_e	
−19.5	9 \big\} 20	4.85 \big\} 14.98	1.682
19.5–24.5	11	10.13	
24.5–29.5	10	22.05	6.585
29.5–34.5	44	37.18	1.251
34.5–39.5	45	48.54	0.258
39.5–44.5	54	49.10	0.489
44.5–49.5	37	38.45	0.055
49.5–54.5	26	23.33	0.306
54.5–59.5	8	10.96	0.799
59.5–64.5	5 \big\} 6	3.98 \big\} 5.39	0.069
64.5–	1	1.41	
Total	250	249.98	$T = 11.494$

To apply the chi-square test of goodness of fit, we take the expected frequencies computed in illustrative example 4.1 of Part II, as shown in Table 8.3. Pooling the first two classes into one cell and the last two classes into another, so that the expected frequency in each cell exceeds 5, we find $T = \Sigma (f_o - f_e)^2/f_e = 11.494$. This is based on nine cells, but two parameters μ and σ have been estimated, and therefore the chi square has $9 - 1 - 2 = 6$ df. The observed value of T is less than $\chi_6^2 (0.05) = 12.592$. Hence the deviation from normality is not significant.

Kolmogorov–Smirnov Tests of Goodness of Fit. To examine, on the basis of a sample of size n from a continuous population with cumulative distribution function $F(x)$, the hypothesis

$$H_0 : \quad F(x) = F_0(x)$$

the test criterion suggested by Kolmogorov is

(8.1.1) $d = \sqrt{n} \sup |\hat{F}(x) - F_0(x)|$.

Here $\hat{F}(x)$ is the empirical cumulative distribution function based on the sample, that is,

$$\hat{F}(x) = \frac{k}{n}, \qquad k = 0, 1, 2, \ldots, n,$$

where k is the number of observations in the sample, not greater than x in magnitude. The supremum ("sup") is taken over all the values of x.

An alternative statistic suggested by Smirnov and Von Mises is

(8.1.2) $$w^2 = n \int_{-\infty}^{\infty} [\hat{F}(x) - F_0(x)]^2 \, dF_0(x)$$

$$= \frac{1}{12n} + \sum_{i=1}^{n} \left[F_0(x_{(i)}) - \frac{2i - 1}{2n} \right]^2,$$

where $x_{(1)} \le x_{(2)} \le \cdots \le x_{(n)}$ are observations in ascending order of magnitude. The hypothesis is rejected at $100\alpha\%$ level of significance if the computed value of the statistic exceeds the $100\alpha\%$ point of the null distribution of the statistic chosen.

If H_0 is true, the sampling distribution of either of the statistics d or w^2 does not depend on the form of the cumulative distribution function $F_0(x)$, and percentage points have been tabulated. In large samples, we have the following:

	Upper percentage points	
Statistic	5%	1%
d	1.36	1.63
w^2	0.461	0.743

These tests cannot be used if parameters involved in the distribution function are unspecified.

Illustrative Example 8.3. We illustrate Kolmogorov's test of goodness of fit by considering the problem discussed in illustrative example 8.1. Arranging in ascending order the observations given in Table 8.1, we have $x_{(1)} = -1.72$, $x_{(2)} = -1.59$, $x_{(3)} = -1.45, \ldots, x_{(100)} = 2.04$. We denote the cumulative distribution function of the standard normal distribution by $F_0(x)$ and the empirical cumulative distribution function by $\hat{F}(x)$. Thus $F_0(x_{(1)}) = 0.0427$, $F_0(x_{(2)}) = 0.0559, \ldots, F_0(x_{(100)}) = 0.9793$, and $\hat{F}(x_{(1)}) = 0.01$, $\hat{F}(x_{(2)}) = 0.02, \ldots, \hat{F}(x_{(100)}) = 1.00$. Writing $e_i = |\hat{F}(x_{(i)}) - F_0(x_{(i)})|$, we get $e_1 = 0.0327$, $e_2 = 0.0359$, $\ldots, e_{100} = 0.0207$, the maximum of which is $e_{max} = e_4 = 0.0620$. Here $n = 100$, and from formula 8.1.1 we get Kolmogorov's statistic $d = \sqrt{n}e_{max} = 0.620$, which is smaller than 1.36, the asymptotic upper 5% point of d. Hence we cannot reject the hypothesis that the observations come from a normal population with zero mean and unit variance.

Tests of Normality. Besides the tests of goodness of fit various special tests are available for examining whether the parent population is normal on the basis of a sample. Two such tests will now be described.

TESTS OF SKEWNESS AND KURTOSIS. Let b_1 and b_2 be the values of the β_1 and β_2 coefficients (coefficients of skewness and kurtosis) computed from a sample of size n from a normal population. Then to test skewness the procedure (in large samples) is to compute

$$(8.1.3) \qquad T \equiv \pm \sqrt{\frac{b_1(n+1)(n+3)}{6(n-2)}} \sim \pm \sqrt{\frac{nb_1}{6}},$$

the sign being the same as that of the third central sample moment. The skewness observed in the sample is significant at (approximate) $100\alpha\%$ level if $|T| > \xi(\tfrac{1}{2}\alpha)$. In the same way, the kurtosis in the sample is regarded as significant at (approximate) $100\alpha\%$ level if $|T| > \xi(\tfrac{1}{2}\alpha)$, where

$$(8.1.4)$$

$$T \equiv \left(b_2 - 3 + \frac{6}{n+1}\right)\sqrt{\frac{(n+1)^2(n+3)(n+5)}{24n(n-2)(n-3)}} \sim (b_2 - 3)\sqrt{\frac{n}{24}}.$$

Illustrative Example 8.4. In illustrative example 2.10 of Part II the values of the beta coefficients for skewness and kurtosis of the distribution of the scores in English were computed from a sample of $n = 250$ observations. They were found to be $b_1 = 0.013937$ and $b_2 = 2.968707$, respectively. These values deviate somewhat from the corresponding values, 0 and 3, for a normal population. To examine whether these deviations are significant we compute the standard errors of $\sqrt{b_1}$ and b_2, which are given approximately by se $(\sqrt{b_1}) \sim \sqrt{6/n} = 0.15492$ and se $(b_2) \sim \sqrt{24/n} = 0.30984$. We then compute the ratio of each deviation to its standard error. From 8.1.3 we get, as the criterion for skewness, $T \sim \sqrt{nb_1/6} = 0.762$, which is not significant at the 5% level. Again from 8.1.4 the criterion for kurtosis is $|T| \sim |(b_2 - 3)| \sqrt{n/24} = 0.010$, which also is not significant at the 5% level.

GEARY'S TEST. The statistic suggested is the ratio of the mean deviation about the mean to the standard deviation:

$$(8.1.5) \qquad T \equiv \frac{\sum\limits_{i=1}^{n} |x_i - \bar{x}|}{\sqrt{[n\Sigma(x_i - \bar{x})^2]}},$$

where $x_1, x_2, \ldots, x_n$ are the observed values in a sample and $\bar{x}$ is their mean. For the normal distribution itself, this ratio has in the population the value $\sqrt{2/\pi}$, a higher value for a platykurtic distribution and a lower value for a leptokurtic distribution. Table 34A of *Biometrika Tables for Statisticians* gives percentage points of the distribution of the statistic when the parent population is normal, and deviation from normality is regarded as significant at a certain level if T exceeds the corresponding percentage point.

8.2 HOMOGENEITY: TWO-SAMPLE CASE

The following procedures are among the many which have been proposed to test the hypothesis H_0 that the two samples $x_1, x_2, \ldots, x_{n_1}$ and $y_1, y_2, \ldots, y_{n_2}$ come from the same population having a continuous probability density function the form of which is unspecified.

Run Test. In an arbitrary sequence of a fixed number of elements, where each element can be one of several mutually exclusive kinds, each sequence of elements of one kind is called a *run* and the number of elements in a run is called its *length*. The total number of runs in a sequence will be denoted by U. For instance, in the sequence $a\,a\,a\,b\,b\,a\,a\,b\,a\,a\,b\,b\,a\,b$ with 14 elements, where each element is of one of the two types a and b, there are $U =$ eight runs: $a\,a\,a$, $b\,b$, $a\,a$, b, $a\,a$, $b\,b$, a, b.

If U denotes the total number of runs of a's and b's in a random permutation of $n_1 + n_2$ letters, n_1 of which are a's and n_2 are b's, the probability distribution of U, under the assumption that all permutations are equally likely, is given by

$$\text{Prob}\,(U = 2k) = 2\binom{n_1 - 1}{k - 1}\binom{n_2 - 1}{k - 1}\Big/\binom{n_1 + n_2}{n_1},$$

$$(8.2.1) \quad \text{Prob}\,(U = 2k - 1) = \left[\binom{n_1 - 1}{k - 1}\binom{n_2 - 1}{k - 2}\right.$$
$$\left. + \binom{n_1 - 1}{k - 2}\binom{n_2 - 1}{k - 1}\right]\Big/\binom{n_1 + n_2}{n_1}.$$

The expectation and the variance of U are given by

$$(8.2.2) \quad E(U) = \frac{2n_1 n_2}{n_1 + n_2} + 1, \qquad V(U) = \frac{2n_1 n_2(2n_1 n_2 - n_1 - n_2)}{(n_1 + n_2)^2(n_1 + n_2 - 1)}.$$

To examine the hypothesis H_0 that two samples $x_i\ (i = 1, 2, \ldots, n_1)$ and $y_j\ (j = 1, 2, \ldots, n_2)$ come from the same population we arrange the $n_1 + n_2$ observations in ascending order and denote by U the total number of runs of x's and y's in this sequence. The hypothesis H_0 is rejected at $100\alpha\%$ level of significance if $U < c$, where c satisfies $\text{Prob}\,(U < c) = \alpha$.

In large samples, H_0 is rejected at (approximate) level of significance α if $T = [U - E(U)]/\sqrt{V(U)} < -\xi(\alpha)$.

Illustrative Example 8.5. We illustrate the use of the run test for comparing two samples with the data relating to heart weights of male and female cats given in illustrative example 6.2.

Arranging all 27 observations in ascending order, we have *7.1, 7.2, 7.3, 7.4,* 7.6, 7.6, 8.0, 8.3, *8.7, 9.0,* 9.1, 9.3, 9.4, *9.5, 9.5,* 9.6, *10.1, 10.1, 10.2,* 10.7, 11.2, 11.7, 12.7, 12.8, 13.6, 14.9, 15.6, where the figures for female cats are in italics. Here the total number of runs $U = 8$ and the sample sizes are $n_1 = 15$, $n_2 = 12$. The expectation and the variance of U are obtained from 8.2.2 as

$$E(U) = 14.33; \qquad V(U) = 6.3248.$$

The statistic $T = [U - E(U)]/\sqrt{V(U)} = -2.517** < -\xi(0.01)$ is significant at the 1 % level. So the samples cannot be regarded as coming from the same population. (See illustrative examples 8.6, 8.7, and 8.8 for other tests.)

Mathiesen's Test. Let $n_1 = 2t + 1$ and $n_2 = 2u$, and let v be the number of y's smaller than the median of the x's. Then the mean and the variance of v if H is true are given by

$$(8.2.3) \qquad E(v) = u, \qquad V(v) = u - u^2 + \frac{u(2u - 1)(t + 2)}{(2t + 3)},$$

and v is asymptotically (as m, n increases indefinitely, the ratio m/n remaining constant) normally distributed.

Let $T = [v - E(v)]/\sqrt{V(v)}$. The hypothesis is rejected at (approximate) level of significance α if $|T| > \xi(\tfrac{1}{2}\alpha)$.

Illustrative Example 8.6. To use Mathiesen's test for comparing the heart weights of male and female cats given in illustrative example 6.2 of Part II, we proceed as follows. Here the median heart weight of the male cats is 10.7, and the number of female cats with heart weights less than 10.7 is 12. Since all the female cats have heart weights less than the median for the males, the two samples are obviously different and a test of significance is hardly needed. The expectation and variance of v and the corresponding standardized deviate T can be computed by using formula 8.2.3.

Dixon's Test. Let $n_1 \leq n_2$. Arrange the x's in ascending order: $x_{(1)} < x_{(2)} < \cdots < x_{(n_1)}$, and let f_1 be the number of y's less than $x_{(1)}$; f_i the number of y's between $x_{(i-1)}$ and $x_{(i)}$, $i = 2, 3, \ldots, n_1$; and f_{n_1+1}

the number of y's greater than $x_{(n_1)}$. The criterion suggested by Dixon is

(8.2.4)
$$D = \sum_{i=1}^{n_1+1} \left(\frac{f_i}{n_2} - \frac{1}{n_1 + 1} \right)^2,$$

and the hypothesis H_0 is rejected if D exceeds a preassigned constant. If H_0 is true, the distribution of kD in large samples may be approximated by the chi-square distribution with N df, where

(8.2.5)
$$k = \frac{n_2{}^2(n_1 + 2)(n_1 + 3)(n_1 + 4)}{2(n_2 - 1)(n_1 + n_2 + 2)(n_1 + 1)};$$
$$N = \frac{n_1 n_2(n_1 + n_2 + 1)(n_1 + 3)(n_1 + 4)}{2(n_2 - 1)(n_1 + n_2 + 2)(n_1 + 1)^2}.$$

The hypothesis H_0 is therefore rejected at approximate level of significance α if $T \equiv kD^2 > \chi_N{}^2(\alpha)$.

Illustrative Example 8.7. To use Dixon's test for comparing the heart weights of male and female cats given in illustrative example 8.5, we proceed as follows. The frequency distribution of the heart weights of male cats in the 13 class intervals determined by the heart weights of the 12 female cats in ascending order is as shown in Table 8.4.

TABLE 8.4

DIXON'S TEST FOR COMPARING THE HEART WEIGHTS
OF MALE AND FEMALE CATS

Serial no.	Class limits	Frequency f_i	Relative frequency Observed f_o	Relative frequency Expected f_e	$(f_o - f_e)^2$
1	–7.1	0	0	$\frac{1}{13}$	0.005917
2	7.1–7.2	0	0	$\frac{1}{13}$	0.005917
3	7.2–7.3	0	0	$\frac{1}{13}$	0.005917
4	7.3–7.4	0	0	$\frac{1}{13}$	0.005917
5	7.4–7.6	0	0	$\frac{1}{13}$	0.005917
6	7.6–8.7	3	$\frac{3}{15}$	$\frac{1}{13}$	0.005155
7	8.7–9.0	0	0	$\frac{1}{13}$	0.005917
8	9.0–9.5	3	$\frac{3}{15}$	$\frac{1}{13}$	0.005155
9	9.5–9.5	0	0	$\frac{1}{13}$	0.005917
10	9.5–10.1	1	$\frac{1}{15}$	$\frac{1}{13}$	0.000105
11	10.1–10.1	0	0	$\frac{1}{13}$	0.005917
12	10.1–10.2	0	0	$\frac{1}{13}$	0.005917
13	10.2–	8	$\frac{8}{15}$	$\frac{1}{13}$	0.208310
	Total	15	1	1	$D = 0.271978$

We next compute k and N from 8.2.5, remembering that, since m denotes the smaller sample size, $n_1 = 12$ and $n_2 = 15$. This gives $k = 71.61804$ and $N = 8.81453$. Thus $kD = 19.479*$, which as a chi square with $N = 8.81$ df is significant at the 5% level.

Wilcoxon's Test. The criterion proposed by Wilcoxon is

$$(8.2.6) \qquad W = mf_1 + (m-1)f_2 + \cdots + 2f_{m-1} + f_m,$$

where f_i's are as defined in the case of Dixon's test. The mean and the variance of W, if H_0 is true, are given by

$$(8.2.7) \qquad E(W) = \tfrac{1}{2}n_1 n_2; \qquad V(W) = \tfrac{1}{12}n_1 n_2 (n_1 + n_2 + 1),$$

and, asymptotically, W is normally distributed.

Let $T = [W - E(W)]/\sqrt{V(W)}$. The hypothesis H_0 is to be rejected at (approximate) level of significance α if $|T| > \xi(\tfrac{1}{2}\alpha)$.

Illustrative Example 8.8. We take the values of f_i's from illustrative example 8.7 to illustrate Wilcoxon's test. Wilcoxon's criterion is $W = \sum_{i=1}^{13} (13 - i) f_i = 39$. The expected value and the variance of W are obtained from 8.2.6 as $E(W) = 90$ and $V(W) = 420$. The statistic $|T| = |W - E(W)|/\sqrt{V(W)} = 2.489*$ is significant at the 5% level.

Randomization Test. Let $d = \bar{x} - \bar{y}$ be the difference between the means of the two samples. Consider all possible partitions of the $m + n$ observations into two groups of m and n, and for each such partition $\mathscr{P}$ compute the value of $d_{\mathscr{P}}$, the difference between the mean of the first group of m observations and that of the other group of n observations. Arrange these values in ascending order: $d_{(1)} \le d_{(2)} \le \cdots \le d_{(N)}$, say, where $N = \begin{pmatrix} m + n \\ m \end{pmatrix}$ is the total number of possible partitions. Let α be the preassigned level of significance and M the greatest integer not exceeding $\tfrac{1}{2}N\alpha$. Then the hypothesis H_0 is rejected at (approximate) level of significance α if d is smaller than $d_{(M)}$ or greater than $-d_{(M)}$.

Illustrative Example 8.9. Eight rabbits were divided at random into two groups of four each, and each group was given a different feed. The increases in weight (in grams) of these rabbits over a period of four weeks were 82, 65, 97, 76 for those given feed A and 89, 72, 66, and 78 for those given feed B. Examine whether the two feeds have significantly different effects on the weights of the rabbits.

Let us number the rabbits serially from 1 to 8 in the order in which their increases in weights are given. The mean increase in weight of the rabbits given feed A is $\bar{x}_A = 80$, and that for feed B is $\bar{x}_B = 76.25$. The difference is $d = \bar{x}_A - \bar{x}_B = 3.75$. Here the total number of all possible partitions is $N = \binom{8}{4} = 70$. For each such partition we compute the values of the difference between the means of the first and the second groups. We arrange them in ascending order and thus obtain $d_{(1)} = -16.75$, $d_{(2)} = -15.75, \ldots, d_{(70)} = 16.75$. We take the level of significance to be $\alpha = 0.05$ and thus obtain $M = 1$. Since $d < -d_{(1)}$, the hypothesis that the two feeds have different effects on the weights of the rabbits is rejected at the 5 % level.

Sign Test. To examine the hypothesis H_0 that two populations are identical on the basis of n pairs of independent samples (x_i, y_i), $i = 1, 2, \ldots, n$, from the two populations, we may use the number R of pairs where x exceeds y. If H_0 is true, R follows the binomial distribution:

$$(8.2.8) \qquad \mathrm{Prob}\,(R = r) = \binom{n}{r}\left(\frac{1}{2}\right)^n,$$

and the problem reduces to that of examining whether the probability of success in a binomial distribution is $\frac{1}{2}$. If n is large, H_0 is thus to be rejected at (approximate) level of significance α if $|T| > \xi(\frac{1}{2}\alpha)$, where $T = (2R - n)/\sqrt{n}$.

Illustrative Example 8.10. Use the sign test to examine whether the difference in weights of anterior muscles of left and right legs of rabbits is statistically significant, on the basis of the data given in illustrative example 6.3.

The excesses of the weight of the muscle of the left leg over that of the right leg for the 16 rabbits are, respectively, 0.1, −0.2, 0.0, −0.2, 0.0, 0.0, 0.2, −0.4, 0.1, −0.2, −0.2, 0.0, −0.3, 0.0, −0.3, 0.0, 0.0, and −0.1. We exclude the rabbits for which this excess is zero, as they do not provide any information. We then have $n = 10$ rabbits, and among them $R = 4$ show positive excess. To examine the significance of R, we compute $T = (2R - n)/\sqrt{n} = -0.632$. As a standardized normal deviate this is not significant at the 5 % level.

8.3 HOMOGENEITY: k-SAMPLE CASE $(k \geq 2)$

Median Test. Let n_i be the size of the ith sample, $i = 1, 2, \ldots, k$; $n = \sum_{i=1}^{k} n_i$. Let m be the greatest integer not exceeding $\frac{1}{2}n$, and denote by m_i the number of observations in the ith sample not exceeding the median (defined as the mth from the bottom) of all the n observations. Thus $m = \sum_{i=1}^{k} m_i$. When the samples are large in size, the hypothesis H_0 that the k samples come from the same population (with a common continuous probability density function) is to be rejected at (approximate) level of significance α if

$$(8.3.1) \qquad T \equiv \frac{1}{m(n-m)} \sum_{i=1}^{k} \frac{(mn_i - nm_i)^2}{n_i} > \chi^2_{k-1}(\alpha).$$

Chi-Square Test. Let the range be divided into c predetermined exhaustive and exclusive classes, and in the ith sample of size n_i let n_{ij} denote the frequency in the jth class, $j = 1, 2, \ldots, c$; $i = 1, 2, \ldots, k$. Let $n = \sum_{i=1}^{k} n_i$, $m_j = \sum_{i=1}^{k} n_{ij}$, so that m_j is the total frequency in the jth class. When samples are large, the hypothesis H_0 is to be rejected at (approximate) level of significance α if

$$(8.3.2) \qquad T = \sum_{i=1}^{k} \sum_{j=1}^{c} \left(n_{ij} - \frac{n_i m_j}{n} \right)^2 \frac{n}{n_i m_j} > \chi^2_{(c-1)(k-1)}(\alpha).$$

Illustrative Example 8.11. Table 8.5 gives the frequency distributions of the duration of fever under three different types of medical treatment. Examine whether the distributions differ significantly from one another.

TABLE 8.5

FREQUENCY DISTRIBUTION OF DURATION OF FEVER
UNDER THREE DIFFERENT TREATMENTS

Treatment	Duration of fever (days)				Total
	1–4	5–6	7–8	9–12	
1	45	27	20	12	104
2	25	10	9	10	54
3	56	47	30	18	151
Total	126	84	59	40	309

Under the hypothesis that the three distributions are identical, the frequencies expected in these cells are given in Table 8.6. These are obtained in the following way:

$$42.41 = \frac{104 \times 126}{309}, \qquad 28.27 = \frac{104 \times 84}{309} \qquad \text{etc.}$$

Then we obtain from formula 8.3.2 $T = \Sigma (f_o - f_e)^2 / f_e = 5.269$, where f_o and f_e are the observed and the expected frequencies. Here $k = 3$ and $c = 4$, so that the number of degrees of freedom is $(3-1)(4-1) = 6$. Since $T < \chi_6^2 (0.05)$, the differences are not significant at the 5% level.

TABLE 8.6

Expected Frequencies

Treatment	Duration of fever (days)				Total
	1–4	5–6	7–8	9–12	
1	42.41	28.27	19.86	13.46	104.00
2	22.02	14.68	10.31	6.99	54.00
3	61.57	41.05	28.83	19.55	151.00
Total	126.00	84.00	59.00	40.00	309.00

Analysis of Variance. The analysis of variance procedure for one-way classification given in Section 7.3 may also be used for testing homogeneity.

8.4 INDEPENDENCE

We are given a random sample of n pairs of observations (x_i, y_i), $i = 1, 2, \ldots, n$, on two variates X and Y having a continuous bivariate probability density function. We will now describe a number of methods which are used to examine whether the two variates are independently distributed.

Median Double-Dichotomy Test. Let m be the greatest integer not exceeding $\frac{1}{2}n$, and let $\tilde{x}$ and $\tilde{y}$ denote the values of the sample median (mth value from the bottom) for the variates X and Y, respectively. Let Z denote the number of observations for which $X \leq \tilde{x}$ and $Y \leq \tilde{y}$. We thus get a 2×2 contingency table of the form

$$\begin{array}{c|c} Z & m-Z \\ \hline m - Z & n - 2m + Z \end{array}.$$

Under the hypothesis H_0 that the variates are independently distributed, the probability distribution of Z is given by

$$(8.4.1) \qquad \text{Prob}\,(Z = a) = \binom{m}{a}\binom{n - m}{m - a}\bigg/\binom{n}{m}.$$

For large samples, the hypothesis H_0 is to be rejected at (approximate) level of significance α if

$$(8.4.2) \qquad T = \frac{n(na - m^2)}{n^2(n - m)^2} > \chi_1^2(\alpha).$$

For small samples the exact procedure given in Section 5.3 for testing independence in a 2×2 contingency table can be used.

Rank-Correlation Tests. Let the rank of the ith pair be u_i when arranged in ascending (or descending) order of values of X, and v_i when arranged in ascending (or descending) order of values of Y. Independence of X and Y can be examined by testing the significance of Spearman's rank correlation coefficient R_S, defined by formula 5.5.1 of Part II, or of Kendall's rank correlation coefficient R_K, defined by formula 5.5.2 of Part II.

SPEARMAN'S COEFFICIENT. Using R_S, the hypothesis H_0 of independence is rejected at (approximate) level of significance α if $|T| > t_{n-2}(\tfrac{1}{2}\alpha)$, where

$$(8.4.3) \qquad T = \frac{R_S}{\sqrt{1 - R_S{}^2}} \sqrt{n - 2}.$$

KENDALL'S COEFFICIENT. If the two variates are independent, the expectation and the variance of R_K are

$$(8.4.4) \qquad E(R_K) = 0, \qquad V(R_K) = \frac{2n + 5}{18n(n - 1)}.$$

Then the hypothesis of independence is rejected at (approximate) level of significance α if $|T| > \xi(\tfrac{1}{2}\alpha)$, where $T = R_K/\sqrt{V(R_K)}$.

Illustrative Example 8.12. The scores in music X and mathematics Y of ten students are given in Table 8.7. To examine whether X and Y are independent, we convert the scores to ranks and obtain Table 8.8.

Computing Spearman's rank correlation coefficient, we obtain $R_S = -0.1515$. Here $n = 10$, and from 8.4.3 we get

$$T = \frac{R_S}{\sqrt{1 - R_S{}^2}} \sqrt{n - 2} = -0.4335 < t_8(0.025),$$

which is not significant at the 5% level. Thus there is not enough evidence of any correlation between the scores in music and mathematics.

The same conclusion is reached if we use Kendall's rank correlation coefficient instead. The value of this coefficient is found to be $R_K = -0.1111$. From 8.4.4 we have $V(R_K) = 0.015432$, so that

$$T = \frac{R_K}{\sqrt{V(R_K)}} = -0.896,$$

TABLE 8.7

SCORES IN MUSIC AND MATHEMATICS OF TEN STUDENTS

Serial no.		1	2	3	4	5	6	7	8	9	10
Score	music X	10	3	24	14	25	26	36	29	40	45
	mathematics Y	30	89	56	23	81	50	17	70	75	40

TABLE 8.8
RANKS IN MUSIC AND MATHEMATICS OF TEN STUDENTS

Serial no.	1	2	3	4	5	6	7	8	9	10
Rank { music	9	10	7	8	6	5	3	4	2	1
Rank { mathematics	8	1	5	9	2	6	10	4	3	7

which as a standard normal variate is not significant at the 5% level.

Contingency Chi Square. The usual contingency chi-square test of independence, given in Section 5.3, can be applied by first preparing a two-way frequency table, using preassigned class limits for X and Y.

8.5 RANDOMNESS

To examine whether a sequence of observations $x_1, x_2, \ldots, x_n$ may be regarded as a random sample from a common but unspecified population, various procedures are available, of which a few are as follows.

Run Test. Convert the sequence of observations x_i into a sequence of the letters a and b, by writing in the ith position a if $x_i \leq C$ and b if $x_i > C$, where C is a preassigned constant. Let U be the total number of runs in this sequence of the letters a and b. The significance of U can be judged by using the procedure given in Section 8.2. Usually we take for C the value of the sample median. A significant value of U indicates that the series is not random.

Rank-Correlation Test. Let u_i be the rank of x_i when the observations are arranged in descending or ascending order of magnitude. Randomness can then be examined by testing the significance of Spearman's or Kendall's rank correlation coefficient between the pairs (i, u_i), $i = 1, 2, \ldots, n$, using the procedures given in Section 8.4. A statistically significant value of the rank correlation coefficient indicates that the series is not random.

Illustrative Example 8.13. Examine the following series for randomness:

t	x_t	t	x_t	t	x_t	t	x_t
1	−0.49	6	+0.67	11	+0.29	16	+2.84
2	−0.92	7	−0.78	12	+1.18	17	+0.94
3	−0.22	8	−0.88	13	+1.15	18	+1.64
4	+0.01	9	+1.56	14	+0.10	19	+2.32
5	+0.47	10	−0.11	15	+0.75	20	+1.03

To apply the run test we convert the above data to a sequence of a's and b's by writing in the ith position a if $x_i \leq 0.67$ and b otherwise, the value 0.67 being the median of the observations. We then get

$$a\,a\,a\,a\,a\,a\,a\,a\,b\,a\,a\,b\,b\,a\,b\,b\,b\,b\,b\,b$$

so that the total number of runs is $U = 6$. Here the number of a's is $n_1 = 11$ and that of b's is $n_2 = 9$, so that from 8.2.2 we obtain $E(U) = 10.9$ and $V(U) = 4.6374$.

Therefore

$$T = \frac{U - E(U)}{\sqrt{V(U)}} = 2.275* > \xi(0.025),$$

which is significant at the 5% level.

Alternatively, arranging the observations in descending order, we find the value of Spearman's rank correlation coefficient between the rank and the initial ordering as $R_S = -0.7429$. From formula 8.4.3 we then obtain

$$T = \frac{R_S}{\sqrt{1 - R_S^2}} \sqrt{n - 2} = -4.708,$$

so that $|T| > t_{18}(0.005)$. Since this value of T is highly significant, we conclude that the series is not random.

8.6 STATISTICAL CONTROL

Consider the distribution of a characteristic at different "states." Consider, for example, the distribution of a quality characteristic of an industrial product manufactured on different days or on different machines or by different groups of workers. If these distributions for all the different "states" or "subgroups" are identical, the process is said to be in statistical control. If they are not, assignable causes must be at work and it is the job of the statistician to determine them.

To examine whether a process is in statistical control, a graphical method is generally used. From each subgroup, a sample is taken and an appropriate statistic t is computed. In industrial applications, statistics generally employed are the sample mean, range, standard deviation, proportion of defectives, and mean number of defects per unit. The values of t are plotted against the serial number of the subgroups on what is called a *control chart*, t being along the vertical axis. On the chart three lines are drawn: a center line and two (upper and lower) control lines. The center line is drawn at $t = \mu_t$, the upper control line at $t = \mu_t + k_1\sigma_t$, and the lower control line at $t = \mu_2 - k_2\sigma_t$, where μ_t and σ_t are, respectively, the mean and the standard deviation of the sampling distribution of t and k_1 and k_2 are constants so chosen that the probability of a value of t being

TABLE 8.9
CONSTANTS FOR CONTROL CHARTS

Statistic used	Control lines	
	Lower	Upper
$\bar{x}$ = sample mean	$\bar{\bar{x}} - A_1\bar{s}$ $\bar{\bar{x}} - A_2\bar{R}$	$\bar{\bar{x}} + A_1\bar{s}$ $\bar{\bar{x}} + A_2\bar{R}$
R = sample range	$D_3\bar{R}$	$D_4\bar{R}$
s = sample standard deviation (divisor n)	$B_3\bar{s}$	$B_4\bar{s}$
p = proportion of defectives in sample	$\bar{p} - \dfrac{3\sqrt{\bar{p}(1-\bar{p})}}{\sqrt{n}}$	$\bar{p} + \dfrac{3\sqrt{\bar{p}(1-\bar{p})}}{\sqrt{n}}$
c = number of defects	$\bar{c} - 3\sqrt{\bar{c}}$	$\bar{c} + 3\sqrt{\bar{c}}$

outside the control lines is very small. Usually we take $k_1 = k_2 = 3$ and the corresponding control lines are called *three-sigma* control limits. Sometimes μ_t and σ_t are given either as hypothetical values or as adequately precise estimates based on past experience. If such values are not available they are estimated from the data itself. In practice, simple to compute but unbiased estimates are preferred.

From such a chart, lack of control may be detected in several ways. When a point falls outside the control limits, when a number of consecutive points fall on one side of the center line, or when they develop a trend, action is recommended to look for assignable causes.

Table 8.9 gives a number of formulae for constructing various types of control charts when parameters are unknown. Three-sigma limits are used throughout. The distribution of quantitative characters is assumed

TABLE 8.10
VALUES OF CONTROL CHART CONSTANTS

Sample size	A_1	A_2	B_3	B_4	D_3	D_4	$1/c_2$	$1/d_2$
2	3.760	1.880	0	3.267	0	3.267	1.7725	0.8865
3	2.994	1.023	0	2.568	0	2.575	1.3820	0.5907
4	1.880	0.729	0	2.266	0	2.282	1.2533	0.4857
5	1.596	0.577	0	2.089	0	2.115	1.1894	0.4299
6	1.410	0.483	0.030	1.970	0	2.004	1.1512	0.3946
7	2.277	0.419	0.118	1.882	0.076	1.924	1.1259	0.3698
8	1.175	0.373	0.185	1.815	0.136	1.864	1.1078	0.3512
9	1.094	0.337	0.239	1.761	0.184	1.826	1.0942	0.3367
10	1.028	0.308	0.284	1.716	0.223	1.777	1.0837	0.3249

to be normal, that of the number of defectives in a sample to be binomial, and that of the number of defects per item to be of the Poisson type. In the table one or two bars over the symbol for a statistic denotes that the value of this statistic has to be averaged over all samples; thus $\bar{\bar{x}}$ denotes the mean of all the subgroup sample means.

Estimates of the standard deviation in a normal population can be obtained from $(1/c_2)\bar{s}$ or $(1/d_2)\bar{R}$. The values of these constants are given in Table 8.10 for $n = 2, 3, \ldots, 10$.

8.7 EXERCISES

Goodness of fit

8.1. The subscribers' numbers in a telephone directory were run through, and a note was taken of the length of the interval (that is, the number of subscribers' numbers) between successive numbers where the final digit was 1. The distribution of length for 80 such intervals is given in Table 8.11.

Examine, so far as these data go, whether the observed distribution is consistent with the supposition that in a telephone directory the final digits in subscribers' numbers occur at random and with equal frequency.

TABLE 8.11

FREQUENCY DISTRIBUTION OF THE LENGTH OF THE
INTERVAL BETWEEN TWO NUMBERS ENDING IN 1 IN
A TELEPHONE DIRECTORY

Length of interval	Frequency
0–3	24
4–6	18
7–9	13
10–12	6
13–15	7
16–18	5
19–21	4
22–24	3

8.2. Table 8.12 gives the distribution of the correlation coefficient r in random samples of size $n = 8$ from a certain bivariate population.

Examine whether the observed distribution is in agreement with the hypothesis that the samples have been drawn from a bivariate normal distribution with $\rho = 0$, in which case the sampling distribution of r is known to be

$$dF(r) = \frac{\Gamma\frac{1}{2}(n-1)}{\Gamma(\frac{1}{2})\Gamma\frac{1}{2}(n-2)}(1 - r^2)^{\frac{1}{2}(n-4)}\,dr.$$

TABLE 8.12
OBSERVED SAMPLING DISTRIBUTION OF r

Class interval for r	Frequency	Class interval for r	Frequency
−1.000 to −0.825	2	0.075 to 0.225	85
−0.825 to −0.675	27	0.225 to 0.375	98
−0.675 to −0.525	44	0.375 to 0.525	65
−0.525 to −0.375	60	0.525 to 0.675	38
−0.375 to −0.225	96	0.675 to 0.825	14
−0.225 to −0.075	115	0.825 to 1.000	3
−0.075 to 0.075	103	Total	750

8.3–8.5. Examine the goodness of fit of the binomial distributions fitted in exercises 3.1–3.3 of Part II.

8.6. Examine the goodness of fit of the hypergeometric distribution fitted in exercise 3.17 of Part II.

8.7–8.10. Examine the goodness of fit of the Poisson distributions fitted in exercises 3.10–3.13 of Part II.

8.11. Examine the goodness of fit of the Pascal distribution fitted in exercise 3.18 of Part II.

8.12–8.13. Examine the goodness of fit of the negative binomial distributions fitted in exercises 3.19 and 3.20 of Part II.

8.14. Examine the goodness of fit of the Neyman's contagious distribution of Type A fitted in exercise 3.21 of Part II.

8.15. Examine the goodness of fit of the truncated binomial distribution fitted in exercise 3.9 of Part II.

8.16. Examine the goodness of fit of the normal distribution fitted in exercises 4.1–4.4 of Part II.

8.17–8.20. Examine the goodness of fit of the normal distribution fitted in exercises 4.1–4.4 of Part II.

8.21. Examine the goodness of fit of the log-normal distribution fitted in exercise 4.6 of Part II.

8.22–8.31. Examine the goodness of fit of the Pearsonian types fitted in exercises 4.16–4.25.

8.32. Given in Table 8.13 are 100 two-digit numbers extracted from a table of random sampling numbers. Examine whether these can be regarded as a random sample from a rectangular distribution in the range (0, 99) by using (a) the chi-square test, with 10 equal classes, (b) the Kolmogorov–Smirnov test.

8.33–8.36. Examine the normality of the distributions given in exercises 2.7, 2.8, 2.10(b), and 2.10(c) of Part II (a) by testing the significance of the sample values of $\sqrt{\beta_1}$ and $\beta_2 - 3$, (b) by using Geary's test.

TABLE 8.13

ONE HUNDRED TWO-DIGIT RANDOM NUMBERS

29	52	66	41	39	92	97	92	79	79
41	67	95	24	15	45	13	96	72	03
27	30	74	83	34	08	27	62	35	63
05	60	52	46	11	12	61	07	60	08
27	54	91	43	14	05	90	25	70	02
58	70	28	59	49	88	16	58	29	22
92	63	24	66	33	98	54	40	87	38
20	02	78	40	16	90	75	05	04	23
95	68	28	35	94	27	36	68	25	96
82	43	15	79	19	30	50	26	34	26

8.37. The 100 values given in Table 8.14 are extracted from Wold's *Random Normal Deviates*. Examine whether these may be regarded as a random sample from a normal population with zero mean and unit standard deviation (a) by testing the significance of the sample values of $\sqrt{\beta_1}$ and $\beta_2 - 3$, (b) by Geary's test, (c) by the chi-square test, using ten classes with the same expected frequency in each class, (d) by the Kolmogorov–Smirnov test.

TABLE 8.14

ONE HUNDRED VALUES TAKEN FROM WOLD'S *Table of Random Normal Deviates*

−0.84	0.68	0.11	1.05	0.09	0.83	1.35	1.01	0.54	0.28
1.37	−0.77	−0.89	0.61	−2.54	1.55	−0.92	−0.20	1.11	−1.52
−0.18	−1.39	0.99	−0.01	−0.22	0.36	1.27	0.45	0.59	1.52
0.35	−1.91	0.50	−0.92	−0.30	0.36	1.28	−0.69	−1.64	0.42
2.82	0.05	−0.95	1.17	1.22	0.14	−2.13	−0.76	0.24	−1.07
2.12	1.32	0.81	−1.91	−1.23	−0.17	−0.38	−0.03	−1.65	−0.35
−0.99	−0.67	−0.28	−0.48	−0.12	−2.21	−0.10	0.40	−0.83	−0.37
0.34	−0.81	−1.64	−0.21	−0.19	0.66	0.12	0.39	1.06	−0.38
0.64	0.96	−1.44	−2.47	−1.69	−0.45	2.31	1.39	−0.17	0.09
0.11	−0.24	0.01	−0.28	0.04	1.28	0.47	0.77	−1.31	−0.38

Homogeneity

8.38. In connection with exercise 6.8, use the following non-parametric tests to find out whether the two samples come from the same population: (a) Wald–Wolfowitz test, (b) Mathiesen test, (c) Dixon test, (d) Wilcoxon test, (e) sign test.

8.39. On the basis of the data in exercise 2.36 of Part II test the hypothesis that the medians of the two populations from which the samples have been drawn are equal. Obtain confidence intervals for the medians separately from the two samples if they are different. If they are equal, obtain a confidence interval from the two samples combined.

8.40. In connection with exercise 7.5 use median and chi-square tests to find out whether there are any differences between the four batches *A*, *B*, *C*, and *D*.

8.41. Table 8.15 shows measurements of tensile strength made on six specimens of rubber randomly selected from each of five different batches.

TABLE 8.15

TENSILE STRENGTH (IN KILOGRAMS PER SQUARE CENTIMETER)
OF SPECIMENS OF RUBBER

	Batch no.				
Specimen no.	1	2	3	4	5
1	177	116	170	181	177
2	172	179	156	190	186
3	137	182	188	210	199
4	196	143	212	173	202
5	145	156	164	172	204
6	168	174	184	187	198

Source: *Biometrika Tables for Statisticians*, Vol. I.

Use non-parametric tests to find out whether there are differences between the batches.

8.42–8.43. Use the tests based on (a) median double dichotomy, (b) rank correlation, (c) contingency chi square, in exercises 5.7 and 5.8 of Part II, to test whether there is any association between the two characters.

Statistical Control

8.44. Samples of five pieces of a certain part of a stove were taken every 15 minutes in order of production from a certain manufacturing process and the length of each piece was measured. From the data given in Table 8.16 examine whether the process is under control by drawing the control charts for the mean and the range. Write a report on your findings.

TABLE 8.16
LENGTH MEASUREMENTS OF STOVE PARTS

Sample	Length (in.)				
1	0.833	0.835	0.834	0.833	0.833
2	0.836	0.834	0.835	0.837	0.836
3	0.832	0.837	0.833	0.837	0.830
4	0.835	0.835	0.836	0.834	0.833
5	0.835	0.835	0.832	0.830	0.833
6	0.833	0.836	0.833	0.837	0.835
7	0.834	0.834	0.834	0.834	0.835
8	0.831	0.832	0.834	0.832	0.831
9	0.834	0.832	0.833	0.832	0.832
10	0.834	0.832	0.832	0.832	0.833
11	0.835	0.833	0.834	0.833	8.831
12	0.837	0.833	0.833	0.834	0.834
13	0.835	0.836	0.835	0.837	0.836

TABLE 8.17
INSPECTION RECORD OF THE NUMBER OF DEFECTIVES

Sample no.	No. of defectives	Sample no.	No. of defectives
1	6	11	2
2	8	12	8
3	9	13	6
4	1	14	4
5	9	15	4
6	3	16	4
7	0	17	13
8	5	18	7
9	6	19	5
10	3	20	5

8.45. The number of articles produced every day by a certain machine is 150, and each article is subjected to a detailed inspection. The number of defective articles detected daily is recorded in Table 8.17. Draw a control chart for the proportion of defectives and examine whether the production process is under control.

8.46. Table 8.18 gives the numbers c of missing rivets noted at the final inspection of aircraft. Plot a control chart for c.

TABLE 8.18

NUMBER OF MISSING RIVETS IN AIRCRAFT

Airplane no.	No. of missing rivets	Airplane no.	No. of missing rivets	Airplane no.	No. of missing rivets
201	8	210	12	218	14
202	16	211	23	219	11
203	14	212	16	220	9
204	19	213	9	221	10
205	11	214	25	222	22
206	15	215	15	223	7
207	8	216	9	224	7
208	11	217	9	225	9
209	21				

CHAPTER 9

Multivariate Analysis

9.1 INTRODUCTION

In this chapter the following topics are discussed: methods of testing various hypotheses concerning the parameters of multivariate normal populations, problems of classification, and factor analysis. When using these procedures in practical situations, we have to be careful about two points. First, these procedures are generally of an omnibus nature; we seek to answer many questions simultaneously by a single test. In order to draw physically meaningful conclusions, it may be necessary at times to examine the variates singly, even though it may not be possible to make precise assessment of the simultaneous level of significance. Second, many of the test procedures, especially those with respect to the dispersion matrix, are valid only for multivariate normal populations, and even small deviations from normality may vitiate them to a great extent.

Notations. A p-variate normal population with mean vector μ and dispersion matrix Σ will be denoted by $\mathcal{N}_p(\mu, \Sigma)$, and a sample of size n from it will be denoted by $((x_{i\lambda}))$, $i = 1, 2, \ldots, p$; $\lambda = 1, 2, \ldots, n$, where $x_{i\lambda}$ is the value of the ith variate for the λth individual. Set

$$\bar{x}_i = \frac{1}{n} \sum_{\lambda=1}^{n} x_{i\lambda} \quad \text{and} \quad S_{ij} = \sum_{\lambda=1}^{n} x_{i\lambda} x_{j\lambda} - n\bar{x}_i \bar{x}_j;$$

the vector $\bar{x} = (\bar{x}_1, \ldots, \bar{x}_p)$ will be called the sample mean vector, and the matrix $S = ((S_{ij}))$ will be called the corrected sum of products matrix or briefly the sp matrix. The dispersion matrix is estimated as $\hat{\Sigma} = S/(n-1)$. If several samples or populations are involved, they will be distinguished by suitable superscripts or subscripts. The symbol e will denote the p-vector $(1, 1, \ldots, 1)$.

412

9.2 TESTS OF THE MEAN VECTOR

Suppose that the problem is to test the hypothesis H_0 that the vector parameter $\boldsymbol{\theta} = (\theta_1, \theta_2, \ldots, \theta_p)$ has a specified value $\boldsymbol{\theta}_0 = (\theta_{10}, \theta_{20}, \ldots, \theta_{p0})$. An estimate $\hat{\boldsymbol{\theta}}$ of $\boldsymbol{\theta}$ is available, whose sampling distribution is a p-variate normal, with mean vector $\boldsymbol{\theta}$ and dispersion matrix $\boldsymbol{\Delta} = ((\delta_{ij}))$, which is non-singular. If $\boldsymbol{\Delta}$ is known, the procedure is to reject H_0 at level of significance α if

$$(9.2.1) \qquad T = (\hat{\boldsymbol{\theta}} - \boldsymbol{\theta}_0)\boldsymbol{\Delta}^{-1}(\hat{\boldsymbol{\theta}} - \boldsymbol{\theta}_0)' > \chi_p^2(\alpha).$$

When $\boldsymbol{\Delta}$ is not known, but an unbiased estimate $\hat{\boldsymbol{\Delta}}$ for it is available, which follows Wishart's distribution with ν degrees of freedom and is statistically independent of $\hat{\boldsymbol{\theta}}$, the procedure is to reject H_0 at level of significance α if

$$(9.2.2) \qquad T \equiv \frac{\nu - p + 1}{\nu p} \cdot (\hat{\boldsymbol{\theta}} - \boldsymbol{\theta}_0)\,\boldsymbol{\Delta}^{-1}(\hat{\boldsymbol{\theta}} - \boldsymbol{\theta}_0)' > F_{p,\nu-p+1}(\alpha).$$

Test for a Specified Value of a Mean Vector. Consider, in particular, the problem of testing on the basis of a sample of size n from $\mathcal{N}_p(\boldsymbol{\mu}, \boldsymbol{\Sigma})$ the hypothesis H_0 that $\boldsymbol{\mu} = \boldsymbol{\mu}_0$. When $\boldsymbol{\Sigma}$ is not known, H_0 is to be rejected at level of significance α if

$$(9.2.3) \qquad T = \frac{n(n - p)}{p} (\bar{\mathbf{x}} - \boldsymbol{\mu}_0)\mathbf{S}^{-1}(\bar{\mathbf{x}} - \boldsymbol{\mu}_0)' > F_{p,n-p}(\alpha),$$

where $\bar{\mathbf{x}}$ is the sample mean vector and $\mathbf{S}$ the matrix of corrected sums of squares and products as defined in Section 6.1.

Illustrative Example 9.1. In a certain examination each student had to answer three essay-type questions which were valued independently by two examiners A and B. The difference between the scores given by the two examiners (A minus B) for the ith question was denoted by x_i, $i = 1$, 2, 3. The mean vector and the dispersion matrix of x_1, x_2, x_3 estimated from a sample of 50 are given in Table 9.1. Examine simultaneously whether, except for sampling fluctuations, the average difference between the two examiners for each question is zero.

The number of variates here is $p = 3$. The dispersion matrix $\hat{\boldsymbol{\Sigma}}$ of the observations was computed by dividing the sp matrix by the error degrees of freedom $\nu = n - 1 = 49$. We first compute the quadratic form $\bar{\mathbf{x}}\hat{\boldsymbol{\Sigma}}^{-1}\bar{\mathbf{x}}'$ by pivotal condensation as shown in Table 9.2, with an additional zero as the last diagonal element. The last element with sign changed gives $\bar{\mathbf{x}}\hat{\boldsymbol{\Sigma}}^{-1}\bar{\mathbf{x}}' = 0.592622$.

TABLE 9.1

MEANS AND DISPERSION MATRIX OF DIFFERENCES IN SCORES

Mean	Dispersion matrix Σ		
	x_1	x_2	x_3
$\bar{x}_1 = 2.54$	16.90	22.01	12.35
$\bar{x}_2 = -1.72$		51.72	19.46
$\bar{x}_3 = 0.94$			28.73

From (9.2.3) we obtain

$$T = \frac{n(n-p)}{vp}\, \bar{\mathbf{x}}\, \hat{\Sigma}^{-1}\, \bar{\mathbf{x}}' = \frac{50 \times 47}{48 \times 3} \times 0.592622$$

$$= 9.473^{**} > F_{3,47}(0.01),$$

which is significant at the 1 % level. The examiners thus differ significantly.

TABLE 9.2

PIVOTAL CONDENSATION FOR COMPUTING $\bar{\mathbf{x}}\hat{\Sigma}^{-1}\bar{\mathbf{x}}'$

	$\hat{\Sigma}$		$\bar{\mathbf{x}}'$	Sum check
16.90	22.01	12.35	2.54	53.80
	51.72	19.46	−1.72	91.47
		28.73	0.94	61.48
			0	1.76
16.90	1.302367	0.730769	0.150296	3.183432
22.01	23.054902	0.146423	−0.091163	1.055260
12.35	3.375774	19.210722	−0.031670	0.968330
2.54	−2.101752	−0.608408	−0.592622	

Equality of Means of Correlated Variates. Consider the problem of testing, on the basis of a sample of size n from a p-variate normal population, the hypothesis H_0 that the means of the p variates are equal to one another. The procedure is to reject H_0 at level of significance α if

$$(9.2.4) \qquad \frac{n(n-p+1)}{p-1}\left[\bar{\mathbf{x}}S^{-1}\bar{\mathbf{x}}' - \frac{(\bar{\mathbf{x}}S^{-1}\mathbf{e}')^2}{\mathbf{e}S^{-1}\mathbf{e}'} \right] > F_{p-1,\,n-p+1}(\alpha).$$

Equality of Two Mean Vectors. Suppose that samples of sizes n_1 and n_2 are available from $\mathcal{N}(\mu^{(1)}, \Sigma)$ and $\mathcal{N}_p(\mu^{(2)}, \Sigma)$, respectively. The hypothesis of equality of the mean vectors, $H_0 : \mu^{(1)} = \mu^{(2)}$, is to be rejected at level of significance α if

$$(9.2.5) \qquad \frac{n_1 + n_2 - p - 1}{p} \cdot \frac{n_1 n_2}{n_1 + n_2} \, dS^{-1}d' > F_{p, n_1+n_2-p-1}(\alpha),$$

where $d = \bar{x}^{(1)} - \bar{x}^{(2)}$ and $S = S^{(1)} + S^{(2)}$, $\bar{x}^{(i)}$ and $S^{(i)}$ being the sample mean vector and corrected sp matrix for the sample of size n_i from $\mathcal{N}(\mu^{(i)}, \Sigma)$, $i = 1, 2$.

Illustrative Example 9.2. Table 9.3 gives the estimates of the means and the common dispersion matrix of three characters:

x_1: length of hind femur,

x_2: maximum width of head in the genal region,

x_3: length of pronotum at the peel,

for two groups of female desert locusts, one in the phase *gregaria* and the other in an intermediate phase between *gregaria* and *solotaria*.

TABLE 9.3

MEANS AND DISPERSION MATRIX OF BIOMETRICAL
CHARACTERS OF DESERT LOCUSTS

	Means			Dispersion matrix Σ		
Character	*Gregaria* $n_1 = 20$	Inter-mediate $n_2 = 72$	Differ-ence d'	x_1	x_2	x_3
x_1	25.80	28.35	−2.55	4.7350	0.5622	1.4685
x_2	7.81	7.41	0.40		0.1413	0.2174
x_3	10.77	10.75	−0.02			0.5702

Source: K. R. Nair, A biometric study of the desert locust, *Bulletin of the International Statistical Institute*, Vol. 33, Pt. 2 (1951).

Test for the significance of the difference in the mean vectors of the two groups of female desert locusts.

Here the dispersion matrix is based on $\nu = n_1 + n_2 - 2 = 90$ df and is obtained by dividing the sum of the sp matrices for the two phases by ν. The number of characters is $p = 3$. Denoting by **d** the difference between the two mean vectors given in the fourth column of the table, we compute first $d\hat{\Sigma}^{-1}d = 9.742116$ by the method of pivotal condensation as shown in Table 9.4.

TABLE 9.4

COMPUTATION OF $\mathbf{d}\hat{\boldsymbol{\Sigma}}^{-1}\mathbf{d}'$ BY PIVOTAL CONDENSATION

$\hat{\boldsymbol{\Sigma}}$			$\mathbf{d}'$	Sum	Check
4.7350	0.5622	1.4685	−2.5500	4.2157	
	0.1431	0.2174	0.4000	1.3227	
		0.5702	0.0200	2.2761	
			0	−2.1300	
4.7350	0.1187328	0.3101373	−0.5385428	0.8903273	0.8903273
0.5622	0.0763484	0.5637433	9.2047587	10.7685020	10.7685046
1.4685	0.0430409	0.0904994	4.5820083	5.5820083	5.5820045
−2.5500	0.7027686	0.4146690	−9.7421163	1	1

From 9.2.5, we then obtain

$$
\begin{aligned}
T &= \frac{n_1 + n_2 - p - 1}{p(n_1 + n_2 - 2)} \cdot \frac{n_1 n_2}{n_1 + n_2} \cdot \mathbf{d}\hat{\boldsymbol{\Sigma}}^{-1}\mathbf{d}' \\
&= \frac{20 + 72 - 3 - 1}{3(20 + 72 - 2)} \times \frac{20 \times 72}{20 + 72} \times 9.742116 \\
&= 49.699^{**} > F_{3,90}(0.01),
\end{aligned}
$$

which is highly significant. Thus the two phases are significantly different with respect to the means of the three characters.

9.3 ANALYSIS OF DISPERSION

General Procedure. Generalization of the analysis of variance procedure to multivariate populations is known as *analysis of dispersion* or *multivariate analysis of variance.* We start with n independent p-dimensional normal variables $\mathbf{y}_i$, $i = 1, 2, \ldots, n$, with a common dispersion matrix $\boldsymbol{\Sigma}$ and expectations given by

(9.3.1) $E\mathbf{y}_i = a_{i1}\boldsymbol{\theta}_1 + a_{i2}\boldsymbol{\theta}_2 + \cdots + a_{im}\boldsymbol{\theta}_m, \qquad i = 1, 2, \ldots, n,$

where a_{ij}'s are given constants and $\boldsymbol{\theta}_j$'s are unknown parameter vectors each with p components. We shall denote the rank of the matrix $((a_{ij}))$ by r. To estimate $\boldsymbol{\theta}_j$'s we use the equations:

(9.3.2) $c_{j1}\boldsymbol{\theta}_1 + c_{j2}\boldsymbol{\theta}_2 + \cdots + c_{jm}\boldsymbol{\theta}_m = Q_j, \qquad j = 1, 2, \ldots, m,$

where $c_{jk} = a_{1j}a_{1k} + a_{2j}a_{2k} + \cdots + a_{nj}a_{nk}$ and $Q_j = a_{1j}\mathbf{y}_1 + a_{2j}\mathbf{y}_2 + \cdots + a_{nj}\mathbf{y}_n$. To estimate the dispersion matrix $\boldsymbol{\Sigma}$, we first compute the matrix of sums of squares and products (sp matrix) due to error. This is given by

(9.3.3) $\mathbf{S}_e = \mathbf{y}_1\mathbf{y}_1' + \cdots + \mathbf{y}_n\mathbf{y}_n' - (Q_1\hat{\boldsymbol{\theta}}_1' + \cdots + Q_m\hat{\boldsymbol{\theta}}_m'),$

where $\hat{\theta}_1, \ldots, \hat{\theta}_m$ is any solution of equations 9.3.2. The sp matrix due to error is said to have $e = n - r$ degrees of freedom, and $\mathbf{S}_e/e$ provides an unbiased estimate of Σ.

Let $\theta = l_1\theta_1 + \cdots + l_m\theta_m$ be an estimable parameter vector. To test the hypothesis H_0 that θ has a specified value θ_0, we proceed as follows. Let $\hat{\theta} = l_1\hat{\theta}_1 + \cdots + l_m\hat{\theta}_m$ be expressed in the alternative form $\hat{\theta} = \lambda_1 Q_1 + \cdots + \lambda_m Q_m$. Then $\hat{\theta}$ is an unbiased estimate of θ, and its dispersion matrix is $(l_1\lambda_1 + \cdots + l_m\lambda_m)\Sigma$. The hypothesis H_0 is to be rejected at level of significance α if

$$(9.3.4) \quad \frac{e - p + 1}{p(l_1\lambda_1 + \cdots + l_m\lambda_m)} (\hat{\theta} - \theta_0)\mathbf{S}_e^{-1}(\hat{\theta} - \theta_0)' > F_{p,e-p+1}(\alpha).$$

To test the hypothesis H_0 that q given functionally independent estimable parameter vectors, say $\phi_j = b_{j1}\theta_1 + \cdots + b_{jm}\theta_m$, have specified values ϕ_j^0, we have first to compute a matrix $\mathbf{S}_h$ known as the sp matrix due to the hypothesis. Let $\hat{\phi}_j = b_{j1}\hat{\theta}_1 + \cdots + b_{jm}\hat{\theta}_m = \beta_{j1}Q_1 + \cdots + \beta_{jm}Q_m$. We then compute

$$(9.3.5) \quad d_{jj'} = b_{j1}\beta_{j'1} + \cdots + b_{jm}\beta_{j'm} = b_{j'1}\beta_{j1} + \cdots + b_{j'm}\beta_{jm}$$

and then

$$(9.3.6) \quad \mathbf{S}_h = \sum_{j,j'=1}^{q} d^{jj'}(\hat{\phi}_j - \phi_j^0)(\hat{\phi}_{j'} - \phi_{j'}^0)',$$

where $((d^{jj'})) = ((d_{jj'}))^{-1}$. An alternative formula is

$$(9.3.7) \quad \mathbf{S}_h = \mathbf{S}_e^* - \mathbf{S}_e,$$

where $\mathbf{S}_e^*$ is the sp matrix due to error when H_0 is true.

Though these formulae look formidable, the actual procedure for computing the sp matrics due to error and due to the hypothesis is not too complicated. As a matter of fact, these matrices can be obtained in exactly the same way as in the univariate procedure of analysis of variance and covariance.

Starting from the matrices $\mathbf{S}_h$ and $\mathbf{S}_e$, three different procedures have been proposed for testing H_0.

$$P_1: \text{Reject } H_0 \text{ if } L = \frac{|\mathbf{S}_e|}{|\mathbf{S}_e + \mathbf{S}_h|} < c'.$$

$$P_2: \text{Reject } H_0 \text{ if } R = \lambda_{\max}[\mathbf{S}_h(\mathbf{S}_e + \mathbf{S}_h)^{-1}] > c''.$$

$$P_3: \text{Reject } H_0 \text{ if } H = \text{tr }(\mathbf{S}_h\mathbf{S}_e^{-1}) > c'''.$$

Here $\lambda_{\max}$ denotes the maximum latent root and tr the "trace" of a matrix, and c', c'', c''' are appropriate constants to ensure attainment of a preassigned level of significance. We shall use procedure P_1, which is based on the likelihood ratio, primarily because the computations involved are less laborious than those required for the other procedures.

When e is moderately large, P_1 reduces to rejecting H_0 at approximate level of significance α if

$$(9.3.8) \qquad T = -\left(e - \frac{p - q + 1}{2}\right) \ln L > \chi^2_{pq}(\alpha),$$

where $L = |\mathbf{S}_e|/|\mathbf{S}_e + \mathbf{S}_h|$.

When $p = 2$, to ensure that the level of significance is exactly α, reject H_0 if

$$(9.3.9) \qquad \frac{1 - \sqrt{L}}{\sqrt{L}} \cdot \frac{e - 1}{q} > F_{2q, 2e-2}(\alpha).$$

Similarly, when $q = 2$, reject H_0 at level of significance α if

$$(9.3.10) \qquad \frac{1 - \sqrt{L}}{\sqrt{L}} \cdot \frac{e - p + 1}{p} > F_{2p, 2e-2p+2}(\alpha).$$

Equality of k Mean Vectors ($k \geq 2$). Let $\bar{\mathbf{x}}^{(i)}$ and $\mathbf{S}^{(i)}$ be, respectively, the sample mean vector and the corrected sp matrix based on a sample of size n_i from $\mathcal{N}_p(\mathbf{\mu}^{(i)}, \mathbf{\Sigma})$, the ith of k p-variate normal populations with a common dispersion matrix, $i = 1, 2, \ldots, k$.

Let $n = n_1 + \cdots + n_k$, $\bar{\mathbf{x}} = (n_1\bar{\mathbf{x}}^{(1)} + \cdots + n_k\bar{\mathbf{x}}^{(k)})/n$, $\mathbf{B} = n_1\bar{\mathbf{x}}^{(1)'}\bar{\mathbf{x}}^{(1)} + \cdots + n_k\bar{\mathbf{x}}^{(k)'}\bar{\mathbf{x}}^{(k)} - n\bar{\mathbf{x}}'\bar{\mathbf{x}}$, and $\mathbf{W} = \mathbf{S}^{(1)} + \cdots + \mathbf{S}^{(k)}$. The matrices $\mathbf{B}$ and $\mathbf{W}$ are known respectively as the "between" and "within" sp matrices. To test the hypothesis of equality of population mean vectors, $H : \mathbf{\mu}^{(1)} = \mathbf{\mu}^{(2)} = \cdots = \mathbf{\mu}^{(k)}$, use 9.3.8 with $\mathbf{S}_e = \mathbf{W}$, $\mathbf{S}_h = \mathbf{B}$, $e = n - k$, $q = k - 1$.

Illustrative Example 9.3. Table 9.5 gives the means and the dispersion matrix (estimated from within groups) of three anthropometric characters: maximum head length x_1, maximum head breadth x_2, and frontal breadth

TABLE 9.5

MEANS AND DISPERSION MATRIX

	Mean			Estimated dispersion matrix based on 803 df within groups		
	Nadia	Dacca	Mymensingh			
	Sample size					
	$n_1 = 170$	$n_2 = 337$	$n_3 = 299$	x_1	x_2	x_3
x_1	182.19	182.54	183.94	41.30	5.47	7.48
x_2	139.79	142.71	141.16		26.89	10.65
x_3	102.37	103.54	103.43			17.81

x_3, for Muslims in three districts of East and West Bengal: Nadia, Dacca, and Mymensingh. Data are from *Race Elements in Bengal* by D. N. Majumdar and C. R. Rao, published by Asia Publishing House.

To examine whether the mean vectors are significantly different we first compute the sp matrix between groups. This comes out as

$$B = \begin{bmatrix} 446.8739 & -47.4447 & 126.8392 \\ & 1024.7685 & 355.7332 \\ & & 169.6726 \end{bmatrix}.$$

For instance,

$$b_{11} = 170(182.19)^2 + 337(182.54)^2 + 299(183.94)^2$$
$$- (170 \times 182.19 + 337 \times 182.54 + 299 \times 183.94)^2/$$
$$(170 + 337 + 299)$$
$$= 446.8739,$$

and

$$b_{12} = 170 \times 182.19 \times 137.79 + 3.37 \times 182.54 \times 142.71 +$$
$$299 \times 183.94 \times 141.16 - (170 \times 182.19 + 337 \times 182.54 +$$
$$299 \times 183.94)(170 \times 137.79 + 337 \times 142.71 + 299 \times 141.16)/$$
$$(170 + 337 + 299)$$
$$= -47.4447.$$

The sp matrix within groups can be expressed as $\mathbf{W} = e\hat{\boldsymbol{\Sigma}}$, where $\hat{\boldsymbol{\Sigma}}$ is the dispersion matrix within groups based on $e = n_1 + n_2 + n_3 - 3 = 803$ df. In 9.3.8, the statistic $L = \dfrac{|\mathbf{W}|}{|\mathbf{W} + \mathbf{B}|}$ can be written alternatively as

$L = \dfrac{|\hat{\boldsymbol{\Sigma}}|}{|\hat{\boldsymbol{\Sigma}} + (1/e)\mathbf{B}|}$. In this case $|\hat{\boldsymbol{\Sigma}}| = 13,928.57$ and

$$\left| \hat{\boldsymbol{\Sigma}} + \frac{1}{e}\mathbf{B} \right| = \begin{vmatrix} 41.86 & 5.41 & 7.64 \\ & 28.17 & 11.09 \\ & & 18.02 \end{vmatrix} = 14,845.77 .$$

Hence $L = 13,928.57/14,845.77 = 0.93822$. Here $p = 3$, $q = 2$, and therefore from 9.3.8 we obtain

$$T = -\left(e - \frac{p - q + 1}{2}\right) \ln L = 51.144^{**} > \chi_6^2(0.01),$$

which is highly significant. The groups are therefore significantly different in respect to the means of these three characters.

9.4 TESTS OF THE DISPERSION MATRIX

Equality of k Dispersion Matrices. On the basis of samples of size n_i from $\mathcal{N}_p(\mathbf{\mu}^{(i)}, \mathbf{\Sigma}^{(i)})$, $i = 1, 2, \ldots, k$, to test the hypothesis that the dispersion matrices are equal,

$$H_0 : \quad \mathbf{\Sigma}^{(1)} = \mathbf{\Sigma}^{(2)} = \cdots = \mathbf{\Sigma}^{(k)},$$

the statistic to use is

$$(9.4.1) \qquad\qquad B = \frac{\prod_{i=1}^{k} |\hat{\mathbf{\Sigma}}_i|^{\nu_i}}{|\hat{\mathbf{\Sigma}}|^{\nu}},$$

where $\nu_i = n_i - 1$, $\nu = \nu_1 + \nu_2 + \cdots + \nu_k$, $\hat{\mathbf{\Sigma}}_i = \mathbf{S}_i/\nu_i$, $\hat{\mathbf{\Sigma}} = (\mathbf{S}_1 + \cdots + \mathbf{S}_k)/\nu$, $\mathbf{S}_i$ being the corrected sp matrix for the ith sample. When samples are large in size, H_0 is to be rejected at approximate level of significance α if

$$(9.4.2) \qquad\qquad T = -\rho \ln B > \chi_f^2(\alpha),$$

where

$$\rho = 1 - \left(\frac{1}{\nu_1} + \cdots + \frac{1}{\nu_k} - \frac{1}{\nu}\right)\frac{2p^2 + 3p - 1}{6(p + 1)(k - 1)}$$

and $f = \frac{1}{2}(k - 1)p(p + 1)$.

Illustrative Example 9.4. Table 9.6 gives the estimated dispersion matrices of three anthropometric characters: maximum head length x_1, maximum head breadth x_2, and frontal breadth x_3, for Muslims in three districts of East and West Bengal: Nadia, Dacca, and Mymensingh. These are computed from the statistics given by D. N. Majumdar and C. R. Rao in *Race Elements in Bengal*, a quantitative study, published by Asia Publishing House.

TABLE 9.6

DISPERSION MATRICES OF ANTHROPOMETRIC CHARACTERS

	Nadia			Dacca			Mymensingh		
	Sample size								
	$n_1 = 170$			$n_2 = 337$			$n_3 = 299$		
	x_1	x_2	x_3	x_1	x_2	x_3	x_1	x_2	x_3
x_1	43.38	4.62	9.90	41.09	7.05	8.66	40.37	4.16	4.79
x_2		27.85	11.60		27.72	10.97		25.37	9.75
x_3			23.05			18.75			13.79

Writing $\hat{\Sigma}_1$, $\hat{\Sigma}_2$, $\hat{\Sigma}_3$ for the estimated dispersion matrices for the districts Nadia, Dacca, and Mymensingh, respectively, we have $|\hat{\Sigma}_1| = 19{,}849.81$, $|\hat{\Sigma}_2| = 14{,}740.42$, $|\hat{\Sigma}_3| = 9853.69$.

The degrees of freedom are $v_1 = n_1 - 1 = 169$, $v_2 = n_2 - 1 = 336$, and $v_3 = n_3 - 1 = 298$, respectively, and $v = v_1 + v_2 + v_3 = 803$. The pooled dispersion matrix is

$$\hat{\Sigma} = (v_1\Sigma_1 + v_2\Sigma_2 + v_3\Sigma_3)/v = \begin{bmatrix} 41.30 & 5.47 & 7.48 \\ & 26.89 & 10.65 \\ & & 17.81 \end{bmatrix}.$$

Therefore $|\hat{\Sigma}| = 13{,}928.57$.

To examine whether the dispersion matrices for the three districts are significantly different, we compute ρ and f from formula 9.4.2, noting that $p = 3$ and $k = 3$ in our case. Thus

$$\rho = 1 - \left(\frac{1}{v_1} + \frac{1}{v_2} + \frac{1}{v_3} - \frac{1}{v}\right) \cdot \frac{2p^2 + 3p - 1}{6(p + 1)(k - 1)} = 0.9940396,$$

$$f = \tfrac{1}{2}p(p + 1)(k - 1) = 12,$$

and

$$T = \rho(v \ln |\hat{\Sigma}| - v_1 \ln |\hat{\Sigma}_1| - v_2 \ln |\hat{\Sigma}_2| - v_3 \ln |\hat{\Sigma}_3|)$$
$$= 24.091* > \chi_{12}^2(0.05).$$

Thus at the 5% level of significance the dispersion matrices can be regarded as different; however, the differences are not significant at the 1% level.

Independence. Suppose that p jointly normally distributed variates are divided into m groups with p_i variates in the ith group, $i = 1, 2, \ldots, m$, so that $p = p_1 + \cdots + p_m$. To examine on the basis of a sample of size n the hypothesis that the m groups of variates are mutually independent, the statistic to use is

(9.4.3)
$$L = \frac{|S|}{\prod_{i=1}^{m} |S_i|},$$

where S is the corrected sp matrix for all the p variates, and S_i is a $p_i \times p_i$ diagonal submatrix of S, being the corrected sp matrix for the p_i variates in the ith group. For large n, the hypothesis is to be rejected at approximate level of significance α if

(9.4.4)
$$T = -(n - \lambda) \ln L > \chi_f^2(\alpha),$$

where

$$f = \tfrac{1}{2}p^2 - \tfrac{1}{2}(p_1^2 + \cdots + p_m^2) \quad \text{and} \quad \lambda = \frac{3}{2} + \frac{p^3 - (p_1^3 + \cdots + p_m^3)}{6f}.$$

Illustrative Example 9.5. Table 9.7 gives the dispersion matrix of the scores x_1, x_2, x_3, x_4 on four tests, the first two on composition and the second two on mathematics, based on a sample of $n = 300$ students.

To examine whether the scores on composition (x_1, x_2) and those on mathematics (x_3, x_4) are independent, we use the statistic L defined by 9.4.3. This can be expressed in the equivalent form $L = |\hat{\Sigma}|/|\hat{\Sigma}_{11}| \, |\hat{\Sigma}_{22}|$, where $\hat{\Sigma}$ is the dispersion matrix of all the four scores, $\hat{\Sigma}_{11}$ is that of (x_1, x_2) only and $\hat{\Sigma}_{22}$ is that of (x_3, x_4) only. We have $|\hat{\Sigma}| = 167{,}198.37$,

TABLE 9.7

DISPERSION MATRIX OF SCORES ON FOUR TESTS

	x_1	x_2	x_3	x_4
x_1	15.129	23.860	1.793	0.998
x_2		54.756	3.633	3.511
x_3			18.225	21.122
x_4				60.516

which was worked out in illustrative example 5.7 of Part I. Also

$$|\hat{\Sigma}_{11}| = \begin{vmatrix} 15.129 & 23.860 \\ 23.860 & 54.756 \end{vmatrix} = 259.1039$$

and

$$|\hat{\Sigma}_{22}| = \begin{vmatrix} 18.225 & 21.122 \\ 21.122 & 60.516 \end{vmatrix} = 656.7652.$$

Therefore $L = 0.98253$.

Here $p = 4$, $p_1 = 2$, $p_2 = 2$, and hence from 9.4.4 we obtain

$$f = \tfrac{1}{2}p^2 - \tfrac{1}{2}(p_1^2 + p_2^2) = 4,$$

$$\lambda = \frac{3}{2} + \frac{p^3 - (p_1^2 + p_2^3)}{6f} = 3.5,$$

and

$$T = -(n - \lambda) \ln L = 5.226 < \chi_4^2(0.05).$$

This is not significant, and we cannot reject the hypothesis of independence.

Illustrative Example 9.6. On the basis of the data given in illustrative example 9.5, can we regard the scores on the four tests as mutually independent?

We have to compute first

$$L = \frac{|\hat{\Sigma}|}{\hat{\sigma}_{11}\hat{\sigma}_{22}\hat{\sigma}_{33}\hat{\sigma}_{44}} = \frac{167{,}198.37}{913{,}649.64} = 0.1830.$$

In this case $p = 4$, $p_1 = p_2 = p_3 = p_4 = 1$, and therefore

$$f = \tfrac{1}{2}p^2 - \tfrac{1}{2}\Sigma p_i^2 = 6$$

$$\lambda = \frac{3}{2} + \frac{p^3 - \Sigma p_i^3}{6f} = 3.16667.$$

Hence from 9.4.4 we have

$$T = -(n - \lambda) \ln L = 504.103 > \chi_6^2(0.01).$$

This being highly significant, we reject the hypothesis that the four variates are mutually independent.

Canonical Correlation. Let the dispersion matrix of the $p + q$ variates $(X_1, \ldots, X_p; Y_1, \ldots, Y_q)$ be written in the partitioned form $\begin{bmatrix} \Sigma_{11} & \Sigma_{12} \\ \Sigma_{21} & \Sigma_{22} \end{bmatrix}$, where Σ_{11} is the $p \times p$ dispersion matrix of $X = (X_1, \ldots, X_p)$, Σ_{22} is that of $Y = (Y_1, \ldots, Y_q)$, Σ_{12} is the $p \times q$ matrix of the covariances of an element of X with an element of Y, and of course $\Sigma_{21} = \Sigma_{12}'$. We shall assume that $p \leq q$.

As a measure of correlation between the p-dimensional variable X and the q-dimensional variable Y, Hotelling proposed the following. Consider a linear function of $X_1, \ldots, X_p$, say $X^* = l_1 X_1 + \cdots + l_p X_p = lX'$, and another of $Y_1, Y_2, \ldots, Y_q$, say $Y^* = m_1 Y_1 + \cdots + m_q Y_q = mY'$, and determine the coefficients l and m such that the correlation between X^* and Y^* is maximum. The maximum value of the correlation, ρ, called the *maximum canonical correlation*, is the proposed measure. It can be shown that ρ^2 is the dominant latent root of matrix $\Sigma_{11}^{-1}\Sigma_{12}\Sigma_{22}^{-1}\Sigma_{21}$ or, equivalently, the maximum root of the determinantal equations

(9.4.5) $$|\Sigma_{12}\Sigma_{22}^{-1}\Sigma_{21} - \rho^2\Sigma_{11}| = 0.$$

Then l is obtained from

(9.4.6) $$(\Sigma_{12}\Sigma_{22}^{-1}\Sigma_{21} - \rho^2\Sigma_{11})l' = 0,$$

and $m = (1/\rho)\Sigma_{12}\Sigma_{22}^{-1}$.

Illustrative Example 9.7. Find the maximum canonical correlation between the scores (x_1, x_2) in composition and the scores (x_3, x_4) in mathematics, using the dispersion matrix of scores given in illustrative example 9.5.

We write the dispersion matrix in the partitioned form $\begin{bmatrix} \hat{\Sigma}_{11} & \hat{\Sigma}_{12} \\ \hat{\Sigma}_{21} & \hat{\Sigma}_{22} \end{bmatrix}$ so that $\hat{\Sigma}_{11}$ is the dispersion matrix of (x_1, x_2) and so on. The square of the

maximum canonical correlation is the maximum latent root of the matrix
$\mathbf{P} = \hat{\boldsymbol{\Sigma}}_{11}^{-1} \boldsymbol{\Sigma}_{12} \hat{\boldsymbol{\Sigma}}_{22}^{-1} \boldsymbol{\Sigma}_{21}$. Direct computation gives

$$\mathbf{P} = \begin{bmatrix} 9.2741 & 12.0230 \\ 2.8692 & 8.2350 \end{bmatrix} \times 10^{-3}.$$

The two latent roots of $\mathbf{P}$ are 0.014651 and 0.0028582. The maximum canonical correlation is thus

$$\rho = \sqrt{(0.014651)} = 0.121.$$

To find the canonical variates we use formula 9.4.6. If coefficients of x_1 and x_4 are taken as unity, the canonical variates turn out to be $X^* = x_1 + 0.4472x_2$ and $Y^* = x_3 - 0.1664x_4$. As a check, we find by direct computation $V(X^*) = 47.420$, $V(Y^*) = 12.871$, and $\mathrm{Cov}\,(X^*, Y^*) = 2.990$ so that the coefficient of correlation between X^* and Y^* is 0.121, which agrees with ρ.

Spherical Symmetry. To examine on the basis of a sample of size n from a p-variate normal population the hypothesis that the variates are mutually independent and have equal variances, the statistic to use is

(9.4.7) $$M = \frac{|\mathbf{S}|}{s^p},$$

where $\mathbf{S}$ is the corrected sp matrix and $s = \mathrm{tr}\,\mathbf{S}/p$. For large n, the hypothesis of spherical symmetry is to be rejected at approximate level of significance α if

(9.4.8) $$T = -(n - \lambda) \ln M > \chi_f^2(\alpha),$$

where $f = \frac{1}{2}p(p + 1) - 1$ and $\lambda = (2p^2 + p + 2)/6p$.

Equality of Means, of Variances, and of Covariances. For a p-variate normal population consider the hypothesis (i) H_{mvc}: that the means are equal, the variances are equal, and the covariances are equal, and (ii) H_{vc}: that the variances are equal and the covariances are equal. In a sample of size n, let $\mathbf{S} = ((S_{ij}))$ be the corrected sp matrix, and $\bar{\mathbf{x}} = (\bar{x}_1, \bar{x}_2, \ldots, \bar{x}_p)$ the sample mean vector. Let

$$s = \frac{1}{p} \sum_{i=1}^{p} S_{ii}, \qquad s' = \frac{1}{p(p-1)} \sum_{i \neq j=1}^{p} S_{ij}, \qquad \bar{\bar{x}} = \frac{1}{p} \sum_{i=1}^{p} \bar{x}_i.$$

Wilks showed that the likelihood-ratio principle yields the following statistics: L_{mvc} and L_{vc} for testing, respectively, the hypotheses H_{mvc} and H_{vc}:

$$(9.4.9) \qquad L_{\text{mvc}} = \frac{|S|}{[s + (p-1)s'] \left[s - s' + \dfrac{n}{p-1} \displaystyle\sum_{i=1}^{p} (\bar{x}_i - \bar{\bar{x}})^2 \right]^{p-1}},$$

$$(9.4.10) \qquad L_{\text{vc}} = \frac{|S|}{[s + (p-1)s'][s - s']^{p-1}}.$$

When n is large, the hypothesis H_{mvc} (or H_{vc}) is to be rejected at approximate level of significance α if

$$(9.4.11) \qquad T = -(n - \lambda) \ln L > \chi_f^2(\alpha),$$

where L is Wilks' L_{mvc} (or L_{vc}) criteria, and λ and f are constants tabulated in Table 9.8 for $p = 4, 5, 6, 7, 8$.

Exact tests are available when $p = 2$ or 3. If $p = 2$ and the level of significance is α, H_{mvc} is to be rejected if

$$(9.4.12) \qquad \frac{(n - 2)(1 - L_{\text{mvc}})}{2L_{\text{mvc}}} > F_{2,n-2}(\alpha),$$

and H_{vc} is to be rejected if

$$(9.4.13) \qquad \frac{(n - 2)(1 - L_{\text{vc}})}{L_{\text{vc}}} > F_{1,n-2}(\alpha).$$

If $p = 3$, H_{mvc} is to be rejected if

$$(9.4.14) \qquad \frac{(n - 3)(1 - \sqrt{L_{\text{mvc}}})}{3\sqrt{L_{\text{mvc}}}} > F_{6,2n-6},$$

and H_{vc} is to be rejected if

$$(9.4.15) \qquad \frac{(n - 3)(1 - \sqrt{L_{\text{vc}}})}{2\sqrt{L_{\text{vc}}}} > F_{4,2n-6}.$$

TABLE 9.8
VALUES OF f AND λ

p	L_{mvc}		L_{vc}	
	f	λ	f	λ
4	11	2.217	8	2.736
5	17	2.485	13	3.019
6	24	2.775	19	3.321
7	32	3.076	26	3.632
8	41	3.385	34	3.950

Illustrative Example 9.8. Table 9.9 gives means, variances, and co-variances for scores on four tests for a sample of $n = 50$ examinees. (a) Can the tests be regarded as parallel? (b) If not, would additive corrections applied to the means make the tests parallel?

Tests are said to be parallel if test scores in the population of examinees have equal means, equal variances, and equal covariances. To answer question (a), the appropriate hypothesis to be tested is H_{mvc}, and for (b) it is H_{vc}.

The sample dispersion matrix here was obtained by dividing the sp matrix by n. We thus have here $p = 4$, and $|S| = 39,750.5n^4$, $s = 24.47055n$, $s' = 13.03058n$, $\Sigma(x_i - \bar{x})^2 = 0.78094$, $s + (p - 1)s' = 63.56229n$, and $s - s' = 11.43997n$. Therefore

$$L_{mvc} = \frac{39,750.5n^4}{(63.56229n)(11.43997n + 0.78094n)^3} = 0.3821.$$

From Table 9.8 we have $f = 11$ and $\lambda = 2.217$. Hence from 9.4.11 we obtain

$$T = -(n - \lambda) \ln L_{mvc} = 45.971^{**} > \chi_{11}^2(0.01),$$

which is highly significant. Thus H_{mvc} is rejected.

To examine H_{vc}, we compute

$$L_{vc} = \frac{39,750.5n^4}{(63.56229n)(11.43997n)^3} = 0.4177.$$

From Table 9.8 we have $f = 8$ and $\lambda = 2.736$, so that from 9.4.11

$$T = -(n - \lambda) \ln L_{vc} = 39.084^{**} > \chi_8^2(0.01),$$

which is highly significant. Therefore tests are not parallel, and even additive corrections in the means would not make them so.

TABLE 9.9

MEANS, VARIANCES, AND COVARIANCES FOR FOUR
TESTS, $n = 50$

Test	Mean	Sample dispersion matrix			
		A	B	C	D
A	14·9048	25.0704	12.4363	11.7257	20.7510
B	15.4841		28.2021	9.2281	11.9732
C	14.4444			22.7390	12.0692
D	14.3810				21.8707

9.5 CLASSIFICATION

The General Problem of Classification. Suppose that an individual is to be classified into one of k populations on the basis of p characteristics $\mathbf{X} = (X_1, X_2, \ldots, X_p)$ of the individual. The a priori probability of the individual's coming from the ith population is p_i, $p_i > 0$, and $\sum_{i=1}^{k} p_i = 1$. The frequency density function of $\mathbf{X}$ in the ith population is supposed to be known and will be denoted by $f_i(\mathbf{x})$, $i = 1, 2, \ldots, k$.

Let l_{ij} be the loss due to misclassification of an individual actually coming from the ith population as belonging to the jth population, $l_{ij} > 0$ for $i \neq j$ and $l_{ii} = 0$. Then the best procedure for classification in the sense of minimizing the average loss due to misclassification is to compute

$$(9.5.1) \qquad F_j(\mathbf{X}) = \sum_{i=1}^{p} l_{ij} p_i f_i(\mathbf{X})$$

for $j = 1, 2, \ldots, k$ and to assign the individual to the jth population if j is the smallest index for which

$$F_j = \min(F_1, F_2, \ldots, F_k)$$

holds.

The Multivariate Normal Case. Suppose that the populations are all multivariate normal with a common dispersion matrix Σ, and let the mean vector for the ith population be denoted by $\mu^{(i)}$, $i = 1, 2, \ldots, k$. Suppose further that the a priori probabilities are equal, $p_i = 1/k$, and that losses due to any type of misclassification are equal, $l_{ij} = l$ if $i \neq j$ and $l_{ii} = 0$. The classification procedure in such a case becomes particularly simple. One has to compute the quadratic forms

$$(9.5.2) \qquad Q_j = (\mathbf{X} - \mu^{(j)})\Sigma^{-1}(\mathbf{X} - \mu^{(j)})'$$

for $j = 1, 2, \ldots, k$ and to assign the individual to the jth population if j is the smallest index for which

$$Q_j = \min(Q_1, Q_2, \ldots, Q_k)$$

holds.

If $k = 2$, the procedure further simplifies to the following. The individual is to be assigned to the first population if

$$(9.5.3) \qquad \sum_{i=1}^{p} \lambda_i X_i \geq \tfrac{1}{2}(\theta_1 + \theta_2)$$

and to the second population otherwise, where

$$\lambda = (\lambda_1, \ldots, \lambda_p) = (\mu^{(1)} - \mu^{(2)})\Sigma^{-1}$$

and $\theta_j = \mu^{(j)}\lambda'$, $j = 1, 2$. The total probability of misclassification when this procedure is followed is given by $2\Phi(-\frac{1}{2}\Delta)$, where

$$(9.5.4) \qquad \Delta^2 = (\mu^{(1)} - \mu^{(2)})\Sigma^{-1}(\mu^{(1)} - \mu^{(2)})'$$

and

$$\Phi(x) = \int_{-\infty}^{x} \frac{1}{\sqrt{2\pi}} e^{-\frac{1}{2}t^2} dt.$$

LINEAR DISCRIMINANT FUNCTION.   The function $\sum_{i=1}^{p} \lambda_i X_i$ defined in formula 9.5.3 is called the *linear discriminant function* for the two populations. The non-negative quantity Δ defined by 9.5.4 was used by Mahalanobis as a measure of divergence between the two populations and is called *Mahalanobis' distance function*.

The problem of classification when the density functions are unspecified or involve unknown parameters has not been satisfactorily solved. All that we can generally do is to substitute estimates for unknown parameters.

The sample analogue of the distance function, namely,

$$(9.5.5) \qquad D^2 = [\bar{x}^{(1)} - \bar{x}^{(2)}]\Sigma^{-1}[\bar{x}^{(1)} - \bar{x}^{(2)}]',$$

is not an unbiased estimate of Δ^2.   To obtain an unbiased estimate we take

$$(9.5.6) \qquad \hat{\Delta}^2 = \frac{n_1 + n_2 - p - 3}{n_1 + n_2 - 2} D^2 - \frac{(n_1 + n_2)p}{n_1 n_2}.$$

Illustrative Example 9.9.   Using the data given in illustrative example 9.2, find the linear discriminant function based on the three characters x_1, x_2, x_3 between the two groups of desert locusts. What is the classification rule in this case? To which group would you assign a locust with measurements $x_1 = 27.06$, $x_2 = 8.03$, and $x_3 = 11.36$?

Estimates $\mathbf{l} = (l_1, l_2, l_3)$ of the coefficients of x_1, x_2, x_3 in the linear discriminant function are obtained from the equations $\mathbf{l}\hat{\Sigma} = \mathbf{d}$, when $\hat{\Sigma}$ is the estimated common dispersion matrix and $\mathbf{d}$ is the difference of the two mean vectors. These can be obtained by back substitution from the pivotal condensation of $\hat{\Sigma}$ and $\mathbf{d}$ given in Table 9.4. Extracting the relevant portion from this table, the equations in triangular form are as follows:

l_1	l_2	l_3	
1	0.1187328	0.3101373	−0.5385428
	1	0.5637433	9.2047587
		1	4.5820083

where only the coefficients are shown. Thus $l_1 = -2.745805$, $l_2 = 6.621684$, $l_3 = 4.582008$, and the linear discriminant function is $L = l_1x_1 + l_2x_2 + l_3x_3$. The mean value of L for the phase *gregaria* is $\theta_1 = 25.80l_1 + 7.81l_2 + 10.77l_3 = 30.22167$, and for the intermediate phase it is $\theta_2 = 28.35l_1 + 7.41l_2 + 10.75l_3 = 20.47954$. Thus $\frac{1}{2}(\theta_1 + \theta_2) = 25.35061$. The value of L for the particular locust is $L = 27.06l_1 + 8.03l_2 + 11.36l_3 = 30.92211$. Since $L > \frac{1}{2}(\theta_1 + \theta_2)$, it has to be classified as belonging to the first population, that is, to the phase *gregaria*. As a check on the computations, we have $D^2 = \theta_1 - \theta_2 = 9.74213$, which agrees with the value found in illustrative example 9.2.

Illustrative Example 9.10. Table 9.10 gives the means of four measurements taken on four series of Egyptian skulls, and Table 9.11 gives their estimated dispersion matrix within groups (Barnard's data, *Annals of Eugenics* (*London*), Vol. 6, 1935). For a newly discovered Egyptian skull, these measurements are $x_1 = 134$, $x_2 = 97$, $x_3 = 52$, and $x_4 = 132$. In the absence of any other information, to which one of the four series should the skull be allocated?

We shall ignore the sampling fluctuations in the estimates of the four mean vectors and the common dispersion matrix and denote them by $\mu^{(i)}$, $i = 1, 2, 3, 4$, and Σ, respectively. We shall write $\mathbf{X} = (134, 97, 52, 132)$ for the four measurements on the new skull. Formula 9.5.2 says that to classify this skull we have to compute $Q_j = (\mathbf{X} - \mu^{(j)})\Sigma^{-1}(\mathbf{X} - \mu^{(j)})$,

TABLE 9.10

MEANS OF MEASUREMENTS ON EGYPTIAN SKULLS

	Series 1 late pre-dynastic	Series 2 6–12th dynastics	Series 3 12–13th dynastics	Series 4 Ptolemaic dynastics
	Sample size			
Measurement	$n_1 = 9_1$	$n_2 = 162$	$n_3 = 70$	$n_4 = 75$
Maximum breadth x_1	133.582	134.265	134.371	135.307
Basialveolar length x_2	98.308	96.463	95.857	95.040
Nasal height x_3	50.835	51.148	50.100	52.093
Basibregmatic height x_4	133.000	134.883	133.643	131.467

TABLE 9.11

ESTIMATED DISPERSION MATRIX WITHIN GROUPS
(BASED ON 394 df)

	x_1	x_2	x_3	x_4
x_1	24.5228	1.1309	2.8696	5.4533
x_2		23.0282	3.1452	5.7254
x_3			9.9957	3.2260
x_4				22.1866

for $j = 1, 2, 3, 4$. Direct computation gives $Q_1 = 0.31922$, $Q_2 = 0.59113$, $Q_3 = 0.66109$, and $Q_4 = 0.25946$. Since Q_4 is the smallest, the skull is to be assigned to series 4.

Test for an Assigned Discriminant Function. To test whether a given linear function $y = c_1 x_1 + \cdots + c_p x_p$ is the discriminant function between two p-variate normal populations with a common dispersion, the first step is to compute the distance due to y, namely,

$$D_y^2 = \frac{(\mathbf{cd'})^2}{\mathbf{c \, \Sigma \, c'}}, \qquad \text{where } \mathbf{d} = \bar{\mathbf{x}}^{(1)} - \bar{\mathbf{x}}^{(2)}.$$

The given function is discarded at level of significance α if

$$(9.5.7) \quad T = \frac{n_1 + n_2 - p - 1}{p - 1} \frac{c(D^2 - D_y^2)}{1 + cD_y^2} > F_{p-1, n_1+n_2-p-1}(\alpha),$$

where D^2 is defined by 9.5.5 and $c = n_1 n_2 / (n_1 + n_2)(n_1 + n_2 - 2)$.

Illustrative Example 9.11. Are the data given in illustrative example 9.2 consistent with the hypothesis that the linear discriminant function between the two groups of desert locusts is $y = -3x_1 + 7x_2 + 5x_3$?

The coefficient vector of this function is $\mathbf{c} = (-3, 7, 5)$.

Using the difference $\mathbf{d}$ between the two sample mean vectors and the estimated common dispersion matrix $\hat{\mathbf{\Sigma}}$ from illustrative example 9.2, we find the distance due to y as

$$D_y^2 = \frac{(\mathbf{cd'})^2}{\mathbf{c \, \hat{\Sigma} \, c'}} = 9.73562.$$

Here $n_1 = 20$, $n_2 = 72$, $p = 3$, and the distance based on three characters was found in illustrative example 9.2 to be $D^2 = 9.7421$. Hence formula 9.5.7 gives $T = 0.0185 < F_{2,88}(0.05)$. Since this is not significant at the 5% level, we cannot reject the hypothesis.

Additional Distance Due to Extra Variates. Let Δ_p denote the distance between two populations based on the p variates $X_1, X_2, \ldots, X_p$, and

Δ_{p+q} that based on the $p + q$ variates $X_1, X_2, \ldots, X_p$; $X_{p+1}, \ldots, X_{p+q}$. Then in general $\Delta_{p+q} \geq \Delta_p$; but when equality holds, the inclusion of the extra q variates, namely, $X_{p+1}, \ldots, X_{p+q}$, does not increase the efficiency of discrimination between the two populations. If the two populations are multivariate normal with a common dispersion matrix, the hypothesis $\Delta_{p+q} = \Delta_p$ is rejected at level of significance α if

$$(9.5.8) \qquad T = \frac{ec(D_{p+q}^2 - D_p^{\ 2})}{q(1 + cD_p^{\ 2})} > F_{q,e}(\alpha),$$

where $\theta = n_1 + n_2 - p - q - 1$, $c = n_1 n_2/(n_1 + n_2)(n_1 + n_2 - 2)$, and D_p and D_{p+q} are the sample analogues of Δ_p and Δ_{p+q}, respectively.

Illustrative Example 9.12. On the basis of the data given in illustrative example 9.2, examine whether it is worth while to include x_3 in addition to x_1 and x_2 for purposes of discrimination between the two groups of desert locusts.

We use formula 9.5.8 with $p = 2$, $q = 1$, $c = 20 + 72 - 2 - 1 - 1 = 88$, $c = (20 \times 72)/(92 \times 90) = \frac{4}{23}$, $D_{p+q}^2 = D_3^2 = 9.7421$, $D_p^{\ 2} = D_2^2 = $ distance due to x_1, and $x_2 = 7.8421$. Hence

$$T = \frac{ec(D_{p+q}^2 - D_p^{\ 2})}{q(1 + cD_p^{\ 2})} = 3.075 < F_{1,88}(0.05).$$

The additional distance due to x_3 is thus not significant at the 5% level.

9.6 FACTOR ANALYSIS AND THE METHOD OF PRINCIPAL COMPONENTS

Sometimes it is of importance to examine whether the joint variation in p observable random variables can be described approximately in terms of the joint variation of a fewer number, say r, $r < p$, of hypothetical variables. Two closely related approaches to the problem are available. One, called *factor analysis*, was developed primarily in connection with psychometric investigations. The other, due to Hotelling, is known as the method of *principal components*.

Factor Analysis. In factor analysis, one starts with a p-dimensional observable random variable $\mathbf{X} = (X_1, X_2, \ldots, X_p)$ so standardized that each of its components has unit variance. It is assumed that

$$(9.6.1) \qquad \mathbf{X} = \boldsymbol{\xi}\mathbf{F}' + \boldsymbol{\eta},$$

where $\boldsymbol{\xi}$ is an r-dimensional unobservable random variable with uncorrelated components, each having unit variance, $\mathbf{F}_{pn}$ is a matrix of constants, and $\boldsymbol{\eta}$ is a p-dimensional random variable with uncorrelated components, which is uncorrelated with $\boldsymbol{\xi}$. In psychometric usage, $\mathbf{X}$ is the standardized score vector in p tests, ξ the set of common factors, $\mathbf{F}$ the matrix of *factor loadings*, and η the sum of specific factors and errors of observation. The problem is to determine, on the basis of observations on $\mathbf{X}$, the number of common factors r, the matrix of factor loadings $\mathbf{F}$, and the factor scores ξ.

From 9.6.1 it follows that

$$\mathbf{R} = \mathbf{FF}' + \Delta,$$

where $\mathbf{R}$ is the correlation matrix of $\mathbf{X}$ and $\Delta = \text{diag}\ (\delta_1{}^2, \delta_2{}^2, \ldots, \delta_p{}^2)$ is the dispersion matrix of η. In psychometry, $\delta_i{}^2$ is known as the *uniqueness* of the ith test, and its complement $r_{ii} = 1 - \delta_i{}^2$ is called its *communality*. The matrix $\mathbf{R}^* = \mathbf{R} - \Delta$ is called the *reduced correlation matrix*. The fundamental equation of factor analysis is thus

$$(9.6.2) \qquad\qquad \mathbf{R}^* = \mathbf{FF}'$$

so that $r = \text{rank}\ (\mathbf{R}^*)$ and $\mathbf{F}$ can be obtained from 9.6.2. Notice that $\mathbf{R}^*$ is the same as the correlation matrix of $\mathbf{X}$, except that the diagonal unities are replaced by the communalities. The resolution 9.6.2 is not unique, and various solutions for $\mathbf{F}$ can be obtained. For instance, if $\mathbf{F}$ is any solution, so is $\mathbf{FC}$, where $\mathbf{C}$ is any $r \times r$ orthogonal matrix. In any particular case, that solution is to be chosen which admits ready interpretation in physical terms. A number of methods of factorization will now be described.

THURSTONE'S CENTROID METHOD. This method is applied when most of the correlations are positive. If they are not, we work with transformed variables $\mathbf{Y} = \mathbf{XP}$, where $\mathbf{P} = \text{diag}\ (\pm 1, \pm 1, \ldots, \pm 1)$ with signs so determined that in the correlation matrix $\mathbf{PRP}$ of $\mathbf{Y}$ most of the elements are positive. This is known as *reflection*. Then, if $\mathbf{G}$ is the matrix of factor loadings for $\mathbf{Y}$, that for $\mathbf{X}$ is $\mathbf{F} = \mathbf{PG}$. Henceforth, we shall assume that most correlations either are positive to start with or have been made positive by reflection.

Thurstone's method of factorization consists of the following operations:

(1) Substitute in each diagonal cell of $\mathbf{R}$ the largest absolute element in the corresponding column. That is to say, take the maximum of the correlations in the ith column as a first estimate of the ith communality.

(2) Compute the column totals $C_1, C_2, \ldots, C_p$ and the grand total G.

(3) The loadings $a_{11}, a_{21}, \ldots, a_{p1}$ for the first factor, which form the first column of P, are obtained as $a_{i1} = C_i/\sqrt{G}$, $i = 1, 2, \ldots, p$.

(4) To obtain loadings for the second factor repeat operations (1) through (3) on a suitably reflected form of the residual correlation matrix $\mathbf{R}_1 = ((r_{ij} - a_{i1}a_{j1}))$.

(5) Repeat operations (1) through (4) to extract more factors if necessary. Stop at the stage where the residual correlation matrix become negligibly small.

THE CASE OF A SINGLE COMMON FACTOR. When there is a single common factor, *tetrad differences* of the type

$$D = \begin{vmatrix} r_{jk} & r_{jl} \\ r_{km} & r_{lm} \end{vmatrix} = r_{jk}r_{lm} - r_{jl}r_{km}, \qquad j \neq k \neq l \neq m$$

should all vanish, except for fluctuations of sampling.

Illustrative Example 9.13. The correlation matrix of the scores of 100 students on four psychometric tests is given in Table 9.12. Obtain factor loadings by Thurstone's centroid method.

TABLE 9.12

CORRELATION MATRIX $\mathbf{R} = ((r_{ij}))$ OF SCORES ON FOUR TESTS

Test	1	2	3	4
1	1.0	0.7350	0.5983	0.6203
2		1.0	0.6049	0.6357
3			1.0	0.5515
4				1.0

Since all correlations are positive, reflection is not necessary to start with. The first step is to replace diagonal unities by maximum absolute correlation in the column, thus obtaining the following reduced correlation matrix:

$$\begin{array}{cccc} 0.7350 & 0.7350 & 0.5983 & 0.6203 \\ & 0.7350 & 0.6049 & 0.6357 \\ & & 0.6049 & 0.5515 \\ & & & 0.6357 \end{array}$$

The column sums are, respectively,

$$c_1 = 2.6886, \quad c_2 = 2.7106, \quad c_3 = 2.3596, \quad c_4 = 2.4432,$$

the grand total being $G = 10.2020$.

The first factor loadings are obtained from the relation $a_{i1} = c_i/\sqrt{G}$. This gives the following:

First factor loadings		First factor residuals $((r_{ij} - a_{i1}a_{j1}))$		
$a_{11} = 0.8417$	a	$+0.0207$	-0.0235	-0.0235
$a_{21} = 0.8486$		a	-0.0220	-0.0134
$a_{31} = 0.7387$			a	-0.0135
$a_{41} = 0.7649$				a

a The diagonal elements are not required.

The residuals are all small, and it may not be necessary to extract any more factors. However, for purposes of illustration, we show how second factor loadings could be computed. Since most of the first factor residuals are negative, we reflect tests 3 and 4, that is, pre- and post-multiply by $P = \text{diag}(1, 1, -1, -1)$ and then write in the diagonal cells the maximum absolute entry in the columns. We then get the following matrix:

$$
\begin{array}{cccc}
\underline{0.0235} & 0.0207 & 0.0235 & 0.0235 \\
 & \underline{0.0220} & 0.0220 & 0.0134 \\
 & & \underline{0.0235} & -0.0135 \\
 & & & \underline{0.0235}
\end{array}
$$

The column sums are as follows:

$$c_1' = 0.0912, \quad c_2' = 0.0781, \quad c_3' = 0.0555, \quad c_4' = 0.0469,$$

and the grand total is $G' = 0.2717$.

The second factor loadings are obtained by first computing $a_{i2}' = c_i'/\sqrt{G'}$ and then reflecting back, by postmultiplication by P. Thus we obtain:

$$a_{12} = a_{12}' = 0.1750,$$
$$a_{22} = a_{22}' = 0.1498,$$
$$a_{32} = -a_{32}' = -0.1065,$$
$$a_{42} = -a_{42}' = -0.0900.$$

We could proceed to compute third factor loadings in the same way, but second factor residuals are too small to warrant continuation. As a matter of fact, if we compute the tetrad differences

$$
\begin{vmatrix} r_{12} & r_{13} \\ r_{24} & r_{34} \end{vmatrix} = -0.0014, \qquad
\begin{vmatrix} r_{12} & r_{14} \\ r_{23} & r_{34} \end{vmatrix} = +0.0037,
$$

and

$$
\begin{vmatrix} r_{14} & r_{13} \\ r_{24} & r_{23} \end{vmatrix} = -0.0051,
$$

we find that they are all quite small, and we might therefore have stopped with the extraction of only one factor.

LAWLEY'S METHOD OF MAXIMUM LIKELIHOOD. Under the assumption that in 9.6.1 ξ and η are multivariate normal variables and that the number of factors r is known, maximum-likelihood estimates of factor loadings F can be obtained by an iterative procedure suggested by Lawley. The computational steps are as follows.

(1) Start with an approximation to the factor loadings, say $F_0 = ((a_{ij}))$, $i = 1, 2, \ldots, p;\ j = 1, 2, \ldots, r$.

(2) Estimate uniqueness by $\delta_i^2 = 1 - \sum_{j=1}^r a_{ij}^2$, and write $\boldsymbol{\Delta}_0 =$ diag $(\delta_1^2, \delta_2^2, \ldots, \delta_p^2)$.

(3) Improved estimates of the factor loadings are given by

$$\mathbf{F}_1 = \mathbf{R}\boldsymbol{\Delta}_0^{-1}\mathbf{F}_0(\mathbf{F}_0'\boldsymbol{\Delta}_0^{-1}\mathbf{F}_0)^{-1}.$$

(4) If necessary, repeat operations (1) through (3), starting with $\mathbf{F}_1$ and improved estimate of uniqueness $\boldsymbol{\Delta}_1$. Continue until the results stabilize.

ESTIMATION OF FACTOR SCORES. When factor loadings F and uniqueness $\boldsymbol{\Delta}$ are known, the factor scores corresponding to a standardized vector of test scores $\mathbf{X}$ are estimated from the formula

$$\boldsymbol{\xi} = \mathbf{X}\boldsymbol{\Delta}^{-1}\mathbf{F}(\mathbf{F}'\boldsymbol{\Delta}^{-1}\mathbf{F})^{-1}.$$

Principal Components. Given a p-dimensional random variable $\mathbf{X} = (X_1, \ldots, X_p)$ with dispersion matrix $\boldsymbol{\Sigma}$, we may like to construct a linear function, say $\boldsymbol{\xi}_1 = \mathbf{X}\mathbf{l}_1'$, with $\mathbf{l}_1\mathbf{l}_1' = 1$, such that $V(\boldsymbol{\xi}_1)$ is a maximum. Let $\lambda_1 \geq \lambda_2 \geq \cdots \geq \lambda_p$ be the latent roots of $\boldsymbol{\Sigma}$. It can then be shown that $\mathbf{l}_1$ is a normalized latent vector of $\boldsymbol{\Sigma}$ corresponding to the latent root λ_1, and when $\mathbf{l}_1$ is so chosen, $V(\boldsymbol{\xi}_1) = \lambda_1$ and $\boldsymbol{\xi}_1$ is then said to be the *first principal component* of X.

If we want next to construct $\boldsymbol{\xi}_2 = \mathbf{X}\mathbf{l}_2'$, with $\mathbf{l}_2\mathbf{l}_2' = 1$, so that it is uncorrelated with $\boldsymbol{\xi}_1$ and has maximum variance, it turns out that $\mathbf{l}_2$ is a normalized latent vector of $\boldsymbol{\Sigma}$ corresponding to the latent root λ_2. Then $\boldsymbol{\xi}_2$ is called the second principal component of $\mathbf{X}$. We can similarly find the third, fourth, $\ldots$, and finally the pth principal component.

The total variation in $\mathbf{X}$ may be measured in terms of tr $\boldsymbol{\Sigma} = \lambda_1 + \cdots + \lambda_p$. The sum of the variances of the first r principal components is $\lambda_1 + \cdots + \lambda_r$, and thus these together account for a fraction $(\lambda_1 + \cdots + \lambda_r)/(\lambda_1 + \cdots + \lambda_p)$ of the total variation. Consequently, we may say that the first r principal components adequately describe the variation if the residual $1 - (\lambda_1 + \cdots + \lambda_r)/(\lambda_1 + \cdots + \lambda_p)$ is small.

If the first r principal components, $\xi_j = l_{1j}X_1 + l_{2j}X_2 + \cdots + l_{pj}X_p$, $j = 1, 2, \ldots, r$, are interpreted as the r common factors, we can then write $X_i = l_{i1}\xi_1 + l_{i2}\xi_2 + \cdots + l_{ir}\xi_r + \eta_i$, $i = 1, 2, \ldots, p$, so that l_{ij}'s would be the factor loadings. This, however, is somewhat different from the model 9.6.1 in that the variables $(\eta_1, \ldots, \eta_p)$ have a singular distribution and are not mutually uncorrelated.

Illustrative Example 9.14. The dominant latent root and the corresponding latent vector of the correlation matrix given in illustrative example 9.13 can be worked out by methods described in Chapter 5 of Part I. We get the dominant latent root as $\lambda_1 = 2.8765$, and the corresponding normalized latent vector is $\mathbf{l}_1 = (0.5162, 0.5203, 0.4754, 0.4866)$.

The elements of this vector are taken as the loadings for the first common factor. The first principal components accounts for a fraction $2.8765/4 = 0.72$ of the total variation. To obtain the second principal component, we have to find the dominant latent root and vector of the residual matrix $R - \lambda_1 l_1' l_1$. In this particular case, this is hardly necessary, because the first principal component itself acounts for a very high fraction of the total variation.

TEST FOR PRINCIPAL COMPONENTS. If $\lambda_1 \geq \lambda_2 \geq \cdots \geq \lambda_p$ are all the latent roots of the correlation matrix of a p-variate normal population, it is not worth while to extract more than r factors if $\lambda_r > \lambda_{r+1}$ but $\lambda_{r+1} = \lambda_{r+2} = \cdots = \lambda_p$, that is, if the smallest $p - r$ latent roots are equal in magnitude. Bartlett has suggested the following approximate procedure for testing this hypothesis.

Let n be the size of the sample from which the correlation matrix R is calculated, and let $\hat\lambda_1, \ldots, \hat\lambda_r$ be the r largest latent roots of R. Then the hypothesis is to be rejected at approximate level of significance α if

$$T \equiv -\left(n - 1 - \frac{2p + 5}{6} - \frac{2}{3}r\right) \ln L > \chi_f^2(\alpha),$$

where

$$L = \frac{|R|}{\hat\lambda_1 \cdots \hat\lambda_r \left(\dfrac{p - \hat\lambda_1 - \cdots - \hat\lambda_r}{p - r}\right)^{p-r}}$$

and $f = \frac{1}{2}(p - r)(p - r - 1)$. Thus if T is not significant we may stop after extraction of r factors.

Illustrative Example 9.15. In illustrative example 9.14 we have $p = 4$, $r = 1$, $\lambda_1 = 2.8765$, $|R| = 0.14583$, so that

$$L = \frac{|R|}{\hat\lambda_1 \left(\dfrac{4 - \hat\lambda_1}{3}\right)^3} = 0.96525$$

and $f = \frac{1}{2}(p - 1)(p - 2) = 3$. The size of the sample $n = 100$, so that

$$T = -(n - 1 - \tfrac{13}{6} - \tfrac{2}{3}) \ln L = 3.401 < \chi_3^2(0.05),$$

which is not significant. Therefore we need not extract any more principal components.

9.7 EXERCISES

Mean vector

9.1. Eggs are classified into two grades A and B by visual inspection. In order to examine whether these grades differ in respect to four important characters: yolk shadow x_1, yolk color x_2, albumen index x_3, and albumen

TABLE 9.13

MEAN VALUES AND CORRECTED SUMS OF SQUARES AND PRODUCTS

Grade A (sample size 25)

	Mean	Corrected sum of squares and products			
		x_1	x_2	x_3	x_4
x_1	7.16	106.36	10.32	3.60	−12.16
x_2	13.92		85.84	−21.80	12.08
x_3	21.60			536.00	−486.60
x_4	26.04				532.96

Grade B (sample size 33)

	Mean	Corrected sum of squares and products			
		x_1	x_2	x_3	x_4
x_1	10.30	40.97	−1.03	146.67	−104.91
x_2	15.30		64.97	−13.33	−5.91
x_3	28.33			1133.33	−640.00
x_4	20.09				506.73

height x_4, 25 eggs of grade A and 33 eggs of grade B were observed for these characters. Table 9.13 gives the mean values and the corrected sums of squares and products.

Analyze the data and give your comments.

9.2. Table 9.14 gives the results of an experiment to examine the possibility of using circular cuts of small size in crop-yield estimating surveys. In a certain locality 15 plots growing paddy were selected, and inside each plot a point was located at random. With this point as center three concentric circles of radii 2 ft, 4 ft, and 5 ft 8 in., respectively, were marked out. The inner circle was harvested first, and the yield recorded. The first and second annular rings were then successively harvested, and the yields were recorded separately. From these records, by suitable addition, was constructed Table 9.14, which gives the yield of paddy in tolas [2.5 tolas = 1 oz (approx.)] from the three circles.

Examine whether the mean yield rates obtained from circles of different sizes are different. Also examine whether the bias, if any, in estimating the yield rate is inversely proportional to the perimeter of the sample cut.

9.3. On the basis of the data in exercise 6.2 of Part II examine whether the mean vectors of height and weight are the same for twin brothers and sisters.

TABLE 9.14

Yield of Paddy from Concentric Circular Cuts

Serial no. of plot	Yield of paddy (tolas) from circle of radius		
	2 ft	4 ft	5 ft 8 in.
1	30	114	213
2	34	109	210
3	34	106	215
4	37	109	216
5	27	85	172
6	28	84	174
7	29	85	170
8	32	111	211
9	29	112	208
10	31	114	215
11	37	110	212
12	19	98	205
13	25	104	206
14	20	103	205
15	23	100	208

TABLE 9.15

Means and Pooled Dispersion Matrix of Scores

Neurotic condition	Sample size	Mean score		
		A	B	C
Anxiety state	114	2.9296	1.1667	0.7281
Hysteria	33	3.0303	1.2424	0.5455
Psychopathy	32	3.8125	1.8438	0.8125
Obsession	17	4.0059	1.5882	1.1176
Personality change	5	1.4000	0.2000	0.0000
Normal	55	0.6000	0.1455	0.2182

Within-dispersion matrix (based on 256 observations)

	A	B	C
A	2.300851		
B	0.251578	0.607466	
C	0.474169	0.035774	0.595094

Source: C. R. Rao and P. Slater, Multivariate analysis applied to differences between neurotic groups, *British Journal of Psychology* (Statistics Section), Vol. 2 (1949).

Analysis of dispersion

9.4. On the basis of the data in exercise 6.1 of Part II examine whether the three species of the iris family are identical in respect to the means of these four characteristics: petal length, petal width, sepal length, and sepal width of the flowers.

9.5. Table 9.15 gives the mean scores and the within-dispersion matrix of scores in three tests *A*, *B*, and *C* of 256 army recruits classified according to their neurotic conditions. Examine whether the scores in the tests are useful in distinguishing different neurotic groups.

9.6. Given in Table 9.16 are the mean values of four characters for

TABLE 9.16

MEAN VALUES BY GROUPS AND CHARACTERS AND THE
WITHIN-DISPERSION MATRIX

Group	Sample size	Head length x_1	Head breadth x_2	Bizygo-matic breadth x_3	Nasal height x_4
Brahmin (Basti, B₁)	86	191.92	139.88	133.36	51.24
Brahmin (other, B₂)	92	191.35	139.50	132.68	50.40
Chattri (Ch)	139	192.58	131.72	131.70	52.72
Muslim (M)	167	190.78	137.40	131.52	51.38
Bhatu (C₁)	148	186.10	138.58	133.55	52.06
Habru (C₂)	124	186.94	137.40	131.16	50.30
Bhil (Bh)	187	181.87	137.62	131.18	48.60
Dom (D)	113	186.40	137.52	132.64	50.34
Ahir (A₁)	68	187.45	138.12	131.70	48.98
Kurmi (A₂)	94	188.86	137.86	131.82	49.22
Other Artisan (A₁)	173	187.69	136.84	131.30	48.72
Kahar (A₁)	57	188.83	136.28	130.70	48.62

Within-dispersion matrix

	x_1	x_2	x_3	x_4
x_1	43.6500	5.8865	8.4396	4.0610
x_2		20.2500	11.1438	2.7326
x_3			20.9764	2.9688
x_4				12.2500

Source: C. R. Rao, The utilization of multiple measurements in problems of biological classification, *Journal of the Royal Statistical Society*, Ser. B, Vol. 10 (1948).

TABLE 9.17
Means and Dispersion Matrices

Normal

Boys — Sample size, $n = 50$

	Mean	Dispersion matrix			
		X_1	X_2	Y_1	Y_2
X_1	57.1	136.21	17.25	13.93	34.64
X_2	25.1		10.87	5.21	7.13
Y_1	36.4			14.96	16.35
Y_2	40.5				46.48

Girls — Sample size, $n = 50$

	Mean	Dispersion matrix			
		X_1	X_2	Y_1	Y_2
X_1	56.5	165.85	18.93	33.27	25.74
X_2	30.2		11.66	2.42	6.81
Y_1	37.8			11.48	9.55
Y_2	42.3				39.60

Deaf and Dumb

Boys — Sample size, $n = 50$

	Mean	Dispersion matrix			
		X_1	X_2	Y_1	Y_2
X_1	48.6	124.02	18.81	19.45	19.74
X_2	20.7		12.73	4.26	8.51
Y_1	21.8			8.90	6.97
Y_2	30.6				19.48

Girls — Sample size, $n = 50$

	Mean	Dispersion matrix			
		X_1	X_2	Y_1	Y_2
X_1	40.7	116.60	10.85	13.97	8.44
X_2	22.6		11.93	5.42	9.85
Y_1	23.4			8.99	2.11
Y_2	31.2				6.52

TABLE 9.18

INITIAL WEIGHTS AND WEEKLY GAINS IN WEIGHT FOR 27 RATS

Group 1: Control						Group 2: Thyroxin						Group 3: Thiouracil					
Rat	y_0	y_1	y_2	y_3	y_4	Rat	y_0	y_1	y_2	y_3	y_4	Rat	y_0	y_1	y_2	y_3	y_4
1	57	29	28	25	33	11	59	26	36	35	35	18	61	25	23	11	9
2	60	33	30	23	31	12	54	17	19	20	28	19	59	21	21	10	11
3	52	25	34	33	41	13	56	19	33	43	38	20	53	26	21	6	27
4	49	18	33	29	35	14	59	26	31	32	29	21	59	29	12	11	11
5	56	25	23	17	30	15	57	15	25	23	24	22	51	24	26	22	17
6	46	24	32	29	22	16	52	21	24	19	24	23	51	24	17	8	19
7	51	20	23	16	31	17	52	18	35	33	33	24	56	22	17	8	5
8	63	28	21	18	24							25	58	11	24	21	24
9	49	18	23	22	28							26	46	15	17	12	17
10	57	25	28	29	30							27	53	19	17	15	18

Source: G. E. P. Box, Problems in the analysis of growth and wear curves, *Biometrics*, Vol. 6 (1950).

twelve castes and tribes of the United Province (present name Uttar Pradesh) and also the corresponding within-dispersion matrix.

Examine whether the groups are different in respect to the means of these four measurements, and if so estimate the "distance" between every two groups.

9.7. In Table 9.17 (p. 440) the means and dispersion matrices of scores on two psychological tests X_1, X_2 and two general proficiency tests Y_1, Y_2 were obtained separately from the scores of 50 normal boys, 50 normal girls, 50 deaf and dumb boys, and 50 deaf and dumb girls.

Examine whether the four groups differ in respect to the mean values of the scores on the two general proficiency tests. Do the differences, if any, arise from differences in sex or physical condition? Can these differences be explained away as being due to the differences in the scores on the psychological tests?

9.8. Table 9.18 (p. 441) shows the weekly gains in weight for 27 rats under three different treatments: (1) control, (2) thyroxin, and (3) thiouracil. Here y_0 represents initial weight of rat, y_1 gain in first week, y_2 gain in second week, y_3 gain in third week, and y_4 gain in fourth week.

(a) Examine whether the three treatments differ in their effects as measured by the four characters—gain in weight in four different weeks— when allowance is made for differences in the initial weight.

(b) Examine separately for each group whether the weekly gain in weight over the different weeks is linear in time.

Dispersion matrix

9.9. Examine on the basis of the data in exercise 9.1 whether the dispersion matrices of the four egg characteristics are the same for the two grades A and B.

TABLE 9.19

MEANS AND DISPERSION MATRIX

	Mean	\multicolumn{8}{c	}{Dispersion matrix based on a sample of 200}
		X_1	X_2	Y_1	Y_2	Y_3	Z_1	Z_2	Z_3
X_1	61	9.82	1.37	1.09	1.32	0.52	1.86	1.52	2.12
X_2	58		7.20	0.85	0.86	0.95	2.14	2.29	2.06
X_1	63			2.97	0.68	0.75	1.00	1.51	0.68
Y_2	68				5.25	1.09	1.66	1.15	2.46
Y_3	65					6.47	0.33	1.11	0.73
Z_1	54						4.49	2.01	2.17
Z_2	51							5.44	2.10
Z_3	43								6.39

9.10. On the basis of the data in exercise 6.1 of Part II examine whether the three species of the iris family are identical in respect to the dispersion matrix of the four flower characteristics.

Independence

9.11. On the basis of the data in exercise 6.2 of Part II examine whether both the height and the weight of the twin brother are uncorrelated with the height and the weight of the twin sister.

9.12. The means, variances, and covariances given in Table 9.19 were computed on the basis of the following marks obtained by a sample of 200 students in India at two different stages of their career in different tests on English and a vernacular language:

X_1	Score in English, Paper I	Preliminary stage
X_2	Score in English, Paper II	Preliminary stage
Y_1	Score in vernacular, Paper I	Preliminary stage
Y_2	Score in vernacular, Paper II	Preliminary stage
Y_3	Score in vernacular, Paper III	Preliminary stage
Z_1	Score in English, Paper I	Final stage
Z_2	Score in English, Paper II	Final stage
Z_3	Score in English, Paper III	Final stage

Is it possible to predict the score of a student on the three papers in English at the final stage from his scores on the two papers in English at the preliminary stage? Does the inclusion of scores on the three vernacular papers as additional predictors increase the accuracy of prediction? Find the maximum canonical correlation between the scores in English at the preliminary and the final stages.

Symmetry

9.13. Using the data in exercise 9.12, examine whether, for the distribution of scores Y_1, Y_2, Y_3 on the three papers in English in the final stage, the means are equal, the variances are equal, and the covariances are equal, except for fluctuations of sampling.

Classification

9.14. On the basis of the data in exercise 9.1 find the linear discriminant function between the two grades of eggs.

9.15. Using the data in exercise 6.1, develop a procedure for classifying a flower into one of the three species of the iris family on the basis of its petal width, petal length, sepal length, and sepal width.

9.16. Using the data in exercise 9.5, develop a method for assessing the neurotic condition of a subject on the basis of his scores on the three

444 STATISTICAL INFERENCE

psychological tests, *A*, *B*, and *C*. Use this procedure to assess a person whose scores on *A*, *B*, and *C* are 3.2, 1.5, and 0.8, respectively.

9.17. In continuation of exercise 9.15, examine whether the statistical "distance" between the species *Iris setosa* and *Iris versicolor* is significantly decreased when sepal measurements are ignored.

9.18. In continuation of exercise 9.6, examine whether the anthropometric character "nasal height" is useful in discriminating between the twelve groups, or whether it is redundant when the other three characters are used.

9.19. On the basis of the data in exercise 9.1, examine whether the best linear discriminant function for the two grades of eggs would be taken as proportional to $12X_1 + 3X_2 + 2X_3 - 3X_4$.

Factor analysis

9.20. Table 9.20 of correlations of eight emotional traits was obtained by C. Burt from a record of 172 normal children. It is expected that there is a general emotionality (GE) factor common to all these traits.

TABLE 9.20

CORRELATION MATRIX OF EIGHT EMOTIONAL VARIABLES

Variable		1	2	3	4	5	6	7	8
Sociability	1	1.00							
Sorrow	2	0.83	1.00						
Tenderness	3	0.81	0.87	1.00					
Joy	4	0.80	0.62	0.63	1.00				
Wonder	5	0.71	0.59	0.37	0.49	1.00			
Disgust	6	0.54	0.58	0.30	0.30	0.34	1.00		
Anger	7	0.53	0.44	0.12	0.28	0.55	0.38	1.00	
Fear	8	0.24	0.45	0.33	0.29	0.19	0.21	0.10	1.00

Source: K. J. Holzinger and H. H. Harman, *Factor Analysis: A Synthesis of Factorial Methods*, University of Chicago Press, Chicago, 1941.

Find out the loadings of this GE factor, using Thurstone's centroid method. Also compute the various tetrad differences to determine whether there is only a single common factor.

9.21. For the data given in exercise 9.20, find out the loadings of the GE factor by using the method of maximum likelihood and taking the estimates obtained in the same exercise as the first approximations.

9.22. For the data in exercise 9.20 find the specific factor loadings and estimate the factor scores of an individial whose standardized scores for these eight emotional traits are 2.50, −1.65, −0.42, 1.70, −0.06, 0.57, 0.08, and 1.20, respectively.

9.23. For the data in exercise 9.20, find the loadings of the GE factor, using Hotelling's method of principal components. Also carry out suitable statistical tests to determine whether there is only a single principal component.

CHAPTER 10

Sequential Procedures

10.1 INTRODUCTION

In the usual test and estimation procedures the sample size is fixed beforehand, and statistical analysis is taken up only after all samples have been collected. It is generally more economic, however, to take samples sequentially in stages and decide at the end of each stage, on examination of data already collected, whether or not more samples are required. This is known as a sequential procedure.

We describe here a number of sequential tests and estimation procedures.

10.2 SEQUENTIAL PROBABILITY RATIO TEST

Let $f(x, \theta)$ be the frequency density (in the continuous case) or the probability law (in the discrete case) for the chance variable x. Suppose that the problem is to examine the simple hypothesis H_0 that the parameter θ has the value θ_0 against the simple alternative H_1 that the value is θ_1. Let the probability of accepting H_1 when H_0 is true be approximately α and when H_1 is true be approximately $1 - \beta$, where α and β are preassigned numbers, $0 < \alpha < 1 - \beta < 1$. Then, the sequential probability ratio test (SPRT) procedure for the situation stated above is as follows.

Let

$$(10.2.1) \qquad a = \log \frac{1 - \beta}{\alpha} \quad \text{and} \quad b = \log \frac{\beta}{1 - \alpha}$$

and denote the logarithm of the likelihood ratio of the ith sample by

$$(10.2.2) \qquad z_i = \log \frac{f(x_i, \theta_1)}{f(x_i, \theta_0)},$$

where x_i is the ith random sample. Random samples are to be drawn one by one, and at the mth stage the cumulative sum $S_m = \sum_{i=1}^{m} Z_i$ is to be computed. If $b < S_m < a$, another sample is to be taken; otherwise

446

sampling is to be discontinued. If $S_m \geq a$, sampling is to be terminated at the mth stage with the rejection of the hypothesis H_0; and if $S_m \leq b$, sampling is to be terminated with the acceptance of H_0, that is, with the rejection of the alternative hypothesis H_1.

The probability $L(\theta)$ that the SPRT procedure will terminate with the acceptance of H_0 when θ is the true value of the parameter is called the *operating characteristic* (OC) *function* of the test and is given approximately by

$$(10.2.3) \qquad L(\theta) = \frac{\left(\dfrac{1-\beta}{\alpha}\right)^h - 1}{\left(\dfrac{1-\beta}{\alpha}\right)^h - \left(\dfrac{\beta}{1-\alpha}\right)^h},$$

where $h = h(\theta)$ is defined as the non-zero root of the equation

$$(10.2.4) \qquad \int_{-\infty}^{\infty} \left[\frac{f(x, \theta_1)}{f(x, \theta_0)}\right]^{h(\theta)} f(x, \theta)\, dx = 1.$$

The average number of observations $E_\theta(n)$ required by the SPRT procedure to reach a decision is called the *average sample number* (ASN) function and is given approximately by

$$(10.2.5) \qquad E_\theta(n) = \frac{bL(\theta) + a[1 - L(\theta)]}{E_\theta(z)},$$

where

$$(10.2.6) \qquad E_\theta(z) = \int_{-\infty}^{\infty} \left[\log \frac{f(x, \theta_1)}{f(x, \theta_0)}\right] f(x, \theta)\, dx.$$

We give below the SPRT procedures for testing simple hypotheses about the parameters of the binomial, Poisson, and normal distributions. In each of these cases, the procedure reduces to the following. At the mth stage, a certain statistic T_m, depending on all the m observations, has to be computed. Continue sampling if $B + mC < T_m < A + mC$, stop sampling with rejection (acceptance) of the hypothesis H_0 if $T_m \geq A + mC$ ($T_m \leq B + mC$), where A, B, C are certain constants that depend on the hypothesis to be tested and are listed below. In the formulae to be given, a and b are defined by 10.2.1.

Test for a Proportion. To test the hypothesis H_0 that the probability of success in a binomial model is p_0 against the alternative H_1 that it is p_1, the constants of the SPRT procedure are

$$(10.2.7) \qquad A = \frac{a}{k}, \qquad B = \frac{b}{k}, \qquad C = \frac{1}{k} \log \frac{1 - p_0}{1 - p_1},$$

where $k = \log [p_1(1 - p_0)/p_0(1 - p_1)]$ and the statistic T_m is the total number of successes up to the mth stage.

Test for the Mean of a Poisson Population. To test the hypothesis H_0 that the mean of a Poisson population is μ_0 against the alternative H_1 that it is μ_1, the constants of the SPRT procedure are

$$(10.2.8) \qquad A = \frac{a}{k}, \qquad B = \frac{b}{k}, \qquad C = \frac{1}{k}(\mu_1 - \mu_0) \log e,$$

where $k = \log (\mu_1/\mu_0)$ and T_m is the total of the first m observations.

Test for the Mean of a Normal Population with Known Variance. For a normal population with known variance σ^2, to test the hypothesis H_0 that the mean is μ_0 against the alternative H_1 that it is μ_1, the constants of the SPRT procedure are

$$(10.2.9) \qquad A = \frac{a}{k}, \qquad B = \frac{b}{k}, \qquad C = \frac{\mu_0 + \mu_1}{2},$$

where $k = (1/\sigma^2)(\mu_1 - \mu_0) \log_{10} e$, and the statistic T_m is the sum of the first m observations.

Test for the Variance of a Normal Population with Known Mean. For a normal population whose mean is known to be μ, to test the hypothesis H_0 that the variance is σ_0^2 against the alternative H that it is σ_1^2 of the constants of the SPRT procedure are

$$(10.2.10) \qquad A = \frac{a}{k}, \qquad B = \frac{b}{k}, \qquad C = \frac{1}{k} \log \frac{\sigma_1}{\sigma_0},$$

where

$$k = \frac{1}{2}\left(\frac{1}{\sigma_0^2} - \frac{1}{\sigma_1^2}\right) \log e \quad \text{and} \quad T_m = \sum_{i=1}^{m} (x_i - \mu)^2,$$

x_i being the ith random sample.

Illustrative Example 10.1. Assuming that the distribution of the score in English given in illustrative example 4.1 of Part II is normal with standard deviation $\sigma = 10$, use the SPRT procedure to test the hyopthesis that the mean is $\mu_0 = 40$ against the alternative that it is $\mu_1 = 43$. Take $\alpha = 0.10$, $\beta = 0.30$.

We shall take logarithms to base 10. Then we have from 10.2.1

$$a = \log \frac{1 - \beta}{\alpha} = \log 7 = 0.8450980,$$

$$b = \log \frac{\beta}{1 - \alpha} = -\log 3 = -0.4771213,$$

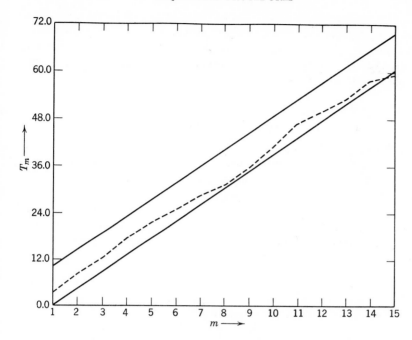

and from 10.2.9

$$k = \frac{1}{\sigma^2}(\mu_1 - \mu_0) \log_{10} e = \frac{1}{100}(43 - 40) \times 0.434294 = 0.0130288$$

so that

$$A = \frac{a}{k} = 64.86, \qquad B = \frac{b}{k} = (-36.62), \qquad \text{and} \qquad C = \frac{\mu_0 + \mu_1}{2}$$
$$= 41.5.$$

We then compute, for successive values of m, the values of the limits $A + mC$, $B + mC$, and T_m. The first time T_m goes outside these limits is when $m = 14$, and the decision at that stage is to reject H_0. The graph at the top of the page shows the values of $A + mC$, $B + mC$, and T_m for $m = 1, 2, \ldots, 15$.

10.3 SEQUENTIAL TESTS OF SOME COMPOSITE HYPOTHESIS

Sequential Test of the Equality of Two Proportions. Let p_1 and p_2 be, respectively, the probabilities of success in the two binomial populations. Take a pair of observations, one from each population. The possible results are *ss*, *sf*, *fs*, or *ff* where the first letter stands for the observation from the first population and the second letter for that from the second population: s for success and f for failure. Ignore observations of the type ss or ff because they do not help in comparing the two populations. Let X denote a random variable which takes the value 1 if the observation is of the type sf and 0 if the observation is of the type fs. Thus X is a binomial variate with Prob $(X = 1) = p$, where

$$(10.3.1) \qquad p = \frac{p_1(1 - p_2)}{p_1(1 - p_2) + p_2(1 - p_1)},$$

and obviously $p = \frac{1}{2}$ if and only if $p_1 = p_2$. The problem of testing the hypothesis that $p_1 = p_2$ is thus reduced to that of testing the simple hypothesis that $p = \frac{1}{2}$ for the binomial variate X.

Sequential t Test. To test sequentially the hypothesis that the mean μ of a normal distribution is equal to μ_0, when the variance σ^2 is unknown, suppose that the acceptance of the hypothesis is to be regarded as an error of practical importance only when $|\mu - \mu_0|/\sigma$ exceeds a preassigned constant δ. Let $x_1, x_2, \ldots$ be the samples drawn, and

$$(10.3.2) \qquad S_m = \frac{[G_m(\delta) + G_m(-\delta)]}{2G_m(0)},$$

where

$$(10.3.3) \qquad G_m(\delta_0) = \int_0^\infty \sigma^{-m} \exp\left[-\frac{1}{2\sigma^2} \sum_{i=1}^m (x_i - \mu_0 - \delta)^2 \right] d\sigma.$$

Continue sampling as long as $b < S_m < a$, where a, b are defined by 10.2.1. Terminate sampling at the mth stage and reject the hypothesis if $S_m \geqq a$ and accept the hypothesis if $S_m \leqq b$. Tables are available (Tables to facilitate sequential t tests, *Applied Mathematics Series* 14, National Bureau of Standards, Washington) for evaluation of $G_m(\delta)$.

10.4 SEQUENTIAL ESTIMATION

A Two-Sample Procedure for the Mean of a Normal Population. To obtain a confidence interval of length $2L$ and confidence coefficient $1 - \alpha$ for the mean μ of a normal population with unknown variance, the following procedure is suggested by Stein. First draw a sample of size m and compute the sample mean $\bar{x}$ and estimate of variance s^2. Let $t_0 = t_{m-1}(\frac{1}{2}\alpha)$. Choose a positive integer n and a real number a to satisfy

$$(10.4.1) \qquad \frac{a^2}{m} + \frac{(1 - a)^2}{n} = \frac{L^2}{t_0^2 s^2}.$$

Draw a second sample of size n and let $\bar{y}$ be the mean of this sample. Compute $Z = a\bar{x} + (1 - a)\bar{y}$. Then $(Z - L, Z + L)$ provides the required confidence interval.

A General Sequential Procedure for Estimation by a Confidence Set. Let $x_1, x_2, \ldots,$ be a sequence of independent observations from a population with probability density function $f(x, \theta)$ involving the parameter θ. The following sequential procedure is suggested by Wald for estimation of θ by means of a confidence set with assigned geometrical properties. Take an arbitrary sequence of fixed functions $p_m{}^*(x_1, x_2, \ldots, x_m, \theta)$ which for any m may be regarded as a probability density function of $x_1, x_2, \ldots, x_m$. Let $A = 1/(1 - \alpha)$, where α is the preassigned confidence coefficient. Denote by W_n the set of all parameter points θ such that

$$\frac{p_m{}^*(x_1, x_2, \ldots, x_m, \theta)}{\prod\limits_{i=1}^{m} f(x_i, \theta)} < A$$

for $m = 1, 2, \ldots, n$. Continue sampling until W_n acquires the assigned geometrical properties. If N is the smallest integer for which the geometrical properties are acquired, then W_N gives a confidence set for θ with confidence coefficient not less than α.

10.5 EXERCISES

10.1. From the data in exercise 2.1 in Part II examine by using a sequential procedure whether the coin is unbiased against the alternative that the probability of a head is 0.6.
Take $\alpha = 0.01$, $\beta = 0.25$.

10.2. On the assumption that the distribution is normal with variance unity, examine by a sequential procedure, using the data in exercise 8.37, whether the mean is zero against the alternative that it is $+0.5$
Take $\alpha = 0.05$, $\beta = 0.50$.

10.3. On the assumption that the distribution is normal with mean zero, examine by a sequential procedure from the data in exercise 8.37 whether the variance is unity against the alternative that it is 2.
Take $\alpha = 0.05$, $\beta = 0.50$.

10.4. Find the percentage saving in sample size attainable by the use of the SPRT procedure instead of the classical procedure for testing the hypothesis that the mean of a normal distribution with known variance σ^2 is μ_0 against the alternative that it is μ_1 when the first kind of error is fixed at α and the second kind of error at β, assuming (a) that the null hypothesis is true and (b) that the alternative hypothesis is true.
Take $\alpha = 0.01, 0.05$, and $\beta = 0.01, 0.05, 0.10, 0.50$.

10.5. Use Stein's two-stage procedure to estimate the mean of the entries in a table of random normal deviates correct to within ± 0.05 with a confidence coefficient of 0.95.

AUTHOR INDEX

453

SUBJECT INDEX

La mer

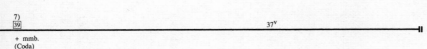

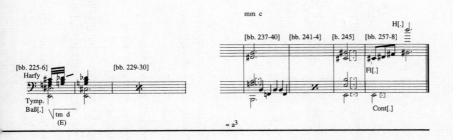

h[armonické] m[otivy]	harmonic motives
m[elodické] m[otivy]/ Mel[lodické] m[otivy]	melodic motives
m[inut]	minutes
nejjednotnější část	most homogeneous part
Proběhlý čas	Time elapsed
stěžejní m[otivy]	pivotal motives
t[o] j[e]	i.e.
tonicky sjednocená vazba archit[ektonická]	tonally unified architectonic structure
t[oninové] m[otivy]/ Toninové m[otivy]	key motives
tři takty	three bars
velké rondo	great rondo
v[teřin]	seconds
výběr	selection
význačné místo	salient point

277

Appendix 10.2   Janáček's *La mer* analysis, fol. 1v

11/III 1921

4.) Písňové melodie: jak dlouho by trval cit hluboký
když by nebyl zažíhán stále?
Slovem atd.........
rozbor ukázal: v době 62ᵛ jediný tm!

Zpívané slov. m.

1.) Slov. m. tkví svým tónem v
hm, v tm silném.
Naopak: hm, mm, mají hlubší
kořeny ve věcech a jejich
citovosti.

2.) Vybroušenost sčasovací.*

3. Zářezy do tónové skladby předmětné[,]
jejich logika[,]srozumitelnost.
Chtělo by se "rozlišovat" – a nelze.
––––––––––––––
Účin hudby odpadnou-li slov. m.

3.) Srozumitelnosti odpadá a tónové** není dostatek.
Důvody logičné, slovesné odpadají.
Ptáme se, proč je tomu konec? Proč už nastu-
puje druhý?

Mluvené slov. m.
Odpoutává se od tónových
hm[,] mm[,] tm[,]: staví
svoje mlhavé,
hatění i sčasovací.*

Texty volí se proto vzrušené,
dějem vynikající.

Hesla slovesná

Odpadne-li slovo – přirozeně nastu-
puje váha barev orchestrových (silou "souhlásek"
orchestr.) [.]

Tu dostává orch. myslení tónové.
Ujmou se v práci složen. tónové** –
vyrůstají volněji.
v symf. básních programových přistupují ještě i
logické svazy tónových představ[,] t.j.jejich složité
reakce
ony vyzdvihují se až vyniknou, až se i samy o sobě líbí.

Translation

Column 1

<u>Sung verbal motives</u>/(1) A verbal motive immerses <u>its own tone</u> in / <u>a harmonic motive</u>, in a strong <u>key motive</u>. / On the other hand: harmonic motives and melodic motives have deeper / roots in <u>things</u> and their / affectivity. / (2) <u>Rhythmic*</u> refinement. / (3) <u>Incisions</u> into an <u>objective tonal structure</u>, / their logic, intelligibility. / It would like to 'differentiate' itself – and that is not possible. / The effect of music if verbal motives are lacking, and the tones** are not sufficient. / Logical, verbal foundations are lacking. / We ask ourselves, why is it the end of this one [motive]? / Why does a second now begin? /

Column 2

<u>Spoken verbal motives</u> / It [a 'spoken verbal motive'] breaks away from tonal / harmonic motives, melodic motives, key motives: / <u>it establishes its own misty ones</u> [harmonic motives etc.]. / Frustration even of rhythm.* / Lyrics therefore are made inflamed, / through a remarkable process. /

Column 3

<u>Verbal captions</u>. / If the word is lacking – naturally / the importance of orchestral colours takes over / (through the strength of orchestral 'consonants'). / In this case, the orchestra receives tonal thought. / They take the lead in the composed work. The tones** – / they grow more freely. / In programmatic symphonic poems are added yet also / <u>the logical connections of the tonal conceptions, that is their complex reactions</u>. / They are highlighted so that they stand out, so that they are satisfying in themselves. /

Addendum (at 180° to the main text)

4) Song melodies: how long would a deep emotion last / if it were not ignited for ever? / through a word etc. . . . / Analysis showed: for the duration of 62 seconds <u>a single key motive</u>!

* See pp. 221–5 above for a full examination of Janáček's terms 'sčasování', 'sčasovací' and 'sčasovka'.

** Janáček here uses the masculine animate plural ending 'ové' – a type of personification for rhetorical effect.

Appendix 10.3 Janáček's *La mer* analysis, fol. 2v; 'Jeux de vagues', Analyses C1–4

[C1:] Hra vln [Game of waves]   (Hra života)

komplikační střety [complicated conflicts]:

stále zmítání [constant agitation]

vyhozená vlnka [a flung-about wavelet]   1   –   až taktu ppp [until the 'ppp' bar]

lehká mysl, sdružení [cheerfulness, association]   2   člověk do osudu [a human being into fate]

těžké chmury [heavy black clouds]   3   4 rozplývá, tesknota, osířelost [dissolves, depression, isolation]

osudem narazí [stroke of fate]!   5   a jednoduché reakce [and simple reactions]

_____

[C2:] žaloba: $(1\ a^2\underset{b}{=}a^2$ mm   )   resignace: $\diagup$ $=3=3=1$
       [argument]   [resignation]

[C3:] Motivy stěžejní [Pivotal motives]

vyniknou slož[itými] reakcemi [they stand out through complex reactions].
Nepodceňovat jednoduché reakce [Not to belittle simple reactions]!

1. a^2 Roz r. rozlišování a opět poznat
                                             [Cor anglais, differentiation and re-recognition]

3.

4. a^2 (a b = a)   "opět poznat"
                        vdrob. rondo. [miniature rondo]

5. a^2 "opět poznat"

2. a^3 $(a^2 b^2 = a^2)$ "opět poznat" a vyspěly do a^3 ["re-recognition" and matured into a^3]

[C4:] Pořádek jejich [Their order]:

       $\{\!\!\{$ | 1 | větší 1 | 2 | $\overline{3}$ = 3 | 4 | = 1 | = 1 | ① | = 1 | $\overline{hn}$ $\overline{tm}$ | 5 | $a^2 b^2 = a^2$ | $d = d$ | 5 | = 3

       [b. 9] [b. 18] [b. 36] [b. 48] [b. 52] [b. 62] [b. 92] [b. 106] [b. 118] [b. 134] [b. 163] [b. 187] [b. 215] [b. 225]

       opět poznat opět poznat opět poznat vyspělost výběr opět poznat

       $\diagup$ opět = 3 | opět = 1
                        [b. 225]   [b. 227]

(Architektonika) [(Architectonics)]

       vedená komplikací [guided by complication].

Index